POISONOUS PLANTS
AND FUNGI IN
BRITAIN

Books must follow sciences,
and not sciences books.
Francis Bacon, 1561–1626

Atropa belladonna
Deadly nightshade

POISONOUS PLANTS AND FUNGI IN BRITAIN

Animal and Human Poisoning

(formerly *Poisonous Plants in Britain and their Effects on Animals and Man*)

Marion R. Cooper
and
Anthony W. Johnson

With collaboration from the Medical Toxicology Unit, Guy's & St Thomas' Hospital Trust, London, and the Royal Botanic Gardens, Kew

London: The Stationery Office

ISBN 0 11 242981 5

Note

The authors and publisher accept no responsibility for any poisoning incident that may result from using information contained in this book. Appropriate veterinary or medical advice should be sought in all cases where poisoning is suspected.

Published by The Stationery Office and available from:

The Publications Centre
(mail, telephone and fax orders only)
PO Box 276, London SW8 5DT
General enquiries 0171 873 0011
Telephone orders 0171 873 9090
Fax orders 0171 873 8200

The Stationery Office Bookshops
59–60 Holborn Viaduct, London EC1A 2FD
temporary until mid 1998
(counter service and fax orders only)
Fax 0171 831 1326
68–69 Bull Street, Birmingham B4 6AD
0121 236 9696   Fax 0121 236 9699
33 Wine Street, Bristol BS1 2BQ
0117 9264306 Fax 0117 9294515
9–21 Princess Street, Manchester M60 8AS
0161 834 7201 Fax 0161 833 0634
16 Arthur Street, Belfast BT1 4GD
01232 238451 Fax 01232 235401
The Stationery Office Oriel Bookshop
The Friary, Cardiff CF1 4AA
01222 395548 Fax 01222 384347
71 Lothian Road, Edinburgh EH3 9AZ
(counter service only)

Customers in Scotland may
mail, telephone or fax their orders to:
Scottish Publications Sales
South Gyle Crescent, Edinburgh EH12 9EB
0131 228 4181 Fax 0131 622 7017

The Stationery Office's Accredited Agents
(see Yellow Pages)
and through good booksellers

Printed in the UK for The Stationery Office
0 11 242981 5 Print No 1 C15   03/98

CONTENTS

LIST OF PLATES (*between pages 270 and 271*)

47. *Colchicum autumnale* Meadow saffron HCB
48. *Convallaria majalis* Lily of the valley HCB
49. *Hyacinthoides non-scripta* Bluebell GTC
50. *Narthecium ossifragum* Bog asphodel GTC
51. *Fraxinus excelsior* Ash HCB
52. *Ligustrum* species Privet (flowers) GTC
53. *Ligustrum* species Privet (fruits) HCB
54. *Oxalis acetosella* Wood sorrel HCB
55. *Chelidonium majus* Greater celandine GTC
56. *Papaver rhoeas* Field poppy GTC
57. *Rheum rhabarbarum* Rhubarb GTC
58. *Rumex acetosella* Sheep's sorrel HCB
59. *Anagallis arvensis* Scarlet pimpernel RBG, Kew
60. *Primula obconica* Poison primrose RBG, Kew
61. *Anenome nemorosa* Wood anemone HCB
62. *Clematis vitalba* Traveller's joy HCB
63. *Helleborus foetidus* Stinking hellebore GTC
64. *Ranunculus* species Buttercup HCB
65. *Aconitum napellus* Monkshood GTC
66. *Rhamnus cathartica* Purging buckthorn HCB
67. *Prunus laurocerasus* Cherry laurel GTC
68. *Ruta graveolens* Rue GTC
69. *Digitalis purpurea* Foxglove GTC
70. *Atropa belladonna* Deadly nightshade (flowers) GTC
71. *Atropa belladonna* Deadly nightshade (fruits) GTC
72. *Datura stramonium* Thorn apple GTC
73. *Hyoscyamus niger* Henbane HCB
74. *Solanum dulcamara* Woody nightshade (flowers) GTC
75. *Solanum dulcamara* Woody nightshade (fruits) GTC
76. *Solanum nigrum* Black nightshade (flowers) RBG, Kew
77. *Solanum nigrum* Black nightshade (fruits) HCB
78. *Solanum tuberosum* Potato (fruits) HCB
79. *Taxus baccata* Yew HCB
80. *Daphne laureola* Spurge laurel PJW
81. *Daphne mezereum* Mezereon HCB
82. *Conium maculatum* Hemlock GTC
83. *Oenanthe crocata* Hemlock water dropwort SB
84. *Heracleum mantegazzianum* Giant hogweed HCB
85. *Lantana camara* Lantana HCB
86. *Viscum album* Mistletoe SB
87. *Amanita phalloides* Death cap DAR
88. *Cortinarius speciosissimus* Cortinarius DAR
89. *Gyromitra esculenta* False morel DAR
90. *Amanita muscaria* Fly agaric GTC
91. *Panaeolus subbalteatus* Panaeolus DAR
92. *Psilocybe semilanceata* Liberty cap BH
93. *Clitocybe dealbata* Clitocybe BMS
94. *Inocybe geophylla* Inocybe RBG, Kew
95. *Coprinus atramentarius* Common ink cap HCB

96.   *Agaricus xanthodermus* Yellow-staining mushroom DAR
97.   *Hebeloma crustuliniforme* Fairy cake hebeloma BH
98.   *Hypholoma fasciculare* Sulphur tuft DAR
99.   *Paxillus involutus* Brown roll rim GTC
100.   *Russula emetica* Sickener GTC
101.   *Amanita rubescens* Blusher GTC
102.   *Lepista nebularis* Cloudy cap GTC
103.   *Claviceps purpurea* Ergot JW

COVER PHOTOGRAPHS

Front, background: *Taxus baccata* Yew HCB
Front, left to right: *Laburnum anagyroides* Laburnum GTC; *Oenanthe crocata*
      Hemlock water dropwort SB; *Solanum dulcamara* Woody nightshade GTC

Back, background: *Bryonia dioica* White bryony GTC
Back, top: *Rhododendron ponticum* Rhododendron GTC
Back, below: *Amanita muscaria* Fly agaric GTC

SOURCES

Most of the photographs were provided by Dr Hugh Baillie (HCB) or taken especially for this edition by Geoff Cooper (GTC), and we are most grateful to them both. For permission to reproduce the line drawing of the death cap (*Amanita phalloides*) on p. 231 and to use some photographs, we are indebted to The Trustees, Royal Botanic Gardens, Kew (RBG, Kew). Other photographs have been kindly loaned by Sylvia Berrett (SB), Barry Hughes (BH), Dr Derek Reid (DAR), Dr Brian Spooner (BMS), Professor John Webster (JW), and Peter Witham (PJW). Almost all of the plants and fungi were photographed in their typical environment in Britain; we should like to thank the many people who told us of locations, particularly Audrey Thomas, who also confirmed the identification of some of the fungi.

FOREWORD TO THE SECOND EDITION

(formerly *Poisonous Plants in Britain and their Effects on Animals and Man*)

Despite, or perhaps because of, our largely urban society, the interest of the public in plants and fungi appears to be on the increase. This is particularly true of garden or house plants and also of those used as herbal remedies. This interest has led to a wide range of plants being imported into this country from all over the world, as well as many new cultivars being developed by plant breeders. Accordingly, in addition to our native species, the population is being exposed to a steadily increasing range of plants whose toxicity may vary considerably.

It is appropriate, therefore, that this new and significantly enlarged second edition of an already classic book, now renamed *Poisonous Plants and Fungi in Britain. Animal and Human Poisoning*, gives more emphasis to human poisoning than the first edition. For this reason the authors have made a special effort to expand the coverage of wild and cultivated plants that may cause problems from either ingestion or handling. In this the National Poisons Information Service and the Medical Toxicology Unit of Guy's & St Thomas' Hospital Trust are honoured to have been able to assist.

In the experience of the Medical Toxicology Unit, children are more likely to be poisoned by plants or fungi than adults, but the latter are also exposed to risks. In particular, those who regularly handle garden and house plants at work or in the home have developed skin reactions. In addition, cases of poisoning continue to arise amongst 'back to nature' enthusiasts keen to explore some of the traditional uses of plants and fungi from the wild, although their skills in identification or knowledge of toxicity may be inadequate.

This new edition includes details of adverse health effects arising from ingestion and skin reactions most likely to be experienced by both these groups who would do well to familarize themselves with this volume before exposure. To them and to the general public the new section on advisory services (Appendix B) will no doubt prove most helpful, as well as to the horticultural, medical and veterinary professions should they require more specialist advice.

The need for a definitive textbook on poisonous plants and fungi is, therefore, undoubted. This new, extensively updated edition, which is based on in-depth knowledge of the scientific, medical, and veterinary toxicology literature, draws upon recent case data and will prove invaluable as an educational and reference tool for schools and medical, veterinary, and horticultural colleges, as well as GPs' practices and hospitals. Indeed, it deserves its place on the shelves of every home.

Medical Toxicology Unit
Guy's & St Thomas' Hospital Trust
London
SE14 5ER

Dr Virginia Murray
Consultant Occupational and
Environmental Toxicologist

FOREWORD TO THE FIRST EDITION

During the preparation of this book a comprehensive search of the published literature was carried out by the authors, a botanist and a veterinarian, who are on the staff of the Commonwealth Bureau of Animal Health which is responsible for documenting world veterinary literature. They consulted over 5000 relevant publications and compiled their findings to produce a book that incorporates the results of the latest studies as well as long established work. Some plants have declined in importance as a cause of poisoning, whilst recent work, as well as expanding knowledge of the subject, has contradicted or disproved some statements which have been repeated from earlier times. In addition to the main poisonous plants native to Britain, this book includes fungi, crop plants and imported feed materials. It should prove of value to the medical and veterinary professions, students, farmers and the public in general in avoiding and dealing with plant poisoning, and assist in their appreciation and understanding of the countryside.

Commonwealth Bureau of Animal Health
Weybridge

Roy Mack FRCVS
Director

PREFACE TO THE SECOND EDITION

(formerly *Poisonous Plants in Britain and their Effects on Animals and Man*)

In preparing this edition a complete revision of the whole subject has been made, and every part of the book updated, modified, or extended as necessary. This has been a major undertaking that has involved the use of several databases and very extensive literature searches. From the searches, any items that seemed likely to be relevant were obtained and consulted, so that almost all of the information presented is taken directly from original publications in scientific journals, specialist books, conference proceedings, etc. (i.e. primary sources); recourse was made to secondary sources (such as books on plant and fungal poisoning from other parts of the world) only in the absence of these.

This new edition is more comprehensive, as most of the 1150 references in the first edition have been retained and about 700 new ones added. Thus the book provides the background as well as the latest information on poisoning by wild plants, crop plants, garden plants, fungi, and mycotoxins; algal toxins are included for the first time. Coverage of the subject has been increased by adding to most families a new section giving brief details of other plants that are of potentially toxicological significance in Britain. In the previous edition the main emphasis was on poisoning in animals, but there is now greater emphasis than before on human poisoning, with some mention of skin contact; a consequence of this is that more information is included on the possible effects of garden and house plants. The problem of identification of plants has been addressed by the inclusion of 60 more photographs than in the first edition, and by a description of an image-based computer system designed for the purpose.

The main part of the text is arranged in the most appropriate way for consultation: the plants alphabetically by family and genus, and the fungi according to the type of poisoning they cause. An entry on poisonous blue-green algae has been added, and a new section on the advisory services available to the medical and veterinary professions and to the public in Britain has been contributed by staff at the National Poisons Information Service (London), and the Royal Botanic Gardens, Kew.

Taxonomic changes continue, with some plants being renamed and others transferred to different families. The authorities used for plant names are: *Vascular Plant Families and Genera*, 1992, by R.K. Brummitt; *The Plant Book. A Portable Dictionary of the Higher Plants*, 1993, by D.J. Mabberley; and *New Flora of the British Isles*, second edition, 1997, by C. Stace. The names of the fungi have been taken from a variety of sources and are believed to be the most recent in current use.

Marion R. Cooper
Anthony W. Johnson

PREFACE TO THE FIRST EDITION

This book is the latest in a series that can be traced back to 1917 when H.C. Long published *Plants Poisonous to Live Stock,* which was followed in 1927 by another book, *Poisonous Plants on the Farm,* by the same author. The latter was reprinted in 1934 as Ministry of Agriculture and Fisheries Bulletin No.75, and was the forerunner of the two editions of *British Poisonous Plants,* Bulletin 161, published in 1954 and 1968 by the late A.A. Forsyth. A reprinted version of the 1968 edition appeared, with a few amendments, in 1979. These books by Long and Forsyth are similar in style and content and provided valuable information on the poisonous plants of Britain for over 65 years. The task of rewriting a book that has become, albeit in a limited field, a standard reference work, is somewhat daunting; the more so while it is in progress than before starting. It was intended originally that the present book would be a revision of Forsyth's work, but the incorporation of recent work made it necessary to make such extensive changes that the result is a completely new book, with a slightly different emphasis. The change of the title of the book from *British Poisonous Plants* to *Poisonous Plants in Britain and their Effects on Animals and Man* is indicative of the changes in content. Not only does it cover native British plants that have caused poisoning in this country, but also those that occur here, and are therefore potentially toxic, although reports of their having caused poisoning have been found only in foreign literature. Potentially toxic, imported feed components (especially seeds) are also included, although the plants of origin may never be grown in Britain. There is more emphasis on human poisoning than in former Bulletins and the section on fungi has been expanded considerably.

Despite recent advances, there is still surprisingly little known about many aspects of plant poisoning, and we can echo what W.J.T. Morton, Professor of Chemistry at the London Veterinary College, wrote in 1840:

> We are, however, in want of more correct information than at present we possess . . .

The relative importance of crop plants and wild or garden plants in the context of poisoning has changed over the years, both as a result of changes in agricultural practice, particularly in the use of herbicides, which have almost eradicated some wild plants, and because there is now more publicity and consequently greater public awareness of the potential dangers of plants. It may be, however, that if the current trend away from such extensive use of agricultural chemicals, and the return to small-scale units run on 'organic' lines persists, some wild plants, including poisonous ones, may become more common, with an accompanying increase in the risk of poisoning. In general, only the more common garden plants are mentioned; house plants have not been covered. Plants having adverse effects by skin contact are mentioned incidentally, and only if they are included in the text because they are poisonous by ingestion; those listed as affecting milk are those recorded in the main text and in the editions by Forsyth.

The basic format of the book follows that of the previous Bulletins, and the practice of describing cases of poisoning has been retained, but to facilitate quick reference, the subject matter has been treated under several headings, used uniformly throughout. Technical terms have been kept to a minimum, consistent with accuracy, and a glossary is appended. The plants are arranged, for convenience, in alphabetical order of plant families and not in the more conventional taxonomic order. The references at the back of the book are grouped in the same way. The botanical names of the plants have been taken from the *Flora of the British Isles,* by Clapham, Tutin and Warburg, and from *A Dictionary of Flowering Plants and Ferns,* by J.C. Willis; where these two authorities differ, the name used by the Kew Gardens Herbarium has been chosen. Names of fungi and common names of plants come from a variety of sources. The descriptions given for most of the plants are included only as a guide; specialist works should be consulted for precise identification.

As it has not been possible to illustrate all of the plants, the selection includes the most important poisonous plants, some of the less well known ones, and some whose identity may be mistaken. The subject matter has been compiled from a very wide range of veterinary, medical, botanical and biochemical publications and from computer searches of four appropriate data bases (AGRICOLA, BIOSIS, CAB, and MEDLINE). Although based mainly on the most recent publications available, older sources have also been consulted to provide background material and also in the few cases where no recent information has been found. The reference material cited represents about one fifth of that read in the course of the revision, and has been chosen to give the most appropriate matter available in English. References in foreign languages have been included only where these are the best available, or where little has been written in English; many of these foreign papers have English summaries. The paucity of recent information on some of the plants is particularly applicable to their poisonous principles. Although every effort has been made to clarify the nature of these, there are still many plants in which the toxins have not been identified or whose toxicity is still attributed to substances isolated and named last century, before modern analytical techniques had been developed, and on which no further work appears to have been carried out. As would be expected, toxins that occur in commercially important crop plants and in the few plants now well recognised to cause serious problems in farm animals have received most attention.

While many plants in Britain are known to be poisonous, few are dangerously so, and cases of severe poisoning in animals or man are relatively rare. The full effects of the toxic constituents of plants are, however, difficult to assess. It may well be that plant toxins are responsible for far more deleterious effects than have yet been recognised. Indefinite characteristics, such as reduced weight gain, poor performance and mild digestive disturbances of animals could be responsible for economic losses that exceed those of the cases of poisoning severe enough to attract attention and be diagnosed.

There is still much to learn, and we share the sentiments of H.C. Long, who wrote in 1916, at the end of his preface to *Plants Poisonous to Live Stock:*

> For any shortcomings I crave the indulgence of my readers, only requesting that they be friendly enough to spare a moment to call my attention thereto.

<table>
<tr><td>*Commonwealth Bureau of Animal Health*</td><td>Marion R. Cooper</td></tr>
<tr><td>*Central Veterinary Laboratory*</td><td>Anthony W. Johnson</td></tr>
<tr><td>*Weybridge*</td><td></td></tr>
<tr><td>*Surrey*</td><td></td></tr>
</table>

ACKNOWLEDGEMENTS

Firstly we should like to acknowledge again the help of the many people who made so freely available to us their knowledge, facilities, and time during the preparation of the first edition.

In the preparation of this second edition we have benefited from the collaboration that exists between the Medical Toxicology Unit (MTU, formerly the Poisons Unit) of Guy's & St Thomas' Hospital Trust and the Royal Botanic Gardens, Kew; staff from both have been most helpful in discussions and in writing contributions for the new advisory services section at the end of the book. Virginia S.G. Murray MB BS, MSc, FFOM, DIH of the MTU has shared her enthusiasm with us, and given great encouragement; we are most grateful to her for agreeing to write the Foreword. In particular we should like to thank Christine J. Leon MSc and Elizabeth A. Dauncey BSc, PhD of the MTU and the Centre for Economic Botany at Kew; they have provided valuable liaison throughout the project, and we have enjoyed working with them. Also from the Centre for Economic Botany, we are pleased to acknowledge the help of J. Morley BSc. From the National Poisons Information Service (London) much useful information has been provided by J.N. Edwards BSc, MIInfSc and F. Northall BSc, RGN, as well as A. Campbell BSc of the Veterinary Poisons Information Service (London).

The sections on fungi have been read by specialists in that field: D.N. Pegler BSc, MSc, PhD, DSc, FLS; B.M. Spooner BSc, PhD; and D. Shah-Smith BSc, PhD of the Mycology Department of the Royal Botanic Gardens, Kew have made constructive comments on the text, and A.E. Gleadle BSc, PhD and S.P. Coleman of the Food Contaminants Division of the Ministry of Agriculture, Fisheries and Food have checked the section on mycotoxins dealing with permitted levels in human food and animal feedingstuffs. Colleagues in the Commonwealth Agricultural Bureaux International (CABI) have again been willing to cooperate: M.R. Hails BSc, Dip Agric Econ. has alerted us to many recent publications, and the bibliographies that he compiled (*Plant Poisoning in Animals. A bibliography from the world literature. Nos 1,2, and 3*) have been a most useful source of references; C.D. Johnson CChem, MRSC has read and checked the chemical aspects of the entries for each plant. We should like to express our thanks to them all.

The library of the Veterinary Laboratories Agency (an executive agency of MAFF) has been invaluable during the writing of this book. We should like to thank the librarians for the use of their facilities and all of the staff for their help and interest. In particular we are indebted to past and present librarians Patrick Ryan, Kevin Jackson, Heather Hulse, and Janet McCappin, and to Rosemary Thomson, who so willingly acquired for us large numbers of journals and books.

In the huge task of typing and preparing the manuscript we were very grateful to receive many hours of help from Geoff and Hilary Cooper, and the practical advice given by Chris Roberts on the finer points of word processing was greatly appreciated. We should also like to thank Dr Chris Aucken for preparing the material in its final form.

We are pleased to record thanks to our publishers, The Stationery Office, in Norwich. In the early stages we were ably steered by Carol Wardle and George Hammond, and for the final design and layout we are indebted to Richard Jones. Dominic Allen saw much of the project through, and we are grateful to him for his sustained interest, and to Janine Eves, who succeeded him. We are particularly indebted to Michele Staple for meticulous editing and her friendly co-operation and guidance in the final stages.

Finally we thank our families and friends who have been so supportive during our long period of preoccupation with this book.

Introduction

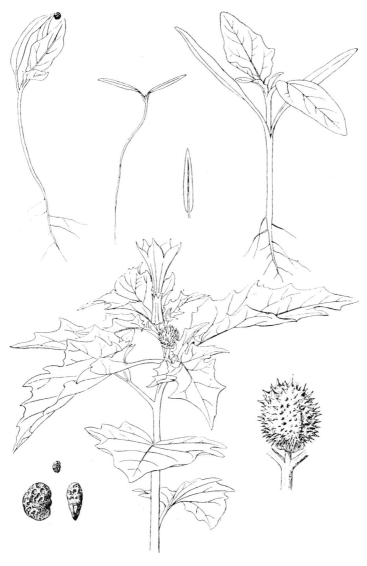

Datura stramonium
Thorn apple

In introducing the subject of plant poisoning and poisonous plants it is necessary to define what is meant by a poisonous plant, but this is not as simple as it may first seem. Broadly speaking the plants considered here are those which, when eaten, can give rise to a departure from normal health. It should be noted, however, that not all such plants are poisonous in all their parts or at all stages of their growth. In addition, the amounts that have to be eaten to produce an adverse effect on health range from relatively small (as in the case of the leaves of yew and the roots of cowbane) to much greater quantities taken over prolonged periods (as in bracken and plants containing pyrrolizidine alkaloids). Another factor complicating the definition of a poisonous plant is the fact that the quantity of a plant that poisons one species of animal may not affect another species; pigs, for example, thrive on amounts of acorns that produce poisoning in cattle.

Several diseases associated with plants cannot really be regarded as poisoning, e.g. the overeating of grain, nutritional deficiencies, skin and respiratory allergies, contact dermatitis, and physical injury, although some mention will be made of such conditions.

Traditionally, and in the previous edition of this book, the fungi have been classified with plants, but they are now recognized as a separate group, one of the five primary divisions of the living world, along with prokaryotes, protista, plants, and animals. To avoid repetition in the following introductory sections, however, 'plant' is still used in its old traditional sense as a collective term, and includes fungi.

HISTORICAL ASPECTS

People have always had to differentiate between those plants that are safe to eat and those that are poisonous. In early times, hunters are thought to have utilized the poisonous properties of certain plants to help catch wild animals, particularly fish, but, in addition to the realization of the potential toxicity of plants, it was also recognized that some could be of benefit in disease conditions. These two aspects of the plant kingdom, the beneficial and also the harmful properties of plants, are described in the early medical literature of classical Greece and Rome (Hippocrates, Theophrastus, Dioscorides).

Publications

The *Materia Medica* of Dioscorides, which was completed about AD 60, describes over 600 plants and plant principles, and was the leading pharmacological work for 16 centuries, being copied and used throughout Europe as the basis for many herbals, including the printed herbals that appeared after 1470. In Dioscorides' work and subsequent herbals, reference is made to the poisonous nature of various plants. Botanical study based on original observations arose again in the first half of the 16th century, and works on poisonous plants began to appear in the 17th and 18th centuries. In 1775 J.F. Gmelin published a German work on poisonous plants that dealt with 56 species, and by the end of the century P. Bulliard's work on French poisonous plants included 86 species, but as W. Woodville states in his *Medical Botany* (1790–1794) writers were still following the authority of Dioscorides for their knowledge of some plants. In 1814/15, however, there appeared a very influential French work on poisons by M.J.B. Orfila; an English translation of this was published in 1818. With the dog as his main experimental animal, Orfila demonstrated the toxicity of some 45 plants and isolated many of their poisonous principles. In 1832, G. Spratt, a surgeon and the editor of the third edition of Woodville's *Medical Botany*, produced *The Medico-Botanical Pocket-Book comprising a Compendium of Vegetable Toxicology*. This describes and illustrates 24 irritant and narcotic plants and four mushrooms, and gives brief details of another 27 poisonous plants. W.J.T. Morton of the London Veterinary College gave a lecture on poisoning in animals to the Veterinary Medical Association in 1836 and referred to the work of Orfila. In 1840 Morton published a Veterinary Toxicology Chart, in which he says 'We are, however, in want of more correct information than at present we possess . . .' A.S. Taylor's *On Poisons in Relation to Medical Jurisprudence and Medicine* (first published in 1848) considers nearly 50 poisonous plants and fungi. More popular works were soon to follow, including *British Poisonous Plants* by C. Johnson (1856) and *The Poisonous, Noxious and Suspected Plants of our Fields and Woods*, by Anne Pratt (1857).

In 1887 was published the first book by a veterinarian on poisonous plants, *Des Plantes Vénéneuses et des Empoisonnements qu'elles Déterminent* by Charles Cornevin, professor at the Lyons Veterinary School. This work has influenced subsequent books on poisonous plants, including *Poisonous Plants in Field and Garden* by G. Henslow (1901), *Veterinary Toxicology* by J.A. Nunn (1907), *A Manual of Poisonous Plants, chiefly of Eastern North America* by L.H. Pammel (1911), *Veterinary Toxicology* by G.D. Lander (1912) and *Plants Poisonous to Live Stock* by H.C. Long (1917). In 1927, Long published *Poisonous Plants on the Farm*, which was reprinted in 1934 as the Ministry of Agriculture and Fisheries Bulletin No. 75, the precursor of *British Poisonous Plants* (Ministry of Agriculture and Fisheries Bulletin 161) by A.A. Forsyth (1954). The latter was reprinted, with small amendments, in 1968 and 1979, but was replaced in 1984 with the first edition of this book (MAFF Reference Book 161).

Research and development

Many of the plants now known to be poisonous were commonly recognized as such by the 18th century at the latest, as indicated by some of their names, English examples of which are cowbane, dead men's fingers, and deadly nightshade. Surprisingly, two of the most important poisonous plants affecting animals in Britain, bracken and ragwort, were not shown to be causes of poisoning until 1893 and 1906, respectively. The late recognition of these types of poisoning was because of their chronicity and confusion with infectious diseases whose nature was not properly understood. Other plants that were significant causes of poisoning, such as corn cockle and the Indian or chickling pea, have declined greatly in importance as the result of changes in agricultural practice.

It is rare for the course of a natural outbreak of poisoning to be studied throughout. The full extent of clinical and pathological signs can be seen only in the (now ethically unacceptable) type of feeding experiments such as were performed in the 19th century, when animals (often dogs) were given repeated doses of plant material to study the effects and allow the determination of lethal doses. Although carefully supervised feeding trials are sometimes conducted with poisonous plants, poisoning is now rarely allowed to proceed so far that the experimental animals die, and little recent information of this type is available.

Apart from some detailed investigations on a few specific plants in Britain, e.g. bracken and those cultivated for animal and human food, there has been little research done on plants from a toxicological point of view. There are various reasons for this: they result in very few fatal cases of human poisoning, they are generally not serious causes of loss in farm animals, and only a relatively few individual cases are seen by medical and veterinary practitioners, who may not have the facilities or time to investigate the cases in sufficient depth to be able to publish their descriptions in the scientific literature. The investigation of plant poisoning requires specialist knowledge from a number of academic disciplines; few investigators are competent in botany, the chemistry of poisonous principles, clinical diagnosis, and pathology. In addition, the special laboratory equipment needed is expensive and this precludes its general use.

Plants have been used medicinally for thousands of years and are the source of some drugs in current use (e.g. digoxin, prepared from some *Digitalis* species). With the increased sophistication and purification methods now available, plants are being investigated more thoroughly as potential sources of novel drugs. The precise mode of action of their individual components is being elucidated, and attempts made to synthesize them. The substances under investigation are of more pharmacological than toxicological interest, because although many of them are toxins, their activity in purified form cannot be extrapolated to apply to cases of ingestion of the plants themselves. Thus the isolation of a pharmacologically useful component from a plant can be taken only as a pointer in plant toxicology. It is, however, appropriate to mention a few examples of the possibilities for therapeutic application that some plant-derived substances appear to have.

At the start of the 1960s extracts of many plants began to be screened for anti-cancer activity; for example, in 1967 a taxane diterpene amide named taxol that had been isolated from the Pacific yew (*Taxus brevifolia*) was found to show cytotoxicity to a range of tumours in laboratory animals. The alkaloids vinblastine and vincristine from the Madagascar periwinkle (*Catharanthus roseus*) also have anti-cancer activity. Mistletoe lectins have been combined with monoclonal antibodies and studied for their selective toxic effects on cancer cells. Some of these substances have been developed for therapeutic use.

In the late 1970s a WHO programme was set up to screen plant extracts for their potential as antifertility agents. Trials have been carried out with gossypol (from cotton plants) as a male oral contraceptive. Some *Allium* species, including onion and garlic, as well as some photoactive plant toxins, such as hypericin (from *Hypericum perforatum*), are being investigated for their antiviral and antidepressant properties.

PREVALENCE

Because of the difficulties in confirming a diagnosis in veterinary and medical practice, and the fact that many cases of plant poisoning recover spontaneously, it is impossible to obtain figures on the prevalence of plant poisoning in Britain, although there are records available that do throw some light on their frequency.

An analysis of the numbers of post-mortem specimens examined at Veterinary Investigation Centres in Britain showed that 15–17% of all poisoning cases were due to plants. Bracken, ragwort, *Brassica* species, oak, yew, and members of the Umbelliferae family were the commonest causes of poisoning between 1975 and 1977. About 10% of the poisoning enquiries received in 1980 at the National Information Centre on Animal Toxicology at the Lyons Veterinary School in France concerned plants, but it is thought there that this represents only a small part of the true situation in that country. In 1990, the American Association of Poison Control Centers received queries concerning the exposure of 28,198 animals (mainly pet animals) to non-drug products; 4539 and 333 were suspected of possible poisoning by plants and fungi, respectively. Of these 4872 queries, 55% were not followed up, no effects were seen in 19%, unrelated effects in 10%, minimal effects in 13%, and moderate or severe effects in 1.8%. Death was reported in 41 (0.9%) of those suspected of being poisoned by plants, and 2 (0.6%) by fungi.

Between 1962 and 1978, some 20,000 enquiries about poisonous plants and their effects were received from the medical profession by the National Poisons Information Service (NPIS) at their five centres (London, Edinburgh, Cardiff, Belfast, Dublin), but only two people are known to have died from plant poisoning in that period, their deaths being due to *Amanita phalloides* and *Laburnum*; more recently, there was a fatal case of poisoning by aconite (*Aconitum napellus*). Spanning the period 1964–1995, the NPIS throughout the country received an estimated 48,000 enquiries about plants. In 1994 the NPIS (London) received about 153,000 enquiries, with about 2.3% relating to plants; 25% of the plant enquiries were concerned with children less than one year old, 23% with children of 1–4 years, and 7% with children of 5–9 years (the age was not known in 33% of the enquiries). Overall, about 4% of the total number of enquiries received by the NPIS concern poisonous plants. The proportion of plant enquiries received by poisons information services in some European countries is much higher.

POISONING: THE PLANT ASPECTS

Poisonous plants and fungi can be classified according to the chemical nature of their toxic constituents, but as these can be either a single substance, several similar substances, or a number of substances with widely different chemical properties, a strictly chemical classification leads to considerable overlapping, with some plants featuring in several chemical groups. Furthermore, in many instances, the poisonous principles have not been characterized. Even the presence of a known poisonous principle in a plant does not mean that consumption of that plant will necessarily produce poisoning.

It is, however, very useful to classify the plant toxins themselves into some chemical grouping and this will be considered later in more detail (see pp. 17–27). Other less precise methods of classifying plant toxins can also be used. These include a classification based on the adverse effects produced, e.g. digestive system disturbances, central nervous system disturbances, or damage to the skin. Such a classification that could lead from clinical signs to the identification of a toxin, and hence to a diagnosis and to the plant responsible for the poisoning, would obviously be extremely useful, but this approach is too simplistic, as the signs are similar for many plant toxins, and an individual toxin may evoke more than one response. An alternative method of classification is based on the ways in which toxic substances can arise in plants. Those that are present naturally, the so-called 'intrinsic' toxins, are the most commonly found. Others, such as the cyanogenic glycosides, are non-toxic in undamaged plant tissue but are rendered highly toxic (by the release of hydrocyanic acid) after the action of enzymes released when the plant is crushed. Plants or plant products may induce adverse effects when infected or contaminated with fungal pathogens that liberate mycotoxins, which are ingested with the plants (e.g. aflatoxins in grain contaminated with *Aspergillus* species; *Sclerotinia* species that cause pink rot in celery and from which furanocoumarins are produced that are responsible for a photosensitization reaction resulting in skin rashes). Storage can also bring about the formation or release of plant toxins, as in potatoes, where the alkaloid solanine may reach highly toxic levels in tubers exposed to light.

Natural (often genetically determined) variations exist between populations of some plants and may affect their toxicity. An example of this is bird's foot trefoil (*Lotus corniculatus*), in different populations of which either cyanogenic glycosides may be absent, or the enzyme that breaks them down to release hydrocyanic acid may be absent, or both of them may be present.

Secondary plant metabolites

Poisonous substances in plants are often termed secondary plant metabolites. Any substance produced within a plant is a metabolite of that plant. For convenience they can be divided into primary metabolites, that is those essential for the basic biochemical reactions required to sustain growth and development of the plant, and secondary (non-nutritional) metabolites that appear to have no such direct role and have even been described as waste products. There is no sharp division, however, between primary and secondary metabolites, and secondary metabolites are now considered to be very necessary to plants, with some functioning as defensive agents against competing plants, pathogenic microorganisms, and herbivorous insects and mammals. A considerable amount of work has been done on the ecological and plant breeding aspects of this protective role, since the increased palatability with lower concentrations of toxins, which is desirable for plants grown for animal or human food, is achieved at the expense of greater susceptibility to predation and to disease caused by invasion of plant pathogens. The reduction or elimination of toxic alkaloids from lupins, to produce the so-called 'sweet' lupin varieties, and the production of rape cultivars with low glucosinolate content are examples of plants in which alterations in the content of secondary (toxic) metabolites of the plant have increased their usefulness as feed plants, but rendered them far more susceptible to insect attack; reducing the secondary metabolites is, therefore, not necessarily economic.

Herbivorous insects are a potential source of major damage to plants, and a fine balance has developed between plants and the insects that feed on them. Secondary metabolites that are toxic to insects are also often toxic to other animals. Whereas some insects have developed specific mechanisms to detoxify or utilize certain otherwise dangerous secondary compounds (e.g. the predilection of cinnabar caterpillars to feed on ragwort), the large herbivorous mammals feed on many more plant species and have developed general, rather than specific detoxification mechanisms. These general mechanisms cannot detoxify all of the many kinds of plant toxins they are liable to meet, and poisoning of varying severity can result.

When the toxic effects of secondary plant metabolites are fatal or severe enough to attract attention, the cause of the deterioration in health can usually be traced, but it is likely that, in animals, considerably greater economic loss is attributable to less obvious effects of plant toxins. They may well contribute to transient digestive disturbances, which can lead to a general loss of condition and performance, affecting weight gain and the quality and production of meat, milk, and wool. Considered in this way, toxic secondary plant metabolites have been referred to as 'antiquality' factors.

Secondary plant metabolites, including the toxic ones, can also affect the taste and smell of plants and, consequently, their palatability. Plants of relatively low palatability

7

will obviously not be consumed to the same extent as more palatable ones, but they may be eaten almost exclusively in times of food shortage. At such times animals may develop a taste for a toxic plant not normally eaten and become addicted to it, still seeking it and sometimes experiencing recurrent episodes of poisoning even when other feed becomes available. Some animal species show preferences for particular plants that are avoided by others; a possible correlation exists between this selective feeding and the ability of the animal to detoxify potentially harmful substances in the plants.

Effects of land management

The occurrence on grazing land of non-cultivated native plants that are poisonous can be influenced by land management. Under recent agricultural policy in the European Union a small percentage of arable land is not used for crops; this is known as set-aside land. It is sown with various seed mixtures and the vegetation cut before it is allowed to produce seed. Mixtures of wild plant seeds are also sown on road verges. In addition to the possibility of these mixtures containing seeds of poisonous plants, the areas where they are sown provide additional land on to which indigenous poisonous plants could spread and become established, thus increasing their occurrence in the country. No links have been made between set-aside land, road verge seeding, and animal poisoning, but as these areas are often adjacent to grazing land, this must be seen as a possibility.

The condition of a pasture can influence the type of plants that grow in it. Some poisonous plants are colonizers that increase in density with overgrazing (e.g. buttercups, docks, ragwort). As desirable forage plants decrease in density, grazing animals consume proportionately larger amounts of the toxic plants, increasing their risk of being poisoned. In addition, animals in poor physical condition from grazing poor pasture are often more susceptible to plant poisons. Poor grazing may frequently drive animals to seek food that they would normally avoid, e.g. horses may consume acorns after a long dry summer period, or cattle and sheep consume poisonous plants such as buttercups, bracken, and umbellifers.

In drought conditions, some plants have a higher concentration of toxic substances, and there may be changes with season and altitude. Snow and severe winter weather can drive animals near to human habitations, which may be surrounded by protective or ornamental hedges such as rhododendron, privet, laurel, or yew, all of which present an available but dangerous source of food. Hedge cuttings and other garden waste thrown on to pasture, or fallen branches from trees are also responsible for many isolated cases of poisoning.

Other agricultural practices that can increase the risk of plant poisoning include herbicide application and other weed control measures. If left on pastures, wilting plants and those treated with chemicals often appear to be more attractive to animals, which may then eat poisonous plants that they would otherwise ignore, or be poisoned by the chemicals themselves.

POISONING: THE ANIMAL ASPECTS

Different species of animals often vary in their susceptibility to individual poisonous plants. In some cases this variation can be explained by differences in the diet of animals, the anatomy of their digestive tracts, and feeding behaviour. Ruminants, such as cattle, sheep, and goats have large forestomachs, where a toxic substance becomes well diluted. Its passage into the intestines, where absorption takes place, is much slower than in non-ruminants, such as horses, pigs, dogs, and cats. Microbial action in the rumen may also destroy the poisonous principles in the plants, although the breakdown of plant material in the rumen can also be detrimental, by promoting the release of toxic constituents. It is often assumed that goats can safely eat almost anything, but this is certainly not so. Under natural conditions, the feeding pattern of the flock is determined by its leader, so that the same plants are eaten at the same site. Flock members learn to avoid the plants actively discriminated against by their leader. Goats not kept as a flock and kids separated early from their mothers show little discrimination.

The most important factors in species differences in susceptibility are probably the detoxification mechanisms specific to each species. These mechanisms can even vary within animals of the same species, e.g. some (but not all) rabbits possess an enzyme, atropinesterase, so that they are not adversely affected by deadly nightshade; goats also possess an atropinesterase that makes them less susceptible to deadly nightshade poisoning. Deer are said to be able to feed on yew and rhododendron, and grey squirrels on toxic fungi (*Amanita* species).

Internal reactions

When a potentially toxic compound is absorbed from the digestive tract, it may remain unchanged, break down spontaneously, or undergo enzymatic metabolism. Enzymatic breakdown to a more water-soluble product than the parent compound is by far the most frequent reaction that occurs. It should be noted, however, that this enzymatic breakdown is not necessarily a detoxification, as it can result in the production of toxic substances from an initially harmless compound. Metabolic breakdown can be conveniently divided into two phases. The first phase involves oxidation, reduction, or hydrolysis to primary products that may be excreted as such or linked, in the second phase, to form an easily excreted conjugated material. The many enzymes involved in these two phases differ with the species of animal, but can also be influenced by a variety of factors such as strain, age and sex of animal, season, time of day, diet, pregnancy, and the amount of the potentially toxic compound absorbed.

After ingestion, poisonous plants may affect the digestive tract in a number of ways. When chewed, some plants, such as the spurges (*Euphorbia* species) and daphne (*Daphne mezereum*), cause an inflammation of the mouth, but the most frequent effect of poisonous plants is an irritation of the stomach and intestines, this being shown by signs including abdominal pain, vomiting (in animals that can vomit) and diarrhoea; a few plants causing gastroenteritis (e.g. oak) cause constipation rather than diarrhoea.

After absorption from the digestive tract the poisonous principles pass first to the liver, the major organ where enzymatic breakdown and detoxification take place. The liver can adapt to the presence of relatively low concentrations of some toxins by developing specific enzyme systems that can break them down. Liver damage can also occur, however, and is seen, in particular, after poisoning by plants containing pyrrolizidine alkaloids (e.g. *Senecio* species). When liver function is impaired, certain bile pigments, instead of being eliminated in the bile, can enter the general blood circulation and reach the capillaries in the skin where they can be activated by ultraviolet radiation and cause the photosensitization syndrome. Other poisonous substances have a direct effect on the blood; those found in rape and *Allium* species can break down red blood cells and cause anaemia. If animals eat plants that contain large amounts of oxalates, such as wood sorrel (*Oxalis acetosella*), the oxalates may combine with calcium in the blood to form insoluble calcium oxalate and lead to hypocalcaemia.

The kidneys, the main organs of excretion, can be damaged by poisonous substances passing through them. For example, degenerative changes are found in them in poisoning by oak and oxalate-containing plants. In many fatal types of poisoning the immediate cause of death is heart failure, which may be the result of a direct effect on the heart muscle, or an indirect effect on the nerve supply of the heart. In addition to the cardiac glycosides (such as those of foxglove), taxine, the main poisonous principle of yew, also has a direct effect on the heart.

Nervous signs are probably second in frequency only to digestive system signs in cases of plant poisoning; they may be characterized as being predominantly excitatory or depressive. When nervous signs are shown, it is usually not possible to find any gross or histological changes in the nervous system to account for them.

POISONING: THE HUMAN ASPECTS

Enquiries related to plants account for only about 4% of those received by poisons units in Britain. In some cases the plant material in question is not toxic, and in many others there are only mild symptoms that resolve spontaneously. Advice is sought, however, because there is a widely known risk of poisoning by plants. Accurate identification of the plants is necessary before advice can be given.

Many of the general principles outlined in the section 'Poisoning: the animal aspects' (see above) also apply to human poisoning. Unlike animals, however, the mixed diet taken by most of the human population ensures that only relatively small amounts of plant material are normally eaten at any one time. Under these conditions the body can tolerate the inclusion of some of the less toxic material without apparent ill effect. It is only when large amounts are taken (e.g. a meal of wild mushrooms), or a dangerously poisonous plant is eaten, that the protective and detoxification mechanisms of the body are inadequate and poisoning results. In times of food shortage, when it is difficult to eat a balanced diet, and plant material not normally regarded as food (e.g. rhubarb leaves and daffodil bulbs) may be eaten, plant poisoning is more likely to occur.

Most human cases of plant poisoning involve certain groups of the population: children, particularly at the crawling and toddling stages with access to house and garden plants; adults gathering wild plants and fungi for food; people using plant materials or mushrooms for their psychoactive effects; and those taking herbal medicines and teas. Occasionally poisonous plants are involved in suicide attempts.

Young children, especially those 2–3 years old, tend to get hold of small objects, such as berries, and put them in their mouth. Older children in the garden are likely to try plant parts to see if they are edible. The house and garden are the most likely sites of ingestion; parks, fields, and woods are other, though less common, sites.

Mistaken identification can occur with those using wild plants as a source of 'natural' food; mushroom gatherers are particularly at risk, as there are some poisonous fungi that are not easy for the non-expert to distinguish from edible species. People using plants and fungi for their hallucinogenic effects can be poisoned by taking too high a dose of the hallucinogen or using a highly toxic plant or fungus in mistake for one thought to be hallucinogenic.

Home-made infusions of plant material that are drunk as herbal teas or taken as herbal remedies can give rise to poisoning, usually after regular consumption over a long period or when large quantities are taken. The 'bush teas' made in some countries abroad often contain high levels of pyrrolizidine alkaloids that are known to be toxic, but poisoning has also occurred in Britain when preparations containing these alkaloids have been used, e.g. the root of comfrey (*Symphytum officinale*). It is also inadvisable to take in excess any of the herbal teas and unlicensed herbal remedies on the market in Britain. The advice of a qualified herbal practioner should be sought as there are possible dangers associated with taking self-prescribed remedies. Although it would appear that the risks associated with the use of unlicensed herbal remedies is low, their potential danger to health is, as yet, largely unknown as they are currently unregulated. The concept that a herbal preparation is 'natural', and therefore safe, is unfounded. There is uncertainty over the actual constituents of some herbal preparations, and their content of active ingredients is very variable; they are not necessarily exactly what they claim to be on the label. Purchasers should be aware that herbal remedies, including some used in traditional medicines, may contain toxic metals, or that pharmaceutical drugs may have been added to enhance the desired effects of the preparation. The amount of research and consequent expense involved in preparing and testing a new drug before it is licensed are so large that, although many plants are screened for their possible pharmaceutical use, only relatively few have gone through the rigorous testing procedures required and are in commercial production.

Poisoning by skin contact

It is not only by ingestion that plants can be dangerous; some can affect the skin. Apart from the spines, hooks, and prickles that can cause mechanical damage, there are some plants that have stinging hairs, notably the stinging nettle (*Urtica dioica*) in Britain, that can introduce chemical irritants into the skin. There are others, such as dumbcane (*Dieffenbachia* species) and the spurges (*Euphorbia* species), whose sap is so irritant that it can cause skin or eye injuries. This type of irritant contact dermatitis is seen particularly in people whose occupation involves handling some plants or plant parts; conditions such as 'daffodil itch' and 'lily rash' and are well recognized among those who work with the bulbs of daffodils or with flowers. An allergic type of dermatitis, in which there is an immunological (hypersensitive) response, can occur in some individuals on contact with certain plants; repeated exposure to the plants can give rise to responses of increasing severity. Allergens that can cause the skin reactions, which often resemble eczema, in sensitized individuals are found in members of many different plant families; the condition called 'tulip fingers' is an allergic contact dermatitis that occurs among people whose work involves handling tulip bulbs.

Other plants, such as rue (*Ruta graveolens*) and giant hogweed (*Heracleum mantegazzianum*), contain furanocoumarins that have photosensitizing properties and can give rise to severe blistering on areas of skin exposed to sunlight. The affected areas of skin commonly develop a persistent brown pigmentation. Such reactions occur among children playing in vegetation, or people gardening. Phototoxic

11

reactions can also be an occupational problem as they may occur when working among crop plants of the Umbelliferae family (such as parsley, parsnips, or celery) in the sun.

Publicity and education

In recent years significant progress has been made in Britain in increasing public awareness to potentially poisonous plants. Collaboration among various organizations (the Poisons Unit of Guy's & St Thomas' Hospital Trust; Health Promotion in Lambeth, Lewisham and Southwark; the Royal Society for the Prevention of Accidents; the Royal Botanic Gardens, Kew; the Horticultural Trades Association; and the Royal Horticultural Society) resulted, in 1994, in the preparation and widespread distribution of posters illustrating and describing some of the poisonous plants that can be encountered in the home, the garden, and the countryside.

Another collaborative venture was the establishment of a voluntary code of practice incorporating a labelling scheme to be used by retailers for potentially harmful plants; the labels carry simple warnings to alert purchasers to any possible dangers from ingestion or skin contact.

Concurrently, an image-based, computerized identification system has been developed jointly by staff at the Poisons Unit of Guy's & St Thomas' Hospital Trust in London and the Royal Botanic Gardens, Kew (see pp. 279–281). It is intended for use in hospital accident and emergency departments, and doctors' surgeries; there is also a simpler version available for educational purposes. The system enables the user to identify a plant suspected of causing poisoning even if only a small part of it is available. Once correctly identified, the toxicity of the plant can be determined and appropriate treatment initiated or specialist advice sought.

DIAGNOSIS

Although the diagnosis of plant poisoning may be fairly obvious in a few cases, such as when cattle break into a garden and are seen eating yew, or when children are found eating berries, it is generally not so easy. The difficulty arises for a variety of reasons: the relative infrequency of plant poisoning in comparison to infectious, metabolic, and other diseases; the variety of potentially toxic plants; the sometimes long period before signs of toxicity appear; the non-specificity of these signs; and the popular tendency to ascribe any disease of obscure origin to poisoning.

To reach a diagnosis on circumstantial evidence, a great deal of information may have to be collected, particularly on the history of the patients, where they have been, and the potentially toxic plants to which they have had access. In a case of suspected plant poisoning it is not uncommon to find that a number of such plants have been available, and after their identification it is important to determine how much of each plant there is growing and if any show signs of having been eaten. The presence of any predisposing factors must be considered, such as the curiosity of a young animal or a recently purchased animal in a new environment, change of pasture, shortage of feed, drought, and application of herbicides or pesticides, or, in cases of human poisoning, the likelihood of plants or preparations of them having been taken by children playing, or by adults for food or as potential hallucinogens.

The clinical signs shown by poisoned animals are usually not very helpful in making a diagnosis; either none may be observed, with the animal being found dead, or they are indefinite and not indicative of any specific cause. There are a large variety of poisonous plants and toxic principles, but only a few ways in which animals or people can react to them: death in a short time, diarrhoea or constipation, excitement or depression, etc. Plants that can produce signs in a short time (within about two hours) include hemlock, hemlock water dropwort, cowbane, yew, foxglove, and cherry laurel and other cyanogenic plants. Those that take 2–48 hours to produce signs include the nitrate-containing plants. Signs of bracken and ragwort poisoning may appear several weeks or even months after their first consumption, and at the time of appearance of signs of toxicity the animals may no longer be consuming them. Plants producing excitement and convulsions include hemlock water dropwort, cowbane, and sometimes ragwort in cattle, whereas depression is the predominant sign produced by hemlock and yew. Many poisonous plants induce diarrhoea, but there is constipation in acorn and ragwort poisoning. Haemoglobinuria occurs with annual and dog's mercury, rape and kale, and haematuria with acorns and bracken. The changes found at post-mortem examination are also generally not specific, although careful examination of stomach contents may reveal pieces of poisonous plant, which may be identified by microscopic examination. Some plants may give a typical odour to the body, e.g. cyanogenic plants, *Allium* species, hemlock. Diagnostic histological changes are found in ragwort poisoning, in which the liver has a characteristic fibrosis.

Many of the remarks on the diagnosis of animal poisoning are also applicable to human poisoning, and some other relevant points are covered in the section on 'Poisoning: the human aspects' (see above). In some respects diagnosis may be easier in human poisoning, as it is not unusual for a patient, or the accompanying adult of children, to link their condition with a specific plant, but there is often a problem in the identification of the plant, and thus in assessing the degree of risk involved. In a confused or unconscious patient, however, plant poisoning is only one of many considerations in differential diagnosis, and it should be remembered that plants are not common causes of poisoning.

Particularly in human poisoning, various methods are used in specialized laboratories to detect and measure the poisonous principles in plants and body fluids. These include thin layer chromatography, high performance liquid chromatography, gas chromatography/mass spectrometry, and nuclear magnetic resonance spectroscopic analysis. Before collecting and despatching any samples for analysis, however, verbal contact should be established with an appropriate laboratory.

TREATMENT

Should there be any suspicion that plants are the cause of animal or human poisoning, the veterinary surgeon or doctor, respectively, should be consulted immediately. They have the training and experience to assess the problem and decide on the appropriate course of action: whether to initiate treatment themselves, request specialist advice from a poisons centre, or refer the case to a hospital. The intention here is to outline the basic principles underlying treatment for poisoning by plants, and not to describe in detail the therapeutic measures available.

The essential first step in both animal and human poisoning is to make sure that there is no further access to the suspected cause of the poisoning. The two other main procedures are (1) the elimination of unabsorbed poisonous material still in the digestive tract as well as that already absorbed, and (2) the support of body functions so that they can respond to, and deal with the toxic agent(s) and the damage caused. The order in which these procedures are taken depends on the condition of the patient. If severe signs, such as convulsions, are present, then their control would have to precede measures to eliminate the poisonous substances. Procedures to eliminate the poisonous plant material from the digestive tract include the adsorption of toxins with activated charcoal, the induction of vomiting, stomach lavage, manual removal of the stomach contents of ruminants, and the use of purgatives.

Absorption of poisonous principles from the digestive tract may be reduced by administering adsorbents, the most effective of which is activated charcoal of vegetable origin. This should be administered after vomiting and gastric lavage. To remove poisonous material that has already reached the small intestines, laxatives such as magnesium sulphate or sodium sulphate or mineral oil should be given. If diarrhoea is already present, the administration of a laxative may add to the risk of dehydration. Colonic lavage can be used to remove poisonous material from the large intestines.

Symptomatic therapy and supportive measures to aid the natural detoxification processes of the body are very important factors contributing to recovery. Supportive measures include control of body temperature, maintenance of respiratory and cardiovascular function, control of pain and central nervous system signs, and treatment of shock.

Specific antidotes are available for only a few types of poisoning, that is those due to cyanides, nitrates, oxalates, and the thiaminase deficiency induced by bracken. Lidocaine has been suggested as treatment for poisoning by yew. General non-specific detoxification measures, however, can be useful, such as the intravenous administration of calcium borogluconate, or of large volumes of fluids to promote renal excretion.

Veterinary treatment
In animals the dosage of activated charcoal for all species is 1–4 g per kg body weight in 50–200 ml of water; a saline laxative should be given at the same time or after about 30 minutes to promote passage of the charcoal and adsorbed toxin through the gastrointestinal tract. In some types of poisoning the administration of repeated doses of activated charcoal may be at least as effective in eliminating the toxins as the use of emetics and gastric lavage, while avoiding the unpleasantness of these procedures. Vomiting can be induced quite readily in some animals (dogs, cats, and pigs), and even if they have vomited already, an emetic should be given to remove any toxic material still in the stomach. Horses, ruminants, rabbits, and rodents do not vomit readily and, if they do vomit, they seldom live long after the event; emetics are not used in these species. In animals that do vomit, the emetics recommended for oral administration are syrup of ipecacuanha for dogs at 1–2 ml per kg body weight, and for cats at 3.3 ml per kg (it is toxic to some cats), and hydrogen peroxide (3%) for both dogs and cats at 1–2 ml per kg. Apomorphine is only recommended for dogs (at 0.03 mg per kg intravenously when the response is almost immediate, and at 0.04 mg per kg intramuscularly or 0.08 mg per kg subcutaneously when vomiting occurs in about 4–5 minutes). Xylazine has an emetic action in cats when given by intramuscular injection at 1 mg per kg, but is followed by sedation. Stomach lavage can be performed in some animals; if not already unconscious they should be anaesthetized, and a cuffed endotracheal tube inserted to prevent stomach contents entering the trachea. In

ruminants the only effective way to empty the stomachs is by rumenotomy, and this has been recommended for yew poisoning in cattle. The contents of the rumen must be replaced at once, however, by warmed feed; rumen fluid aspirated from a healthy animal may be required to restore proper rumen function.

Medical treatment

In human poisoning the principles of treatment are basically the same as those described for animals. The use of emetics, such as syrup of ipecacuanha, is now generally not recommended, as it can aggravate a patient's condition and a previously symptomless patient may develop symptoms. In addition, the clinical effects of a poison may be masked by the possible adverse effects of ipecacuanha (nausea, vomiting, drowsiness, lethargy). Stomach lavage is usually recommended only up to two hours after ingestion of a potential poison. It involves the passage of a tube into the stomach, removal of its contents by gravity or suction, replacement of the contents with water or normal saline, and repetition of this removal and replacement until the washings are clear and free of the toxic material; the final replacement is with a suspension of some adsorbent material such as activated charcoal. Human stomach lavage is an unpleasant procedure for adults, and in children should only be used when absolutely necessary; it should be remembered that berries may block the stomach tube. In cases of poisoning by some of the highly toxic larger fungi, several sophisticated methods, including forced diuresis, haemodialysis, and haemoperfusion are used to assist in eliminating toxins from the body. Specific (Fab) antibody fragments have been used in cases of poisoning by digitalis and other cardiac glycosides.

Poisonous Principles

Conium maculatum
Hemlock

Biochemically, the poisonous plants may be grouped according to their toxic principles, whether these have been synthesized by the plant or selectively concentrated from the soil. These toxic principles include a vast range of compounds that have been classified traditionally as alkaloids, glycosides, saponins, nitrates, oxalates, tannins, phenols, volatile oils, photodynamic substances, minerals, etc. There is some structural overlap between these simple groups and other classifications are possible, but it must be borne in mind that little is known of the poisonous principles of many plants and that the poisonous properties of a plant may be due to more than one substance. In addition, the method used for extracting the toxic constituent from a plant may predetermine the type of poisonous principle found. In Britain most poisonous principles of plants are alkaloids or glycosides.

ALKALOIDS

The alkaloids are not a homogeneous group of compounds that can be defined solely on their chemical structure or pharmacological activity. The term 'alkaloid' (alkali-like) was proposed by the German pharmacist K.F.W. Meissner in 1819, after the first recorded isolation of a crystalline constituent (narcotine) from opium in 1803, although alkaloid-containing plants have been used for their medicinal or toxic properties since very early times. By 1850 a large number of alkaloids had been isolated and characterized, and now about 6000 are known, although it is estimated that they are present in less than 10% of all plant species.

In general, it is recognized that an alkaloid must be a product of plant or animal metabolism, and must contain at least one nitrogen atom that can act as a base. Two further qualifications are that it has a complex molecular structure with the nitrogen atom being part of a heterocyclic ring and that it shows pharmacological activity. As many alkaloids were isolated before their chemical structure was determined, they generally bear names derived from the Latin botanical name of their plant source, with the ending -ine (e.g. berberine from *Berberis*); a few have been named after their physiological action (e.g. emetine from *Cephaelis ipecacuanha*).

They have been isolated from the roots, seeds, leaves, or bark of some members of at least 40% of plant families, with a number of the families being particularly rich in alkaloids, e.g. Amaryllidaceae, Buxaceae, Compositae, Euphorbiaceae, Leguminosae, Liliaceae, Papaveraceae, Ranunculaceae, and Solanaceae. Two very poisonous groups of alkaloids, however, are from yew and hemlock, which belong, respectively, to the Taxaceae and Umbelliferae, families that are otherwise relatively poor in alkaloids. Within a given plant species the content and pattern of alkaloids frequently vary from tissue to tissue and from time to time. Climate, soil, and other environmental factors can modify the alkaloid content within a genetically homogeneous group, while geographical races characterized by different alkaloid content are known within a single species.

The alkaloids are often grouped according to their chemical structure, the plants in which they occur, or their physiological action. There are a variety of structural types, and those of interest here are: piperidines (e.g. the hemlock alkaloids), tropanes (e.g. atropine), pyrrolizidines (in *Senecio* species), indoles (the ergot alkaloids, psilocybin, and heliosupine), isoquinolines (berberine, emetine), quinolizidines (lupinine, cytisine), steroid alkaloids (solanine, the *Buxus* group), and diterpenes (aconitine). There are still other alkaloids that do not fit neatly into such classes or whose structure has not been determined. When grouped by physiological effects, there are, in addition to those recognized principally for their poisonous effects, those with therapeutic uses, for example, as analgesics (morphine), cardiac depressants (quinidine), respiratory stimulants (lobeline), vasoconstrictors (ergometrine, ephedrine), and muscle relaxants (tubocurarine). It is rare, however, for an alkaloid to induce only one type of physiological response, and this limits their therapeutic value.

On the basis of studies carried out on the pharmacologically useful alkaloids, it has been concluded that, after consumption and absorption, the alkaloids present in plants generally undergo some metabolic transformation before being excreted. This transformation may involve only a few structural modifications produced by enzyme reactions in the liver, such as oxidation, hydrolysis, or condensation with other molecules.

Structural similarities have been demonstrated between various alkaloids and the nerve transmitter substances acetylcholine, norepinephrine, dopamine, and serotonin, and it is thought that many toxic alkaloids produce their effects by mimicking or blocking the action of these nerve transmitters. Some clinical features common to the acute poisoning produced by such alkaloids are excess salivation (or its absence), dilatation or constriction of the pupil, vomiting, abdominal pain, diarrhoea, incoordination, convulsions, and coma (as in poisoning by aconitine, atropine, the *Buxus* group, colchicine, coniine, cytisine, galegine, lupinine, solanine). Poisoning by the pyrrolizidine alkaloids is very different; it is usually chronic and the principal organ affected is the liver. Some alkaloids (e.g. from *Conium maculatum*, *Lupinus*, *Nicotiana*, and *Veratrum*) are teratogenic, causing defects in the foetus when plants containing them are eaten by the mother.

The alkaloid-containing plants have a bitter taste and are generally not eaten, although individual animals can become addicted to them. Treatment of poisoned animals is with drugs that counteract the central nervous system effects of the alkaloids; the poisoning, however, is often fatal, and in animals that do survive, recovery is frequently never complete.

GLYCOSIDES

The term glycoside is applied to a large group of organic substances in which a carbohydrate portion, consisting of one or more monosaccharide molecules, is combined with a non-sugar entity called an aglycone. The glycosides are easily hydrolysed by enzymes or acids to the parent sugar and the water-insoluble aglycone.

Glycosides are widely distributed in plants, and many are not toxic. The toxicity of a glycoside is determined by the aglycone, and the properties of the latter can be used to classify the toxic glycosides into cyanogenic, goitrogenic, cardiac, and saponic glycosides. There are other toxic glycosides that do not fit into these groups, e.g. the coumarin glycosides such as esculin in the horse chestnut and those of the spurge laurel (*Daphne laureola*), the norsesquiterpene glycoside ptaquiloside in bracken, and the glycoside ranunculin, whose aglycone is a volatile, strongly irritant oil protoanemonin, which is the poisonous principle of buttercups.

Cyanogenic glycosides

These are not toxic as such, but only through their release of hydrocyanic acid (HCN) that occurs when they have been broken down either after ingestion or as a result of plant cell damage before ingestion.

Trace amounts of cyanogenic glycosides are widespread in the plant kingdom, but relatively high concentrations are found only in certain plants. There is no obvious pattern in the family or genus where they occur, and even closely related species and individual plants of the same species may differ greatly in their production of these glycosides. Most cases of cyanide poisoning, however, are caused by consumption of plants of the families Rosaceae, Leguminosae, and Gramineae. In general the highest concentrations are found in the leaves, but cyanogenic compounds also occur in seeds, roots, and other plant tissues.

Cyanogenic plants contain an enzyme system capable of converting the cyanogenic glycoside to sugar, HCN, and an aldehyde or ketone. In the intact plant the enzyme system and the cyanogenic glycoside are separated, but on disruption of the plant cell they come together to release HCN. Maceration by the animal of the fresh plant tissue as it is ingested initiates the enzymatic breakdown of the glycoside. The acidic environment in the human stomach and that in the stomach of monogastric animals, such as horses, pigs, dogs, and cats, inhibits the action of the plant enzymes, although these may be active during subsequent digestion in the duodenum. It has been suggested that the acidity of the stomach contents may not be great enough to hydrolyse cyanogenic glycosides. In ruminants (cattle, sheep, and goats) the cyanogenic material remains in the rumen at neutral pH, which favours plant enzyme action, while the material is physically broken down further by rumination and the action of rumen bacteria; bacterial enzymes play a principal part in hydrolysing the glycoside. This may explain the greater susceptibility to cyanogenic plants that has been reported for ruminants. Even if a potential danger exists, the actual quantity of available HCN absorbed within a short period determines whether or not poisoning will occur.

When cyanide is absorbed it reacts readily with the trivalent iron of cytochrome oxidase in mitochondria; cellular respiration is thus inhibited and cells become deficient in oxygen; this particularly affects tissues with high oxidative metabolism (e.g. the central nervous system and cardiac muscle). As oxygen transfer to tissues is blocked, venous blood is oxygenated and becomes almost as bright red as arterial blood.

After absorption of HCN, animals do have some ability to detoxify it. A major mechanism is by combination with thiosulphate to form thiocyanate and sulphate; this is catalysed by the enzyme rhodanese, which is widespread in animal tissues (particularly the liver, kidneys, thyroid, adrenals, and pancreas). The thiocyanate is excreted in the urine and saliva. For poisoning to occur the body must absorb HCN more quickly than it can be detoxified. However, cyanide absorption is very rapid, and if sufficient is available (the minimum oral lethal dose is 2–4 mg per kg body weight) its toxic action is also very rapid, with death occurring from a few minutes to an hour after ingestion. The clinical signs are an initial stimulation of respiration that rapidly changes to laboured breathing, excitement, gasping, prostration, convulsions, coma, and death. There are no specific post-mortem lesions; the blood is bright red and stomach contents may smell of bitter almonds.

For ruminants, the recommended treatment is the intravenous injection of sodium thiosulphate at 0.5 g per kg body weight initially, and sodium nitrite at 10–20 mg per kg. Sodium thiosulphate administration can be repeated if symptoms reappear. The sodium nitrite promotes the formation of methaemoglobin, which competes with cytochrome oxidase for the cyanide ion, whereas the thiosulphate acts as a sulphur donor for the enzyme rhodanese to enhance the conversion of cyanide to thiocyanate.

For treatment of human poisoning, the nitrite–thiosulphate combination has been supplemented to good effect with oxygen and sodium pyruvate; the successful use of dicobalt edetate has also been reported, but should be reserved for severe, confirmed cases because of the possible side-effects of cobalt itself.

Goitrogenic glycosides

These are glucosinolates (formerly termed thioglucosides) that are hydrolysed by an associated enzyme, thioglucosidase, whenever wet, raw plant material is crushed; they yield glucose, an acid sulphate ion, goitrogens (thiocyanate, isothiocyanate, goitrin), and nitriles.

Most of the plants containing glucosinolates are in the Cruciferae family, and many different glucosinolates have been isolated from wild plants of this family and also from those cultivated as fodder plants, but only one or two glucosinolates are present in relatively large amounts in a given plant species. Some of the glucosinolates have been named after the plants from which they were first isolated, e.g. sinigrin after the old name for black mustard *Sinapis* (now *Brassica*) *nigra*, but in later nomenclature the prefix gluco- is linked to the plant name, e.g. glucobrassicin.

Glucosinolates are responsible for the hot pungent flavour of several of the Cruciferae (e.g. radish and mustard) and may be found in all parts of the plant, but are often at their highest concentrations in seeds, so that animal feed mixes containing such ingredients as rapeseed meal are potentially toxic, as well as foliage. In young pigs, calves, and lambs high glucosinolate diets have been associated with reductions in feed intake and growth rate that may be the result of direct effects on thyroid function.

The goitrogenic effects of these substances in animals cannot be alleviated by giving iodine, as the mechanism of the goitrogenicity is different from that involved in goitre resulting from the iodine deficiency that occurs in some hardwater areas. Plant goitrogens act by interfering with the uptake of iodine by the thyroid gland, limiting the formation of the iodine-containing precursors of thyroxine, the production of which is therefore decreased. The size and mass of the thyroid glands increase, presumably so that thyroxine production can be increased. The thyroid gland, thus enlarged, is recognized clinically and pathologically as goitre. Although work in experimental animals has indicated a direct correlation between increased thyroid gland size and the consumption of glucosinolates, the development of goitre, solely as a result of eating plants containing these substances, has not been demonstrated conclusively. It seems reasonable to assume, however, that the effects of dietary deficiency of iodine can be exacerbated by eating large quantities of plant material containing goitrogens. The possible depression of thyroid gland activity and the development of goitre as a result of drinking milk from cows fed on large amounts of glucosinolate-containing plants has also been postulated, but is open to question.

Thiocyanate ions may also be present in plants of families other than the Cruciferae as a result of the breakdown of cyanogenic glycosides. Goitrogens of undetermined chemical structure have been reported in other plants but little is known about them.

Cardiac glycosides

On hydrolysis, these yield aglycones that have a steroid structure and a highly specific action on the heart, increasing contractility of heart muscle and slowing the heart rate. The sugar portion of the glycoside has no physiological activity of its own but often greatly enhances the cardiac activity of the aglycone, by affecting its lipid solubility and cell penetrability. The best-known members of this group are the digitalis glycosides present in the foxglove (*Digitalis purpurea*); these have long been used in medicine to strengthen the action of a weakened heart.

Over 400 cardiac glycosides have been isolated and, in addition to those in foxgloves, they are also found in Britain, in the spindle tree (*Euonymus europaeus*), lily of the valley (*Convallaria majalis*), and *Helleborus* species. Besides the effects on heart function, the cardiac glycosides can also cause gastroenteritis and diarrhoea; many of the other signs are a direct result of the inability of the heart to circulate blood. Signs of poisoning usually develop 4–12 hours after ingestion of the plants and, if lethal quantities are eaten, death occurs in 12–24 hours. With sublethal quantities the clinical signs many persist for 2–3 days. Activated charcoal adsorbs cardiac glycosides in the gastrointestinal tract and is an effective treatment of acute poisoning.

SAPONINS

These are water-soluble plant constituents that are distinguished by their capacity to form a soapy foam even at low concentrations, and by their bitter taste and ability to haemolyse red blood cells. They are glycosides with a non-sugar aglycone portion, which is termed a sapogenin. Saponins are classified according to the chemical nature of the sapogenin into two major groups: steroidal and triterpenoid saponins. Almost all the saponins in food and forage plants are of the triterpene class.

Saponins are widely distributed in the plant kingdom and are found in various forage legumes such as lucerne (*Medicago sativa*) and some clovers (*Melilotus alba, Trifolium pratense, Trifolium repens*), as well as in other plants in Britain such as bird's foot trefoil (*Lotus corniculatus*), beech, and horse chestnut. Saponins can occur in all parts of plants, although their concentration is affected by variety and stage of growth; they appear to be concentrated particularly in the roots and rapidly growing shoots. Saponins are more poisonous by injection than by ingestion, and are generally harmless to mammals when ingested, although large quantities can be irritant and cause vomiting and diarrhoea. They are, however, highly toxic to fish and snails. The saponins of lucerne can inhibit the growth of pigs and chicks and depress egg production.

NITRATES/NITRITES

Plants absorb nitrates from the soil and generally convert them into other nitrogenous compounds. Under certain conditions, however, some plants may accumulate quite high concentrations of nitrates. Nitrates are not very toxic, but they are readily converted by bacteria in the alimentary tract into the much more toxic nitrites.

Several factors can increase the accumulation of nitrates by plants and these include drought, shade, the use of herbicides and, in particular, application of nitrogenous fertilizers. In Britain the plants most likely to accumulate nitrates are beet, mangels, turnips, swedes, rape, and kale.

Nitrites pass easily from the gastrointestinal tract into the blood, where they combine with haemoglobin in the red blood cells to form methaemoglobin, a compound that is incapable of taking up and transporting oxygen. Consequently the clinical signs of nitrite poisoning are those of oxygen deficiency and include weakness, depression, a rapid weak pulse, and a fall in blood pressure, while breathing becomes quicker and laboured. The visible mucous membranes become purplish and dark in colour; examination of the vaginal mucous membranes of cows can be used to assess the nitrate status of their feed. There may be muscular tremors and recumbency. Death from asphyxia can occur within a few hours of eating nitrate-rich plants, although it is more usual for a few days to elapse before signs of poisoning appear. During this period the digestive-tract bacteria become adapted to nitrates, which they break down more quickly. Pregnant animals may abort, even in the absence of clinical signs of poisoning. High-nitrate feeds have also been associated with infertility, and with vitamin A deficiency in cattle, nitrates destroying the vitamin A content of hay and silage. Post-mortem examination frequently shows small haemorrhages on the heart and in other internal organs. The blood is often a dark reddish brown. Most cases of nitrite poisoning have been reported in cattle, although sheep, goats, horses, and pigs may also be affected.

Treatment for affected animals is the intravenous injection of a 2–4% aqueous solution of the dye methylene blue at 4.4 mg per kg body weight. This can be repeated if clinical signs recur. Experimental work has indicated that tungsten (as sodium tungstate) given orally to cattle inhibits the formation of nitrites from nitrates in the rumen.

OXALATES

Oxalic acid and its salts, the oxalates, occur naturally in nearly all forms of living matter, but some members of certain plant families (e.g. Chenopodiaceae, Oxalidaceae, and Polygonaceae) can contain relatively large and potentially toxic amounts, mainly as the soluble sodium or potassium salts and the insoluble calcium salts.

While the oxalate content of plants is principally a species characteristic, wide variations can occur within the same species, depending upon the age of the plant, the season, the climate, and the type of soil. Anatomical variations also occur, the highest concentrations commonly being found in the leaves and the lowest in the roots. The oxalate content of many plants tends to increase as the plants mature, an example being the leaves of rhubarb. Other plants show a rapid rise in oxalate content during the early stages of growth, followed by a decrease as the plants mature, examples being *Atriplex*, mangels, and sugar beet leaves and sugar beet roots. To be potentially dangerous the plants must contain 10% or more oxalic acid on a dry weight basis.

Under natural conditions the plants with a high oxalate content are readily eaten by livestock, but if large amounts of such plants are eaten over a short period, acute poisoning can occur. When oxalates are ingested by ruminants, they may be broken down by the rumen microorganisms, they may combine with free calcium in the digestive tract to form insoluble calcium oxalate that is excreted in the faeces, or they can be absorbed into the blood stream. What actually happens to the oxalates depends upon a variety of factors, including the amount and the chemical form of the oxalates, their rate of ingestion, the previous grazing history of the animal, the amount of calcium in the diet, and the nutritional status of the animal. Ruminants can become adapted to a high oxalate intake by developing a ruminal flora that can break down and utilize oxalates. Horses and pigs can also become adapted by developing a similar type of flora in their large intestines. Hungry or undernourished animals are less tolerant of oxalates, as they absorb a higher proportion of those present. Oxalate poisoning occurs principally when hungry cattle or sheep are allowed to graze heavy growths of plants with a high oxalate content.

Such plants are toxic because of the chemical reaction of the oxalates after absorption. Their primary adverse effect is hypocalcaemia that results from the combination of the oxalates with calcium in the blood stream. The calcium oxalate produced is deposited in various tissues, and especially in the kidneys.

Signs of acute poisoning in cattle and sheep include rapid and laboured breathing, depression, weakness, staggering gait, recumbency, coma, and death. There is a fall in the blood calcium concentration. Gross lesions are usually confined to haemorrhages and oedema of the rumen wall, with the abomasum sometimes being affected. Histologically, calcium oxalate crystals may be found in the tubules of the kidneys and in the rumen wall. A chronic form of poisoning with kidney damage has been reported in sheep grazing *Oxalis* in Australia.

Calcium borogluconate given intravenously to correct the hypocalcaemia is the recommended treatment. It produces a rapid improvement but does not always prevent death, as other factors may also be involved in fatal cases: kidney damage with associated uraemia, and interference with energy metabolism.

Fatal human poisoning has occurred after ingestion of the leaves of rhubarb (*Rheum rhabarbarum*) and curled dock (*Rumex crispus*). Another form of oxalate poisoning is produced by contact with calcium oxalate crystals present in some ornamental plants of the Araceae family (e.g. *Dieffenbachia*); the crystals can cause severe irritation of the mouth, throat, and eyes.

PHOTOSENSITIVE AGENTS AND PHOTOSENSITIZATION

Some plants contain substances that can make non-pigmented or slightly pigmented skin hypersensitive or hyper-reactive to the ultraviolet radiation in sunlight; allergic mechanisms are not involved. After ingestion, these substances are absorbed unchanged into the circulating blood and thus reach the skin, where they may be excited by ultraviolet rays and then induce chemical changes that lead to cell damage. Some of these photosensitive substances, the psoralens (tricyclic furanocoumarin compounds), do not require ingestion of the plant to produce hypersensitivity to sunlight; this can arise just by contact of the plant with the skin.

The body responds to the resulting cell damage by itchiness, redness, heat, oedema, and swelling of the affected skin. Blisters may develop and break, giving rise to scabs and secondary infections; skin necrosis may occur. Animals with photosensitive substances in their skin are said to be in a state of photosensitivity, whereas the reaction that occurs in photosensitive animals after exposure to sunlight is called photosensitization. The severity of the clinical signs of photosensitization is determined by the amount of photosensitive substance in the skin, the intensity of the ultraviolet radiation, and the duration of exposure.

In addition to the primary photosensitivity in which the photosensitive agent remains unchanged during its transfer from the plant to the skin, there is a secondary or hepatogenous photosensitivity in which the photosensitive substance is a normal breakdown product of digestion, usually eliminated by the liver. One such substance, phylloerythrin, is formed in the digestive tract of ruminants during the microbial degradation of chlorophyll, and, after absorption, is transported to the liver, where it is excreted in the bile. Any liver damage affecting bile excretion, however, can lead to the accumulation of phylloerythrin in the blood and thus in the skin, where it can be excited by ultraviolet rays. The liver damage leading to this secondary photosensitivity can result from disease, hepatotoxic drugs, industrial or agricultural chemicals, mycotoxins (produced by fungi infecting plant material), as well as from plant toxins themselves.

In Britain there are two plants that can cause primary photosensitivity when eaten by animals: St John's wort (*Hypericum perforatum*) and buckwheat (*Fagopyrum esculentum*). Human cases of primary photosensitivity may result from contact with giant hogweed (*Heracleum mantegazzianum*) and rue (*Ruta graveolens*), and have also occurred after handling vegetables of the Umbelliferae family, such as parsnips, carrots, and celery. In at least some of these the furanocoumarin content increases as a result of the presence of fungal pathogens on the plants (e.g. *Sclerotinia* species on celery). The consumption of cooked or raw fat hen (*Chenopodium album*) can also cause human photosensitization. The furanocoumarins in plants of the Umbelliferae family are not inactivated by cooking; severe photosensitization reactions have occurred after eating cooked food (e.g. celery soup) in patients receiving PUVA therapy (oral psoralens with ultraviolet light) for eczema. In New Zealand, white-skinned pigs have developed vesicles on their snouts and, less frequently, on their feet after contact with waste vegetable material containing parsnips and celery, and exposure to bright sunlight; this condition can be confused with foot and mouth disease and other viral vesicular diseases of pigs.

The photosensitization occurring with bog asphodel (*Narthecium ossifragum*) in sheep is of the hepatogenous type as is also that occurring with ingestion of mycotoxins in dead plant material. Facial eczema, a condition mainly affecting sheep and resulting from ingestion of the mycotoxin sporidesmin produced by *Pithomyces chartarum* on rye grass, has been suspected in south-east England.

Treatment of photosensitization includes removal of the animals from the plant involved in the photosensitization, protection from sunlight, and symptomatic measures.

PROTEINS, PEPTIDES, AND AMINO ACIDS

In addition to the alkaloids and cyanogenic glycosides, there are some other nitrogen-containing organic compounds that are responsible for poisoning caused by plants. The toxic amino acids of plants do not usually produce such spectacular signs of poisoning as some of the peptides and proteins. Cases of poisoning produced by the lathyrogenic amino acids found mainly in the seeds of *Lathyrus* species have been reported in Britain, but only very rarely and not recently. Cyclic polypeptides, known as amatoxins, are the poisonous principles of the most toxic fungus in Britain, *Amanita phalloides*. Viscotoxins, the poisonous principles of mistletoe, are also polypeptides. The poisonous blue-green algae (*Microcystis* species) that form blooms on still or sluggish freshwater (see pp. 267–269) contain poisonous cyclic heptapeptides; poisoning by such algae was not confirmed in Britain until 1989, although it had been recognized in Australia over 100 years before this and diagnosed in many other countries since then.

Complex proteins of plant origin that have caused poisoning in Britain include ricin (said to be the most toxic naturally occurring compound), a lectin found in the seeds of the castor oil plant (*Ricinus communis*). Other plant proteins are haemagglutinins from kidney beans (*Phaseolus vulgaris*) and soya beans (*Glycine max*), and the enzyme thiaminase from bracken and horsetails (*Equisetum* species).

Certain individuals may show a more or less violent local or generalized reaction (allergy) after ingestion or contact with a particular plant protein that does not have any adverse effect on most other individuals. An example of this is an allergy to peanuts. Unlike the effects of other toxic principles, the intensity of the reaction does not depend on the quantity of the toxin but on the sensitivity of the affected individual. These allergens are not toxic constituents in the strict sense, their toxic action being the result of an altered immune response in those who ingest or otherwise come in contact with them.

TANNINS

These are complex phenolic polymers that vary in chemical structure and biological activity. They bind to proteins, produce an astringent reaction in the mouth, and have the ability to tan leather. On the basis of their chemical structure they can be classified into two main groups: the condensed tannins and the hydrolysable tannins. The former are the more widely distributed in plants, but pass through the digestive tract unchanged and are generally not toxic, although large quantities can give rise to gastroenteritis. The condensed tannins have also been reported to cause growth depression in chicks. The hydrolysable tannins have a basic structural unit, D-glucose, whose hydroxyl groups are esterified by gallic acid (gallotannins) or hexahydroxydiphenic acid (ellagitannins).

In Britain it is only the oak that is considered to cause tannin poisoning, the acorns and leaves containing hydrolysable tannins of relatively low molecular weight. These tannins are broken down and absorbed in the digestive tract of cattle and sheep, the breakdown products including gallic acid and pyrogallol. The toxicity of these breakdown products is not clear; it is claimed that absorbed tannins are responsible for the liver and kidney lesions reported in cattle and sheep.

Poisonous Plants

Senecio jacobaea
Ragwort

PLANT FAMILIES

ALLIACEAE

In this family it is members of the *Allium* genus that are of toxicological interest in Britain. Dogs are particularly susceptible, but farm animals can also be poisoned and their milk and meat may be tainted. Parts of several plants in the genus are used raw or cooked for flavouring food, but no specific case of human poisoning by any member of this family has been recorded.

Allium species

A characteristic feature of plants in this genus is the strong smell emitted when they are crushed. There is considerable variation in the form of the plants, although all have parallel veins in the leaves. Onions and shallots (*Allium cepa*) and garlic (*Allium sativum*) have single or multiple bulbs enclosed by a thin, papery covering. The shape of the leaves varies considerably among the species, being long, narrow, and flat in the leek (*Allium porrum*), long, thin, more or less cylindrical, and hollow in the cultivated onion (*Allium cepa*) and chives (*Allium schoenoprasum*), and stalked, oval, and pointed in ramsons (*Allium ursinum*). The inflorescence is usually a terminal head, either globular or hemispherical, and has white or pale purple flowers in spring or summer. Bulbils develop in the inflorescence of some species. There are also some species, often with attractive, showy flower heads, that are grown as ornamentals. The most common wild species in Britain are ramsons (*Allium ursinum*) and crow garlic (*Allium vineale*). Other wild *Allium* species (some introduced) also occur, but are rare or more localized in distribution.

Allium cepa Onion

Onions are cultivated in many countries for their bulbs, which are eaten raw or incorporated into a wide variety of cooked dishes. The bulbs develop, almost always singly, at or slightly above ground level, where the sturdy base of the plant is formed from the overlapping sheaths of the semi-transparent leaf bases. The upper part of each leaf is thin, hollow and roughly cylindrical in section. The flowers, which are very numerous and greenish white, develop in the second year in a crowded, spherical inflorescence at the top of the stiff stem. When mature, the bulbs are covered with layers of thin, brown, smooth, papery skin.

Poisonous principles
Various sulphur-containing volatile substances with an oxidative action on red blood cells are present in *Allium* species; the main toxic substance in onions is *n*-propyl disulphide, but recently a phenolic compound with haemolytic effects has also been found.[1]

Animal poisoning
Most outbreaks of *Allium* poisoning involve the cultivated onion (*Allium cepa*), whose cooked or uncooked bulbs (occasionally whole plants) are sometimes fed to animals.

Farm animals, particularly sheep, eat onions readily, and are often fed with them over long periods apparently without ill effect. Poisoning usually occurs when animals are fed with them exclusively, or in large quantities; their use as part of a mixed diet is unlikely to cause problems. Domestic pets (especially dogs), however, seem more susceptible, and it is inadvisable to give them food containing onions.

The main effect of onions on all animal species is the development of a haemolytic anaemia[2] involving the breakdown of haemoglobin, with the formation in red blood cells of minute inclusion bodies (Heinz bodies) from the broken-down haemoglobin; there is also damage to the cell membrane and destruction of red blood cells. Red discoloration of the urine, which contains these breakdown products, is often the first sign of poisoning. The toxic constituents also cause disturbances in fat metabolism and enzyme activity in chicken liver.[3] Some dogs have an inherited (autosomal recessive) condition in which their red blood cells have higher than normal levels of potassium and reduced glutathione, and are more susceptible to injury by oxidative substances (including those found in onions).[4]

Most cases reported in farm animals involve cattle. In one outbreak, cows and calves showed depression and paralysis, and a bull died after being fed onions for two weeks.[5] When 85 young cattle were given 1000 kg of onions daily, 22 showed signs of poisoning within five days, and one died.[6] The onions were withdrawn, but further cases continued to occur for another five days. Clinical signs included a rapid heart rate, staggering and collapse, yellowing of the conjunctivae, and haemoglobin in the urine; Heinz bodies were seen in red blood cells. Experiments on the feasibility of incorporating cull onions in cattle feed were carried out in the USA. For 119 days, 36 animals were given onions at 5–25% (dry matter) of their feed; this did not result in anaemia, but blood tests showed that red blood cell counts and haemoglobin concentrations were decreased initially, and the percentage of Heinz bodies was generally proportional to the amount of onions fed. The 25% level was thought to be approaching the toxic threshold.[7] A heifer that ate 6 kg of onions showed signs of poisoning within six hours, and, in a separate incident, in a bullock fed with onion foliage and bulbs,[8] rumination, urination, and defaecation ceased and there were muscular tremors, subnormal body temperature and pale conjunctivae. Reddening of the urine was observed in another bullock. Onion peelings[9] or rotting onions[10] have also caused illness in cattle. Transient anaemia with haemoglobin in urine occurred in a pregnant cow that ate a large amount of onion leaves; the foetus appeared to be unaffected.[11]

Sheep appear to be less susceptible than cattle to onion poisoning. Ewes given cultivated onions with their feed for about four months[12] remained clinically normal, even when pregnant, and their lambs were unaffected. Anaemia developed in the ewes within three weeks, but red blood cell counts had begun to recover before the end of the feeding period.

Horses are also susceptible to onion poisoning. One of two animals died after being fed cultivated onions when their pasture was covered with snow,[13] and in another outbreak seven of nine horses died with clinical signs including increased respiratory rate when forced to move, jaundice of oral mucous membranes and conjunctivae, and coffee-coloured urine.[14]

Dogs have been used in experimental work on poisoning with onions[15] and n-propyl disulphide.[16] They seem to be very sensitive to eating onions in any form, and develop Heinz body anaemia rapidly; numerous incidents of this type of poisoning have occurred, often after the animals have been given portions of their owner's food. Within a few hours the urine becomes red, then later coffee-coloured; the dogs may vomit and show signs of depression and weakness. Even a single meal with a high onion content can have adverse effects: ingestion of onion soufflé resulted in depression, increased frequency of urination, dark urine and anaemia in one dog;[17] dark red and then coffee-coloured urine was produced by a miniature poodle given fried onions;[18] a puppy with a preference for raw onions collapsed on exercise and was anaemic;[19] frequent feeding of raw onions to another dog led to extreme lethargy, depression, and loss of appetite.[20] In these cases and also in dogs given dehydrated onions experimentally[21] there was the typical evidence of red blood cell damage. Cats can be affected similarly but less severely than dogs. Giving onion soup to two cats[22] resulted in anaemia, although they remained clinically healthy. The condition was reproduced by experimental feeding of onion soup or raw onion to other cats. It should be noted, however, that Heinz bodies are frequently seen in the blood of apparently healthy cats.[23] Anaemia has also been seen in poultry fed on boiled onions.[14] No mention has been found of the effect of onions on pigs.

The post-mortem findings are similar in all species and include jaundice of mucous membranes, subcutaneous tissues, and muscles, inflammation of the digestive tract, dark or blood-stained urine, enlarged kidneys, and fatty degeneration of the liver, which is usually pale brown in colour. In all cases the tissues have a strong odour of onions.

Symptomatic treatment may be given, but, in most animals, gradual recovery occurs spontaneously after removal of onions from the diet. In rabbits fed on boiled onions, an improvement of the anaemic state induced was achieved by treatment with methionine.[24]

Human poisoning

Although generally not considered toxic, possible anti-thyroid activity of the volatile constituents of onions has been reported.[25] The sulphur-containing volatile oils in onions have a local irritant effect on the nose and eyes.[26]

Allium ursinum Ramsons (Plate 1)

Other common name: Wild Garlic

This plant is common throughout Britain in woods and damp, shady places where it is sometimes dominant. The plant grows from a single, narrow bulb and has (usually two) bright green, oval leaves, pointed at the tip. They may grow up to 25 cm long (usually shorter) and are up to 7 cm broad. The leaf stalks are 5–20 cm long and twisted. The flat-topped inflorescence, borne on a semi-cylindrical or three-angled stalk, is composed of 6–20 small white flowers.

Poisonous principles

This plant is known to contain di-(2-propenyl) disulphide, which is also probably a haemolytic agent.[27]

Animal poisoning

Ramsons, the leaves and flower heads of which had been extensively grazed in woodland in late spring, was thought to have caused the death of ewes in Britain in an area where unexplained deaths had been reported for several years. The carcasses and rumen contents smelt of garlic, and there was evidence of anaemia, jaundice, darkening of the kidneys, and haemoglobin in the urine.[28]

Allium vineale Crow Garlic

This is another fairly common species that grows in England and Wales beside roads or in arable land, where it may be a troublesome weed. It has a main bulb with smaller ones (offsets) growing from it. The leaves are grooved, hollow, and up to 60 cm long. The rather loose inflorescence bears greenish flowers, bulbils, or both, depending on the variety.

Poisonous principles
This plant contains similar substances to those in onions.

Animal poisoning
Allium vineale was strongly suspected as the cause of outbreaks of poisoning in cattle in East Anglia.[29] Annually recurring episodes of illness, with a drastic drop in milk yield, were associated with the animals being turned on to poor pasture containing crow garlic. Affected animals had a weak pulse, cold skin, jaundice, and diarrhoea that was initially black then later watery and yellow.

Other members of the Alliaceae family

As *n*-propyl disulphide or compounds similar to it are found in varying amounts in all plants in this family, it is possible that any of them could cause poisoning or taint the meat of animals that have eaten them. When mixed vegetable waste containing leeks (*Allium porrum*) was fed to young bulls, their breath smelt strongly of the plant, and at slaughter their carcasses had the same unpleasant odour.[30] At the time of the incident it was estimated that their feed contained 1–2% of leeks. A case of allergic dermatitis in a horse, which developed weals over the whole body, was associated with garlic (*Allium sativum*) in a feed additive.[31] Wild onions (*Allium validum*) have caused poisoning similar to onion poisoning in horses[32] and sheep[33] in the USA. An allergic contact dermatitis, especially to garlic, can develop on the fingers of people preparing food,[34] and skin rashes and blistering have been reported after crushed garlic has been applied to the skin as a compress.[35]

AMARYLLIDACEAE

This family includes the wild spring-flowering bulbs, daffodil (*Narcissus pseudonarcissus*) and snowdrop (*Galanthus nivalis*), both of which are native, although localized in distribution in Britain. Many varieties are grown commercially. Other members of the family are grown as house or garden plants.

Narcissus species Daffodils (Plate 2)

These spring-flowering plants grow from bulbs. The long thin leaves develop first, and are followed by large flowers of various colours (mainly shades of yellow or cream). The wild plants grow up to about 15 cm in height, but the cultivated ones (of which there are several thousand varieties) may be up to 50 cm tall. The flowers of most develop singly on stalks slightly longer than the leaves; some that are referred to as narcissi bear more than one flower on each stem. The flowers consist of a trumpet, surrounded by an outer ring of petal-like perianth segments.

Poisonous principles

The whole plant, particularly the bulb, contains toxic substances. These include the alkaloids lycorine (narcissine) and galanthamine, a glycoside scillaine (scillitoxin), and calcium oxalate crystals.

Animal poisoning

The growing plants are seldom eaten by animals, although the death of a tortoise, 11 days after eating leaves of wild daffodil (*Narcissus pseudonarcissus*) has been reported.[1] The animal gradually lost its appetite, stopped defaecating and became lethargic. Post-mortem examination revealed severe gastritis and ulceration of mucous membranes. In the Netherlands, deaths were reported in cattle given *Narcissus* bulbs to eat when feed was scarce during the Second World War.[2] Dogs sometimes eat daffodil bulbs; clinical signs including vomiting, diarrhoea, and hypothermia have been reported.[3] A puppy that ate 12 daffodil flowers vomited several times over a 2-hour period and became drowsy, but soon recovered.[3]

Human poisoning

Consumption of raw or cooked *Narcissus* bulbs, usually as a result of mistaking them for onions or shallots,[4] has caused symptoms including dizziness, abdominal pain, nausea, vomiting, and diarrhoea.[3] Cases of poisoning, with similar symptoms, have also been reported after eating cooked daffodil flowers, stalks (mistaken for a Chinese vegetable), or soup made from daffodil leaves (mistaken for leeks).[5] It is reported that trembling, convulsions, and death may result,[6] but spontaneous recovery usually occurs within a few hours. Those who handle large numbers of the bulbs and flowers often develop an irritant dermatitis (daffodil itch) as a result of contact with the calcium oxalate crystals present; an allergic dermatitis is relatively uncommon.[7]

Other members of the Amaryllidaceae family

Poisoning similar to that described for daffodils has occurred with Kaffir lilies (*Clivia miniata*), Cape lilies (*Crinum* species), snowdrops (*Galanthus nivalis*), blood lilies (*Haemanthus* species), amaryllis (*Hippeastrum* species), snowflakes (*Leucojum* species), and nerines, including Guernsey lilies (*Nerine* species). Most incidents have involved the bulbs or bulb-like underground parts of the plants.

APOCYNACEAE

In addition to the highly toxic oleander, this family includes other house and garden plants that can cause poisoning.

Nerium oleander Oleander (Plate 3)

Oleander is a native of southern Europe, but can survive most winters without protection in Britain, where it is grown as an ornamental or glasshouse plant. It is a flowering shrub or small tree, which, if left untrimmed, can grow to 3 m in width and height. The leaves are elongated and pointed, with a prominent midrib. Large clusters of flowers are produced in late spring or early summer. These are usually shades of red or pink, but may be white or yellow; some varieties are fragrant. The fruits are long and slender, and contain many seeds with silky hairs.

Poisonous principles

The plant contains glycosides that affect the action of the heart in a similar way to the drug digoxin that is used to slow down the heart rate. The names of most of the glycosides have been derived from the botanical names of the plant, e.g. oleandrin, oleandroside, neriine, nerioside; oleandrin is the most important of these. Among the many other constituents that have been identified is another with cardiac effects, digitoxigenin. All parts of the plant are poisonous, whether fresh, cooked, or dried.

Animal poisoning

As oleander is grown only as an ornamental in Britain, it is unlikely to be a frequent cause of animal poisoning here. It is possible, however, that animals could inadvertently gain access to it, if shrubs overhang their enclosures, or if the plant is incorporated in hay or present in garden trimmings thrown on to pasture. Oleander poisoning has been reported from several countries in many animal species.

In California, 37 outbreaks involving mainly cattle and horses, but also llamas, a bighorn sheep and a rhea were diagnosed in the period 1989–1995.[1] Sudden death was the most frequent finding. In animals examined before death, the clinical signs seen were non-specific; they included colic, diarrhoea, pulmonary oedema, and disturbances of cardiac rhythm. In Hong Kong three ponies died 24–48 hours after they had had access to oleander.[2] In New Zealand three cows were found dead after eating prunings of oleander found among rubbish;[3] leaves and twigs of the plant were found in the rumen of the dead animals. Other animals in the herd were weak and unsteady, and had weak, irregular heart beats. They recovered after treatment that included the injection of atropine. When cattle in Italy were fed with cut vegetation including oleander, they became restless, vomited (a rare occurrence in cattle), and showed signs of colic. Later there were convulsions, an irregular heart beat, and laboured breathing; blood-stained faeces were produced. Eleven of the 23 animals involved in the incident had to be slaughtered within 24 hours; the others recovered steadily after atropine injections.[4] Other cattle were affected similarly in Morocco.[5] In four cows in Iran,[6] signs including a slow heart rate and irregular heart beats, followed the consumption of hay containing large quantities of dried oleander leaves; one animal died. Changes in cardiac rhythm were detected in a three-day-old calf of one of the cows, suggesting that oleander glycosides can be passed through milk. Atropine injections (at 0.04 mg per kg body weight) were ineffective (possibly because given too late), but as the ruminal fluid was very alkaline, diluted vinegar was given orally for five days and the animals recovered. In experimental studies, also in Iran, it was shown that the lethal dose of powdered oleander leaves was 50 mg per kg for cattle and 30 mg per kg for donkeys;[7] when vinegar was given with or following these lethal doses, all animals recovered.[8] In addition to irregular heart beats, respiratory difficulty, and slight muscular tremors, acidosis was recorded in sheep given fresh oleander leaves orally;[9] the lethal dose was 0.5–1.0 g per kg body weight. Necrosis of large areas of cardiac muscle and nerve tissue was seen when the dead animals were examined. Poisoning (fatal in some cases) has also been reported following the ingestion of oleander in swans,[10] geese,[11] and in feeding experiments in budgerigars[12] and canaries.[13]

At post-mortem examinations, parts of the plant are often found in the rumen. Gastroenteritis is a common finding, as are haemorrhages of the digestive system and heart. Diagnosis can be confirmed by the use of thin layer chromatography to detect oleandrin in the contents of the gastrointestinal tract.[1]

Human poisoning

Although most cases involve children, accidental and intentional poisoning by oleander has been reported in adults, with varying numbers of leaves (seven to a handful) being ingested.[14–16] Burning in the mouth is often the first symptom, followed by abdominal pain, nausea, vomiting and diarrhoea (sometimes with blood). Dizziness, drowsiness, a slow irregular pulse, unconsciousness, a drop in blood pressure, and irregularities of heart function may develop,[17] depending on the quantity ingested and whether vomiting is induced or other treatment given. Abdominal pain, which persisted for three days, and vomiting occurred in a man who drank an infusion prepared by boiling three oleander leaves in a litre of water.[18] Fatal poisoning occurred in a woman who drank herbal tea prepared from oleander mistaken for eucalyptus.[19] In addition to the more usual symptoms she experienced numbness of the tongue, and became disorientated. In several cases reported,[15,16,20] digoxin was present in the blood, although there had been no intake of this substance. The possibility of digoxin being a metabolite of the oleander glycosides has been discussed, but not established.[20] Visual disturbances similar to those encountered with digitalis poisoning, with dilatation of pupils and the perception of patterns and yellow and green colours, have been reported.[17]

Skin reactions to oleander may occur.[21] A rash and blisters developed in a woman who had been in contact with the shrub while sunbathing;[22] the reaction appeared to be due to photosensitization.

Except in very mild cases, treatment should be sought urgently; stomach lavage should be considered. The injection of 1% atropine is often beneficial if given at the first stages of heart failure. Success has been claimed for the infusion of digoxin-specific Fab antibody fragments.[15,23]

Other members of the Apocynaceae family

Allamanda (*Allamanda* species) and dipladenia or mandevilla (*Mandevilla* species) can cause severe diarrhoea; the sap is irritant to the skin. Madagascar periwinkle (*Catharanthus roseus*) contains toxic alkaloids.

AQUIFOLIACEAE

Included in this family are the hollies, the commonest in Britain being *Ilex aquifolium*, whose berries have occasionally caused mild poisoning.

Ilex aquifolium Holly (Plate 4)

Holly grows wild, as an evergreen shrub or tree, throughout Britain, and its varieties are widely cultivated as ornamentals. The bark of the tree is dark grey and the leaves are thick, dark green and glossy above. They vary in shape from oval, with a smooth edge and terminal point, to those of more characteristic shape, having a deeply undulating margin with spine-pointed teeth. Small clusters of inconspicuous white flowers develop in spring, and bright red spherical berries often remain throughout the winter.

Poisonous principles

Several glycosides have been found in the plant, and one of these, named ilicin (from the botanical name of the plant), is often referred to as the toxic agent of holly, but little is known about them, or the other possible toxins present (saponins and triterpene compounds).

Animal poisoning

Few cases have been reported. In France two heavy horse foals of three and nine months of age were found dead on poor hill pasture in November. The caecum of each animal was impacted with holly leaves; no other abnormalities were detected.[1] In south-west England young lambs have been choked by a holly leaf becoming lodged in the back of the throat at the entrance to the oesophagus.[2]

Human poisoning

Children are attracted by the berries and if more than about 20 are eaten they can have an emetic or purgative effect.[3] In two-year-old twins a 'handful' of berries of the American holly (*Ilex opaca*) produced repeating vomiting within 90 minutes of ingestion, and diarrhoea 20 hours later; one of the twins became drowsy. The symptoms had disappeared 30 hours after eating the berries.[4] Some of the effects in these twins could have been due to the treatment they received (syrup of ipecacuanha). A two-year-old girl experienced nausea lasting for about two hours after ingesting two berries.[5] In a survey in 12 American states, 21 of 1051 cases of ingestion of poisonous plant parts in 1959–1960 involved holly.[6]

The symptoms are usually mild and do not require treatment, but if large quantities of berries have been eaten, stomach lavage should be considered, although the berries may block the tube.

ARACEAE

Many plants in this family are poisonous, including cuckoo pint (*Arum maculatum*), a common wild plant in Britain, and several popular house plants, the most poisonous of which are the dumb canes (*Dieffenbachia* species).

Arum maculatum Cuckoo Pint (Plates 5 and 6)

Other common names: Wild Arum; Lords and Ladies; Wake Robin

Cuckoo pint is generally distributed throughout Britain, except for Scotland where it is relatively uncommon, particularly in the north. It is a shade-loving plant, growing in woods and hedge banks, and may be a persistent garden weed. The leaves appear on long stalks in spring from the perennial white rootstock. The leaf blades are dark green and glossy, up to 20 cm long, triangular or arrow-shaped and often spotted dark purple. The flowers, which appear in late spring, consist of an erect, yellowish-green, partial sheath (spathe), usually 15–25 cm long, within which is a dull purple cylindrical structure (spadix). The fruits develop at the base of the spadix as a closely clustered group of shiny green berries that become reddish orange when ripe, at which time the leaves and spathe die down. (The common name Lords and Ladies relates particularly to the fruiting stage of the plant.)

Poisonous principles

An acrid juice which acts as an acute irritant when applied to the skin or eaten is present in all parts of the plant; drying or boiling reduces, but does not eliminate, its activity. Starch extracted from the roots was used formerly for laundry work but was abandoned because of the irritation it caused to the hands. Food preparations from the baked and powdered root were known as Portland arrowroot and Portland sago. The nature of the toxic principle is uncertain, but most reports suggest that a saponin (saponic glycoside), aronin(e) or aroin, which occurs in all parts of the plant, is the active substance. Little is known about aronin except that it is volatile and unstable and that, if ingested, it ultimately affects the central nervous system. In other poisonous members of the Araceae family that are not native to Britain but which produce similar symptoms to those caused by *Arum maculatum* poisoning, calcium oxalate has been identified as a toxic agent.[1]

Animal poisoning

Poisoning by *Arum maculatum* is rare as, under normal circumstances, animals make no attempt to eat the plants, probably being discouraged by their pungent taste. Outbreaks of poisoning have been reported in spring in Ireland among cattle on poor pastures; they had grazed in hedgerows where *Arum maculatum* was abundant.[2] The clinical signs varied, probably because different amounts of the plant had been eaten. The signs included salivation, swelling of the neck, incoordination, and convulsions, followed by collapse and death. Post-mortem examination revealed inflamed mucous membranes of the mouth, abomasum, and intestines, and inflammation of the gall bladder.

A ewe in a paddock, in which there was a dense patch of *Arum maculatum* that showed signs of having been liberally eaten, developed intermittent muscular weakness in the hind legs, and within two days a profuse greenish-yellow diarrhoea with a strong smell.[3] Its three-week-old lamb became depressed. As soon as the ewe recovered, it started to eat the plant again. Other ewes in the paddock remained healthy.

Arum poisoning was suspected in seven separate cases in horses in Britain over a period of five years.[4] All were pregnant mares that aborted about five days after the onset of clinical signs, which included inflammation of the conjunctivae and the mucous membranes, particularly those of the mouth. Initial constipation was followed by scouring; five of the horses died. In Romania, horses were poisoned after eating *Arum maculatum* growing at the edge of a wood;[5] an aqueous extract of the plants injected into dogs caused a fall in blood pressure, and respiratory changes led to asphyxia.

Human poisoning

This usually involves children who eat the attractive berries, which are particularly poisonous.[6] However, a small boy was poisoned after chewing the leaves;[7] he developed a sore mouth and abdominal pain and became drowsy. The acrid juice is a deterrent to eating large amounts of cuckoo pint, but if sufficient is eaten there may be sore throat, gastrointestinal irritation and pain, with severe diarrhoea, irregular heartbeat[8] and, in extreme cases, coma and death.[9] Poisoning is not usually severe, however, and treatment is rarely necessary.

Dieffenbachia species Dumb Canes (Plate 7)

These popular house plants are grown for their foliage; the flowers, partially enclosed in green sheaths, are less attractive. In its natural habitat (Brazil and the West Indies) dumbcane may grow up to 2 m high, but as a pot plant it rarely exceeds 60 cm. The upright stem is partly sheathed by the base of the leaf stalks, giving a somewhat jointed appearance. As a continuation of the stalk, the leaves have a prominent midrib, particularly on the underside. The young leaves are loosely curled along their long axis, but when expanded they are bright or dark green, broad and oval, but taper at the tip and towards the stalk. They can be up to 40 cm long, but in many specimens they are less than 20–30 cm. *Dieffenbachia seguina*, *Dieffenbachia picta* and *Dieffenbachia bausei* are particularly common as house plants; there are many varieties and some hybrids. They are distinguishable by the characteristic markings on the upper side of the leaves. These may be white or yellowish lines following the main veins, or an irregular pattern of whitish blotches.

Poisonous principles

It is generally agreed that the constituent causing most of the symptoms is calcium oxalate or oxalic acid, which is present in the sap as needle-shaped crystals, but an enzyme (a proteinase) may also be involved. These plants are a potential danger to both children and domestic pets, and should be kept out of their reach.

Animal poisoning

Pets in the home can often gain access to house plants, and may be badly affected by them. In France a dog that ate a *Dieffenbachia* leaf that was on the floor developed repeated vomiting and diarrhoea; it started to recover in about three days.[10] Similar cases have been reported in Britain.[7]

Human poisoning

Although the whole plant is poisonous, poisoning usually results from the leaves being chewed. A sharp, pricking sensation, sometimes likened to chewing glass splinters, is experienced in the mouth, and it is probable that mechanical damage by the sharp crystals precedes poisoning by the oxalates. An intense burning pain, accompanied by reddening and swelling of the mouth, tongue, and throat, occurs very quickly after chewing the plant; the swelling may be so severe that the throat becomes partly blocked, restricting breathing. In some cases the voice is partially or completely lost for a while, hence the common name, dumb cane.[11,12] Oral contact with the plant for even a very short time can produce severe, local damage in the mouth and on the tongue.[13] Symptoms are usually restricted to the mouth and throat, but occasionally nausea and vomiting have been reported. A four-year-old boy, who drank water that had contained *Dieffenbachia* cuttings, rapidly developed swelling of the lips, tongue, and throat;[14] there was pain on palpation of the upper abdomen. These symptoms declined over the next three days.

Care should be taken when tending these plants as eye injuries lasting for up to four weeks have resulted from sap squirting into the eyes when the plant is being trimmed.[15,16]

Other members of the Araceae family

Bog arum (*Calla palustris*), a plant introduced to Britain, and growing wild in some areas, can cause poisoning similar to that associated with wild arum (*Arum maculatum*). Some other house plants of this family can give rise to poisoning similar to that caused by *Dieffenbachia*, although the symptoms are generally less severe. In this category are elephant's ear (*Alocasia* species), Jack in the pulpit (*Arisaema* species), elephant's ear (*Colocasia* species), devil's ivy (*Epipremnum pinnatum*), the cheese plant (*Monstera deliciosa*), elephant's ear (*Philodendron* species), syngonium (*Syngonium* species), and arum lilies (*Zantedeschia* species).[17] *Philodendron* poisoning has been reported in cats, but could not be reproduced experimentally.[18] An 11-month-old child, who chewed the leaves of a *Philodendron* plant, developed mouth and oesophageal erosions and died suddenly 18 days later.[19] This appears to be a very unusual case, as, in general, *Philodendron* species seem to be of low toxicity.[20]

ARALIACEAE

The only member of this family that is native to Britain is the ivy (*Hedera helix*); many varieties (some variegated) are cultivated as garden or house plants. These *Hedera* species should not be confused with other plants with the common name ivy, and in particular with the poison ivy (*Toxicodendron radicans*), a member of the Anacardiaceae family, that has been introduced into Europe, and which causes a very severe form of contact dermatitis.

Hedera helix Ivy (Plate 8)

Ivy is a native woody evergreen plant, which creeps along the ground, often forming dense mats, or climbs up trees or walls by means of numerous short roots that grow from the stem. The plant is very tolerant of shade. The leaves, which arise from the main stems, are 4–10 cm across, dark green above and paler beneath, and have 3–5 triangular lobes, the central one being the longest; those on the flowering stem tend to be more oval in shape. The flowers grow in autumn in a terminal group on the stem. They have yellowish-green petals 3–4 mm across, and smooth, black, globular fruits 6–8 mm in diameter develop after flowering.

Poisonous principles

The plant contains triterpenoid saponins (hederasaponins A, B, and C), which undergo partial hydrolysis, with loss of sugars, to form the toxic substances α- and β-hederin.

Animal poisoning

In small quantities, the plant is not considered harmful to livestock and is said by some to be beneficial. In larger quantities, however, it is of potential danger to animals, and care should be taken in the disposal of ivy stripped from walls or trees. Ivy poisoning has been reported in cattle, deer, sheep, and dogs[1] with clinical signs that include vomiting, diarrhoea, excitement, muscular spasms, paralysis, and initial dilatation and later contraction of blood vessels. After consuming large quantities of leaves and berries, when pasture was scarce, two dairy cows started to stagger, became excitable and occasionally bellowed loudly as if in pain. A strong odour of crushed ivy leaves, both in the breath and in the milk, persisted for about three days, after which recovery was complete and uneventful.[2] In Germany, during heavy snow, a deer was found in a disorientated state and with early signs of paralysis. Ivy leaves were found in the mouth and stomach.[3] Vomiting has been reported in two dogs in Britain.[4] Another report states that ivy seeds were responsible for the death of poultry in France.[5]

Human poisoning

Ivy is often listed among plants that can cause poisoning in children who eat the berries. Emetic and purgative effects have been reported, together with laboured breathing, excitation, convulsions, and coma,[6] but no recent reports of such severe symptoms have been found. The sap of the plant can cause both irritant and allergic dermatitis,[7] sometimes with severe blistering and inflammation.[8] In one incident recorded, a severe skin reaction occurred after pruning ivy.[9] An eczematous dermatitis and blistering developed, and there was swelling and pain around the eyes. The affected areas healed slowly over three weeks. In another case, a man who pulled ivy from his garage developed red blotches and irritation over most of his body, with swelling of the hands, arms, and eyelids, and blister formation of the backs of both hands. The skin peeled from his hands and arms. He did not feel unwell, but the skin lesions took about ten days to clear.[4]

If a large number of berries has been eaten, stomach lavage may be performed, but the berries are liable to block the tube.

BERBERIDACEAE

Berberis vulgaris Barberry (Plate 9)

Barberry occurs locally throughout Britain, where it is probably an introduced species rather than a native plant. Many varieties are cultivated in gardens. It is a spiny shrub 1–2.5 m high, with pointed oval leaves 2–4 cm long, that have serrated edges, the serrations often terminating in a small spine. Clusters of yellow flowers, 6–8 mm in diameter, appear in summer, and rectangular red fruits 8–12 mm long develop in autumn. Some of the cultivated varieties have bluish or blue-black berries.

Poisonous principles

An isoquinoline alkaloid, berberine, has been isolated from the roots and stems of several *Berberis* species; the highest alkaloid content is in the bark. The berries of wild barberry are not poisonous,[1] but the seeds of at least some of the cultivated species and varieties contain appreciable quantities of alkaloids. No authenticated cases of animal or human poisoning by any part of the plant have been found. Berberine extracted from the plant is being investigated for its possible pharmacological activity on some tumours. It is an ingredient of some herbal (mainly Chinese) medicines.

Human poisoning

Reports of children having eaten the berries of wild barberry or those of cultivated species and varieties of *Berberis*, or those of the related shrub mahonia (*Mahonia* species) are received frequently by poisons information services,[1,2] although these berries are apparently not toxic. However, medicinal preparations containing berberine have caused poisoning, with vomiting and diarrhoea being the most common symptoms. Abdominal pain and diarrhoea have been reported in those who handle the wood.[3] Injury by the spines can cause papular dermatitis,[3] although it is possible that this may be due, at least in part, to the introduction of bacteria or fungi from the spines into the skin.

BORAGINACEAE

The poisonous plants in this family include some native wild plants that have caused poisoning abroad (*Cynoglossum* and *Echium* species), and the heliotropes (*Heliotropium* species) that are sometimes cultivated here, but in Britain in recent years most attention has been paid to comfrey (*Symphytum officinale*) since it has been found to be harmful, although widely used as a herbal remedy.

Cynoglossum officinale Hound's Tongue

Hound's tongue is a native British plant that is common in some areas, but found only occasionally in others. It is widely distributed in southern and eastern England, where it grows on dry soils (sand, gravel, chalk, and limestone) often near the sea. It is an erect biennial that grows up to 90 cm high and is covered with long, silky hairs, giving it a greyish appearance. Purple funnel-shaped flowers develop in summer.

Poisonous principles

The plant contains pyrrolizidine alkaloids, variously named as cynoglossine, consolidine, echinatine, and heliosupine. The pyrrolizidine base, heliotridine, that is present in hound's tongue differs structurally from the more familiar pyrrolizidine alkaloids present in other plants, but it produces a similar type of toxic reaction.

Animal poisoning

Hound's tongue began to thrive in Britain in the mid 1950s as myxomatosis killed the rabbits, which had previously kept it in check. In 1959, pregnant Friesian cows were poisoned when they gained access to waste land where hound's tongue was growing in profusion.[1] When found several hours later, the animals had staring expressions, rapid breathing, and varying degrees of tympany and diarrhoea. Increased thirst was a prominent sign and a drop in milk yield was recorded. Post-mortem examination of animals that died revealed congestion of the lungs and large quantities of hound's tongue leaves in the rumen, where there was considerable inflammation. Other parts of the stomach were inflamed, and mesenteric lymph nodes were swollen, oedematous, and haemorrhagic. Cattle that grazed hound's tongue growing with sainfoin in Russia[2] developed nervous signs and diarrhoea 12–24 hours (6–12 hours in calves) after first eating the plants. Many cattle in the herd had failed to recover three months later and were slaughtered. *Cynoglossum officinale* has become established in parts of the USA after it was inadvertently introduced into the country, and has caused much poisoning of animals there. Evidence that the toxicity of the plants remains after drying was found when a calf from a group of nine became ill after being fed with chopped hay from a pasture containing the plant, and died of liver failure;[3] the post-mortem examination showed changes indicative of pyrrolizidine alkaloid toxicity. Other calves given daily, by stomach tube, a slurry containing the ground, dried plant in water for 21 days developed liver damage of dose-related severity.[4] The death of ten horses that also suffered severe liver damage was attributed to feeding with dried grass that contained *Cynoglossum officinale*.[5] From an experimental feeding trial in horses[6] it was concluded that hound's tongue at the early flowering stage, when it is likely to be harvested with forage plants, generally contains about 0.8% total pyrrolizidine alkaloids. At this concentration, a lethal dose for a 500-kg horse would be about 900 g of the dried plant (about 6% of the daily intake of a horse). The intake of such an amount is possible in the USA, where hound's tongue has become widespread in certain areas, but is most unlikely in Britain.

Echium plantagineum Purple Viper's Bugloss

Other common names (mainly in Australia): Paterson's Curse; Salvation Jane

This is a native plant that grows in a few areas near the coast in south-west England, and occasionally elsewhere as a naturalized garden escape. The leaves are coarsely hairy, oval in shape, but pointed at the tip and where they join the stem. The plant grows up to 75 cm tall, and bears clusters of purple, lipped, tubular flowers.

Poisonous principles
The plant contains the closely related pyrrolizidine alkaloids echimidine and echiumine. There is variability in the total content of toxic alkaloids among different populations of the plant.[7]

Animal poisoning
Purple viper's bugloss has not been associated with poisoning in Britain. Ingestion has caused nervous signs in a colt,[8] and the death of horses in Australia.[9] In all cases the animals gradually lost condition and appetite and became listless over a period of 4–6 weeks. Nervous signs, including incoordination, circling, and blindness, were seen in some cases. Examination of dead animals revealed liver damage with bile duct proliferation. An outbreak of poisoning in Brazil in which 28 of 77 Holstein cattle died

was attributed to the plant.[10] The animals showed digestive and nervous system disturbances and, in some, photosensitization. In the dead animals examined the liver was small and hard, the gall bladder enlarged, and there were lesions in the liver and degeneration of nervous tissue. The disease was reproduced experimentally in calves and chickens when the dried plant was added to their feed. Sheep are also susceptible to poisoning by *Echium plantagineum*, but in these animals two distinct diseases occur; one typical of pyrrolizidine alkaloid poisoning, and the other a form of chronic copper poisoning.[11-13] It is thought that damage to the liver cells caused by the alkaloids results in the enhanced uptake and accumulation of copper. There have also been reports of poisoning in free-range pigs in New South Wales, and in other pigs fed experimentally with the plant.[7] The toxicity of the plant has been studied in experiments on sheep[14] and rats[15] fed pelleted feed containing 20–80% of the plant.

Human poisoning

No cases associated with ingestion have been found, but the rough hairs on the plant are a cause of dermatitis.[16,17]

Symphytum officinale Comfrey (Plate 10)

This plant grows in damp places, often beside streams, and is generally distributed throughout Britain, although found less commonly in the north. It is an erect, coarsely hairy plant, 30–120 cm high. The leaves are 15–25 cm long, tapering towards the tip and narrowing towards the base which continues down the stem, giving it a winged appearance. The flower heads form in summer at the ends of the branches, where a cluster of blue, pink, purple or yellowish-white, bell-shaped flowers are borne on separate stalks. The comfreys grown commercially, mainly for use in a variety of herbal preparations, are vigorous hybrids, usually crosses between *Symphytum officinale* and the rough comfrey (*Symphytum asperum*). These hybrids, known as Russian or blue comfrey (*Symphytum* × *uplandicum*), are sometimes found naturalized in Britain, especially along roadsides.

Poisonous principles

Symphytum species contain numerous pyrrolizidine alkaloids, many of which are named after poisonous plants in the Boraginaceae family, e.g. symphytine, cynoglossine, heliosupine, lycopsamine, echimidine, and lasiocarpine. Quantitative studies of Russian comfrey (*Symphytum* × *uplandicum*), which contains at least eight alkaloids, showed that the concentrations of alkaloids are highest in small, young leaves early in the season, decrease as the leaf grows heavier, and are lowest in the large, mature leaves.[18] In general, the concentrations of alkaloids are higher in roots than in leaves. Nitrates may accumulate in some plants.

Animal poisoning

Comfrey appears to cause animal poisoning only rarely; possibly they find it unattractive to eat because of its bristly hairs. Nitrate-nitrite poisoning has been reported in pigs given rough comfrey (*Symphytum asperum*) as green fodder.[19] (This species is seen occasionally in Britain where it has become naturalized in waste places.) General apathy, laboured breathing, and cyanosis, typical of nitrite poisoning, were observed. The blood was dark reddish brown indicating the presence of methaemoglobin, a stable compound (of nitrites and haemoglobin) that does not take up oxygen.

Therapeutic veterinary use of the plant has been reported. Preparations (sometimes called kytta) made from comfrey roots have been applied topically to promote healing of tongue ulcers in cats,[20] and skin lesions associated with lameness in cattle,[21] or given internally for the treatment of inflammatory conditions of the digestive and reproductive systems.[22]

Human poisoning

Comfrey has long been regarded as a mild astringent, and extracts of boiled roots or leaves have been used as herbal teas, as a tonic, or for treating numerous maladies[23] – old herbals on the subject make fascinating reading. The plant and its hybrids have been grown commercially in Britain and other countries for medicinal use. It has also been listed as edible,[24] and its potential as a food plant has been investigated;[25] the Japanese have used it as a green vegetable.[26] Although there are relatively few reports of poisoning after eating comfrey, its consumption in herbal tea can lead to serious liver damage.[27] The plant is, therefore, a cause for concern because of its widespread use. Veno-occlusive disease, which is similar to the Budd–Chiari syndrome, has been diagnosed in people taking relatively large amounts of comfrey preparations regularly over a long period.[28–31] The precise mechanism of this type of toxicity is unknown, but the presence of an unsaturated pyrrolizidine ring seems to be essential. Veno-occlusive disease occurs particularly in the West Indies, where so-called bush teas are taken. These often contain only harmless plants, but others such as *Crotalaria* and *Senecio* species, which contain pyrrolizidine alkaloids, are also included. A woman who took two comfrey preparations several times daily (comfrey tea and comfrey-pepsin capsules) had progressive swelling of the abdomen and extremities (due to fluid accumulation), and enlargement of the liver.[29] There were structural changes in the liver, including dilatation of some of the larger blood vessels, almost total obliteration of some of the smaller ones, and the development of fibrous tissue. General malaise accompanied by abdominal distension and peripheral oedema developed in a 23-year-old man who had eaten 4–5 comfrey leaves daily for 1–2 weeks.[30] His liver was enlarged, and small samples of tissue from it showed narrowing or blocking of blood vessels, and small haemorrhages. The man developed a deep vein thrombosis and died. A similar, but less severe, condition was reported in a 13-year-old boy, with a history of Crohn's disease, who was given comfrey root and tea preparations.[31] The regular consumption, over long periods, of herbal teas or herbal remedies containing comfrey should be avoided.[32] Preparations containing the dried, powdered roots of comfrey (sometimes called Radix symphyti or Symphyti radix) are also used, as are a variety of aids to digestion, taken in the form of capsules or pills, each of which may contain as much as 500–600 mg of alkaloids.[33] The harmful effects of comfrey on the liver were confirmed in experiments on laboratory rats, in which dose-related liver damage occurred when they were given pyrrolizidine alkaloids from Russian comfrey.[34] Other experiments have shown that comfrey can be carcinogenic in rats;[26] tumours developed in the liver and bladder of those fed comfrey leaves at 8–33%, or comfrey roots at 1–8% of their diet. Liver damage was apparent after six months, and tumours developed from 14 months onwards with leaf, and seven months onwards with root preparations. There is some evidence that intermittent feeding of the plant to rats is more damaging than continuous feeding.[28] As the potential dangers of comfrey have been recognized, the plant has fallen into disrepute, and a request for the immediate withdrawal from sale of medical oral preparations (tablets and capsules) containing it was made by the Food

Minister in Britain in March 1993.[35] At the same time the trade was asked to consider labelling the packaging of comfrey roots and leaves with a warning against their ingestion, and the public advised against the use of comfrey leaves as a vegetable, or of the roots to make tea.[36] No action was suggested on comfrey leaf teas, as these contain lower concentrations of pyrrolizidine alkaloids, or on comfrey preparations for external use. Applied to the skin, comfrey is said to have healing properties, which are attributed to the allantoin present in the plant.[23] As assessed by the excretion of the alkaloids in the urine, the absorption of pyrrolizidine alkaloids by the skin of rats was 20 times less than that by the gastrointestinal system,[37] indicating that the occasional external use of comfrey preparations should not be hazardous. Contact with the bristly hairs of the plant is known to cause irritant contact dermatitis.[38,39]

Other members of the Boraginaceae family

Borage (*Borago officinalis*) and common viper's bugloss (*Echium vulgare*) contain small amounts of pyrrolizidine alkaloids, but no cases of poisoning by them have been found in Britain. Heliotropes (*Heliotropium* species) that are occasionally found naturalized as garden escapes in Britain have caused poisoning in other countries; they contain pyrrolizidine alkaloids. *Heliotropium europaeum* has been associated with outbreaks of liver cirrhosis that closely resembles poisoning by ragwort (*Senecio jacobaea*) in cattle[40,41] and sheep[13,42] in Australia, and also in calves in Israel.[43,44] In some of these cases the plant was present in hay. Fatal poisoning has been recorded in pigs and poultry given feed contaminated with *Heliotropium europaeum* seeds.[45] There have been several cases reported of outbreaks of human poisoning, mainly in India, Central Asia and Barbados, after ingesting various *Heliotropium* species[33] in the form of herbal teas, herbal remedies, or flour from grain contaminated with seeds of the plant.

BUXACEAE

Buxus sempervirens Box (Plate 11)

Box is an evergreen shrub or tree, which is native in Britain but limited in its distribution to a few areas of southern England, where it is locally abundant on chalk or limestone in beech woods and scrub. Box is cultivated widely as an ornamental or hedging plant. The bark is grey and the twigs are angled and covered with short hairs. The leaves, borne close together on short stalks, are elliptical or oval in shape, 1.0–2.5 cm long, darker green and somewhat glossy above, paler and dull below. The inconspicuous flowers are borne in clusters in the axils of the leaves, each cluster terminating in a female flower with several male flowers below it. The fruit is an ovoid capsule containing shining black seeds.

Poisonous principles

All parts of the plant are poisonous. The active agent was believed to be an alkaloid, buxine, but this is now recognized to be a complex group of steroidal alkaloids rather than a single substance. Many names, derived from the generic name *Buxus*, have been applied to individual alkaloids within the group, but nomenclature based on their structure is also used. There is still little known about the toxicity of the individual alkaloids.

Animal poisoning

Box is usually avoided by animals, possibly because of its disagreeable odour when bruised and its bitter taste, but, when it has been eaten, severe illness and death have occurred in several animal species. A fatal dose for a horse is reported to be 750 g of leaves,[1] and of a group of pigs that died after eating box, one had almost 500 g of leaves in its stomach.[2] The cases of poisoning reported in horses,[3] cattle,[4-6] and pigs[2,4,7] have generally resulted from the animals having had access to garden hedges, trees, or clippings. The clinical signs are similar in all species and have included vomiting, abdominal pain, diarrhoea, incoordination, convulsions, and coma. Death from respiratory failure may occur very rapidly. Transient paralysis of the throat, with consequent inability to swallow, was reported in a heifer that recovered.[6] Aquarium fish have been killed by sprigs of box being placed in their tanks.[3] Post-mortem examination reveals acute irritation of the gastrointestinal tract, with box leaves in its contents, and congestion of the lungs.

Human poisoning

No reports of poisoning by ingestion of box have been found, but skin reactions may follow contact with the sap, and asthma has developed after exposure to the sawdust.[8]

CACTACEAE

Lophophora williamsii Peyote Cactus

This spineless cactus has been used for its hallucinogenic properties for at least 2000 years in the parts of the world where it is native (southern Texas and north and central Mexico). Each plant grows from a fleshy rootstock, and consists of one or more squat, rounded, green, succulent stems (crowns), usually 2–8 cm in diameter, that are ridged longitudinally and divided near the top into small sections, each of which bears a tuft of white or yellowish hairs. The flowers develop centrally and are white or pink; the fruit is a pinkish, spherical structure and the seeds are black.

Poisonous principles

Peyote contains over 30 alkaloids, many of which have been given very similar names; they include mescaline (about 30% of the total alkaloid content), pellotine, anhalamine, anhalinine, anhalonine, and lophophorine.[1] It appears that mescaline (3,4,5-trimethoxy-beta-phenylethylamine) is the most hallucinogenic, with actions similar to those of lysergic acid diethylamide (LSD). Mescaline and other related drugs, such as Ecstasy (3-methoxy-4, 5-methylene dioxyamphetamine), have been synthesized for their hallucinogenic properties. Lophophorine (*N*-methylanhalonine), a minor alkaloid constituent, is the most toxic and has strychnine-like effects.

Human poisoning

The dried, brown, disc-shaped crowns (mescal buttons) are generally swallowed, or sometimes soaked in water, which is then drunk. Shortly after ingestion there may be a hangover-like phase with nausea, flushing of the face, light-headedness, dizziness, chills, headache, abdominal pain, vomiting, anxiety, dilatation of the pupils, and muscular relaxation.[2] Any unpleasant symptoms subside in 1–2 hours and are followed by a dream-like hallucinatory state with brilliantly coloured visual effects; this phase lasts for 5–12 hours. Enquiries about *Lophophora* are received occasionally by poisons units in Britain. Supportive treatment is generally all that is required, but in some cases stomach lavage may be necessary.

CAMPANULACEAE

Lobelia species Lobelias

Acrid lobelia (*Lobelia urens*) occurs occasionally as a wild plant in Britain, where it is very limited in distribution, but said to be increasing in frequency. Several *Lobelia* species are grown in gardens; the cultivated forms vary greatly in appearance.

Poisonous principles
The plants contain a piperidine alkaloid, named lobeline, and other related alkaloids; these have a nicotine-like action. Dried plant material has little toxic activity.

Animal poisoning
Some species of *Lobelia* have been implicated in cases of poisoning in the USA; after an outbreak of poisoning in cattle that had been grazing pasture in which *Lobelia berlandieri* was one of the dominant plants, feeding trials were carried out on sheep.[1] Clinical signs including dilated pupils, sluggishness, loss of appetite, and diarrhoea developed initially, followed by nasal discharge and ulceration of the mouth; coma preceded death.

Human poisoning
Acrid lobelia was reported in early literature[2] to cause inflammation if applied to the eyes, and symptoms similar to poisoning by deadly nightshade (*Atropa belladonna*), with inflammation, if taken internally. No evidence of such poisoning has been found in later literature. Drinking or smoking herbal preparations containing the leaves of some *Lobelia* species can cause poisoning.[3] Because of the unpalatability of *Lobelia* species, human poisoning by the plants is rare, but they can irritate the skin.[4,5]

CANNABACEAE

Cannabis sativa Hemp

Other common name: Cannabis

In warmer parts of the world, hemp is cultivated for fibre production and its oil-rich seeds, as well as for the narcotic drugs it contains. The species is highly variable, and varieties have been developed for these different end-products. A strain of cannabis, called skunk, has been produced recently by genetic engineering; the plant grows faster than normal cannabis plants, yields a bigger crop, and is highly hallucinogenic. Another variety has been developed in which the psychoactive ingredient has been reduced to 'virtual insignificance'; this could be a useful fibre crop in Britain. In addition to illegal cultivation in Britain, it is occasionally found growing wild around rubbish dumps and places where birds have been given seed mixtures containing hemp seed not rendered completely incapable of germination. Cannabis is one of the earliest known narcotics. It was used in human and veterinary medicine as a hypnotic and sedative, but is now used almost solely for its psychedelic effects. There is conflicting information on the therapeutic value of the drug (e.g. to control spasticity in multiple sclerosis); this aspect is being reinvestigated in a clinical trial in Britain.[1]

Hemp is an erect annual, generally unbranched and growing 1–2 m in height, the varieties grown for fibre often being considerably taller. The leaves are alternate on the upper, and opposite on the lower part of the stem, and are compound, being divided into up to seven long narrow lobes with serrated margins; they are rough to touch. The male and female flowers are usually borne on separate plants in the axils of the leaves, the male flowers being in loose clusters, while the short spikes of the female flowers open only enough for the small feathery stigmas to protrude. After flowering, the leaves on the male plants turn yellow and these plants die, while the female plants remain dark green for about a month longer until the fruits ('hemp seeds') ripen.

Poisonous principles

The active agents are cannabinoids, especially tetrahydrocannabinols, which are found in the resin and occur in greatest concentration in the female flowers. Most of the characteristic psychoactive properties of cannabis are thought to be due to Δ^1-tetrahydrocannabinol. The content of tetrahydrocannabinols varies with the variety of the plant, its stage of growth, and the climatic conditions. When grown for drug production, the male plants are removed as soon as they can be distinguished. The name of the plant, cannabis, is often used for the drug derived from it, but the drug is also known by many other common names. The flowering tops of the plant (marijuana or grass) are chopped for smoking in cigarettes, while the dried resin (hashish) is usually smoked in a pipe. Hashish oil, an extract of flowering tops, contains the highest concentration of tetrahydrocannabinols (up to 60%). The drug is absorbed more rapidly and in higher concentration when smoked, but is also absorbed readily from the gastrointestinal tract if taken orally.

Animal poisoning

The plant has a bitter taste and is generally avoided by animals, although there is a report from Greece of poisoning in horses and mules who ate illegally grown plants and showed excitement, respiratory distress, muscular tremors, hypothermia, foaming at the mouth, sweating, and recumbency; they died 15–30 minutes after the appearance of clinical signs.[2] Cases of poisoning have occurred in dogs that have had access to cannabis resin or preparations (hashish, 'hashish cookies', marijuana cigarettes) used by their owners,[3–11] and in police dogs trained to find drugs.[12] Clinical signs include muscular weakness, incoordination, salivation, vomiting, drowsiness, mild hypothermia, prostration, and coma; some animals show excitability, muscular tremors, and convulsions, and some have diarrhoea. Recovery usually occurs within 24 hours, and oral doses of 3 g of crude marijuana extract per kg body weight have not been lethal for dogs.[13] In separate incidents, the ingestion of hemp seed by two dogs caused lethargy, depression, and (in one case) vomiting.[14]

In dogs it is recommended that vomiting is induced as soon as possible (up to one hour after ingestion), and that activated charcoal is given to adsorb any residual toxin. Also in dogs, a central nervous system stimulant such as pentetrazol (0.25 mg intramuscularly) has been reported to aid recovery.

Human poisoning
Although there is now widespread use of cannabis, it is still illegal to grow or use it in Britain, and there are significant dangers (short and long term) associated with its use.[15-17] The desired effects (relaxation, elevation of mood, euphoria, changes in perception) appear to users to be reversible in a short time, but it takes one month to eliminate completely a single dose of tetrahydrocannabinols from the body, and regular use (more than once a week) leads to the storage of tetrahydrocannabinols in the body. Physical effects reported with the use of the drug are an increased heart rate, conjunctivitis, a dry mouth, and increased appetite.[16] Possible long-term adverse effects[15-17] include impairment of memory, concentration, and learning ability, reduced ability to control and coordinate physical skills (e.g. driving and handwriting), and cancer of the mouth and lungs that develops much more quickly than with tobacco smoking. Fertility may be affected, and there is some evidence of harm to babies born to mothers who use the drug during pregnancy as it can cross the placenta. It has been found that tetrahydrocannabinols are concentrated and secreted in human milk and are absorbed by babies fed by mothers who use the drug.[18] Prolonged or heavy use may lead to coma, or there may be extremely unpleasant mental experiences, with flash-backs, panic, anxiety and disorientation. Taking cannabis may precipitate psychotic illnesses,[19,20] and increases the chances of relapse.[20] The ingestion of hashish resin by babies and young children is potentially life-threatening, and medical help should be sought urgently.[21]

There is no specific treatment; supportive care, reassurance, and possibly sedation are generally all that is required unless there is coma or difficulty with breathing.

CAPRIFOLIACEAE

Lonicera species Honeysuckles

The common wild honeysuckle (*Lonicera periclymenum*) is found in Britain in hedgerows, or growing up trees or along the ground in light shade in woods. There are many cultivated species and varieties in gardens. The honeysuckles are shrubs or perennial woody climbers that twine clockwise around other plants or trees and may reach a height of 6 m. The leaves arise in pairs on the stem, and are oval with pointed tips and, in some species, are slightly downy, giving a bluish-green appearance; most honeysuckles are deciduous. Clusters of flowers develop in summer, often in a compact head. Each flower has a long, basal, tubular portion, at the top of which are two broad, reflexed lips through which the stamens project. The flowers vary in colour according to species and variety, and may be cream, yellow, or shades of pink; many are fragrant. The fruits are shiny, spherical, red berries.

Poisonous principles

These plants and their berries are usually considered to be of low toxicity; it has been suggested that the symptoms seen after ingestion of about 30 or more berries are due to saponins.

Animal poisoning

Vomiting, diarrhoea, and lethargy have been reported in dogs.[1]

Human poisoning

Children sometimes taste the berries, but these are generally bitter so that only a few are eaten, and not enough to produce symptoms. Honeysuckle is reported to cause contact dermatitis.[2] If a large number, especially of unripe berries, are swallowed, stomach lavage is recommended.[3]

Sambucus nigra Common Elder (Plate 12)

Elder is a common shrub or small tree, which grows on waste land and in hedgerows, scrub or woodland, especially on alkaline and nitrogen-rich soils. It may reach 3–4 m in height, and has branches that are often arched and have brownish grey, deeply furrowed, corky bark. The twigs are stout and greyish, and prominent brown or white pith is apparent when they are cut. The branches and twigs snap readily, and partially broken trees are often seen. The leaves are compound, each being divided into oval, pointed leaflets usually numbering 5–7. The inflorescence is flat-topped, with five primary rays, and is composed of numerous, small, cream-white flowers. The purplish-black, globular fruits (elderberries) hang in conspicuous clusters in autumn.

Poisonous principles

Elder contains sambunigrin and other cyanogenic glycosides from which hydrocyanic acid is released by enzyme action. Heating is reported to destroy the toxic activity.

Animal poisoning

Elder appears to be unattractive to animals, which seldom eat it (possibly because of its unpleasant odour when bruised or crushed), but the bark, leaves, and berries may cause poisoning. In Romania, pigs that ate young elder leaves developed signs of poisoning the following day.[4] Salivation, vomiting, abdominal pain, diarrhoea, accelerated respiratory and heart rates, paralysis of hindquarters, trembling, and unsteadiness were recorded. Of the 50 animals affected, 14 died. Cases have also been reported in cattle[5] and turkeys,[6] but most are not well authenticated.

Human poisoning

The roots and stems of elder have caused poisoning, and are known purgatives. The ripe berries are often considered non-poisonous, but, if eaten in quantity, raw berries can cause nausea and vomiting.[1] A group of people in the USA who drank juice prepared from the pressed fruits and leaves of elderberry (*Sambucus mexicana*) developed nausea and diarrhoea, with abdominal pain and weakness.[7] Some became dizzy and numb. The severity of symptoms was related to the amount of juice drunk; all recovered quickly. Both berries and flowers have long been used, apparently safely, after cooking or in wine-making, despite incomplete elimination of cyanogenic material.[8]

Symphoricarpos albus Snowberry (Plate 13)

Snowberry is sometimes still referred to by its synonym *Symphoricarpos rivularis*. It is not native to Britain but is cultivated here and has become naturalized in many places. This bushy shrub reaches a height of 1–3 m, depending on where it is growing. It has dull green oval leaves, small pink flowers and characteristic waxy, white, spherical berries, up to 1 cm in diameter.

Poisonous principles
A reputedly poisonous substance, viburnine, is found in the plant. Several alkaloids, including chelidonine, a narcotic constituent of greater celandine (*Chelidonium majus*), are also found in *Symphoricarpos*, but the toxicity of most of these has not been determined.[9] Saponins, tannins, terpenes, triglycerides, and coumarins are also stated to be present.[5]

Animal poisoning
There are no reports of animal poisoning, and *Symphoricarpos oreophilus* is browsed by sheep in the USA.[10]

Human poisoning
Snowberry is said to cause gastrointestinal irritation, vomiting, and blood-stained urine.[11] *Symphoricarpos* berries have a long-standing reputation for poisoning, an early report from Norfolk[12] describing gastrointestinal symptoms, delirium, and a semi-comatose state in four children whose 'vomit left no doubt of their having eaten largely of snowberries'. (The plant in this report is mistakenly spelt *Lymphoricarpos* and has the old specific name *racemosus*.) More recent cases of snowberry poisoning have been recorded in children in the USA and Poland,[13] and in Britain, where vomiting, slight dizziness, and mild sedation occurred after a child ate three berries.[1]

Other members of the Caprifoliaceae family

Some that are popularly considered to be poisonous include danewort (*Sambucus ebulus*), the wayfaring tree (*Viburnum lantana*), and the guelder rose (*Viburnum opulus*), and queries relating to these plants, especially their berries, are often received by the veterinary and medical professions. However, the plants are generally harmless or of very low toxicity, and there are usually no symptoms following ingestion. Occasionally they may cause poisoning, as in the case of a two-year-old child who ate an unknown number of *Viburnum* berries;[1] vomiting for 12 hours and diarrhoea for two days were reported.

CARYOPHYLLACEAE

Agrostemma githago Corn Cockle (Plate 14)

In the past, corn cockle was an important cause of animal and human poisoning.[1] Although not native in Britain, this plant spread extensively and was formerly a common weed among cereal crops. As a result of changes in agricultural practice and the use of weedkillers, it had virtually disappeared from British arable land and was rarely seen in this country. Corn cockle is, however, included in some seed mixtures intended for set-aside land. Vegetation on such land should be cut before the plants seed, but there is a possibility that the plant could be reintroduced.

Corn cockle is an erect annual plant, growing 30–100 cm in height. The stem is simple or sparingly branched, and both it and the narrow, pointed leaves, are covered with white hairs, giving the plant a greyish-green appearance. The leaves are narrow and pointed, up to 12 cm long, and, at the base, they clasp the stem from which they usually arise in pairs. The flowers, 3–5 cm in diameter, are borne singly at the end of the main stem or branches and have purplish-pink petals. The plant is readily recognizable by the single pink flowers, the buds that have a slightly bulbous base and long, pointed, leafy teeth at the tip, and by the seed capsule, which becomes light brown on drying and opens by five more or less erect teeth to reveal the black seeds, 3–3.5 mm across. The seeds used to be threshed out with cereal grains and either sown with them for future crops or ground with them into flour.

Poisonous principles

These are colloidal glycosides with the properties of saponins. They are so called because, although they do not dissolve in water, they remain suspended in it and impart to it a lathering or frothing action, similar to soap. The saponins are not inactivated by heat, and the consumption of bread made with contaminated flour can cause poisoning. Such flour has a greyish colour, a bitter taste and an unpleasant odour.[2] Should these saponins enter the blood, they cause a breakdown of red blood cells (haemolysis).

Animal poisoning

There were 30 outbreaks of corn cockle poisoning in Poland between 1951 and 1963, with high mortality among pigs, cattle, horses, silver foxes, fowls, geese, and ducks.[3–5] More recently in Italy,[6] three outbreaks were recorded in cattle as a result of giving forage containing the plant; severely affected animals died. Poultry are said to be more sensitive to corn cockle poisoning than carnivores, while carnivores are more sensitive than herbivores,[7] the young of all species being more sensitive than adults. Saponin-containing plants are not eaten readily, probably because of their bitter taste. When poisoning does occur, however, the clinical signs are similar in all animals and include salivation and gastrointestinal disturbances (often with ulceration and frothy diarrhoea); muscular tremors and general paralysis may develop.

At post-mortem examination, necrotic lesions may be found in the liver, spleen, and lungs as well as in the intestines, which are often severely inflamed; there may be haemorrhages and haemolysis. Microscopic examination of the rumen contents for the presence of corn cockle seeds is important in differential diagnosis.

Treatment is mainly symptomatic, and similar to that used for any poison causing gastrointestinal irritation. Demulcents, sedatives, and pain-killing drugs may be given; stimulants may be required after the acute stage has passed. If laxatives are needed, only very mild ones should be given until it can be reasonably supposed that ulceration of the intestinal walls has healed. Obviously the use of contaminated feed, or access to the plants, should be discontinued.

Human poisoning

A chronic form of human poisoning, known as githagism, can occur.[2] It is caused by the presence of ground corn cockle seeds in flour. Lassitude, yawning, weight loss, and gastrointestinal disturbances are the chief symptoms, the patient weakening progressively and possibly dying if the contaminated diet is continued. The treatment is the same as for animal poisoning.

Other members of the Caryophyllaceae family

This family also contains the soapworts (*Saponaria* species), sandworts (*Arenaria* species), and stitchworts and chickweeds (*Stellaria* species) that grow wild in Britain, as well as some well-known garden plants such as pinks and carnations. It seems highly probable that all members of the family contain saponins but, with the exception of corn cockle, they have only very rarely been associated with poisoning. Old reports in veterinary literature state that chickweed (*Stellaria media*) has caused digestive system disturbances and death in lambs[8,9] in which the plant material formed indigestible masses in the stomach. Poisoning of horses by this or another similar species has also been recorded.[2] Chickweed is sometimes recommended as a salad ingredient, but should be used with caution as there is anecdotal evidence that it can cause severe digestive problems.

CELASTRACEAE

Euonymus europaeus Spindle (Plate 15)

Other common name: Skewer Wood

Spindle is found in woods, scrub and hedges throughout Britain, mostly on calcareous soils. It is a deciduous shrub or small tree growing 2–6 m high, with many erect branches, giving a stiff appearance. The bark is grey and smooth and the young twigs green and four-angled. The leaves are 3–13 cm long and arranged in pairs on the stem. They are oval, with pointed tips and short stalks and usually turn reddish in the autumn. The small, inconspicuous, yellowish-green flowers, up to 1 cm across, form in summer in clusters near the tips of the twigs. The fruit capsules are dark pink, four-lobed, and 10–15 mm across. When ripe, they split open from the top, revealing a bright orange, fleshy seed covering (the aril), with one seed in each lobe. The wood is hard and was sought after for the manufacture of spindles, knitting needles, skewers, and pegs, and for burning, to make charcoal sticks for drawing.

Poisonous principles

All parts of the plant, except possibly the fleshy part of the fruit, are said to be poisonous, although the precise nature of the toxins is uncertain. In early literature[1] a toxic substance, evonymine (the plant name being given as *Evonymus*) is mentioned, while later publications refer to evobioside, evomonoside, evonoside, evonine, euonymin, and triazotin or triacetin. From the effects of poisoning by *Euonymus*, it is clear that some of these toxic substances are cardiac glycosides. An unnamed glycoside isolated from *Euonymus europaeus*, given by intravenous injection to pigeons and cats, stimulated the action of the heart muscles.[2] Alkaloids (evonine and related compounds) are present in the seeds; they have pharmacological activity, but their toxicity has not been studied.

Animal poisoning

Sheep and goats have been poisoned by eating the twigs and leaves of the plant,[3] and fatal poisoning in two horses that ate shoots of the plant is recorded.[4] The horses were adequately fed in stalls, but allowed out to graze in the evenings in a meadow, on the edge of which spindle bushes were growing. Considerable amounts of the shoots were eaten, and the animals became restless and suffered paralysis of the digestive tract, with consequent constipation. Their pulse became rapid and both animals died four days later. Inflammation of the intestines was evident at post-mortem examination. No recent case reports have been found.

Human poisoning

This usually involves ingestion of the fruits and is followed 10–12 hours later by vomiting, diarrhoea, and stimulation of the heart. In severe cases, persistent vomiting, hallucinations, drowsiness, and loss of consciousness may occur, and convulsions and symptoms similar to meningitis have been reported.[5] In one fatal case, blood-stained diarrhoea and convulsions preceded death. Accounts of serious poisoning by spindle have been found only in older literature; the symptoms described more recently have been relatively mild.

Other members of the Celastraceae family

This family also includes khat (*Catha edulis*), a bush whose leaves are chewed for their stimulant properties in parts of the Yemen and East Africa. Excessive use may damage the lining of the gastrointestinal tract, and lead to liver and kidney damage.[6]

CHENOPODIACEAE

Many of the *Beta* species, subspecies, and varieties in this family are grown as crop plants for animal and human food; the inappropriate use of these and other members of the family that grow wild in Britain can lead to poisoning.

Beta vulgaris Mangels and Beet

Other common names: Mangold; Mangel-wurzel; Mangold-wurzel; Fodder Beet; Sugar Beet

These are plant breeding selections and varieties of the subspecies *vulgaris* or *maritima* of *Beta vulgaris*. They are distinguishable visually by the size, colour, and shape of the roots, and by the proportion of the swollen root (or lower stem and root) visible above the soil surface. The other main difference is in the dry-matter content of the roots, which is lowest in mangels, intermediate in fodder beet, and highest in sugar beet. Varieties known as mangels have been cultivated for animal feed in Britain since early last century; sugar beet was introduced in the 1920s and fodder beet around the middle of this century. The roots of mangels and fodder beet and the tops (leaves and crown of the root) of sugar beet are used for animal feeding, and the main part of sugar beet roots for sugar production. Sugar beet pulp, a by-product of processing for sugar, is an excellent but expensive feed.

It should be emphasized that these plants are a valuable and generally safe livestock feed, and it is only under certain circumstances that their consumption by ruminants can give rise to adverse effects that include lactic acidosis (accumulation of lactic acid in the rumen) and ketosis (a metabolic disorder in which the ketone content increases and that of glucose decreases in blood), as well as true poisoning. The high carbohydrate content of the roots of these plants can lead to lactic acidosis if this feed is introduced too rapidly into the diet. Decreases in appetite, milk yield, and fat content of milk may be associated with this condition.[1] A high lactic acid content in the rumen occurred in sheep given fodder beet juice, equivalent to 11.7 g sucrose per kg live weight.[2] Because of their high dry-matter content, excessive amounts of *Beta* roots in feed may cause rumen impaction. Ketosis may occur among cattle fed on freshly harvested fodder beet,[3] sugar beet tops,[4] and sugar beet pulp.[5]

Poisonous principles

Nitrates (readily converted to toxic nitrites) accumulate in these plants and are present in freshly harvested roots and sugar beet tops; oxalates occur in the roots and foliage, and saponins in leaves. Nervous disorders sometimes occur and may be due to one of these or to another unidentified substance; goitrogens are also present.

Animal poisoning

• NITRATE–NITRITE POISONING Freshly harvested *Beta* roots may contain high levels of nitrates. These, and possibly other constituents of the roots, have an irritant action and can cause severe diarrhoea (sometimes fatal) in cattle.[6] To avoid this, the roots need to be 'ripened' by storage in clamps for 3–4 months before feeding. It is also recommended by some that fodder beet should be allowed to mature before feeding.[7] Sugar beet tops should be left to wilt for at least a week before feeding in order to avoid severe diarrhoea in cattle.[7] Spraying beet crops with the herbicide 2,4-D can lead to accumulation of toxic levels of nitrates (up to 8.8%) in the foliage.[8] Nitrates are reduced to highly toxic nitrites in the rumen of cattle and sheep. Nitrite poisoning is characterized by weakness, laboured breathing, staggering, and recumbency, and can be fatal. The nitrites combine with haemoglobin in the blood to form methaemoglobin, preventing the uptake of oxygen and giving the blood a characteristic brownish colour. In an outbreak of nitrite poisoning in Canada,[9] 41 of 70 cattle were poisoned by eating frosted, green sugar beet tops that contained 1–6% nitrate. Despite treatment by intravenous injection of 10–30 ml of a 2% aqueous solution of methylene blue, 19 of the affected animals died. The conversion of nitrates to nitrites does not occur to any great extent in pigs. During cooking of roots containing nitrates at too low a temperature or for too short a time, nitrites are formed. Feeding with such cooked roots has led to poisoning in pigs, which are more susceptible to nitrites than are other farm animals.[10] Beet has also caused nitrate-nitrite poisoning with diarrhoea and 1–2% mortality in hens.[11]

• OXALATE POISONING Some members of the Chenopodiaceae family, including the beets, contain soluble sodium oxalate and insoluble calcium and magnesium oxalates[12] in the roots and leaves (beet foliage may contain up to 12% oxalates).[13] Soluble oxalates are very largely detoxified in the rumen, being converted into carbonate and bicarbonate. If a large enough quantity of oxalate is ingested, however, some of it will be absorbed unchanged and thus lead to oxalate poisoning. The ability of the rumen to prevent this depends on the state of nutrition of the animals and the efficiency of ruminal function. Oxalate poisoning can occur in several forms:[12,13] calcium deficiency (hypocalcaemia), leading to rapid death; breakdown of red blood cells (haemolysis); kidney damage due to blockage of tubules by calcium oxalate crystals; and crystallization of oxalates in brain tissue, causing paralysis and other disorders of the central nervous system. In castrated male sheep and cattle fed on mangels, particularly those grown on chalky soils, the urethra may become obstructed by calcium oxalate crystals. In Yugoslavia, metabolic disorders and poisoning occurred among cattle that had been fed intensively for a long period on sugar beet leaves.[14] An acute form of oxalate poisoning occurred, with lesions in the central nervous system, the digestive system, and organs involved in blood formation;[14] there were disturbances in blood chemistry and blood coagulation.[15] When sugar beet tops were fed to cows for five days, some showed ruminal overload, loss of appetite, increased urine excretion, and blood in the urine; some died.[16] Mildew on the leaves did not increase their toxicity for cows or sows.[17]

• OTHER TOXIC EFFECTS A chronic form of poisoning, also seen in the cattle fed sugar beet leaves in Yugoslavia,[14] and attributed to saponins, was characterized by bone diseases resulting in lameness, reduced fertility, increased incidence of milk fever (paralysis at parturition, due to hypocalcaemia), dark-coloured urine, and a tendency to haemorrhages. Bone and joint disorders have also been reported in Russia in intensively reared young bulls fattened on beet pulp.[18] Feeding cows on sugar beet leaves (40–70 kg for 46 days) has produced slight goitrogenic effects, but without clinical signs of goitre; by the end of the trial the yield of milk and its fat content had fallen.[19] If fed to dairy cows, sugar beet tops should always be given immediately after milking, to avoid taint.[7]

Sugar beet can be a very dangerous feed for horses. In 1934–1936 in Hungary, hundreds of horses fed ensiled sugar beet tops died, with nervous signs: throat paralysis and, more frequently, spinal paralysis.[20] Horses may also choke on sugar beet pulp.[10]

Chenopodium album Fat Hen (Plate 16)

Fat hen is a common plant of waste places and poor cultivated land and is by far the most frequently occurring *Chenopodium* species in Britain. The whole plant, including the tightly clustered flower heads, is green and may have a powdery appearance. It often exceeds 50 cm in height. The form of the plant is variable, but it is usually branched, the terminal spike being the largest. The leaves are oval or diamond shaped with variably toothed edges. The stem, leafstalks and upper leaves are sometimes tinged reddish purple.

Poisonous principles
Although known to accumulate nitrates,[21, 22] the high oxalate content of *Chenopodium* is thought to be responsible for most of its poisonous properties. When absorbed during digestion, soluble oxalates combine with calcium, resulting in a reduction in the blood calcium concentration (hypocalcaemia).

Animal poisoning

Ingestion of the plant has caused muscular incoordination among lambs in Australia;[23] shallow respiration, weak heart beat, recumbency, and death in ewes in the Netherlands;[24] and similar clinical signs, with loss of consciousness and death in some cases, in cattle in the west of England.[25] In New Zealand, listlessness and staggering when driven were observed in 40 milking cows the day after they had eaten considerable amounts of fat hen.[26] Milk production decreased and two animals became deeply comatose. A soluble oxalate content of 7.22% was found in the plants. In most cases of poisoning reported in livestock, the affected animals had been allowed to graze in pastures heavily overgrown with fat hen. For treatment, calcium borogluconate should be given intravenously.

Human poisoning

Consumption of the plant, either raw or cooked, followed by exposure to sunlight has caused a photosensitization reaction characterized by severe necrotic ulceration of the skin.[27,28] Gangrenous areas developed and the lesions were slow to heal. In general there were no effects on internal systems, but blood-stained diarrhoea occurred in two cases.[27] In both the reports cited, fat hen had been eaten in fairly large quantities during a time of acute food shortage in Poland. Under similar conditions in Dresden in 1947, *Chenopodium album* and the related plant common orache (*Atriplex patula*) were eaten 2–3 times a day.[29] Weakness and fatigue developed gradually, followed by oedema, particularly of the head, hands, and legs. A yellow pigmentation appeared on parts of the skin exposed to light.

COMPOSITAE

This family includes one of the most important causes of plant poisoning in animals in Britain, that is ragwort (*Senecio jacobaea*); poisoning by ragwort is covered in detail. Brief mention is also made of other *Senecio* species and plants in some other genera that are native in Britain or are commonly grown here.

Arctium lappa Greater Burdock

This native plant occurs in waste places and beside paths or roads throughout the lowlands of Britain. The lesser burdock *(Arctium minus)*, with many variable forms including the burdock formerly known as *Arctium pubens,* also occurs in this country.

Greater burdock has large, basal leaves, and a flowering stem that may exceed 150 cm in height. The flowers are reddish purple and crowded together in heads that are surrounded by numerous bracts; these become woody and hooked at the tips to form burs.

Attachment of burs to the coats of animals can cause skin irritation, particularly in long-haired dogs and cats. When animals remove the burs by licking and chewing, the hooked scales can penetrate the mucous membranes of the mouth and tongue. The resulting granular stomatitis, with clinical signs that include salivation, oral discomfort on eating, and ulceration of affected areas, is said to be a common condition[1] resulting from contact with burdock, but is rarely reported. Mechanical obstruction of the oesophagus with burs has caused mortality in pheasants.[2]

Symptoms of mild atropine-like poisoning have been reported in a woman after drinking burdock root tea.[3]

Centaurea solstitialis Yellow Star Thistle

Other common name: St Barnaby's Thistle

This plant occurs only occasionally in Britain as an annual or biennial weed on cultivated land, but several other *Centaurea* species are native in this country. Yellow star thistle grows 30–60 cm high and is mostly covered with cottony hairs. It has branched, winged stems, and the flower head is composed of an ovoid mass of stiff, overlapping bracts and a terminal cluster of yellow flowers.

Although sesquiterpine lactones from *Centaurea solstitialis* have proved toxic in neuron cultures, recent research suggests that a neuroexcitatory amino acid may be the poisonous principle in yellow star thistle.[4]

Yellow star thistle and, to a lesser extent, some other species of *Centaurea* are responsible for a nervous syndrome (nigropallidal encephalomalacia), of sudden onset, in horses.[5] Affected animals may be sleepy or move aimlessly, and involuntary movements of the mouth, with puckering of the lips and protrusion of the tongue, are characteristic signs. The outcome may be fatal, and areas of necrosis can be seen in the brain. Poisoning has been reported mainly from California and Oregon in the USA, but horses in Argentina and Australia have also been affected.[5] As the disease occurs only after prolonged ingestion of the plants under climatic conditions that do not permit good growth of other forage plants, it is unlikely that horses would be affected in Britain.

Cichorium intybus Chicory

This plant is probably native to Britain and is sometimes cultivated, the leaves being used in salads or as a vegetable, and the dried, ground roots in beverages. For culinary use the compact mass of tightly overlapping leaves is used (generally blanched), but under natural conditions the stem can grow up to 1 m high, and bears terminal and axillary clusters of bright blue flowers.

Cattle readily eat the leaves,[6] but feeding the roots to heifers in Poland (18 kg per animal daily) resulted in loss of appetite, thirst, diarrhoea, paralysis of extremities, and, in some cases, death.[7] At post-mortem examination, gastrointestinal inflammation, oedema, and congestion of the liver, kidneys, and lungs were seen. After chicory was withdrawn from the feed, the remaining animals recovered within a few days.

Helianthus annuus Common Sunflower

Sunflowers are not native in Britain, but are cultivated for their oil-bearing seeds or as ornamentals; escapes sometimes grow in a semi-wild state. The plant has a tall, erect, usually unbranched stem with large, broad leaves covered with stiff hairs. The flower head of some garden sunflowers is very large (up to 30 cm across); all have conspicuous, bright yellow ray florets.

Under some growing conditions the plants are known to accumulate nitrates that can give rise to nitrite poisoning.

Cattle have been poisoned by eating sunflower plants in several countries including Germany[8] and Bulgaria.[9] In these outbreaks the plants were young and the seeds not formed or still green. Clinical signs included circulatory failure, swaying of hind quarters, and excitation with subsequent collapse 1–3 hours after eating the plants. Post-mortem examination showed oedema of the lungs, dark-coloured blood, congestion of intestinal blood vessels, and small haemorrhages, typical of poisoning by nitrites, to which nitrates are converted in the rumen.

Inula conyzae Ploughman's Spikenard

This plant grows, and is locally common, on some types of chalky soil in Britain. The stems of the plant are tough, up to 1 m tall, and branch near the top, where there are terminal and axillary clusters of small, tightly packed, yellow, tubular flowers surrounded by overlapping bracts, the inner ones of which are often purple.

The toxic principle is not known with certainty, although a substance isolated from elecampane (*Inula helenium*) and designated helenin(e) (probably a lactone of a volatile, aromatic oil) was toxic for laboratory animals.[10]

Large-scale poisoning of cattle that ate *Inula conyzae* growing with lucerne was reported from Poland.[11] In Germany, 16 cattle died or were slaughtered 7–12 hours after eating green fodder containing about 30% of *Inula conyzae*.[12] Salivation, gastrointestinal disorders with blood-stained faeces, circulatory disturbance, and muscular tremors were the principle clinical signs. At post-mortem examination, swelling and degeneration of the liver, kidneys, and heart, and haemorrhages of the intestinal mucous membranes were found. Also in Germany, in a separate incident, ten sheep died or were slaughtered, with similar clinical signs, after grazing pasture on which *Inula conyzae* was abundant.[12] The related plant stinking fleabane (*Dittrichia graveolens*) is reported as poisonous in Western Australia.[13]

Senecio species

There are about 20 *Senecio* species that are native in Britain and many more worldwide, of which at least 100 are known to contain pyrrolizidine alkaloids.[14] Ragwort (*Senecio jacobaea*) has caused major problems in grazing animals because it is so widely distributed on pastures.

Senecio jacobaea Ragwort (Plate 17)

Other common names: Benweed; Staggerweed; Tansy Ragwort; St James's Wort

Ragwort is abundant throughout Britain on waste land, beside roads, and in pastures where it can be a troublesome weed. No accurate estimates have been found of the amount of ragwort in the country as a whole, but surveys conducted annually from 1979 in north-east Scotland indicate a strong natural tendency to increase, although herbicide spraying has kept the level fairly constant at around 18% of the grassland area.[14]

Ragwort usually grows as a biennial, but if flowering does not occur in the second year (e.g. because of grazing), it can be perennial. It is an erect plant usually 30–90 cm high, but may exceed 1 m. The stems are tough and often tinged red near the base, but brighter green and branched above the middle. A basal rosette of leaves usually dies before flowering, but the stem leaves persist. They are deeply dissected, with irregular, jagged-edged lobes (hence the most common name, ragwort). All the leaves are dark green and rather tough and may be sparsely hairy on the lower side. The inflorescence is a conspicuous, large, flat-topped head of densely packed flowers with ray florets and disc florets, all of which are bright yellow. The seeds are borne singly and have a downy appendage (pappus) making them readily dispersable. Details of poisoning follow the description of *Senecio vulgaris* (see below).

Senecio vulgaris Groundsel

Groundsel is a native plant that is distributed throughout the country in a wide range of habitats. It usually grows as an annual, but occasionally overwinters. The plant is very variable in form, but is usually about 30 cm tall, and has irregularly lobed leaves with rather jagged edges. The flower heads develop on branched stalks, and consist of tightly packed yellow flowers that (in most forms) have no ray florets and are more or less enclosed by overlapping green bracts. The ripe seeds have a white downy appendage that aids their dispersal by the wind.

Poisonous principles

Ragwort contains pyrrolizidine alkaloids, many of which have been characterized and named, often from the name of the plant (e.g. senecionine, seneciphylline, jaconine, jacobine). Their proportions can vary with stage of growth, season, and district. The most toxic pyrrolizidine alkaloids are cyclic diesters. Although their toxic effects are most apparent in the liver, there is evidence that the alkaloids themselves are not hepatotoxic, but that they may be metabolized in the liver to bound pyrrole derivatives that are toxic. These metabolites are either water-soluble *N*-oxides (detectable in urine) or lipophilic pyrroles (detectable in body tissues). The poisonous principles are not destroyed by drying.[14]

Animal poisoning

Ragwort is one of the commonest causes of plant poisoning in Britain.[15,16] The signs of ragwort poisoning are usually slow to develop, and may not become apparent until animals have been eating it for several weeks or months; signs may even appear after consumption of the plant has ceased.[17]

Occasionally, however, poisoning develops less than a week after eating ragwort. Once clinical signs have appeared, it is not unusual for affected animals to die within a few days. The disorders of the digestive and nervous systems that result from eating the plant bear superficial resemblances to some other diseases. It is not surprising, therefore, that the association between the disease syndrome and ragwort was not recognized until this century. The discovery was made in Canada in 1906, where the condition (known as Pictou disease, after the town of that name in Nova Scotia) became established following the introduction of ragwort from Scotland in 1852.[18] The occurrence of poisoning by ragwort in Britain was first demonstrated in 1917,[19] although the poisonous properties of this plant had been suspected before this.

At pasture, poisoning is most likely to occur when there is heavy infestation of ragwort and alternative plants are scarce. Under such conditions ragwort may be grazed heavily, despite its apparent unpalatability. Some animals develop an addiction to or preference for the plant once they start eating it. The toxicity remains in ragwort in hay and dried grass; it is reduced in silage but not sufficiently for it to be safe for cattle to consume even when it contains a low percentage of *Senecio* plants.[20] In one outbreak hay containing 5% ragwort caused poisoning, with some mortality in heifers.[21] Dried grass, hay, or silage are the most common sources of ragwort poisoning in Britain.

There are considerable differences in the susceptibility of animals to pyrrolizidine alkaloid toxicity. Cattle and horses are very susceptible and are the most often involved in ragwort poisoning,[22] although sheep[23] and pigs[24] are also susceptible. The practice of allowing sheep access to ragwort-infested pasture to assist in clearing it of the plants is sometimes recommended, and there is experimental evidence that the ruminal metabolism of these animals gives some protection against pyrrolizidine alkaloid poisoning.[25] No liver damage was found when sheep were used for this purpose in New Zealand.[26] Deer appear to be resistant to ragwort poisoning,[27] and experiments on rabbits showed that intestinal absorption of alkaloids was low[28] and urinary excretion efficient;[29] guinea pigs were also resistant.[29]

Clinical signs of ragwort poisoning are similar in cattle and horses. Initially there are digestive system disturbances, usually including abdominal pain and diarrhoea (sometimes with blood) or constipation, both associated with persistent straining, and often resulting in rectal prolapse.[30,31] There may be emaciation and jaundice. Nervous signs may develop, particularly in horses. They include restlessness and aimless, uncoordinated movement;[32] the names 'walking disease' and 'sleepy staggers' have been applied to this condition in horses. Affected animals of both species may appear blind, press their heads against solid objects,[32,33] and become at least partially paralysed. Weakness progressing to recumbency[18] and 'hepatic' coma (due to an increase in blood ammonia) may precede death.[32] There appears to be little correlation between the severity of the reaction and the amount or duration of ragwort ingestion.[34] In experimental feeding, cattle tolerated up to 1.5% of their body weight of the dried plant, eaten in a 15-day period, but died if given 2% of their weight within 20 days.[35]

Ragwort poisoning in horses is usually associated with the feeding of ragwort-contaminated hay,[36] but has also been reported in horses at pasture.[36,37] Secondary gastric impaction and subsequent gastric rupture may be a fatal complication in horses.[38] Stress can result in the appearance of clinical signs. Cases have been reported in cows after parturition[39] and lactation,[40] and in horses after exercise;[41] the horses (in the USA) had been given hay containing about 25% groundsel (*Senecio vulgaris*).

Post-mortem examination of cattle and horses reveals inflammation of the digestive tract, often with ulceration and small haemorrhages,[30] and cirrhosis of the liver, with characteristic histological changes.[30,32] Accumulation of ammonia, as a result of liver damage, is responsible for a spongy degeneration of the brain and spinal cord.[33,42]

Sheep fed experimentally with 3 g of dried *Senecio jacobaea* per kg body weight daily for 16 days did not develop clinical signs, but liver function was impaired and there was 70% mortality during the next six months.[23] A severe disease with emaciation and, terminally, aggressive behaviour, occurred in Iraq in sheep grazing vegetation, one-third of which was *Senecio cineraria*.[43] Post-mortem examination revealed congestion and inflammation of the liver and superficial haemorrhages of abdominal organs. In a feeding experiment the susceptibility of goats differed little from that reported for sheep.[44] It is not clear whether the difference in the susceptibility of cattle and sheep is due to differences in their hepatic metabolism or in the protective role of the ruminal microflora.[45] Recent work in the USA has shown that bacteria isolated from the ruminal contents of sheep can degrade pyrrolizidine alkaloids; cultures of the bacteria are being fed to cattle to protect them from ragwort poisoning.[46]

Ragwort poisoning has not been reported in pigs under natural conditions, but their susceptibility to it was demonstrated experimentally[22] by the inclusion of 5–10% dried ragwort in the diet of seven pigs for 1–3 months. The animals developed laboured breathing and fluctuating, elevated body temperatures. In contrast to the post-mortem findings in sheep and cattle, the only lesion in the liver was enlargement of cell nuclei. The most severe effects were in the lungs, which were firm, heavy, reddish purple, and haemorrhagic.

In chicks fed, from one week old, for six weeks on a diet containing 7% dried, ground ragwort, there were progressive degenerative changes in the liver.[47]

Liver biopsy has proved to be a reliable method for confirming diagnosis in horses poisoned by *Senecio vulgaris*[48] and calves by *Senecio jacobaea*.[49]

There is no specific treatment for ragwort poisoning, but supportive treatment for the digestive disturbances and removal of affected animals from pasture containing ragwort may assist in recovery. It is recommended that dietary protein should be limited at this time[33] as exacerbation of the nervous disorders often follows intake of a high-protein feed. In rats it has been shown that the inclusion of 1% cysteine in the diet provides some protection against ragwort poisoning by enhancing the pyrrole-conjugating ability of the liver.[50] In subsequent tests on ponies and cattle, however, a dietary additive containing sulphur amino acids and antioxidants did not provide protection.[22]

Human poisoning

A disease, called seneciosis, is recognized in some parts of the world, but it is doubtful if there are any adverse effects of ragwort on the human population in Britain. The question of the transfer of alkaloids to milk from cattle grazing ragwort remains open. The presence of at least one alkaloid (jacoline) was demonstrated in the milk of cows given 10 g of dried ragwort per kg body weight by stomach tube daily for two weeks, but careful monitoring did not reveal any change in their calves.[51] In rats given the milk of goats fed for four weeks on a diet containing 25% dried, ground *Senecio jacobaea*, there was a reduction in the activity of some liver enzymes.[52] The potential human danger of the consumption of milk from animals poisoned by ragwort is generally considered to be slight.[22]

In the USA, toxic alkaloids from *Senecio jacobaea* have been detected in honey produced from the nectar of the plant and are considered a potential health hazard.[53] In some states, bees visit ragwort particularly from mid to late summer when there is a dearth of other suitable flowers. These conditions may occur during drought in Britain, when ragwort survives better than other nectar-producing plants. The resulting honey is deep yellow in colour and has a strong, unpleasant taste and smell.[54] There is, however, no evidence that, in this country, such honey contains sufficient quantities of ragwort alkaloids to be toxic.

A severe disease of the liver, veno-occlusive disease, can result from drinking herbal teas made from several plants, including some *Senecio* species;[14] this has occurred mainly in Jamaica, India, and Afghanistan.

Control of ragwort

Hand-pulling and removal of the plant from pasture is practised to some extent, but is obviously impracticable for heavy infestation or large areas. Ploughing of infested pasture is recommended and herbicide spraying is effective, but expensive. There is evidence that, at least in north-east Scotland, spraying areas where 22% (or more) of the fields are infested with ragwort decreases the level of infestation, but the infestation increases where less than 22% of infested fields are sprayed.[55] The herbicides MCPA and 2,4-D are recommended, but a single spray treatment is not necessarily sufficient as there may be regeneration of plants from residual roots.[56] Animals should not be allowed on to recently sprayed pasture as they will eat wilted plants or those treated with weedkiller even more readily than fresh plants. An increase in water-soluble carbohydrates (and hence greater palatability) has been demonstrated in ragwort after treatment with 2,4-D; there is also evidence that the weedkiller increases the alkaloid content of the plants.[57]

Ragwort was designated as an injurious weed in the Weeds Act, 1959, as, particularly in cattle, ragwort poisoning has been said to cause higher economic losses in Britain than all other plants combined.[43] Under the Act, a landowner can be required to prevent the plant from spreading, and failure to do so within a specified time renders that person liable to prosecution and a fine.[56]

Silybum marianum Milk Thistle

This is not a native plant but has become naturalized in some parts of Britain. The milk thistle has erect stems that are up to 120 cm tall and are covered with cottony hairs. The leaves are smooth, with spiny margins and white veins. The flower heads develop singly and are often drooping at maturity. The base of the inflorescence is ovoid and composed of overlapping bracts, some of which have a triangular, spiny tip; there is a terminal cluster of reddish-purple flowers.

Nitrites produced in the rumen from nitrates in the plants are thought to be the poisonous principles. Milk thistle has caused poisoning in cattle in New South Wales[58] and South America,[59] where affected animals developed gastrointestinal disturbances, slow heart beat, and difficult breathing. Post-mortem examination revealed congestion of the stomach and intestines with chocolate-brown-coloured blood. Cases of poisoning have occurred only in winter. Frequent injection of 2–4% methylene blue is recommended for nitrite poisoning; dramatic recovery has resulted from the use of a 20% solution of this dye.[60]

Xanthium strumarium Cocklebur

In Britain cocklebur is described as an introduced plant with local distribution. The seeds of *Xanthium* have been so widely distributed, unintentionally, by attachment of the burred flower heads to animals or clothing, that the true place of origin of the plants is difficult to determine.

There are many variations in the size, form, and flower colour of cocklebur plants. They are generally erect, up to 120 cm high, much branched, often hairy, and sometimes aromatic. The male and female flowers are separate, the males being small and inconspicuous, and the bracts of the females developing hooked spines to form burs.

A glycoside, named xanthostrumarin, was first thought to be the poisonous principle, and later hydroquinone was suspected, but carboxyatractyloside has now been shown to be the toxic agent.[61]

No reports have been found of poisoning by this plant in Britain, but in the USA all classes of domestic livestock have been affected,[62] with pigs being particularly susceptible to the toxic two-leaf stage in spring.[63] Depression, ataxia, convulsions, and death have been reported in pigs[64] and also in cattle.[65,66] Oedema of the gall-bladder wall, accumulation of fluid in the abdominal cavity, and haemorrhages of the heart, liver, and kidneys are seen at post-mortem examination. Although the toxin is also contained in the seeds, these are rarely eaten as they are surrounded by the burs of the flower head, but depression, after eating cocklebur seeds, has been reported in poultry.[64] When crushed cocklebur plants formed 25% of a feed mixture given to chicks for three weeks, the only effect noticed was a decrease in body weight gain.[67] The toxicity of the plant remains after drying.

Other members of the Compositae family

These include various thistles (*Carduus* and *Cirsium* species) and golden rod (*Solidago* species) that are known to accumulate nitrates[68] in potentially toxic amounts, but no reports of their having caused poisoning have been found. Wormwood (*Artemesia absinthium*), mugwort (*Artemisia vulgaris*), leopard's bane (*Doronicum* species), and the Jerusalem artichoke (*Helianthus tuberosus*), all of which occur in Britain, have poisoned animals in other countries. Several plants in the family can cause an unpleasant taint in the milk of dairy cows.[43] Human poisoning has occurred by medicinal use of the aromatic oil or infusions of tansy (*Tanacetum vulgare*);[43] these plants can also give rise to allergic contact dermatitis, as can other members of the Compositae family.[69] Some of the florists' chrysanthemums (*Dendrathema* species), and also chamomiles (*Anthemis* species) and mayweeds (*Matricaria* species), can cause symptoms resembling hay fever.[69]

CONVOLVULACEAE

Convolvulus arvensis Field Bindweed (Plate 18)

This plant is widely distributed through most of the temperate regions of the world in waste places or cultivated ground, where it is a persistent and troublesome weed. Bindweed is a climbing perennial that is hard to eradicate because of its underground rhizomes, which penetrate deeply into the soil. New shoots develop from the rhizomes, and the long slender stems climb by twisting anti-clockwise, usually around the stems of other plants. The leaves, which are about 5 cm long, are stalked and variable in shape; often they are more or less triangular, or shaped like a spear head. The flowers are also stalked, each stalk bearing 1–3 flowers, which are fragrant and trumpet shaped, up to 3 cm across, and pink or pink and white.

Poisonous principles
Bindweed contains several alkaloids, including pseudotropine, a tropane alkaloid, and cuscohygrine, a pyrrolidine alkaloid.

Animal poisoning

Bindweed is not readily eaten by animals, but has been grazed by horses on pasture overrun by the plant in the USA. A disease syndrome in the horses characterized by weight loss and recurrent colic, with fibrosis, vascular lesions, and shortening and thickening of the small intestine was described,[1] and later suspected to have been caused by eating bindweed.[2] Laboratory analysis of aerial parts of bindweed plants from a pasture on which horses had been kept showed the presence of various alkaloids, including pseudotropine,[3] which may have caused the chronic poisoning of the horses, as tropane alkaloids are known to decrease secretory activity and motility in the digestive tract. Mice fed exclusively on bindweed for 5–6 days became excited, then depressed before dying with liver and stomach lesions.[2] There are no reports of adverse effects associated with this plant in Britain, but in view of the widespread occurrence of the plant and the toxins it contains, it has been suggested that it could be a previously unrecognized hazard, especially to hungry animals.

Cuscuta species Dodder

Large dodder (*Cuscuta europaea*) is a slender, twining, annual parasite that is yellowish green or reddish in colour and twists in an anti-clockwise direction. In Britain it is found chiefly on nettles and hops, to which it attaches by suckers; but it is stated to be rare and is probably decreasing. Common dodder (*Cuscuta epithymum*) is similar but smaller (its stem is thread-like, with a diameter of 0.1 mm compared with 1.0 mm for large dodder); it is common locally on gorse (*Ulex*) and heather (*Calluna*). The leaves are small, inconspicuous scales, and the flowers develop in tightly packed groups that appear at intervals along the otherwise bare stems. The individual flowers are small, pinkish, and fragrant.

Poisonous principles
The poisonous principles of dodder are not known.

Animal poisoning
Dodder poisoning has not been reported in Britain, but species in Russia, including *Cuscuta europaea*,[4] that parasitize lucerne, have caused chronic poisoning in horses when more than half of the plants fed have been affected. Clinical signs are those of gastroenteritis, with loss of appetite, diarrhoea, constipation, and colic; death has resulted from intestinal perforation or intraperitoneal haemorrhage.[5] Horses are said to be more susceptible than other animals.

Ipomoea species Morning Glory (Plate 19)

These plants are not native in Britain, although they can sometimes be found in waste places, where seeds (usually bird seeds or soya bean waste) have been discarded. Some species such as *Ipomoea purpurea* and *Ipomoea tricolor* are cultivated as ornamentals.

Morning glory is an annual with climbing stems bearing heart-shaped leaves up to 12 cm long and clusters of 1–5 funnel-shaped flowers up to 8 cm long. The flowers of many are shades of blue or purple, sometimes with white, while others are pink, red, or uniformly white.

Poisonous principles

The seeds of the plant contain varying concentrations of derivatives of *d*-lysergic acid, which is a well-known hallucinogen. Ergot alkaloids are also present, with large variations in content occurring in different varieties of the plant.[6]

Animal poisoning

There are no reports of consumption of any parts of *Ipomoea purpurea* or *Ipomoea tricolor* by domestic animals. The toxicity to livestock (mainly sheep and goats) of other species of *Ipomoea* (notably *Ipomoea carnea*) has been reported in natural outbreaks[7] and feeding experiments[8,9] in other countries. In a feeding study in which rats were given ground seed of *Ipomoea hederacea* and *Ipomoea lacunosa* at 0.8–8% in their diet,[10] there were dose-related decreases in body weight, and 40% mortality in males and 10% in females. This experiment was designed to set tolerance limits for levels of *Ipomoea* seed in grain, in which it can be present as a contaminant.

Human poisoning

Cases of the deliberate ingestion of up to 300 morning glory seeds for hallucinatory purposes have been reported. The symptoms produced include facial flushing, stomach-ache, nausea, vomiting, and diarrhoea, but are mainly a result of disturbances of the central nervous system, such as agitation, disorientation, blurred vision, dilated pupils, and hallucinations.[11] Altered perception of surroundings and permanent psychological disturbance, sometimes leading to death, have been recorded.[12] Stomach lavage is indicated where the patient is not hallucinating. Sedation may be required.

CRASSULACEAE

Sedum acre Common Stonecrop

This small plant grows in crevices in walls and rocks, and is often used as a rockery plant in gardens. Common stonecrop is an evergreen perennial with numerous creeping stems, often forming mats 15–30 cm across, and bearing short succulent leaves which often develop a yellow or reddish tinge. The flowers are about 12 mm in diameter and have bright yellow, pointed petals.

Poisonous principles

This plant, and some other species of *Sedum*, have a hot bitter taste and are reputed to be poisonous. There is some justification for this as the piperidine alkaloids sedamine and sedridine are found in the plants.[1]

Animal poisoning

Because of the habitat of many of the *Sedum* species, the plants are often inaccessible to animals and are unlikely to be eaten in sufficient quantity to cause poisoning. It is probable that the reputation of stonecrop as a poisonous plant is attributable to old reports[2] of clinical signs, including salivation, muscle tremors, rapid respiration, and coma in dogs fed with 7 g of *Sedum acre* per kg of body weight. More recently, in Hungary, the garden plant *Sedum spectabile* was implicated as the probable cause of poisoning of pigs that had eaten considerable amounts of discarded plants, including flowering parts.[3] The pigs appeared slightly bloated and depressed, showed some inappetence and loss of balance when walking, and their body temperature was raised. Vomiting was induced and purgatives given; the animals recovered.

Human poisoning
The sap of the plant is irritant to the skin.[4]

Other members of the Crassulaceae family

Various pigmyweeds (*Crassula* species) grow wild or in cultivation in Britain; they can cause poisoning similar to that described for the *Sedum* species above.

CRUCIFERAE

The name of this family is derived from the cross-shaped arrangement of the four petals of the flowers. It contains about 1900 species, including many garden flowers (stock, wallflower, candytuft), and weeds of arable land (charlock, wild radish) as well as plants that provide food: vegetables (cabbage, turnip, radish), condiments (mustard, horseradish), forage plants (kale, rape), and oilseed plants (rape).

Most of the crucifers are herbaceous, with spirally arranged, lobed leaves, the terminal lobe being the largest. The earliest flowers appear as a compact group which gradually lengthens into a loose inflorescence with the youngest flowers at the apex. The flowers have four yellow or white petals. The fruit is usually a capsule which is divided into two cells by a thin longitudinal partition. Seeds usually occur in one or two rows in each cell. The shape of the fruit is important in distinguishing between species.

Poisoning may be due to mustard oil, as in the weeds charlock and wild radish, and the condiment plants white mustard and horse radish. Another type of poisoning is associated with the forage and oilseed crops. The chief toxic constituents are glucosinolates, although kale and, to a lesser extent, rape also contain an amino acid, *S*-methyl cysteine sulphoxide (SMCO), which is a haemolytic toxin. All species of Cruciferae so far investigated contain glucosinolates, which usually occur as potassium salts. By hydrolysis with the plant enzyme, thioglucosidase[1] (sometimes still referred to by the older names myrosinase or glucosinolase), potentially toxic substances are released. These include isothiocyanates, nitriles, and thiocyanates. Glucosinolates occur in all parts of the plant, but are usually more concentrated in the seeds.[2] Thioglucosidase does not normally come into contact with glucosinolates, unless the plant cells are crushed in the presence of water. The first glucosinolate to be isolated was named sinigrin (allyl glucosinolate) from black mustard (*Brassica nigra*). On hydrolysis this yields mustard oil (allyl isothiocyanate), the pungent substance that contributes to the characteristic flavour of black mustard and other cruciferous plants. Most plants that produce allyl isothiocyanate are listed as poisonous to livestock. The immediate effect of mustard oil on contact with the skin is acute inflammation.[3] Most of the known glucosinolates are converted to stable isothiocyanates or nitriles, but some isothiocyanates are unstable and react further to form either ring compounds or the thiocyanate ion. Prior treatment of the plant material, and the conditions under which the hydrolysis occurs, influence the course of the reaction.

The main compounds formed from the glucosinolates, and their effects on animals are: goitrins and the thiocyanate ion that inhibit thyroid function by different mechanisms, but both lead to thyroid gland enlargement; isothiocyanates that are irritant to skin and mucous membranes, and are also goitrogenic; nitriles that interfere with growth and cause pathological changes in the liver, kidneys, and other organs, without any effect on the thyroid gland.

In the period 1975–1977, crucifers accounted for 57 of the total of 145 cases of plant poisoning referred to the Veterinary Investigation Centres of England and Wales. These included 17 cases of *Brassica* poisoning in sheep and 38 in cattle, and a single case of horse-radish poisoning in birds.[4]

Armoracia rusticana Horse Radish (Plate 20)

Horse radish is cultivated for use as a condiment (the whitish flesh of the root is crushed for this purpose), but is also found growing wild in many parts of the country. The plant is a perennial with large leaves and a long tapering root. The basal leaves are rough to touch, but are not hairy; they grow up to 50 cm in length on stalks up to 30 cm long and are undivided. They are toothed at the edges, and 10–15 cm broad. The stems are 60–125 cm tall, and bear tiny white flowers in a terminal group. The pods, even if they form, seldom ripen in the British climate.

Poisonous principles
The root and leaves of horse radish contain sinigrin (allyl glucosinolate) and 2-phenylethyl glucosinolate. Allyl glucosinolate is hydrolysed to allyl isothiocyanate, which is a potent irritant of the eyes and skin.

Animal poisoning
Horse-radish poisoning is rare, possibly because of the pungent flavour of the leaves and roots, but there have been reports in Britain of poisoning of cattle,[5] ponies,[5] pigs[5] and a bird.[4] In cattle the clinical signs were lowing and excitement followed by collapse and death. Six ponies, found dead after having broken into an orchard in which horse radish was growing in profusion, had large amounts of the leaves and flowering stems in their stomachs, which were acutely inflamed and smelt typically of horse radish. There were no other lesions. There was evidence that the animals had struggled violently before dying. Two fattening pigs were found dead about three hours after being fed uncooked hotel garbage. Post-mortem examination showed acute inflammation of the stomach walls, which, even after washing in water, smelt strongly of horse radish. There were no other lesions. It was estimated that the pigs had eaten 55–85 g of the grated root between them.

Brassica campestris Turnip Rape
Brassica napus Rape (Plate 21)

Other common names: Cole; Colza

Almost all of the rape grown in Britain is *Brassica napus*, but the turnip rape, *Brassica campestris*, also occurs. Both of these plants are variable in form, and there are several cultivars and hybrids to which a variety of other common names is applied. These differ in their growth habit, their toxicity, and their suitability for use, either as forage or as an oilseed crop. Forage rape is usually eaten as a standing crop by sheep and cattle. Oilseed rape is grown for its seed, from which the extracted oil (often called colza oil after an alternative name for the plant) is widely used for human consumption or industrial purposes (including lubrication). The residue of the seeds after extraction (rapeseed meal) is incorporated into animal feeds, mainly for pigs and poultry. Rapeseed meal is a good source of protein, but the amount used is limited by its toxic effects. There are now varieties of rape with lower concentrations of glucosinolates, and meal prepared from these can, therefore, be fed in larger quantities.

Poisonous principles

Although rape is a valuable and widely used feed, all parts of the plant can contain toxic levels of several potentially harmful substances. The foliage contains glucosinolates, the amino acid *S*-methyl cysteine sulphoxide (SMCO), and, under certain growing conditions, nitrates; the seeds contain glucosinolates, sinapine (the choline ester of 4-hydroxy-3,5-dimethoxycinnamic acid and usually associated with the glucosinolate complex), and tannins and saponins (whose effects have not been investigated).[6] Rapeseed oil, extracted from the seed for human use, contains erucic acid, a long-chain fatty acid, that has caused various abnormalities in experimental animals, although there is no evidence that it harms the human consumer. New varieties of rape (the so-called double low varieties) are low in both erucic acid and glucosinolates.

Of the glucosinolates, the most important in rape are progoitrin, gluconapin, and glucobrassicanapin; these yield the goitrogens 3-butenyl isothiocyanate and 5-vinyl-2-oxazolidenethione. Isothiocyanates are not only goitrogenic, but are also irritant to the skin and mucous membranes. Goitre does not occur in animals grazing on rape, but can develop among pigs and poultry given feed containing a high proportion of rapeseed meal. This is probably because the leaves contain less progoitrin than the seeds. Under some conditions, progoitrin is hydrolysed to non-goitrogenic, organic nitriles instead of goitrins, and these nitriles have been shown to damage the liver and kidneys of rats. SMCO is a haemolytic factor that was first identified in kale; there is much less SMCO in rape than in kale. There is variation in the toxicity of rape related to season, year, and crops, this being attributed to differences in the content of glucosinolates and SMCO. The glucosinolate content is also influenced by the age of the plant, the environment, and genetic factors. The SMCO content of rape plants increases with age.[7]

Animal poisoning

Several disease syndromes have been associated with rape, although in many cases it is not possible to correlate these with the individual toxic constituents. Rape poisoning is most likely to occur in cattle and sheep from forage rape, and in pigs and poultry from rapeseed meal.

Main types of forage rape poisoning
Most accounts of this are based on observations made in Canada in the 1940s.[8] At that time four types of disease were recognized: respiratory, urinary, nervous, and digestive. These designations remain applicable to current outbreaks, except that, in older reports, the respiratory form may have been confused with fog fever (acute bovine

pulmonary emphysema) or a similar condition in some cases, and that the urinary type refers to the haemolytic anaemia which is now associated with SMCO. It is now clear that these four types are not specific forms of rape poisoning and may occur concurrently or sequentially.

The post-mortem findings vary slightly with the four types of poisoning. In all forms, however, there is inflammation of the intestinal tract, with patchy necrosis and congestion of the liver; often the bladder contains dark-coloured urine. There is also an accumulation of dark-coloured intestinal contents. In the digestive type, the rumen contains a black, solid, doughy mass, and there is no gas; the folds of the omasum have a burned appearance, and the mucous membrane peels easily from them.

• HAEMOLYTIC ANAEMIA   Particularly in the older literature, this is reported to be the commonest form of rape poisoning; it is often accompanied by haemoglobinuria. In the rumen SMCO is converted to dimethyl disulphide, which leads to the denaturation and precipitation of haemoglobin to form Heinz bodies in the red blood cells.[9] Haemoglobin released from the red blood cells is excreted in the urine, which becomes reddish or dark in colour. Affected animals may be jaundiced, and liver damage sometimes occurs; the photosensitization reactions recorded are not necessarily related to this liver damage. The presence of a haemolytic substance in rape was suspected in the 1940s in Canada, where, particularly in Ontario, an association between overfeeding on rape and a condition characterized by anaemia and haemoglobinuria had been recognized in cattle for many years. Experimental work has confirmed that feeding rape to ruminants induces anaemia but that haemoglobinuria occurs in only a few animals.[10] The selenium status of ruminants influences their susceptibility to rape-induced Heinz body anaemia.[11] There is evidence that increased production of red blood cells can compensate for their loss by haemolysis.[12] In Britain, anaemia and haemoglobinuria have occurred in cattle,[13] and anaemia in sheep[14] after grazing rape.

Cattle are not often fed on rape and little work has been done on its toxic effects in this species. In addition to the haemoglobinuria type reported in cattle in Britain,[13] an outbreak has been described in which the main clinical feature was blindness, associated with dullness, lack of ruminal movements and constipation.[15] Diarrhoea is occasionally reported in cattle but constipation is a more common occurrence.[13]

In Scotland, jaundice developed in some sheep that had grazed on rape for a part of each day during a month; three died.[14] The clinical signs were depression, rapid breathing, a rapid heart beat, and considerable diarrhoea. Visible mucous membranes were dark yellow or brown, and the skin was yellow. Haemoglobinuria was observed in one sheep. The haemoglobin content of the blood was 3.6 g per 100 ml. The anaemia appeared to be associated with a low content of inorganic phosphate in the blood. A similar incident has been reported among lambs in New South Wales.[16] Anaemia and deaths have been reported on the Continent in roe deer, a large proportion of whose diet was rape.[17]

• NERVOUS TYPE   This is characterized by the sudden onset of blindness, and can occur in both cattle and sheep. More severe nervous signs include head-pressing and violent excitement. The eyes appear normal on ophthalmoscopic examination. The pupils show some response to light and may or may not be dilated. Affected animals usually recover, but this may take several weeks.[15, 18, 19] This type has been found in sheep in Britain, blindness being the main clinical sign. On removal from rape, most of the animals recover their sight.

• DIGESTIVE TYPE   This is seen 3–4 days after the consumption of excessive amounts of rape. The affected animal stops feeding, is constipated, and there are no ruminal sounds. The rectum and colon are empty, except for small amounts of sticky black faeces. Bloat may also occur. In Britain, bloat and constipation have been seen, along with other clinical signs of rape poisoning, in cattle[20,21] and sheep.[22]

• RESPIRATORY TYPE   Despite confusion with fog fever in some cases, respiratory distress can be a feature of rape poisoning in both cattle[20] and sheep.[23]

Other types of forage rape poisoning

Also associated with the consumption of forage rape are nitrite poisoning,[24,25] liver damage,[26] and photosensitization.[13,27] Rape, in common with turnips and swedes, is capable of taking up large amounts of nitrate when grown on soil containing a lot of nitrogen, whether occurring naturally or as the result of application of nitrogenous fertilizer.[24] In this state it is not safe to feed it to cattle and sheep. Nitrite poisoning resulting from feeding on second growth rape caused the death of 20 lambs in a flock of 337 in New Zealand.[25] In contrast to kale, there are no reports of goitre in animals grazing rape, except for one experiment with lambs,[28] although glucosinolates are also present in rape. A photosensitization reaction, known as 'rape scald', occurs in lambs in New Zealand;[27] clinical signs include oedema and necrosis of the skin, but liver damage has not been linked with this condition. A similar photosensitization has also been recorded in a cow in Britain.[13] Ensiling reduces the glucosinolate and SMCO concentrations in rape.[29]

Rapeseed meal poisoning

Rapeseed meal is generally not so well accepted as other meals, such as the more expensive soya bean meal. The depression of weight gain associated with rapeseed meal feeding can occur without other clinical signs, and may be only the result of lower feed intake, because of unpalatability. Other explanations have, however, been suggested for this reduced weight gain. These include depression of thyroid activity, and the formation of toxic nitriles[1] from glucosinolates in rape seed. The reduced feed consumption and growth rate are associated with increases in the weights of the liver, kidneys, and thyroid glands, and lower secretion of thyroid hormones.[30]

• GOITRE   The most common adverse effect of feeding rapeseed meal is enlargement of the thyroid gland (goitre), which occurs in pigs and poultry and, to a very small extent, in ruminants.[6] This condition is almost invariably associated with increased weight of the thyroid glands that occurs as a result of goitrin (a hydrolysis product of progoitrin) interfering with the synthesis of thyroid hormones. It does not respond to treatment with iodine as do some other forms of goitre, such as that caused by thiocyanate (present in kale), which competes for iodine with the thyroid gland. The seed of *Brassica napus* is more goitrogenic than that of *Brassica campestris*, because it contains more oxazolidenethione, produced by hydrolysis of glucosinolates. It appears that the increase in size of the thyroid glands enables sufficient thyroxine to be produced, thus compensating for the depressing effect of rapeseed meal on thyroid hormone production.[6] When cows received up to 3.4 kg (dry matter) of rapeseed meal daily during three consecutive lactations, there were mild suppressive effects on thyroid hormone release but no adverse effects on health or fertility.[31]

• LIVER HAEMORRHAGE   This is another effect seen in poultry fed with rapeseed meal; it is often responsible for high mortality. This condition caused widespread losses in

British flocks in 1971–1972,[32] although it had been seen earlier, in experimental work.[33] The severity of the haemorrhages varies with different types of rapeseed and different breeds of bird. Higher mortality rates have been recorded in laying hens than in broilers or cockerels; it has been suggested that the transitory increase in blood pressure at egg-laying is responsible for this. The constituent of rapeseed meal causing this has not been identified with certainty, but the glucosinolate complex may be involved.[34]

• LEG ABNORMALITIES   Perosis (shortening and thickening of bones) can occur in poultry fed rapeseed meal.[35] This condition is often associated with thyroid enlargement and growth depression. The legs are weak; bent hock joints are a typical feature. A higher incidence of leg weakness occurs in birds fed seed residues of *Brassica napus* than those of *Brassica campestris*. The causative agent is not known, although the incidence of the condition is higher with high glucosinolate meals. Chicks given a diet containing 12.5% rapeseed meal for ten weeks developed leg abnormalities that included swollen hocks and tenosynovitis.[36]

• EFFECTS ON REPRODUCTION   Diets containing a high (20%) content of rapeseed meals (particularly those from *Brassica napus*) depress egg production in pullets.[6] No adverse effects on reproductive efficiency have been reported in sows, but in gilts given 8–10% rapeseed meal there have been reductions in litter size and weight and, in some cases, delayed conception.[37] Rapeseed meal of low glucosinolate content did not affect fertility of gilts, but the first observed oestrus was delayed in others given high glucosinolate meal.[38] Some experiments have shown, however, that feeding rapeseed meal to pregnant sows can result in increases in embryonic mortality, stillbirths, and/or postnatal mortality.[39]

• EGG TAINT   An effect of feeding rapeseed to poultry that is of particular concern to poultry farmers is a taint in eggs, described as a 'fishy', 'crabby', or 'off' taste; it is mainly brown eggs that are affected.[40] It was found in the early 1970s that this taint is due to the presence of trimethylamine in the eggs. Trimethylamine is a product of the breakdown of sinapine, and other dietary sources of choline, by intestinal bacteria. Egg taint is linked with a genetic defect impeding the synthesis of the enzyme trimethylamine oxidase[40] that breaks down trimethylamine. Impaired thyroid function was thought to account for the reduced production of trimethylamine oxidase, but experiments have shown that the enzyme is inhibited by goitrin (from glucosinolates in the plants).[41] A biochemical test has been developed to identify, while still chicks, birds with defective trimethylamine metabolism.[42,43]

• MEAT TAINT   The meat of sheep that have grazed on rape may have a disagreeable aroma and flavour, which could be due to metabolites of glucosinolates.[44] Similar taint has been suspected in the carcasses of broiler fowls fed on rapeseed meal.[35]

Human ingestion
Rapeseed oil is used in foods such as margarine and cooking fats. The oil contains erucic acid that is not readily absorbed from the intestines and is, therefore, an undesirable constituent of food. Under experimental conditions, it has caused damage to the heart of pigs and rats,[45] but no adverse effects have been observed in people eating products containing it. New varieties of rape have a low erucic acid content.

Brassica oleracea var. *acephala*   Kale

The two main types of kale traditionally grown in Britain, marrowstem and thousand-head (tall and dwarf, respectively), were developed by selection and cultivation from the wild cabbage (*Brassica oleracea*). Kale is an excellent, succulent feed for cattle that is of high digestibility and rich in protein (17% crude protein in the dry matter) and carotene.[46,47] It is particularly valuable as a green winter feed. Traditionally, marrowstem kale is grown for autumn use, and the more frost-resistant thousand-head kale late in winter, but these have now been largely replaced by hybrid cultivars, such as Maris Kestrel which is a short, winter-hardy, thick-stemmed type. Kale grows well under a wide range of conditions, but is found mostly in the south and south-west of England. Problems have long been associated with the feeding of large amounts of kale over a prolonged period.

Poisonous principles

Toxic constituents of kale include the amino acid, *S*-methyl cysteine sulphoxide (SMCO), which is converted in the rumen during normal fermentation to dimethyl disulphide, a compound that destroys red blood cells[48] and causes an acute haemolytic anaemia. The characteristic smell of dimethyl disulphide can be detected in the breath of animals consuming brassicas. Also present are goitrogens, mainly the thiocyanate ion, but also some isothiocyanates, derived from glucosinolates.[49,50] Glucosinolates that have been identified from kale include sinigrin, glucobrassicin, progoitrin, gluconapin, neoglucobrassicin, glucoiberin, and glucobrassicanapin.[51] The SMCO content can vary with fertilizer application; it increases with nitrogen application but only when soil sulphate values are high.[52] Under certain conditions kale can accumulate nitrates.

Animal poisoning

The two main disorders produced by kale feeding are haemolytic anaemia and goitre. The plant can also have adverse effects on fertility, and nitrate/nitrite poisoning has been reported in cattle in New Zealand.[27]

• HAEMOLYTIC ANAEMIA When ruminants are fed largely or exclusively on kale, or on other brassica crops, such as rape, cabbage, Brussels sprouts, and swede tops, they may develop severe haemolytic anaemia as a result of SMCO present in the plants.[9] Clinical signs depend on the extent of haemolysis (breakdown of red blood cells), and the ability of the animal to replace the cells destroyed. Recently calved cows or those in late pregnancy are at greater risk, as are animals with a high milk yield. An obvious clinical sign of this acute anaemia in cattle is the presence of haemoglobin in the urine (haemoglobinuria); the urine is reddish brown or black. Other signs are loss of appetite, weakness, a fall in milk yield, jaundice, increased heart rate, and diarrhoea. An affected cow soon becomes weak, and ceases to feed; this is followed by a rapid loss of condition. Collapse and sudden death may also occur.

The first evidence of anaemia, usually after 1–3 weeks of kale feeding, is detectable in the blood; microscopic examination reveals stainable granules (Heinz bodies) in the red blood cells. Subsequently, blood haemoglobin falls, usually over 1–2 weeks, from the normal 11 g per 100 ml to 6 g per 100 ml or lower. The dimethyl disulphide levels in the blood increase as the intake of SMCO progresses.[53] When kale feeding is stopped, haemoglobin levels return to normal in 3–4 weeks. If kale feeding continues even until haemolysis becomes severe, the animals may still recover by producing new red blood cells.

Post-mortem examination of animals that die reveals emaciation and jaundice. The bladder may contain black, tar-like urine, the spleen is pale brown, the liver swollen and pale (with distinct lobules), and the kidneys are a uniform dark brown. Histological examination of the liver shows wedge-shaped areas of necrosis. Extensive vacuolation of kidney cells and degeneration of nuclei in the renal epithelium are also seen, together with the presence of large, irregular masses of an iron-containing protein, haemosiderin, within macrophages of the spleen.[54] The findings are similar to those in another form of haemoglobinuria that occurs after calving and is not always due to kale feeding.[55]

In a survey of 83 dairy farms in 1969 (49 in southern England and 34 in south-west Scotland), 6.4% of cows fed kale developed anaemia (as shown by a low haemoglobin content of blood), although in 36% the red blood cells contained more Heinz bodies than normal. In most of the herds, the disorder was not serious because the animals were seldom fed kale alone.[56] The livestock most at risk are sheep and cattle fed almost entirely on brassica fodder crops.[57]

The SMCO content of kale increases as the plant matures, and as secondary growth and flowering begin. Flowers contain twice as much SMCO as the whole plant (up to 20 g per kg dry matter), and they are very toxic to cattle. At one farm in Scotland, yearling cattle strip-grazing on Maris Kestrel kale crossed an electric fence and ate the flowers; several developed severe anaemia.[58]

Care should be taken when feeding kale and other brassica crops to ruminants, to limit the intake of SMCO by restricting the amount fed and/or by using cultivars low in SMCO (e.g. Maris Kestrel and Cauletta). It has been estimated that a daily intake of 15 g SMCO per 100 kg live weight is required to produce acute haemolytic anaemia, and that 10 g or less produces only mild anaemia.[46] In one survey of kale cultivars and types, plants sampled at various stages of growth contained between 3.8 and 14.4 g SMCO per kg dry matter.[58]

Kale is one of the crops used for the production of leaf protein extracts and as a feedstuff for poultry. Heinz body anaemia similar to that found in ruminants has also been produced in adult fowls (male and female) fed with dimethyl disulphide at up to 600 µg per head per day for 12 days. Haemoglobin and haematocrit values were also reduced.[59]

• GOITRE This condition has been produced by kale in adult sheep,[60] in lambs born to ewes that had been fed on kale during pregnancy,[61,62] and in cattle.[63] The goitre is due to secondary iodine deficiency, as thiocyanate competes with the thyroid gland for uptake of iodine and thus prevents accumulation of iodine in the thyroid gland. This effect can be corrected by feeding extra iodine.[50] The thiocyanate content of kale varies according to the part of the plant sampled and the time of year. Small, young leaves contain about five times more thiocyanate than large leaves, and twice the content of intermediate-sized leaves. Thiocyanate content doubles during late September and October, then declines subsequently. Variations in different crops and years have also been noted.[64]

A common sign of iodine deficiency is the birth of offspring that are weak or die soon after birth. Such animals have an enlarged thyroid gland. The offspring may be born dead, or the thyroid gland may be so large that it interferes with breathing and sucking.[65] Loss of hair is another feature. Iodine deficiency is not now of major economic importance because it is easy to recognize and to correct.[66] Goitre takes a long time to develop in adult animals. Ewes fed unrestricted amounts of kale (daily intake averaging 4.5 kg) for 17 weeks developed thyroid enlargement, and histological signs of goitre; the thyroid gland and the blood contained subnormal amounts of iodine.[67]

• REDUCED FERTILITY This has been associated with kale feeding in cows and ewes. A definite correlation between kale feeding and low winter fertility in cows, particularly Friesians, was established by a survey of 100 farms in Somerset,[68] and a similar effect was reproduced experimentally in Friesians each fed about 50 kg kale daily. Amounts of copper and haemoglobin in the blood were much lower than in cows not fed kale.[69] Herd infertility, manifested by prolonged absence of oestrus, may occur among cows with anaemia due to kale feeding.[70] Simultaneous deficiencies of phosphorus, copper, manganese, and iodine can contribute to the infertility of kale-fed dairy cows.[46] Ewes fed kale have shown brief oestrus and an increased occurrence of abnormal embryos.[62] Feeding kale throughout the winter to a herd of goats in France was suspected to be the cause of the birth of mummified or weak, non-viable kids 5–15 days after the expected date of parturition.[71] Oestrogenic substances have not been demonstrated in kale,[72] and it appears that the goitrogenic properties of kale may be responsible for infertility, suppression of oestrus, reduced conception rate, embryonic mortality and stillbirth.[73]

Human ingestion

Goitrogens circulating in the blood stream are excreted in the milk of lactating animals fed goitrogenic plants. The milk of a goat fed on thousand-head kale was found to contain 4.6 mg thiocyanate per 100 ml.[74] Evidence from Tasmania in 1949–1954 suggested that enlarged thyroids in children might have been caused by drinking milk from cows fed large amounts of marrowstem kale.[75] The pastures in Tasmania harboured various cruciferous weeds, particularly turnip weed (*Rapistrum rugosum*), but extensive investigations failed to produce definite evidence of goitrogens in milk from cows grazing on kale or on cruciferous weeds.[76] In Finland, the thiocyanate content in milk was shown to increase from 2 to 5.8 mg per litre when cows were fed large quantities of brassica forage, but even at levels of 18 mg per litre, there was no evidence that the milk was goitrogenic, although the iodine content of the milk fell with the increase in its thiocyanate content. These findings indicate that iodine deficiency would develop in young children only if such milk were the sole source of nourishment.[49]

Raphanus raphanistrum Wild Radish

Wild radish is an annual or a biennial plant, 20–60 cm tall, very branched, with divided or lobed, rough leaves, which are larger at the base than near the top of the stem. The flowers are white or very pale lilac (occasionally pale yellow) with veined petals.

Poisonous principle

The active constituent is allyl isothiocyanate, derived from sinigrin (allyl glucosinolate).

Animal poisoning

There are no records of poisoning by wild radish in recent British literature, but it has always been regarded as harmful to livestock if eaten in quantity. However, lambs and adult sheep failed to develop signs of poisoning when fed large amounts of the freshly cut plants or ripe seeds. Similarly, no poisoning or abortion occurred among pregnant ewes given up to 600 g of wild radish pods a day, neither were yearling sheep poisoned by eating up to 1 kg of pods mixed with grain. The seeds contained 0.17–0.29% allyl isothiocyanate.[77] Diets that contained as much as 15% wild radish seed pods did not produce any clinical signs of poisoning or lesions in growing pigs.[78] Poisoning was suspected after 50 lambs had been allowed to graze a field covered with wild radish in an advanced stage of flowering. One died on the same night and five others were found dead the next morning; others in the flock were unable to rise. Post-mortem examination within two hours of death showed the rumen to be filled with the plant; the abdominal muscles were congested and the tissues yellow in colour. The heart and lungs were normal, but the liver was friable, the kidneys were congested with blood, and the bladder was filled with blood-stained urine.[79]

Sinapis alba White Mustard

White mustard is the cultivated mustard, which is grown as a forage crop for sheep, as a green manure, and for the manufacture of the condiment, mustard. The stem grows to a height of 30–60 cm, and is usually covered with stiff hairs. The leaves are rough, hairy, lobed, and up to 15 cm long; the flowers have yellow petals, up to 15 mm across. The pod grows up to 40 mm long and 3–4 mm wide. It has a flat hairy beak that takes up over half of its total length, and contains one seed at its base.

Poisonous principles

The seed of white mustard contains sinalbin (*p*-hydroxybenzyl-glucosinolate). On hydrolysis, this forms an unstable isothiocyanate, which breaks down into thiocyanate and *p*-hydroxybenzyl alcohol.[2] Under some conditions, toxic quantities of nitrates may be present.

Animal poisoning

In Britain, when lambs grazed for two days and nights on a white mustard crop in which seed pods had formed, five died and 40 were ill and unable to stand.[80] Others, which could walk, had frothy salivation and diarrhoea. Clinical signs and post-mortem findings were almost identical with those of charlock poisoning.[81] Sheep fed 600 g of extracted mustard seed cake a day for several days, or 1–2 kg in one feed, had a blood haemoglobin value twice that of normal. Their respiration and pulse rates increased and the sheep died; oedema was found at post-mortem examination. However, 290 g of mustard cake fed every day for 100 days in 1 kg of concentrate, with maize silage and hay, produced no adverse effects. The seed cake contained 1.1% mustard oil.[82]

Poisoning has also occurred in cattle. Some bullocks died after grazing white mustard stubble. Post-mortem examination showed that the rumen was packed with coarse fibrous mustard stems and the lining membrane was more easily detached than usual. There was inflammation in the abomasum, small intestines, and lungs.[83] Eight of 54 dairy cows died within two to three days of having had access to a heap of about 16 kg of white mustard seed, which had been deposited in the field where they were grazing.[84] The effects of poisoning commenced with staggering and walking around in circles, then the cows became recumbent with arched neck and profuse salivation; there was no diarrhoea. Post-mortem examination revealed inflammation of the abomasum and intestines, and also patchy congestion and inflammation in the kidneys. The rumen contained much fibrous material, and an abundance of mustard seeds. Mustard seed poisoning has also been reported from India[85] in a bullock given 'conditioning powder' containing 50–60 g of mixed, ground mustard seed, once daily for some days. Clinical signs were those of severe gastroenteritis. In Switzerland, 19 of 48 heifers died two hours after being fed on white mustard.[86] This crop had been cut and fed to the cattle because development of the plants had been inhibited at the preflowering stage by a sudden drop in temperature. The plants contained 6.2% nitrate in dry matter, 10–20 times the toxic level; the glucosinolate content was below that considered dangerous.

Sinapis arvensis Charlock

Charlock is an annual weed of arable land, and thrives on calcareous and heavy soils. It is less common in Britain than in the past. The leaves are rough and slightly hairy. The flowers are bright yellow, and flowering continues for most of the summer; the pods have a beak that takes up about one-third of their length. The seeds are capable of remaining dormant in soil for many years, and germinate only when conditions are favourable. Selective weed killers have been aimed at this weed, particularly in cereal crops. Charlock is now easily controlled in cereals and in oilseed rape.

Poisonous principles
Charlock is not poisonous until the pods have formed. The poisonous constituent of the seeds is the volatile mustard oil, allyl isothiocyanate.[2] This is released from sinigrin (allyl glucosinolate) present in charlock seed.

Animal poisoning
Toxicity has been demonstrated in chickens, especially when fed crushed charlock seed.[87] Sheep fed crushed seed developed slight bloat, while in those fed large amounts of the plant (30–35 kg) rumination ceased.[88] Poisoning occurred in lambs folded on a field of rape in which charlock with well-formed pods was abundant.[81] The clinical signs were those of acute gastroenteritis: abdominal pain, slight frothing around the mouth and nose, grunting, and diarrhoea. Post-mortem examination revealed acute inflammation of the rumen, intestines, and kidneys. Poisoning of horses by charlock has been reported in the Ukraine[89] and Yugoslavia.[90] Cattle have been poisoned by hay containing 20–30% of charlock; allyl isothiocyanate, however, has not been found in silage.[91] In the Republic of Georgia,[91] cattle had access to charlock growing in profusion to a height of 70–80 cm in fields after the potato harvest. Temperatures were low (−5° C), so these plants had probably been damaged by frost. Small amounts eaten by cattle resulted in frequent urination, reddening of visible mucous membranes, and slight bloat; they recovered within 24 hours. When large amounts were eaten, animals died of asphyxia in 1–1.5 hours. Clinical signs were bloat, open-mouth breathing, groaning, shuffling or standing with legs wide apart, bulging of eyes with dilated pupils, bluish coloration (cyanosis) of visible mucous membranes, and inability to urinate. Treatment was symptomatic and included puncture of the rumen to relieve bloat.

Other members of the Cruciferae family

Cabbage (*Brassica oleracea* var. *capitata*), Brussels sprouts (*Brassica oleracea* var. *gemmifera*), swede (*Brassica napus* var. *napobrassica*), turnip (*Brassica campestris*), and brown mustard (*Brassica juncea*) all contain the haemolytic factor *S*-methyl cysteine sulphoxide (SMCO),[48,58] but they are seldom eaten in amounts large enough to cause trouble. Haemolytic anaemia, with or without haemoglobinuria, has been reported in cattle[70,92,93] and in sheep[93,94] fed large amounts of cabbage, and in cows given free access to Brussels sprouts.[70] Although swede roots have always been regarded as safe, anaemia can be produced experimentally in cattle and sheep[94] and in goats[92] by feeding them on swede roots and tops. The SMCO content of turnips is generally quite low, but one cultivar, Tokyo Top, contains moderate amounts; mild anaemia occurred in lambs fed on young stubble turnip,[48,95] a *Brassica campestris* hybrid. Young lambs grazing turnips had enlarged thyroid glands when slaughtered at four months of age.[96] Outbreaks of polioencephalomalacia, pulmonary emphysema, bloat, and haemolytic anaemia have been reported in cattle grazing turnips in the north-western USA.[97]

Turnip plants are capable of taking up and accumulating large amounts of nitrates that can be converted to nitrites, which can cause poisoning in cattle.[92,98,99] When 22 cows were fed, in error, seeds of turnip and swede, they developed acute haemorrhagic gastroenteritis and colic, and seven died. This feed had been imported as 'linseed cake' from Ethiopia into Belgium, and it contained 0.5–0.7% isothiocyanate.[100]

CUCURBITACEAE

Bryonia dioica White Bryony (Plates 22 and 23)

Other common name: British Mandrake

This is a climbing plant that is common in England and Wales, except in the north; it has been introduced locally in Scotland. The name and habitat of the plant cause confusion with black bryony (*Tamus communis*), another poisonous climber, but of a different family (Dioscoreaceae).

White bryony has trailing stems, branching especially near the base and sometimes exceeding 5 m in length. The plant climbs by means of spirally coiled tendrils that arise from the stem beside the leaf stalks. The leaves are up to 10 cm across, have 3–5 pointed lobes, and they, and the stems, are covered with minute, stiff hairs making the plant rough to touch. Greenish-white flowers appear in clusters in the leaf axils in summer, the males (12–18 mm across) and the females (10–12 mm across) being similar in appearance, but borne on separate plants. The flowers have pointed sepals, larger triangular, net-veined petals and yellow anthers in the males and a prominent bifid stigma in the females. White bryony has a massive, tuberous root, consumption of which has caused poisoning when mistaken for parsnip or turnip, hence the French name 'navet du diable' (devil's turnip). The ripe fruit is a red berry with a dull surface and contains flat, black- and yellow-mottled seeds. The whole plant, but particularly the root, contains an acrid milky juice, the unpleasant odour of which persists after drying.

Poisonous principles
Little is known of these, except that they include a glycoside (variously named as bryonin(e) or bryonidin), which is a drastic purgative, and an alkaloid (bryonicine).

A group of irritant tetracyclic triterpenes, cucurbitacins, that are mainly confined to the Cucurbitaceae family, are present in the roots of white bryony; their possible presence in other parts of the plants has not been established. Brydiofin, a toxic protein, has been isolated from the fruits. The toxicity of the plant decreases with drying.

Animal poisoning

Under normal conditions, poisoning of domestic animals by white bryony is rare, although early literature[1] reports that ingestion of the root by pigs, and the berries by poultry, may prove fatal. Poisoning of a herd of 40 milking cows occurred when the animals had access to white bryony roots exposed during excavation for a pipe line.[2] Within a few hours the animals had collapsed, their bodies were cold, and their eyes deeply sunk in their sockets. Despite treatment with stimulants, all the animals became comatose and died. Post-mortem examination revealed large quantities of chewed, fleshy root in the rumen, the walls of which were inflamed. Two other cows that ate white bryony, but recovered, developed a craving for the plant and, during the following summer, ate any part of it which was available. This caused acute digestive disturbance, with diarrhoea, and almost complete, but temporary, cessation of milk secretion. In another more recent case in Britain where white bryony foliage with berries had been eaten liberally from a hedge, a five-year-old cow collapsed and was unable to stand until the following day.[3] There were signs of respiratory distress and milk production ceased for four days, after which it rose gradually, but never reached its former level.

In addition to diarrhoea, horses poisoned by eating white bryony[4] exhibit copious urination, sweating, and, occasionally, complete cessation of defaecation. Other clinical signs reported in horses are respiratory difficulty, incoordination, and convulsions; intestinal ulceration has been seen.

In Britain, a dog that collapsed and had an increased body temperature, and rapid respiratory and heart rates, was found to have eaten white bryony berries, and then vomited.[5] After further vomiting and also defaecation, the dog died suddenly 22 hours after being examined. Large numbers of seeds of the plant were found in the intestines, and haemorrhagic fluid was present in the abdominal and chest cavities. The post-mortem examination also revealed peritonitis and enteritis.

In Romania, 18 ducklings gorged themselves on bryony when food was scarce.[6] All died within 10–24 hours, after showing apathy, staggering gait, recumbency, trembling, convulsions, diarrhoea, and laboured breathing.

There is no specific treatment, but stimulants, as well as fluids to replace those lost in diarrhoea, are recommended.

Human poisoning

The juice of white bryony irritates the skin[7] and poisoning has resulted from eating the root[1] and the berries, which are particularly attractive to children. Vomiting is usually the only symptom when small numbers of berries have been eaten, while more severe reactions occur with larger numbers of berries.[6-8] Fluid replacement is usually the only treatment necessary, but activated charcoal can also be given.

CUPRESSACEAE

Cupressocyparis leylandii Leyland Cypress

This is a hybrid derived by crossing the Monterey cypress (*Cupressus macrocarpa*) with the Nootka cypress (*Chamaecyparis nootkatensis*); it is popular as a screening hedge plant. If left untrimmed Leyland cypress can reach 30 m in height. The small, scale-like leaves are green, yellowish green, or blue-green according to the variety, and may appear all round the stems or be pressed flat in one plane. The young growth, in particular, is very flexible and the foliage forms drooping sprays.

Poisonous principles
Little is known about these, but Leyland cypress is thought to contain the terpenes and phenol derivatives present in the parent trees.

Animal poisoning
From the few cases that have been reported, it appears that Leyland cypress can cause serious poisoning. Weakness, depression, trembling, and loss of appetite have been reported in horses,[1] scouring and rectal prolapse in cattle,[1] and hypersalivation and death in goats.[1]

Human poisoning
No reports of cases of poisoning by ingestion have been found, but contact dermatitis can occur after pruning or handling the foliage. There is a link between this reaction and an allergy to collophany (present in sticking plaster).[2]

Cupressus species Cypresses (Plate 24)

There are many species and varieties of *Cupressus*, of which the best known is probably the Monterey cypress (*Cupressus macrocarpa*), sometimes referred to simply as macrocarpa. Cypress trees are frequently planted in large gardens, and may be trimmed to form a screen. They are evergreen trees that may grow up to 25 m tall. They have ascending branches, reddish-brown fissured or scaly bark, small, scale-like triangular leaves closely pressed in one plane against each other and the stem, and unisexual cones, which rarely exceed 3 cm across.

Poisonous principles
Various terpenes, pinenes, and phenol derivatives are present, as well as some essential oils.

Animal poisoning
Poisoning by *Cupressus* has been reported mainly in cattle,[3,4] in which loss of condition, weakness, staggering gait, and sunken eyes are consistently found. The foliage and woody parts of felled cypress trees (*Cupressus sempervirens*) were responsible for the death of two heifers in Britain,[5] and a cow in Ireland that ate trimmings from a cypress hedge (*Cupressus macrocarpa*) became dull and slightly bloated and was found dead among the felled branches the next day;[6] the animal was eight months pregnant. A large quantity of foliage was found in the rumen, and there was blood-stained fluid in

the abdominal cavity. The other 18 animals grazing in the same field were apparently unaffected, although some were seen eating the cypress trimmings. In Australia, ingestion of foliage from felled *Cupressus macrocarpa* trees induced abortion 1–3 weeks later in nine of 25 cows.[7] Some of the calves were stillborn, some died a few days after birth, and all cows retained the foetal membranes for five to more than seven days. There is a risk of abortion in cows that eat cypress in the last three months of pregnancy. Persistent, severe straining occurs, the cervix does not dilate fully, the foetal membranes are retained, and the maternal cotyledons are greatly swollen. Animals that recover give very little milk initially. Post-mortem examination of foetuses aborted by cows that ate *Cupressus macrocarpa* revealed areas in the white matter of the brain in which the cells had softened and degenerated (cerebral leukoencephalomalacia).[8] None of the adverse effects that occur in cows could be induced in pregnant sheep fed experimentally with *Cupressus macrocarpa* foliage.[9]

Juniperus species Juniper

Juniper is a shrub or small evergreen tree with thin bark, which often peels in longitudinal strips. Depending on the species, the leaves may be scale-like, resembling cypress, or needle-like. The scales of the female flowers become fleshy and form a berry-like structure.

Poisonous principles
The leaves and shoots contain juniper oil, terpene derivatives, and a bitter substance, probably an alkaloid, called juniperine.[10]

Animal poisoning
Species of juniper, particularly *Juniperus sabina*, which is not native but sometimes planted in Britain, have poisoned animals. The clinical signs include gastrointestinal disturbances, muscular cramps, and abortion,[11] especially in the last three months of pregnancy. Poisoning occurs most frequently in cattle, but has also been recorded in a goat, which ate juniper and developed gastrointestinal disorders and had blood-stained urine.[12] Post-mortem examination reveals inflammation of the digestive and urinary tracts. *Juniperus communis* grows on calcareous soils throughout Britain, although it is rather local in distribution. It contains similar toxic principles to other *Juniperus* species, but no specific cases of poisoning have been attributed to it in this country.

Human poisoning
Contact dermatitis can occur in individuals previously sensitized to collophany (present in sticking plaster).[2]

Other members of the Cupressaceae family

The Chinese, western red, and white cedars (*Thuja* species) are not native in Britain, but are very commonly planted in parks or large gardens as specimen trees or for hedging; they make good windbreaks. *Thuja* species have caused severe digestive disturbances, and liver and kidney damage. In a recent incident in Britain, weakness and profuse watery diarrhoea were reported in ten cattle that ate hedge trimmings; they all survived.[1] An allergic contact dermatitis can occur in people who handle the trees (particularly the wood).[2]

CYPERACEAE

Carex species Sedges

This large group contains perennial plants that grow in tufts or from an underground stem (rhizome). The leaves are grass-like in shape; they are curved downwards in many species, and some have overlapping, sheathing bases, are channelled along their length or have inrolled margins. The stems of the British species range in height from 20 cm to over 1 m; they are triangular in section and bear separate male and female flowers arranged in a variety of ways in relation to each other, but on the same inflorescence. The structure of the ripe fruits needs to be studied to identify the species with certainty.

Poisonous principles
The plants contain cyanogenic glycosides. Saponins, tannin, resin, and traces of an essential oil are also said to be present in the whole plant.[1]

Animal poisoning
Sedges are rarely eaten by animals as they contain silicates, which make them coarse and hard, and consequently unpalatable. Consumption of *Carex vulpina*, a sedge native in Britain, has poisoned cattle in Romania,[2] where ten of 62 animals died or had to be killed after eating the actively growing green plant in early summer. The clinical signs described, which apply equally to cattle that have eaten other *Carex* species, are typical of cyanide poisoning. They occurred within a few minutes of eating the plant, and included excess salivation, clenching and grinding of teeth, dilatation of pupils, congestion of mucous membranes, diarrhoea, muscular spasms, unsteady gait, posterior paralysis, recumbency, deep respiration becoming shallower, weak pulse, and groaning. Coma usually preceded death, which often occurred 30–60 minutes after eating the plants. Post-mortem examination revealed haemorrhages in the conjunctivae, muscles, bone marrow, and intestines, the contents of which, in some cases, smelt of bitter almonds. The blood was bright red, and the lungs were oedematous and congested with blood.

If given immediately, and before too much sedge has been eaten, intravenous injection of sodium thiosulphate and sodium nitrite solutions may be effective in treating poisoned animals.

DENNSTAEDTIACEAE

Pteridium aquilinum Bracken (Plate 25)

Other common name: Brake

Bracken is the commonest fern in Britain, and is found on light, acid soils in a variety of habitats including woodland, heath, moorland, and hills up to about 600 m. It has become widely disseminated, and invaded large areas of land, where it is often the dominant plant. No accurate, up-to-date figures are available for the area infested by bracken in Britain, but it is still increasing and was estimated to be over 450,000 hectares in 1993.[1,2]

Bracken is a coarse fern with a creeping underground stem (rhizome) from which solitary leaves develop annually in spring and die down when brown in autumn. The young leaves bear numerous, coarse, brown scales and are rolled tightly inwards from the tip. The scales are lost as the leaves uncurl. When fully grown their height may exceed 2 m, but this varies according to the habitat, usually measuring 1 m or less. The leaves are compound and have a long, tough stalk with (usually three) main pointed fronds near the top; there may also be smaller stalked fronds, in pairs, further down the main stalk. Deeply indented leaflets arise in one plane on the stems. Brown, spore-bearing structures develop all round the margins of the segments of some leaves.

Poisonous principles

The whole plant contains toxic constituents, at least some of which remain after cutting and drying. There are several harmful constituents in bracken, but the only ones that have been identified satisfactorily are a cyanogenic glycoside (prunasin) usually present in harmless quantities, an enzyme (thiaminase) that leads to thiamine deficiency in horses and pigs, and a carcinogen (ptaquiloside). The carcinogenic and immunosuppressive effects of bracken are being studied, and the full picture is not yet clear.

• PRUNASIN Cyanogenic glycosides are toxic because they yield hydrocyanic acid when hydrolysed by enzymes released if the plant tissue is crushed. The presence of prunasin appears to act as a deterrent to grazing, but bracken shows a phenomenon known as biochemical polymorphism, and although most populations of the plant are cyanogenic, some are not because they lack the enzyme and/or prunasin. When non-cyanogenic plants dominate in a population, bracken is grazed heavily.[3] In some parts of the country sheep are said not to graze bracken at all under normal circumstances, but under some conditions, usually when there is no other forage available, they will graze it[4] and seem to become addicted to the plant.[5,6] This preferential eating of bracken was reported recently in a horse.[7] Despite the fact that the prunasin content of bracken is usually too low to harm grazing animals,[3] sudden death, thought to be due to hydrocyanic acid, has been recorded in animals fed on young fronds.[8]

• THIAMINASE Bracken contains thiaminase type I, an enzyme capable of destroying thiamine (vitamin B_1) and thus inducing thiamine deficiency in non-ruminant animals such as the horse and the pig.[9] Thiaminase activity is highest in the rhizomes and very young leaves, and decreases rapidly in the fronds as the aerial parts of the plant unfold. A heat-stable anti-thiamine factor (possibly caffeic acid) has also been shown to be involved in the disease in horses.[10,11]

• CARCINOGENS Ptaquiloside, a water-soluble, norsesquiterpene glycoside of the illudane type, was first reported to be the major carcinogenic agent in bracken in 1983.[12] In alkaline conditions (in the intestines) it is converted to a dianone intermediate that either reacts with water to form the inactive pterosin B or combines with DNA to give rise to changes in chromosomes. These changes can lead to the formation of neoplasms, in whose development other factors, such as the immunosuppressive effects of bracken and the potentially oncogenic papillomaviruses, also play a role.[13–15]

Some preliminary work indicated that ptaquiloside is involved in both the acute haemorrhagic syndrome and enzootic haematuria in cattle,[16] and also in 'bright blindness' (retinal degeneration) in sheep.[17] Other work has shown that ptaquiloside, as well as quercetin and shikimate, which have been suggested previously to be the carcinogens of bracken, have low acute toxicity on some cells in culture, from which it was assumed that these bracken constituents are not the direct causal agents of the acute haemorrhagic syndrome;[18] it has also been shown that neither quercetin nor shikimate cause the severe depression of bone marrow activity that is characteristic of this disease.[19]

Animal poisoning
There are several types of poisoning caused by bracken; these fall into two main groups, acute and chronic, according to whether the disease develops rapidly or gradually from the onset of clinical signs.

Acute types
Before the 1960s, only the acute (rapidly fatal) forms of poisoning were clearly recognized. There are two distinct forms of acute disease: thiamine deficiency (in horses and pigs) resulting from the presence of the enzyme thiaminase in the plant, and the haemorrhagic syndrome that may be caused by ptaquiloside (in cattle and sheep).

• THIAMINE DEFICIENCY This occurs sporadically in Welsh mountain ponies and other horses on bracken land.[9] The main clinical signs are inappetence, incoordination, very pronounced heart beat after mild exercise, and, as the disease progresses, severe muscular tremors. These are followed by convulsions, opisthotonos (backward flexing of the neck), and death. These clinical features have given rise to the name 'bracken staggers' for the condition in horses. There is usually a rapid, dramatic response to the administration of thiamine if given at the onset of clinical signs.[9] Fatal poisoning has occurred in mules in Brazil,[20] where the disease has also been reproduced experimentally in horses.[21]

Bracken-induced thiamine deficiency in pigs appears to be rare, mainly as a result of the conditions under which pigs are generally kept, but, even when it does occur, it is not easy to diagnose because of the non-specificity of the clinical features. In the few cases that have been reported in Britain, the pigs were either found dead or died quickly, after a short period of heavy breathing.[22] The condition has been reproduced experimentally in pigs by feeding a diet containing 25–33%, by weight, of dried, powdered bracken rhizomes.[23] Loss of appetite and vomiting appeared after about seven weeks on this ration, and listlessness after eight weeks. Terminal signs of recumbency and heavy breathing appeared suddenly at 8–10 weeks, after which death occurred within six hours. The most striking post-mortem lesions were in the heart, which was enlarged and mottled with yellow and red patches. Histologically, the heart lesions were similar to those described in experimental thiamine deficiency in pigs. Depression and vomiting occurred in two of three pregnant sows in a paddock into which cut garden weeds, including bracken, had been thrown.[24] If bracken poisoning is suspected in pigs, they should be removed from the bracken-infested land and given thiamine. The thiaminase in bracken does not induce thiamine deficiency in cattle and sheep under normal conditions; these animals are not dependent on a dietary source, as thiamine is synthesized by rumen bacteria. However, the experimental inclusion of 15–30% powdered bracken rhizome in the diet of adult sheep produced clinical signs of thiamine deficiency in 1–3 months.[25]

The thiamine deficiency induced in horses by bracken should be treated by daily injection of 100 mg thiamine (vitamin B_1). This is very successful if begun at the onset of clinical signs. Injection of thiamine is of no use in cattle and sheep.

• ACUTE HAEMORRHAGIC SYNDROME   This is often referred to simply as 'bracken poisoning', but the latter term should be avoided as it is non-specific, and bracken can have several different toxic effects. In Britain in 1893, during a severe drought in which bracken was eaten as it was the only food available, a haemorrhagic syndrome was reported in cattle, and it was suspected that bracken was the cause.[26] In 1894, the disease was reproduced by feeding bracken,[27] but because of later failure with experimental feeding, and because of some confusion with anthrax, the explanation that bracken was the cause was not generally accepted until over 50 years later, when indisputable experimental evidence was obtained.[28] An increase in cases of poisoning by plants, including bracken, was reported in Britain during the droughts of 1976[29] and 1984.[30] According to the diagnoses made at the Veterinary Investigation (VI) Centres in Britain in the 12-year period 1983–1994 there were 225 cases of poisoning of cattle attributed directly to bracken, compared to 152 cases of ragwort poisoning.[31,32] The numbers of outbreaks recorded by the VI Centres indicate seasonal variations with most cases occurring in late summer and autumn.[33]

Clinical signs of this syndrome do not usually develop until animals have been eating bracken for several weeks, and sometimes not until they are no longer grazing the plants. Once clinical signs have developed, however, death may occur within a week; even more rapid death (within 48 hours) has been recorded.[34,35] Poisoning usually follows eating green bracken fronds, but rhizomes of the plant, exposed during ploughing, have caused death;[36] fronds cut when green and dried for use as bedding can cause poisoning when eaten (dry brown bracken, cut in winter, is safe to use for this purpose).

Internal haemorrhage, the principal effect, is revealed by the presence of blood in faeces (firm at first, then fluid) and sometimes in urine. Initially there is often a watery discharge from the eyes, nose, and mouth, followed by bleeding from these sites and from the genital tract. Small haemorrhages are usually apparent on visible mucous membranes. Affected animals often lose their appetite, rumination ceases, and they become weak and unable to stand; the pulse is often feeble, and body temperature may rise. This 'enteric' form of the disease is more common in adult cattle. It is more usual for calves to develop a 'laryngitic' form of the disease, with oral and nasal discharge of mucus, and oedematous swelling of the throat, leading to difficult, noisy breathing. The cause of the haemorrhages is a blood coagulation disorder arising from severe depression of bone marrow activity;[16] fewer blood platelets are produced, resulting in an increase in blood coagulation time. A reduction in the number of white blood cells leads to a greater susceptibility to infection, and a decrease in red blood cell formation, to anaemia; the term 'aplastic anaemia' is sometimes applied to this disease.[37] An increase in the level of heparin-like anticoagulant substances in the circulating blood[38] may be an additional cause of the haemorrhages. Experimental administration of ptaquiloside to a six-month-old calf for 42 days resulted in a severe depression in bone marrow activity and decreases in the blood neutrophil and blood platelet counts, but not the classical clinical signs of the acute haemorrhagic syndrome.[16, 39]

In the acute haemorrhagic syndrome in cattle, batyl alcohol, a substance known to stimulate the activity of bone marrow, was found to be effective in some trials when injected subcutaneously at 1 g in 10 ml olive oil for five consecutive days, or in suspension given by slow intravenous injection daily.[37] However, doubts have been expressed about its efficacy and there are various problems associated with its use. Other treatments that have been suggested are combined therapy consisting of intramuscular injections of mepyramine, streptomycin, penicillin, and prednisolone, and intravenous injections of toluidine blue (250 mg in 250 ml saline) and batyl alcohol (500 ml dispersed in saline). Blood transfusions (4.5 litres of citrated blood, followed by a second transfusion of half this quantity) can be given; a single intravenous injection of 10 ml of 1% protamine sulphate is advised to counteract the anticoagulant effect of the heparin released. Supportive therapy consists of injections of B complex vitamins and oral administration of a drug to stimulate appetite.

The haemorrhagic syndrome also occurs in sheep that eat bracken, although it is slower to develop and is a much rarer occurrence in this species than in cattle. On the North York Moors, losses have been recorded among sheep grazing pastures containing bracken,[40] and in a survey in 1964,[5] the haemorrhagic syndrome was present in 16 of 43 dead sheep that were examined. The white blood cell and blood platelet counts of five severely ill sheep were consistent with the disease. Following an outbreak of the haemorrhagic syndrome in a sheep flock during a drought in Western Australia when there was little else to eat but bracken, two yearling sheep were given a diet containing chopped fresh young bracken fronds. One sheep that died after eating nearly 4.8 kg of the chopped bracken in 24 days had the typical haemorrhagic lesions with complete absence of blood-forming tissue in rib bone marrow. There were no lesions in the other sheep, which was killed after eating 3.4 kg in 36 days.[41] Post-mortem examination of cattle and sheep reveals extensive bleeding in many sites.

Chronic types
In the 1960s, it was established that bracken is the cause of two chronic conditions: enzootic haematuria in cattle and bright blindness in sheep. These conditions had been recognized as specific diseases much earlier, although their cause was not known. More recently bracken has also been associated with intestinal tumours in cattle and sheep. Chronic poisoning by bracken may well prove to be of greater economic importance than the acute condition, but at present there is little information on the prevalence of this type of poisoning.

• ENZOOTIC HAEMATURIA The bracken carcinogen, ptaquiloside, in association with bovine papillomavirus type 2, is reported to be involved in chronic enzootic haematuria.[13] This form of poisoning is found in cattle after prolonged feeding of bracken in small amounts, and has been produced experimentally in sheep. In addition to loss of blood in the urine, it is associated with the development of benign and malignant tumours in the wall of the bladder; the carcinogen has also been found in the urine of cows grazing bracken. It has been suggested that the acute haemorrhagic syndrome and enzootic haematuria are two clinical forms of the same disease, and that the different clinical signs are associated with differences in the amounts of bracken eaten.[42, 43]

Enzootic haematuria is found in cattle throughout the world, but is always limited to areas where cattle graze on bracken or where it is used as bedding.[42] The extent and importance of haematuria in cattle in Britain is not known. Affected animals excrete red or brownish urine, but show no obvious disturbances of their general condition. In contrast to haemoglobinuria, in which the urine is clear and varnish-coloured, in haematuria the urine is always cloudy and opaque, because of the excretion of whole blood, and sometimes it is also floccular. Cattle with haematuria do not show jaundice. Red blood cells can be detected microscopically in urine weeks or even months before the obvious appearance of blood in urine, and diagnosis can be confirmed by cystoscopy (endoscopic examination of the bladder wall in a living animal). During haematuria there is a fall in the number of red and white blood cells and in the haemoglobin concentration of the blood. In advanced cases there is also slight to moderate reduction in the numbers of blood platelets. The course of the disease is generally intermittent, with each episode being worse than the preceding one. Later, during a stage of severe bleeding, the flow of urine may be temporarily or permanently interrupted by blood clots.[42]

Post-mortem examination shows characteristic bladder lesions consisting of small red to black haemorrhagic foci. In some cases these may measure up to 1 cm across. Histological examination of the bladder shows dilatation of blood capillaries, the formation of angiomas (tumours of blood vessels) and growth of tumours infiltrating the whole bladder wall. Bleeding occurs from the angiomatous capillaries.

The link between bracken and bovine enzootic haematuria was demonstrated in 1960 in feeding trials.[44] Prolonged (more than one year) feeding of cows and calves with bracken led to signs typical of enzootic haematuria, but some animals finally died with signs of acute haemorrhage indicating that haemorrhage and haematuria are two clinical manifestations of poisoning by bracken.[42] In a five-year investigation of tumours in sheep, five of eight animals fed on dried bracken (prepared in a pellet form) died of uraemia following haematuria, and one died half-way through the trial with the acute haemorrhagic syndrome.[45] A diet containing ptaquiloside produced haematuria and bladder tumours in rats.[46] A subcutaneous injection of ptaquiloside resulted in a haemorrhagic cystitis in guinea pigs but not in rats or mice;[47] the agent causing the cystitis was carried by the blood and not by the urine.[48]

Other work has shown that the immunosuppressive effects of bracken can activate latent bovine papillomavirus type 2 infection; this virus can give rise to premalignant changes in the bladder, and these can then become malignant under the influence of ptaquiloside.[13,49] In the USA, enzootic haematuria with severe anaemia was reported in a 13-year-old llama that had been pastured for seven years on land where bracken was abundant.[50] Malignant tumours were found in both kidneys (transitional cell carcinomas) and the left ureter (a transitional cell papilloma); the bone marrow and bladder were not kept for examination. Bovine papillomavirus was detected in the ureteral papilloma. The findings in the llama were very similar to those reported in cattle.

• BRIGHT BLINDNESS   This progressive degeneration of the retina of the eyes of sheep is another long-term effect of bracken feeding. It was first described in 1965 in hill flocks in the West Riding of Yorkshire, although it was said to have been known to hill sheep farmers in that county for at least 50 years.[51] It is also well recognized in the Yorkshire Dales, Lower Weardale and Teesdale, and in the Lake District. By 1971 it had been confirmed in 253 flocks in northern England and in one in Scotland. Although found widely in northern England, it has also been reported from South Wales.[6] The term 'bright blind' signifies absence of cloudiness of the eye that characterizes some other forms of blindness.[2] The sheep are permanently blind. They adopt a characteristic, alert attitude. Both eyes are affected and the pupils become circular, responding poorly to light. Histological changes are confined to the retina; when the disease is advanced, the layer of the rods and cones and the outer nuclear layers are completely destroyed, together with parts of the inner nuclear layer.[40, 52] The condition was reproduced experimentally in sheep by feeding them with a concentrate ration containing 50% dried bracken at about 1 kg daily for up to 63 weeks.[5] The peak incidence of bright blindness is found in sheep 3–4 years old, indicating that most sheep require to graze on bracken for two or three summers before blindness develops. In 1978 bright blindness was reported in sheep in South Wales for the first time (on two farms, with little bracken, in Gwent).[6] These sheep had been bought from local hill farms where they had had access to heavy growth of bracken. The previous apparent absence from Wales of bright blindness is interesting in that hill sheep there often have ready access to bracken, but are rarely seen to eat it. This outbreak may have been caused by the drought of 1976 when grass was very scarce and sheep were forced to look for other food; they must also have continued to eat bracken in the following year. Sheep with bright blindness have very low blood platelet and white blood cell counts. A condition resembling bright blindness has been reported in cattle grazing on bracken land in south-west Wales.[53] Bright blindness was reproduced experimentally in sheep by various methods: giving a diet containing powdered bracken for about four months, administering ptaquiloside through an intestinal catheter every other day for six months, or by weekly intravenous injections of ptaquiloside for six months.[17]

• TUMOURS   In addition to the association between bracken feeding and bladder tumours in cattle with enzootic haematuria, bracken feeding also seems to be related to the very high incidence of tumours of the digestive system of beef cows in upland areas of northern England and Scotland.[54] This has been found only on farms with bracken-infested land. The lowlands next to these areas show almost no incidence of these particular tumours. In a study of 80 cases,[54] four types of tumour were found, of which the most widespread was squamous carcinoma (a malignant tumour developed from squamous epithelium and having cuboid cells). Large numbers of cows had these tumours in the mouth, oesophagus, and rumen. Co-existent tumours of the intestine and bladder were found in a large proportion of cases. Papillomas (benign tumours derived from epithelium) were found in the upper alimentary tract of 96% of cows. Bovine papillomavirus type 4 was isolated from the papillomas;[17] these tend to increase in number and become malignant. As a result of the immunosuppressive effect of bracken, cattle are unable to mount their normal immune response to such tumour-producing viruses.[14, 15] More than 70% of the cattle with tumours were found on farms on the west coast of Scotland, particularly in Argyll, and, where it was possible to trace the farm of origin, all had bracken-infested land. A survey conducted in the 1980s showed that Argyll had about 25% of all the bracken-infested land in Scotland.[55] Sheep in north-east Yorkshire have also been found with tumours of the intestine (adenocarcinoma) and the jaw (fibrosarcoma), and bladder tumours and fibrosarcoma have also been induced experimentally in sheep by feeding them on bracken for a long period.[45] Tumours have occurred in mice given bracken spores in their feed or in their drinking water. When a grain diet containing 0.2% of bracken spores was fed to mice for 48 weeks, they showed loss of weight, a shorter life span, and increases in the frequencies of lung and stomach tumours in comparison with controls not receiving bracken spores;[56] spores have also given rise to leukaemia in mice.[57]

Control of bracken

Mechanical and chemical control of bracken are sometimes used to prevent disease in grazing animals, but the areas involved are so large that control is very expensive and often impracticable.[2] The chemical commonly used is asulam (methyl 4-aminobenzenesulphonyl carbamate), an aqueous solution of which sprayed on to thick stands of bracken gives a reasonable kill without affecting other herbage too much. Other chemicals that are effective are glyphosate and metsulfuron.[58] As the carcinogen ptaquiloside and its analogues have been eliminated by composting summer-cut bracken for 16 weeks and autumn-cut bracken for 12 weeks,[59] it has been suggested that such composted material would be safe to use by the following spring, and could be of commercial value as an alternative ingredient to peat in compost mixtures sold for horticultural use.[60]

Human poisoning

The existence of carcinogens in bracken has important public health implications. The fern is consumed as a food in several parts of the world, notably Japan, Brazil, and north-eastern USA and Canada. In certain prefectures of Japan, human consumption of bracken has been associated with an increased incidence of oesophageal and stomach tumours;[61] a similar association has been reported from Brazil.[62] The part of the plant commonly eaten is the uncurled frond (known as fiddleheads in the USA) and this contains high concentrations of carcinogenic agents. Indirect exposure might also occur since the active material is readily passed into the milk of cows fed or grazing on bracken[63] as well as through the placenta in mice.[61] Thus the human foetus could be exposed to the carcinogen when pregnant women eat the fern. Exposure of babies and very young children could also occur through mothers' milk, and people of all ages could be exposed to it by consumption of milk from cows grazing bracken-infested pastures. When a cow was given orally 6 kg of freshly cut, young bracken with grass and molasses for seven days, the animal remained in apparent good health, but ptaquiloside was detected in its milk; ptaquiloside was not found, however, in the milk of another four cows that developed enzootic haematuria after grazing a bracken-infested plot for 24 months.[64] Further work has shown that a person, who drinks daily about half a litre of milk from a cow eating 6–7 kg of bracken a day, could ingest an amount of ptaquiloside that is potentially carcinogenic to animals, but there is no information on the human toxicity of ptaquiloside.[65] A high incidence of pulmonary and mammary gland neoplasms occurred in mice given milk from cows fed a bracken-containing diet.[66] It has been concluded, however, that the dilution effects resulting from the bulk collection of milk reduce the human risk.[67] It has been suggested that potentially carcinogenic bracken spores, besides contaminating water supplies, could be inhaled, trapped in bronchial mucus, and eventually swallowed to be a cause of stomach cancer.[56, 68]

Epidemiological studies in Costa Rica showed a significant correlation between the prevalence of enzootic haematuria in cattle and human oesophageal and stomach tumours,[69] while a survey in North Wales demonstrated a significantly increased risk of stomach cancer in people who had spent their childhood in bracken-infested areas.[68] There is thus some epidemiological evidence that the bracken carcinogen (ptaquiloside) may be associated with human cancer; the possibility of this link deserves more attention.

DIOSCOREACEAE

Tamus communis   Black Bryony (Plates 26 and 27)

Black bryony grows in scrub, hedgerows, and at the edges of woods and is common throughout southern England, the Midlands, and Wales, decreases in frequency further north, and is absent from Scotland. Its common name is likely to cause confusion with white bryony (*Bryonia dioica*), which is also a climber with a similar habit and habitat, but is botanically a very different plant, belonging to another family (Cucurbitaceae).

The plant grows in hedges from an irregular, blackish tuber and climbs by means of its slender, unbranched stems, which twine anticlockwise and grow up to 4 m long. Dark, shining, heart-shaped leaves are borne on long stalks along the stem, and yellowish-green, unisexual flowers appear in the leaf axils in early summer. The male flowers are stalked and loosely clustered and the females have very short stalks, are fewer in number and more compact. The berries are up to 12 mm in diameter and are shining and green when first formed, but red when ripe. They contain 1–5 rough-coated yellow seeds.

Poisonous principles
A glycoside with a similar action to that of bryonine (in *Bryonia dioica*) is said to be present.[1] Skin irritants found in the plant are calcium oxalate and a histamine-like constituent.[2]

Animal poisoning
Reference is often made to the toxic nature of black bryony, but there are few reports of animals having been poisoned by it. Early literature[3] states that the leaves are eaten by sheep and goats without adverse effects, but that the berries are narcotic and irritant. Fatal poisoning was suspected in three horses that had grazed in fields where the stems, leaves, and berries of the plant had been pulled from the hedge and showed signs of having been chewed.[4] In one case the plant was identified in ingested material taken at a post-mortem examination. The horses refused food and became dull; severe abdominal pain, accompanied by elevated temperature and profuse sweating, developed before death.

Human poisoning

If eaten, the plant can cause burning and blistering of the mouth, followed by vomiting and diarrhoea; death may result.[5] Sap from the plant can cause dermatitis. When the skin was rubbed with either the juice of ripe berries or mucilage from the rhizome, mechanical irritation by the needle-shaped calcium oxalate crystals was produced. The histamine-like constituent present in the rhizome mucilage also appears to play a role in the skin irritation. Anti-inflammatory and analgesic activity of an alcoholic extract of the plant has been reported.[6] External application of a commercial ointment prepared from the roots of black bryony is effective in treating chilblains,[7] but skin irritation with dermatitis and blistering resulted from massaging with an extract of *Tamus communis*.[8] Treatment with demulcents is recommended if the plant is ingested.

DRYOPTERIDACEAE

Dryopteris species Male and Buckler Ferns

Several of the *Dryopteris* species native in Britain are uncommon or limited in their distribution, but the male fern (*Dryopteris filix-mas*) occurs throughout the country and is common in woods, hedges, and rocky places including steep hillsides, usually on acid soils. There are other similar, though taxonomically distinct ferns, often bearing older generic names, such as *Aspidium* or *Polystichum*, with the specific name *filix-mas;* hybrids of plants within the group are found. Various buckler ferns also occur in this country, but less commonly than the male fern.

Dryopteris filix-mas Male Fern (Plate 28)

The bright, deep-green leaves grow from a short, stout, scaly underground stem (rhizome), forming a crown. Each leaf is composed of rows of numerous leaflets that are themselves deeply divided, almost to the stem. Spore-bearing structures develop in a row down each side of the small subdivisions of some leaves. The stalk is almost as long as the spreading blade of the leaf and together they may sometimes exceed 150 cm in length. The stalk bears brownish or orange scales. Some leaves may persist into the winter.

Poisonous principles

These ferns contain thiaminase, the agent responsible for thiamine deficiency in horses and pigs that have eaten bracken (*Pteridium aquilinum*), but thiamine deficiency has not been reported with *Dryopteris* species. The plants contain filixic acid (filicin), a mixture of ether-soluble substances. The main toxic activity is due to a phloroglucinol derivative of filicin. Extracts of male fern have anthelmintic properties and have been used medicinally; the toxicity of these extracts is well recognized. The rhizome was used formerly as a flavouring for food, but this has been prohibited since 1976.

Animal poisoning

There are few reports of *Dryopteris* poisoning. All have involved cattle and occurred in winter, when the ferns were eaten as fresh food was scarce. Poisoning was reported in

Ireland in three herds in 1964–1965, when cattle on pastures with very little available herbage fed on rhizomes of buckler fern (*Dryopteris* species) growing in the hedgerows.[1] Poisoning due to male fern (*Dryopteris filix-mas*) occurred in Kirkudbright, Scotland, in 1967[2] and in 1976.[3] In both of these Scottish outbreaks the cattle were on an adequate diet of winter feed (silage and hay), but appeared to have eaten growing rhizomes of the fern, possibly to satisfy a desire for fresh feed. The 1976 outbreak was more severe than that of 1967; this may have been due to the combined toxic effects of male fern and rusty male fern (*Dryopteris borreri*), which were growing together in the same field. In another incident in Scotland in 1983,[4] three of a herd of 40 yearling cattle became blind and ataxic; one remained permanently blind.

Clinical signs found in this type of poisoning are blindness, often with widely dilated pupils, staggering gait, and hard, dark-brown faeces. In some cases the animals stand or lie in water; mortality is low. The blindness, which is sometimes permanent, is a characteristic feature of *Dryopteris* poisoning. Results of detailed examination of eyes of blind calves[5] revealed haemorrhages of the retina, oedema of the optic disc, and damage to the optic nerve. In some animals, however, there may be loss of the pupillary reflex without obvious structural change.[6]

Post-mortem examination of a cow from the 1967 outbreak in Scotland[2] showed the animal to be in good condition. The rumen contents were very dry and contained partly chewed pieces of male fern. The walls of the abomasum and small intestine were thickened and acutely inflamed, the gall bladder was enlarged, and there was a small haemorrhage on the heart. In animals that died or were slaughtered in the 1976 outbreak,[3] there were numerous small haemorrhages along the major blood vessels of the thorax and abdomen and on the heart; ulcers were found in the digestive tract. Microscopic examination of the brain showed spaces around the nerve cells and blood vessels, particularly in the cerebrum. Apart from a few animals that remain permanently blind, recovery is usually spontaneous after removal from access to the ferns.

In treatment, calcium and B complex vitamins have been injected, but with no apparent effect. They may have been given because of the known thiaminase content of the ferns, but, in ruminants, thiamine deficiency does not occur from this source, as it is synthesized by ruminal bacteria. Purgatives can be given to treat the constipation.

EQUISETACEAE

Equisetum species Horsetails (Plate 29)

Other common name: Mare's Tail

Horsetails are found throughout the country and can be troublesome weeds of pastures and arable land, especially in damp areas. At least ten species occur in Britain, the common horsetail (*Equisetum arvense*) and the marsh horsetail (*Equisetum palustre*) being widely distributed, while the others are more local.

Horsetails have a branching, underground rhizome from which green, vegetative, jointed stems grow in spring. These stems are hollow, ridged longitudinally and up to 80 cm tall. Whorls of slender green branches radiate from the main stem at the joints (nodes). The leaves are represented only by a small, toothed sheath extending 4–12 mm up the main stem above each node, and by minute scales at the nodes of the branches. Erect brownish branches also develop; these have toothed sheaths, but no whorled branches at the nodes, and terminate in a cone-like structure which consists of closely crowded rings of spore-bearing organs.

Poisonous principles

The plants contain varying quantities of silicates, rendering them harsh to touch and rather unpalatable in the fresh state. A variety of toxic principles, including an alkaloid named palustrine,[1] have been extracted from horsetail, but the most important one is an enzyme, thiaminase,[2] which also occurs in bracken (*Pteridium aquilinum*), and which destroys vitamin B$_1$ (thiamine). The clinical signs of poisoning caused by eating horsetail closely resemble those of vitamin B$_1$ deficiency.

Animal poisoning

Despite the similar action of different horsetail species, it is most usual for horses to be poisoned by *Equisetum arvense*, and cattle (and to a less extent, sheep) by *Equisetum palustre*. Poisoning results less frequently from ingestion of the growing plants than from hay in which as little as 5% horsetail may produce clinical signs. The poisonous principle is not destroyed by drying and storage, and a case is reported in which bullocks were poisoned by eating hay containing horsetail, which had been stored for at least 16 months.[3] Horses may eat the plant from their bedding in preference to clean hay.[4] However, *Equisetum* poisoning is rarely reported in Britain. The clinical signs in poisoned animals may be acute or take several weeks to develop. It is said that grain-fed animals are less severely affected than those not given grain.[5] Horses lose condition, become weak, and show incoordination (especially of the hindquarters). This may progress to posterior paralysis, muscular exhaustion, and rigidity, and inability to stand despite extreme efforts made to do so. The appetite is not usually lost; there may be either constipation or diarrhoea. In severely affected horses there may be a rapid, weak pulse, opacity of the cornea of the eye, coldness of extremities, and, in fatal cases, convulsions and coma may precede death.[5,6] Pregnant animals may abort.[7]

Cattle are less severely affected than horses, but may lose condition, and develop diarrhoea and muscular weakness, particularly of the hindquarters.[5,8] The milk yield of lactating animals falls, and the milk may be watery and have a bitter taste.[9] In addition, sweating and swaying were prominent features in calves poisoned by eating growing horsetail.[10] Poisoning in sheep is rarely described, but the clinical signs are similar to those in cattle.[9] Post-mortem findings are not specific, but include varying degrees of jaundice of the subcutaneous connective tissue, degenerative changes in the brain, liver, and kidneys, congestion of the lungs,[7] catarrhal inflammation in the digestive tract,[6] and exudation of serum from the membranes around the brain and spinal cord.[11]

The administration of large doses of vitamin B$_1$, or yeast, or preferably the intravenous injection of thiamine, is recommended for treatment. Injection of 2.5 g thiamine hydrochloride (in 25 ml of solution) was effective in saving six of seven horses and a calf.[12] Recovery, particularly without treatment, is often slow.[6]

ERICACEAE

The only poisonous member of this very large family that grows wild in Britain is *Rhododendron ponticum*, which has become naturalized here after its introduction. Some other rhododendrons (including the azaleas) that are cultivated here are poisonous, but the toxicity of most of the individual species and varieties is not known. *Pieris* species, which are popular garden shrubs, can produce a similar type of poisoning.

Pieris species (Plate 30)

Several *Pieris* species, including *Pieris japonica* and *Pieris formosa,* are grown as ornamental shrubs in gardens in Britain. The height of the shrubs varies with the species; some can grow to 5 m. The leaves are long, narrow, and pointed and grow on short stalks; they are usually dark green but some are variegated. The young leaves of some are shades of red, and form bright, attractive compact tops to the stems. The small waxy, bell-shaped flowers hang on short stalks close together in clusters near the tips of the shoots. They are white, cream, or various shades of pink; some are perfumed.

Poisonous principles
These are nitrogen-free, non-glycosidic polycyclic diterpenes, the main one responsible for the toxicity of *Pieris* species being grayanotoxin I (acetylandromedol), which is also present in rhododendrons.

Animal poisoning
Most of the cases reported have been in goats that gained access to the plants in gardens.[1-5] The clinical signs are similar to those of rhododendron poisoning, with vomiting or attempts to vomit being characteristic. Goats do not normally vomit but do so when poisoned by *Pieris.* Other clinical signs seen in goats are those of abdominal pain, grinding of the teeth, shivering, and, in one case, soft, blood-stained faeces; sometimes the poisoning can be fatal. An outbreak also occurred in sheep that broke into a garden in very cold weather.[6] Some were found dead, others showed signs of abdominal pain, staggering, and lateral recumbency with paddling movements of the limbs; ten of 18 affected sheep died. Poisoning has occurred in zoo animals (Barberry sheep,[7] a camel,[7] guanacos,[7] a black bear,[7] llamas,[8] African pygmy goats,[8] and alpacas [8]) that were given leaves of the plant by visitors, or browsed the shrub growing near their enclosures. Vomiting has also been reported in dogs that ate *Pieris* berries or flowers.[9]

Human poisoning
Few reports of poisoning by eating any parts of the plant have been found, but a two-year-old child who ate some buds of *Pieris japonica* had burning sensations in the mouth about an hour later, followed by salivation and vomiting.[10] When examined in hospital his heart rate was slow, but improved after the intravenous administration of atropine; he had recovered the following day. As with rhododendron (see below), honey produced by bees that have foraged on *Pieris* can be toxic.[11]

Rhododendron ponticum Common Rhododendron (Plate 31)

Other common name: Pontic Rhododendron

This plant is a branched, evergreen shrub, commonly cultivated and often planted in woods where it may become dominant beneath trees. It grows up to 4 m high, and has hard, elongated, elliptical leaves which are pointed at the tip and taper towards the stalk. The mature leaves are 6–12 cm long, dark green but not glossy above, and paler green beneath. The young leaves are brighter green and less hard. The inflorescence develops in spring and is a hemispherical or more or less spherical group of wide-mouthed, bell-shaped flowers each up to 5 cm across. They are dull purple in colour, spotted with brown, and have a cluster of stamens (usually ten) projecting from them. There is a wide range of flower colours in cultivated varieties.

Poisonous principles

The leaves, flowers, pollen, and nectar of many *Rhododendron* species contain several toxic diterpenoids (grayanotoxins). One of these, grayanotoxin I, is also known as rhodotoxin, acetylandromedol, or, more often, as andromedotoxin, although there is some confusion over the latter name, which has been used to describe two different toxic substances.

Animal poisoning

Animals rarely graze in woodland areas in Britain and are therefore unlikely to eat rhododendrons under normal conditions, but all classes of livestock are at risk if they gain access to gardens or garden refuse containing the plant. Under adverse conditions, when food is scarce, animals are more likely to eat evergreen plants including rhododendron. Poisoning is most common in sheep[12–19] and goats.[8, 20–24] Losses have been reported annually in the north and west of Britain when hill sheep, brought down for the winter, eat rhododendron leaves.[12] Rams appear to be particularly susceptible to poisoning by this plant. Poisoning has been reported in south-west England among cattle that ate rhododendron leaves when they strayed into a plantation during severe winter weather,[25] and also in calves and goats in Wales.[26] Poisoning has also occurred in sheep during mild weather when they were moved to pasture bordered by rhododendrons.[14, 18, 19] It appears that many animal species are susceptible to rhododendron poisoning, which has been reported in donkeys in Britain,[27] buffaloes during drought conditions in India,[28] wolves that ate leaves from a rhododendron hedge in a zoo in Germany,[8] circus elephants,[29] and coypu given a few picked rhododendron leaves before feeding[30] at a time when green feed was scarce. It was estimated that the coypu had consumed 2–3 g of the leaves per kg of their body weight. Clinical signs developed very rapidly but began to decline after one hour, recovery being complete in three hours. When fed *Rhododendron* leaves experimentally, guinea pigs ate reluctantly, whereas rabbits ate readily initially, but soon stopped. Four dogs, which ate rhododendron hedge clippings, became weak and uncoordinated, vomited, and had diarrhoea.[9] Dogs, whose paws and muzzles had come into contact with a mulch made from shredded rhododendrons, became lethargic and had an unsteady and staggering gait.[31] The rapid development of adverse effects may act as a safeguard to animals and prevent them from consuming a lethal dose. Clinical signs seen in cases of poisoning are similar for all animal species and include salivation, vomiting (frequently projectile), abdominal pain (which is often intense), diarrhoea, constipation, trembling, weak pulse, slow and difficult breathing, staggering, falling, and exhaustion. Vomiting, a very unusual occurrence in cattle, was seen in Wales in calves that broke into a thicket in which rhododendrons were abundant.[26] Milk production is reported to decline and almost cease for up to three days in poisoned cows.[25] In fatal cases, death is due to respiratory failure and may occur within a few hours of first eating the plant.

Rhododendron macrophyllum, which is sometimes grown in gardens in Britain, caused typical signs of *Rhododendron* poisoning in sheep and goats in the USA when clippings were thrown on to their pasture.[32]

It seems possible that bees can be poisoned when they visit some *Rhododendron* species (especially *Rhododendron thomsonii*) and their hybrids.[33] In parts of Scotland where ornamental rhododendron gardens have been planted, some of the early spring-flowering species appear to attract bees, mainly as a source of pollen, although nectar is also collected. It was reported that affected bees emerge from the hive entrance as if propelled, and land on their back or sides. They then spin round in a characteristic manner or lie twitching, with their abdomen curled; death occurs within ten minutes. Whole colonies die out in two to three days if not removed from the area. Serious losses of bees at this time of year are said to have made bee-keeping uneconomic in these areas.

Post-mortem examination reveals plant fragments in the stomach of animals, but little inflammation, the vomiting being caused by the action of the toxins on the nerve endings of the stomach walls. Haemorrhages around the heart and inflammation of the respiratory system have also been reported in sheep.[34] A chromatographic method has been described that can detect acetylandromedol in rumen contents, kidney and lung tissue, and urine.[35]

The administration of stimulants is recommended for treatment, and surgical removal of stomach contents may prevent death. In goats the subcutaneous injection of morphine (60–200 mg depending on the size of the animal) has been reported to bring about recovery within four hours.[22] The use of purgatives is recommended.

Human poisoning

All parts of the plant can cause poisoning, the symptoms being similar to those in animals, including salivation, watering eyes, nasal blockage, vomiting, convulsions, slow pulse, low blood pressure, and paralysis.[36] Human poisoning is unlikely in Britain, but in an unusual incident in a National Trust garden in Scotland a man licked some drops of rhododendron nectar off his hand. In a very short time he experienced tingling in his fingers and toes, followed by numbness and lack of coordination in his limbs; he was unable to stand, but recovered completely in a few hours.[37] A woman who drank rhododendron tea showed typical symptoms, with vomiting, dizziness, low blood pressure, slow heart rate, and a transient episode of complete heart block. She recovered in 1–2 days after supportive therapy that included intravenous fluids and atropine.[38]

Some of the grayanotoxins from rhododendrons are present in the honey[39] produced by bees that have collected nectar, or possibly honeydew, from these plants. In 400 BC, Xenophon reported poisoning of Greek soldiers who had eaten honey made by bees from wild rhododendrons. The men had vomiting and diarrhoea, became unsteady and were unable to stand; all recovered. In some parts of the world, such as Turkey [40-42] and Nepal,[43] where rhododendrons are a major source of nectar for bees, the honey produced from them is known to be poisonous when eaten fresh.[44] The toxicity is said to be lost as the honey ripens during storage or when it is heated. The symptoms are similar to those reported by other parts of the plants. Poisoning by rhododendron honey is almost unknown in Britain as hive bees do not generally collect much nectar from these flowers.[45]

The azaleas, which are mainly deciduous, appear to be less toxic than *Rhododendron ponticum*. An analysis of 152 reports of ingestion of the leaves, flowers, or nectar in the USA showed that symptoms developed in only nine cases, all of whom were children.[46] The symptoms were mild; four of the children vomited. Contact dermatitis can develop when handling azalea cuttings for propagation.

Other members of the Ericaceae family

Some cultivated shrubs, such as species of *Andromeda, Gaultheria, Kalmia,* and *Menziesia,* can cause poisoning similar to that described for rhododendrons. The toxicity varies among individual species and varieties.

EUPHORBIACEAE

Several members of this family are poisonous, but the castor oil plant, whose seeds are responsible for many outbreaks of poisoning in animals and also for occasional human poisoning, is the most important. The cultivated and wild spurges (*Euphorbia* species), the common house plant, poinsettia (*Euphorbia pulcherrima*), and the wild plants annual and dog's mercury (*Mercurialis* species) are also causes of poisoning in Britain.

Euphorbia species

The *Euphorbia* genus contains over 1600 species, 16–20 of which occur in Britain, some having become naturalized after introduction. Unlike many temperate and tropical members of the genus, no British species are shrubs or trees. Many *Euphorbia* species are grown in this country as house or garden plants. The earliest reports refer to the medicinal uses of the plants, which were named after Euphorbus, physician to King Juba II of Mauritania in AD 18.

Euphorbia helioscopia Sun Spurge

Sun spurge grows mainly on or at the edges of cultivated land, and is found throughout the lowland areas of Britain. It is a smooth erect annual, up to 50 cm high. The leaves have finely toothed edges, and are oval in shape, but blunt at the tips, and tapering towards the stalk. The bracts are similar to the leaves, and form a ring around the stem beneath the inflorescence, which is 2–5-rayed and yellowish green. The seed capsule is 3–5 mm long, smooth, and somewhat three-sided but generally rounded; the seeds are brown. Details of poisoning follow the description of *Euphorbia peplus* (see below).

Euphorbia lathyrus Caper Spurge

It is doubtful if caper spurge is native in Britain, although it appears to grow naturally in a few woodland areas. It is more common locally as a garden escape. The plant is a bluish-green biennial. The first year it has a short, erect, leafy stem and in the second year the stem elongates and the inflorescence develops. The leaves grow without stalks in opposite pairs on the stem and are narrow and up to 20 cm long, the upper ones being broader at the base than the lower ones. The prominent bracts are triangular, giving the 2–6-rayed inflorescence (umbel) a spiky appearance. The seed capsule is 8–20 mm across, three-sided, and smooth; the seeds are brown. Details of poisoning follow the description of *Euphorbia peplus* (see below).

Euphorbia peplus Petty Spurge (Plate 32)

This small green annual is very common on waste and cultivated land throughout Britain. It grows 10–30 cm tall, with a single or branched stem. The leaves are oval or rounded, 0.5–3 cm long, and arranged alternately on the stem. The inflorescence (umbel) is 3-rayed, with rather insignificant, yellowish-green flowers, and bracts that are similar to the leaves. The seed capsule is about 2 mm long and three-sided, with two narrow wings on each side. The seeds are pale grey and pitted.

Poisonous principles

These three spurges, as well as other *Euphorbia* species, contain a milky latex, which exudes from the plant when it is cut or crushed. The nature of the toxic principles requires further elucidation, but a resin, an alkaloid (euphorbin, euphorbine, or euphorbane), a glycoside, a dihydroxycoumarin, and a complex substance named euphorbiosteroid have been reported to occur in various *Euphorbia* species. More recent work has demonstrated that the latex contains polyhydric diterpene esters (phorbol, daphnane, and ingenane). The activity of the toxins is not affected by drying and storage, so that feeding dried fodder crops containing spurges could poison animals.

Animal poisoning

Despite their known toxic properties, very few cases of poisoning by *Euphorbia* species have been reported in Britain. However, sun spurge (*Euphorbia helioscopia*) caused severe swelling and inflammation of the mouth, salivation, and some diarrhoea in sheep allowed to graze a field of kale that had not grown well and in which sun spurge was the dominant weed. The animals recovered fully when transferred to good pasture.[1] Petty spurge (*Euphorbia peplus*) caused poisoning when fed experimentally to dogs and rats[2,3] and has caused illness and losses among horses and cattle in Australia, and sheep in New Zealand.[1]

Human poisoning

This has resulted from the use of the seed capsules of caper spurge, mistaken for true capers (the flower buds of *Capparis spinosa*) to which they bear a superficial resemblance. One of two children died after sucking the juice of sun spurge (*Euphorbia helioscopia*).[4] Both children experienced burning of the mouth, oesophagus, and stomach, salivation, vomiting, stomach pain, convulsions, narrowing of the pupils, and symptoms of lung oedema. Coma preceded death. The strong irritant nature of the latex has caused intense irritation and burning of the lips and tongue in children who have handled the plant then licked their fingers, and *Euphorbia* species are frequent causes of skin reactions.[5,6] Experimentally, pieces of leaf applied to the skin have caused rashes and blistering.[6] Conjunctivitis was recorded in six patients in Germany[7] after latex of *Euphorbia* species had come into contact with their eyes either directly or by rubbing with the hands after touching the plants. Reddening of the eyes and blistering of the eyelids developed after an hour, but all recovered. Three similar cases have also been reported in Britain in gardeners in contact with caper spurge (*Euphorbia lathyrus*).[8] Application of the latex has been recommended in the past to remove warts or freckles. A woman who used the latex of petty spurge to treat a wart on a lower eyelid developed a very sore eye and blurred vision that persisted for nearly a week.[9] Preparations of the plants were taken formerly as purgatives and emetics, but the action was drastic and now they are rarely used.

Euphorbia pulcherrima Poinsettia (Plate 33)

Large numbers of these ornamental plants are now grown, particularly for sale at Christmas time. As pot plants they grow up to 40 cm high and wide, and are characterized by the brightly coloured, leaf-like bracts (usually red, but sometimes pink or cream) that develop close together, forming a flattish top to each shoot; the flowers are small and inconspicuous.

Poisonous principles
The watery or slightly milky sap of these plants may contain small quantities of various diterpene esters. The toxicity of this plant is relatively low; it has been suggested that this could have been reduced during intensive cultivation.

Animal poisoning
Pet animals sometimes eat parts of poinsettias, and often no clinical signs develop. Sometimes mild digestive disturbances (vomiting, diarrhoea, signs of abdominal pain) occur in dogs,[10,11] and salivation in cats,[10] but in Switzerland one case was recorded in which a dog developed severe gastrointestinal signs, an elevated body temperature and died 12 hours after eating some leaves of the plant.[12] Another fatal case in a dog was reported from the USA; the animal had persistent vomiting and kidney failure with coma.[13] In feeding experiments, laboratory rats showed no damage to the mouth and no clinical signs of poisoning.[14,15] Post-mortem examination of the rats did not show any evidence of gastrointestinal irritation.

Human poisoning
Despite the impression given in older literature, including a much-quoted report of a fatality in 1919,[16] it appears that the toxicity of poinsettias is low, and that eating them causes no, or only mild symptoms (usually limited to nausea and vomiting). In one case, however, burns (described as white areas) developed in and around the mouth of an eight-month-old girl who chewed a poinsettia leaf;[17] she recovered completely.

Contact with the plant does not often result in skin damage, but widespread eczema was reported in a woman,[18] and dermatitis with painful blistering and itching (possibly a hypersensitive reaction) in a man[19] who had been working among the plants.

Mercurialis species

The only two species of this genus that grow wild in Britain are annual mercury (*Mercurialis annua*) and dog's mercury (*Mercurialis perennis*).

Mercurialis annua Annual Mercury

Although possibly not a native plant, annual mercury is widespread locally in southern England in waste places and as a garden weed. In Wales and northern England it is rare. It is a smooth plant with erect, branched stems 10–50 cm high, elongated oval leaves, pointed at the tip and narrowing towards the stalk and arising in opposite pairs on the stem. The leaf margin may be slightly serrated and the surface bright green and slightly shiny. The inconspicuous, greenish male and female flowers are borne on separate plants in axillary clusters, the females having only very short stalks. The fruits are hairy, globular, and 3–4 mm across. Details of poisoning follow the description of *Mercurialis perennis* (see below).

Mercurialis perennis Dog's Mercury (Plate 34)

This native plant grows throughout most of Britain, except northern Scotland. It is often the dominant ground cover plant in woods. The plant is similar to annual mercury but grows from a long, creeping rhizome; it has an erect, usually unbranched stem up to 40 cm tall, leaves that are lightly hairy, giving them a dull appearance, and female flowers borne in clusters on long stalks.

Poisonous principles
Several constituents of *Mercurialis* have been incriminated, but their separate or combined effects have not been studied in detail. They are methylamine (isolated from the plants in the last century and named mercurialine), trimethylamine, and several poorly defined substances including hermidin(e), saponins, and a volatile oil. The plants appear to be most toxic at the flowering and early seeding stages.

Animal poisoning
Both annual and dog's mercury can cause the same type of poisoning in animals. Although the plants are not eaten readily (possibly because of their unpleasant odour when bruised) some animals seem to acquire a taste for them.[20] Most cases of poisoning have occurred in late summer and autumn when good pasture plants tend to be scarce. There is experimental evidence that, in cattle, acute poisoning only follows the feeding of seeding plants,[21] but rabbits have been poisoned fatally not only by seeds but also by stems and roots.[22] *Mercurialis* poisoning has been recorded in several countries, including Britain; hill sheep in Wales ate dog's mercury when snow covered their pasture,[23] and lambs in southern England died on fallow arable land where *Mercurialis annua* had been heavily grazed.[24] Other outbreaks in sheep have involved cut forage[25] and pasture heavily infested with annual mercury.[26] In Italy, poisoning, with anaemia being the prominent sign, but also weight loss and cessation of milk production, followed experimental feeding of sheep for 28 days with a ration containing 0.25–0.75% of *Mercurialis annua*.[27] Cattle appear to be more susceptible than sheep;[28] and have been poisoned by eating these plants.[29-34] In a recent incident

in Tunisia,[33] dairy cows were poisoned when *Mercurialis annua*, cut from an orchard, was mixed with their hay as green feed was scarce. The morning after they had each been given 10–20 kg of the plant, two of 18 cows were found dead. A drop in milk production and lethargy was observed in all of the animals, and some showed greenish diarrhoea, anaemia, and dark-brown urine (haemoglobinuria); the animals were slow to recover. Horses can be affected,[35] and poisoning has been suspected in goats.[36]

The effects are similar in all animal species, with the characteristic feature being a haemolytic anaemia. Initially there are acute gastrointestinal signs, accompanied by salivation, loss of appetite, and watery diarrhoea (sometimes preceded by constipation). Affected animals become weak and lethargic, milk production in lactating animals decreases or stops, jaundice of oral and genital mucous membranes and eyes develops, followed by the most characteristic sign of pinkish or obviously blood-stained urine. Urination is often painful. In fatal cases, coma may precede death. Poisoning by *Mercurialis* species in cattle can be confused with the tick-transmitted protozoal disease piroplasmosis.[37] Two dogs that ate *Mercurialis perennis* showed signs of poisoning in eight hours;[11] these included loss of appetite, salivation, abdominal pain, vomiting, diarrhoea, pin-point haemorrhages, blood in the urine, collapse, and coma. The dogs had recovered in 24 hours.

The typical post-mortem findings are subcutaneous oedema, haemorrhages of liver, kidneys and heart, enlargement of the liver, degeneration and dark coloration of kidneys, and gastrointestinal inflammation.

Human poisoning

There are some old records of irritant, narcotic poisoning, with some fatalities, after eating annual mercury.[22] More recently, two adults ingested a quantity of boiled leaves of dog's mercury which they had mistaken for brooklime (*Veronica beccabunga*).[11] Symptoms developed within three hours and included profuse vomiting and diarrhoea, facial flushing, abdominal and bilateral loin pains, and haematuria. The patients were given rehydration therapy; antihistamines and sodium bicarbonate were also administered. Particular support was given to renal function. Symptoms persisted for 24 hours, but full recovery was achieved within 48 hours. The possibility of human poisoning from eating meat from poisoned animals has been considered and condemnation of the offal recommended,[1] but no definite information is available.

Ricinus communis Castor Oil Plant (Plates 35 and 36)

This plant is not native in Britain, although it is sometimes grown indoors and in gardens as an ornamental. However, there is considerable interest in *Ricinus* as a poisonous plant in this country because oil expressed from the seeds (castor beans), and detoxified residues of the seeds (pomace) are given to animals.

The castor oil plant is an annual herbaceous shrub which, under favourable conditions, may grow up to 4 m in height, although in Britain the plants seldom exceed 1.5 m. There are numerous cultivated forms which vary in their foliage, fruit, and seed characteristics. On larger plants the leaves may be up to 1 m across. They are dark green, often tinged with red or purple, and have up to 12 (usually eight) pointed lobes, which radiate from the point of attachment of the stalk. The flowers are of separate sexes but borne on the same inflorescence. The males, which open to reveal a mass of stamens, are at the base, and the females, with prominent red stigmas, are near the apex.

The fruit is a green or reddish capsule with fleshy spines and contains glossy, elliptical seeds, up to 1 cm long, and attractively mottled in black, white, grey, or brown.

Poisonous principles

The chief poisonous constituent of the plant is a lectin, ricin, a simple protein (a toxalbumin) that is reputed to be one of the most toxic naturally occurring substances; the ricin content is highest in the seeds. Ricin is soluble in water, and therefore not present in extracted oil, but remains in the husks, which may be incorporated into oilseed cake or meal for animal feed, or used in fertilizers. It has been known since the 1880s that substances extracted from castor beans (and some other seeds) coagulate red blood cells; these have therefore been called phytohaemagglutinins. It was thought until recently that ricin was both the toxic agent and the haemagglutinating agent, although it was known that, on heat treatment, the haemagglutinating activity of pomace disappeared before its toxicity.[38, 39] It is now clear that another lectin (other than ricin) in castor oil seeds is the haemagglutinin.[40] This protein is called ricinus agglutinin or sometimes, rather confusingly, ricine. Failure to distinguish between these two proteins may explain the apparent failure of some detoxification processes. Heat (usually steam) treatment of the pomace is carried out to denature the toxic protein before the product is used in feed preparations. However, the usual test made to check for completion of the detoxification process is a haemagglutination test, which indicates only that the agglutinin, and not necessarily all of the ricin, has been destroyed. The problem is decreasing as a result of more careful quality control of animal feeds. Accidental contamination by castor beans at harvesting of commercial crops (e.g. soya bean)[41] for human and animal consumption remains a problem in countries where the plant is widespread, but is unlikely to occur in Britain. A neurotoxic alkaloid, ricinine, has been extracted from the leaves of the plant.[42] Experimental studies showed that its action inhibits tissue respiration in a similar manner to that in cyanide poisoning.[42] The plant also contains a potent respiratory allergen, but, unlike ricin, repeated exposure to this increases sensitivity. The allergen remains stable in boiling water.[39]

Animal poisoning

There is wide variation in sensitivity to ricin in different animal species[43] and different individuals of the same species, but in all cases the lethal doses are very small. It has been estimated that a dose as small as two-millionths of the body weight would be fatal by injection,[44] the oral dose being somewhat greater due to losses of the toxin in the digestive tract. The lethal oral doses frequently quoted for castor beans vary from 0.1 g per kg body weight in the horse, to 5.5 g per kg in the goat; the lethal dose for cattle, pigs, sheep, rabbits, and chickens is between 1 and 2 g per kg.[45] Depending on the concentration of the toxin present, animals poisoned by eating feed containing ricin may show clinical signs within an hour, or up to three days later. Those which do not die often take many weeks or even months to recover[46] because of the severe tissue damage.[47] Ricin inhibits the synthesis of some essential enzymes,[45] increases the production of others as well as the levels of bilirubin and blood urea nitrogen, and decreases blood sugar. As ricin is a protein, antibodies to it are produced by the body and animals can be immunized, by repeated small doses, to withstand up to 800 times the lethal dose.[44]

The oil fraction of castor beans contains hydroxy fatty acids, up to 90% being ricinoleic acid,[48] considerable amounts of which may be absorbed and utilized if fed to animals. Castor oil is a well known laxative, which acts by stimulating motor nerve activity of the small intestine, causing local irritation which may lead to diarrhoea. Because of this action, ricinoleic acid is sometimes classified as a toxic lipid.

Most outbreaks of poisoning in animals result from their being fed with improperly detoxified castor bean products. In one episode, traces of ricin were found in a batch of cattle cake.[49] The animals suffered severe diarrhoea with blood clots in the faeces. The milk yield was drastically reduced and there were two abortions. In another incident in which cows received 1 kg castor bean cake daily, nine of 25 newborn calves died 1–2 days after birth.[50] Their clinical signs were weakness, feeble pulse, shortness of breath, watery faeces, and swollen joints. Calves born to cows 10–15 days after withdrawal of the cake from their diet were healthy. After eating groundnut meal, later found to contain 25% castor bean husks, 10 cows died and another had to be killed.[51] The animals could not stand, were groaning, and passing fluid faeces with blood and mucus. Their temperature was subnormal and their pulse fast and weak. The lethal dose was estimated as approximately 250 g of husks.

In contrast to cattle, sheep tolerate one-third castor bean meal in their diet, although such feed is not readily eaten.[52] Experimental feeding of sheep for eight months with a ration that included up to 30% castor bean meal (0.22% ricin)[53] resulted in dark brown urine and faeces, but no other clinical signs of illness. At post-mortem examination, however, there were significant pathological changes in the intestines, kidneys, and thyroid glands.[54]

The clinical signs in horses fed castor beans mixed with maize[55] were similar to those described for cattle. In the horse, the early clinical signs of castor bean poisoning could be confused with respiratory infection. Accidental incorporation of some castor beans with grain from burst bags in a shipping consignment resulted in the poisoning of 48 horses in a stud;[56] on the same premises, two chickens and a rabbit given the same food died. Clinical signs in the horses varied in intensity but included sweating, rocking gait, elevated temperature, rapid pulse, muscle spasms, and abdominal pain. In Britain, castor beans were found in the stomach of a goat that died after showing acute abdominal pain and profuse diarrhoea.[57]

Poisoning occurred when three dogs ate 'biological' fertilizer,[58] containing 25% extracted castor seed, direct from the packs, and also in two others that ate the product after it had been spread on the land. One dog died within 20 hours and two others had to be killed. It was estimated that the lethal dose was 1–2 g per kg body weight (100 g of the fertilizer for a 10–25-kg dog). There was gastrointestinal disturbance, with haemorrhage; death resulted from circulatory failure. A dog that ate a castor bean necklace died after showing signs of abdominal pain, accompanied by vomiting and diarrhoea, both with blood.[59] Another two dogs that ate castor oil seed cake vomited, collapsed, and died from intestinal haemorrhages 36 hours later.[45]

Pigs poisoned by eating meal, subsequently found to contain 0.3–1.4 g castor seed husk per 100 g, developed severe vomiting and diarrhoea and became weak and uncoordinated. One weaned pig died in a convulsion, and two of ten piglets of a poisoned sow also died.[46] On the same farm, poultry were fed a mash made from the contaminated meal. Their condition deteriorated rapidly, with drooping wings, ruffled feathers, and greyish combs and wattles. Their crops remained impacted for several days, they had diarrhoea, egg production ceased, moulting commenced, and several birds died.[46] The surviving pigs and poultry had not completely recovered three months after the episode. In Britain, a Vietnamese pot-bellied pig ate leaves from a castor oil plant; it became lethargic and bloated, but recovered after supportive treatment.[59] Poisoning by feeding with castor beans or ricin has been induced experimentally in horses,[60] cattle,[61] rats,[43] and mice.[62]

In four naturally occurring outbreaks, several thousand wild ducks died in Texas,[63] in an area where castor oil plants were grown; fragments of castor beans were found at post-mortem examination of stomach contents. Clinical signs of poisoning (blood-stained droppings with mucus, and progressive paralysis) and pathological changes, including fatty liver, gastroenteritis, and intestinal haemorrhages, developed in mallards force-fed with 1–8 whole castor beans. Poisoning with similar clinical signs and pathological changes has also been recorded in geese[64] and chicks[65] given raw castor beans or castor bean meal. Some of the standard detoxification procedures used did not render the beans safe for chicks.[66, 67]

The post-mortem findings are similar for all animal species and include haemorrhages in the heart, degeneration of kidneys and liver, and intense inflammation and erosion of intestinal membranes.

Human poisoning

Chewing castor beans is the most frequent cause of human poisoning by *Ricinus*.[68] (If swallowed without chewing, the hard seed coat prevents release of the toxin.) Necklaces made from the attractively mottled seeds were imported and sold in charity shops in Britain in 1993.[69] When their potential toxicity was realised, they were withdrawn from sale and requests made for the return of those already purchased. In the USA in recent years, 104 cases (of which 98 were children) were recorded of eating castor beans.[70] In two adults and two children, poisoning was fatal.

The symptoms usually appear within a few hours, and are similar to those in animals, with severe irritation and haemorrhage of the digestive tract, resulting in profuse vomiting and diarrhoea. Dehydration and scanty urination are often recorded. Severe poisoning can occur with only a few beans, but from a retrospective study of 746 cases of accidental and deliberate ingestion of varying numbers of chewed or unchewed castor beans, only 14 fatalities were found.[71] It can be concluded, therefore, that, despite the potential danger, castor bean poisoning is not necessarily severe, and in some cases no symptoms develop.

A much publicized case of the homicidal use of ricin involved a Bulgarian broadcaster who died as a result of a small, perforated metallic sphere being inserted forcibly into his leg in London.[44] The coroner was satisfied that the sphere contained ricin.

Treatment should be sought urgently; all suspected cases should be admitted to hospital, and stomach lavage carried out immediately. Fluid and electrolyte therapy, and treatment for shock, are of great importance in reducing the severe effects. Methods for eliminating the toxins from the blood should be considered. Antibodies to ricin have been shown to protect against its toxicity.

Respiratory allergy (mucosal irritation and asthma) has been reported among workers handling pomace in ports[72] or in oil mills.[73] Typical symptoms of ricin poisoning also occur in individuals exposed to castor bean products.[74] Allergic dermatitis can result from contact with the plant or with castor oil.[75] Ricinoleic acid, which is present in castor oil, is thought to be the allergen.[76]

Other members of the Euphorbiaceae family

Members of the family that are used in Britain as house plants include croton (*Codiaeum* species), the zig-zag plant (*Pedilanthus tithymaloides*), and the African milkbush (*Synadenium grantii*). They can cause reactions that are similar to those of spurges, but varying in intensity.

FAGACEAE

Fagus sylvatica Beech (Plate 37)

This tree is found mainly in south-east Britain on calcareous soils, where it is often the dominant species in woods. Beech and its varieties (including the ornamental copper beech) can, however, grow on a variety of soils, and are often planted and used for hedges. Beech is a large tree, 30–40 m high, with a smooth, grey bark, spreading branches, slender elongated brown buds, and stalked leaves that are broadly oval, 4–9 cm long, and have paired veins. The seeds are triangular nuts, up to 1 cm long, covered by a brittle brown shell and contained, usually in a closely packed group of three, in a four-lobed woody husk covered with coarse bristles. Only the fruit and seeds (mast) of the tree have been reported as poisonous.

Poisonous principles
A substance usually called fagin has been known for many years; it is sometimes referred to as an alkaloid, although its precise composition has yet to be investigated. Saponins are also said to be present.

Animal poisoning
Beech mast is less likely to cause poisoning now than formerly, when the residues left after extraction of oil from the nuts were used to make cake for animal feed. Most reported cases of poisoning refer to the ingestion of such cake, which was apparently particularly poisonous when made from residues that included the husk.[1] It is often stated that the nuts themselves are not poisonous, although there are conflicting reports on this point. Residues that have been boiled and the water discarded have been considered by some to be safe, but others state that the toxic principle is insoluble in water.

It is inadvisable to feed beech nuts or cake to horses, which seem particularly susceptible (300–500 g can be fatal).[2] Severe signs of colic were shown by two ponies in a paddock, in which high winds had brought down a large number of beech nuts.[3] Staggering, muscular tremors over the hindquarters, and dilatation of the pupils were followed by recumbency, rapid and laboured respiration with expiratory grunts, rigid extensor spasms of hind legs, and convulsive paddling of the forelegs. At post-mortem examination broken beech nuts and husks predominated in the stomach contents. Most cases of poisoning reported have involved cattle, which may become critically ill. Local irritation and burning occur initially and affected animals have periods of severe abdominal pain, violent cramps, and staggering, alternating with periods of complete paralysis, collapse, and unconsciousness.[2,4] Death from asphyxia may occur within 12 hours; animals surviving longer than this usually recover. Post-mortem findings are not characteristic. They include signs of suffocation and sometimes severe oedema of the brain and spinal cord, and inflammation of the intestines.

Human poisoning

If eaten in sufficient quantity, the kernels of beech nuts cause soreness of the mouth and throat, and the ingestion of 50 or more nuts can produce headache, abdominal pain, vomiting, diarrhoea, vertigo, and elevated body temperature.[5] Extreme fatigue, pallor, and fainting may also occur. The symptoms usually develop within an hour of eating the nuts and last for up to five hours. Treatment is symptomatic; the use of purgatives and tranquillizers may be indicated.

Quercus species Oaks (Plate 38)

There are two native oak trees in Britain, *Quercus robur* and *Quercus petraea*, both of which are deciduous. The former is a gnarled, spreading tree found on clay soils and is the common oak of the greater part of England and southern Scotland. The leaves have little or no stalks, but the acorns have stalks (peduncles), hence the alternative name pedunculate oak. *Quercus petraea* is a less spreading tree, with a straight trunk and stalked leaves with hairs on the underside; the acorns, however, have very short stalks, or none at all, hence the name sessile oak. It is the oak of light and shallow soils and is found particularly in the north and west of the British Isles. Where the two species occur together there are many intermediates. Other species of exotic origin are naturalized in plantations and gardens; some, like the holm or holly oak (*Quercus ilex*), are more or less evergreen; others are little more than shrubs.

The leaves of most oaks have deeply indented margins, with rounded or pointed lobes with or without serrations, according to the species. All oaks have separate male and female flowers, both growing on the same tree. The males are in slender pendulous catkins and the females solitary or clustered, each one surrounded by small scales. The fruit, or acorn, is ovoid and protrudes from a woody cup formed from the scales.

Poisonous principles

Tannins are found in all parts of the tree, with relatively high levels of hydrolysable tannins occurring in young leaves and green acorns; extracts of the bark were used for tanning skins and hides to make leather. In the gastrointestinal tract of herbivores, the hydrolysable tannins can be broken down by bacterial action into low molecular weight phenolic compounds such as gallic acid and pyrogallol.[6-8] Pyrogallol has been reported to give rise to toxic reactions similar to those of oak poisoning.[8] The identity and toxicity of the other phenolic compounds is not yet clear. Pyrogallol oxidizes haemoglobin to methaemoglobin.[9] Despite contrary claims,[8] it appears that tannic acid, a typical hydrolysable tannin, can be absorbed through the lining of the gastrointestinal wall and cause liver and kidney damage.[9] It has been suggested that mycotoxins may also be present in acorns and be responsible for at least some of their toxicity.[10]

Animal poisoning

This is usually seasonal, occurring in spring (when the tannin content of the sap is highest) from eating buds and young leaves, and in the autumn, from the ingestion of acorns. The tannic acid content of acorns is variable, but higher when they are green than when they are ripe.[11] Although in most years it is normal for animals, particularly horses[12,13] to eat acorns as a highly nutritious pre-winter feed, severe poisoning may occur in some animals. The ingestion of small quantities of acorns and oak leaves may cause no clinical signs at all or mild transient indigestion. Animals may acquire a craving for oak and even eat both leaves and green acorns directly from the trees.[13,14] They may injure themselves in attempts to gain access to them, and poisoning may recur several times in the same season.[15]

Oak poisoning in cattle[16–19] occurs in many parts of the world and is of major economic importance in some places, e.g. south-western USA,[19] where young leaves and buds may be eaten in spring when grazing is scarce. In Britain, poisoning is more common in autumn when acorns are eaten. Acorn poisoning in cattle was more prevalent than usual in this country after the drought and bumper crops of acorns of 1976 and 1995, as well as when storms brought a lot of acorns down in 1984.[20] The Veterinary Investigation Diagnosis Analysis records showed 18 cases in 1976–1977 compared with only two cases in 1975–1976.[21] Although their ingestion does not necessarily result in poisoning, it is more likely to do so when other feed is scarce or absent.[22] Calves are reputed to be more susceptible than older cattle, although there are reports of poisoning in lactating and dry cows. In autumn 1976, in Britain, ten of 60 cows in a herd became ill, and two died, after grazing parkland where many acorns had fallen.[23] In acorn and oak leaf poisoning of cattle, several days may elapse between eating them and the occurrence of clinical signs, which are progressive, beginning with cessation of rumination, lack of appetite, and refusal to drink. After initial constipation, dark-coloured faeces are passed in small quantities and in the later stages may be accompanied by a little blood. Other clinical signs from case reports include dullness, distended rumen, weakness and staggering, stilted gait, pale mucous membranes, watery discharge from the eyes, nose, and mouth, low body temperature, and irregular, slow heart beat. In chronic cases there is considerable wasting. Cases that are likely to prove fatal show aggravated clinical signs, with flatulence and abdominal pain, and death may occur suddenly during a convulsion. Increases in blood urea nitrogen and creatinine have been reported in poisoned cattle[17,18] and also in horses;[24] a return to normal values indicates recovery.[17] Young beef animals put on weight rapidly after recovery.[25] The milk from lactating animals is often bitter and unusable for any purpose.

As the grazing habits of sheep differ from those of cattle, they do not usually eat a significant quantity of leaves or fallen acorns. In Britain, however, cases of acorn poisoning were recorded in 1976–1977[21] and 1984.[26,27] The clinical signs included constipation, blood in faeces, and dehydration; some animals died. In an earlier incident eight sheep died after grazing young oak shoots.[28] The sheep were in a semi-starved state when released on to land where the stumps of felled oak trees were sprouting. Local sheep farmers claimed that they had grazed sheep successfully on young oak shoots and that it was a recognized method for killing off old tree stumps. Poisoning of sheep has also been reported after eating green acorns in Germany[29] and Romania.[30] Clippings from an oak caused the death of a two-month-old pygmy goat in the USA,[31] and oak poisoning was suspected in four goats that died in Turkey.[32] Tannic acid was found in concentrations of 15–25 mg per 100 ml of ruminal contents.

Horses may also be affected, and numerous fatalities were reported in Britain in the autumn of 1976 when, after the exceptionally dry summer, there was a large crop of acorns and other food was scarce.[12] Poisoning, with some fatalities, also occurred after the heavy acorn crops in 1984[24] and 1995.[27] The clinical signs included depression, flatulence, abdominal pain, loss of appetite, and initial constipation often followed by (sometimes black) diarrhoea. In severe cases the stomach may be ruptured.[33]

Occasionally pigs have been poisoned by eating excessive quantities of acorns, but such an occurrence is very rare. These animals usually thrive on them, and many farmers turn pigs into the pastures and woods where acorns abound, to eat them as they fall. In many parts of Europe, particularly Germany, acorns have been gathered and dried, then ground into a meal for use in combination with other foods for pig feeding.[15]

The post-mortem findings are similar in all animal species and include intestinal inflammation and haemorrhages, thickening of intestinal walls, and distension of the stomach with gas. Degenerative changes in the kidneys are characteristic, and it is nephritis that causes death in chronic cases. The liver may be enlarged, pale, and friable and body cavities often contain excess fluid (sometimes blood-stained).

Feeding with bran and hay may reduce the severe effects of poisoning. In general, treatment is symptomatic, and demulcents and purgatives are often given. Calcium hydroxide, however, minimized the toxic effects of feeding oak leaf preparations to rabbits,[34] and experimental calves fed with foliage of post oak (*Quercus stellata*) with 15% (by weight) calcium hydroxide were unaffected, whereas similar animals fed with the oak alone became ill and some died.[35] The intravenous or intramuscular injection of 10% sodium thiosulphate daily for 1–3 days has been reported to aid recovery in experimentally poisoned cattle.[8]

Human poisoning
Children may occasionally eat a few acorns, but, apart from the obvious risk of choking, this is no cause for alarm.

FUMARIACEAE

Dicentra spectabilis Bleeding Heart

Other common name: Dutchman's Breeches

This plant is not native to, and rarely naturalized in Britain, but it and other *Dicentra* species are frequently grown in gardens, and have been recorded as escapes. *Dicentra* species have finely divided fern-like leaves that are bluish green in some varieties. The flowers are usually shades of pink, but may be white. They are bell-shaped, with wide lips, and hang on short stalks near the arching tip of the main flower stalk.

Poisonous principles
Various species of *Dicentra* have been shown to contain protopine and related groups of isoquinoline alkaloids,[1] protopine itself being the only alkaloid found in *Dicentra spectabilis*.

Animal poisoning

Clinical signs seen in cattle fed experimentally with *Dicentra cucullaria* and *Dicentra canadensis* (described under the old name for the genus, *Bikukulla*)[2] were similar to those reported in field cases in the USA where poisoning by *Dicentra* species is reported annually in early spring in areas where the animals graze woodland pastures. The plants are apparently unpalatable, but are eaten when other forage is scarce. The experimental animals refused the plants unless mixed with grass. Feeding the whole plant to a steer resulted in violent trembling, agitation, and frothing at the mouth. Partly digested stomach contents were ejected forcibly. Convulsions with rigid extension of neck and limbs, difficult breathing, glassy eyes, abdominal pain, and diarrhoea occurred. Other animals fed with the plants experienced only slight restlessness. In all cases recovery was rapid and complete.

Human poisoning

Vomiting, diarrhoea, incoordination, trembling, respiratory distress, and convulsions can occur,[3] but there are few reports. Treatment should include removal of stomach contents; tranquillizers may be required. Skin contact with the plants can cause a recurrent dermatitis in sensitive individuals.[4]

GERANIACEAE

Erodium cicutarium Common Stork's Bill

The common stork's bill, whose taxonomy is not clearly definable, as there are subspecies and intermediate forms, is native in Britain, mainly on dry grassland and near the sea. It is an annual plant that may lie along the ground or be partially erect; the stems are up to 60 cm long, but often shorter. The leaves are finely divided, and the flowers pink or pale purple.

Poisonous principles

These are not known.

Animal poisoning

There have been no reports of animal disease associated with this plant in Britain, but sporadic outbreaks of photosensitization in sheep[1] and cattle[2] have been reported, mainly from Australia and New Zealand. A condition called staggers, with leg weakness in lambs and cattle that had eaten the plant, has also been reported.[3]

Other members of the Geraniaceae family

Geraniums (*Pelargonium* species) that are widely cultivated in this country have not been reported to cause animal or human poisoning by ingestion, but they can cause a mild dermatitis.[4]

GRAMINEAE

Although native grasses are the major source of food for many animal species and are often dominant plants in pasture, some of them are capable of poisoning animals. The cereals, which are cultivated for the nutritional value of their grain, can also give rise to signs of ill-health. The relevant individual grasses and cereals are not described here.

Poisonous principles

The plants themselves may contain substances that can lead to poisoning if present in sufficient concentration. These include tryptophan, oestrogens, a metabolic inhibitor, cholecalciferol, and compounds from which hydrocyanic acid can be released. Toxins from fungi that infect grasses can also have adverse effects on animals.

The action of ruminal microorganisms on the amino acid, tryptophan, produces a toxic metabolite, 3-methylindole, which is thought to be the cause of fog fever (acute bovine pulmonary emphysema), a disease that can develop in cattle after consuming large amounts of tryptophan-containing herbage. Significant concentrations of oestrogens occur in young plants of short rotation ryegrass (*Lolium* species) and perennial ryegrass (*Lolium perenne*). In Britain there are no reports of problems associated with oestrogens from grasses. A metabolic inhibitor, which interferes with cellulose digestion and adversely affects the growth of lambs, has been isolated from cock's foot (*Dactylis glomerata*).[1] Cholecalciferol, or a similar vitamin D-like substance, is the calcinogenic constituent of yellow oatgrass (*Trisetum flavescens*), which has caused calcinosis in cattle in the alpine regions of Germany, Austria, and Switzerland.

Animal poisoning

There are various types of poisoning associated with pasture grasses and cereals in this family.

Poisoning by pasture grasses

The various types of poisoning in this category are discussed under the relevant diseases. Some of the diseases are known to occur in Britain, while others are associated with grasses that grow here but have only caused disease abroad. The diseases result from: the toxins that some of the grasses contain (calcinosis, cyanide poisoning, darnel poisoning); from animals being allowed to eat too much fresh grass (fog fever); from fungal infection of a grass in hay or silage (sweet vernal grass poisoning); or from toxic metabolites (mycotoxins) produced by fungi that have colonized grasses (facial eczema, ryegrass staggers).

• CALCINOSIS   This abnormal deposition of calcium salts in tissues (calcinogenesis), first noticed in Austria in 1962, has been the subject of much research since 1970.[2] The cause of this calcinosis is a water-soluble 1,25 dihydroxyvitamin D_3 glycoside[3] in yellow oatgrass (*Trisetum flavescens*), a loosely tufted perennial; this grass is common in England and Wales, but infrequent in Scotland and Ireland.[4] Although readily consumed by cattle and sheep, it is not known to have any adverse effect on grazing animals in Britain. Young growing plants are much more calcinogenic than mature plants, while flowering plants and hay are not at all calcinogenic. In alpine pastures, flowering is delayed and leaf growth encouraged by increase in altitude, and this probably accounts for its calcinogenicity in cattle in these areas.

• CYANIDE POISONING   Among the grasses, compounds with cyanogenic potential are found in Britain in Yorkshire fog (*Holcus lanatus*) and reed sweet-grass (*Glyceria maxima*). In this country these compounds are present at such low concentrations that they are usually harmless, but an incident in goslings has been reported from Romania in which *Holcus lanatus* caused nervous and respiratory signs and death from hydrocyanic acid poisoning.[5]

• DARNEL POISONING The only grass that grows in Britain and can cause both animal and human poisoning is darnel (*Lolium temulentum*). It has become rare in this country, and the following account is included only for its historical interest. Darnel is an erect annual grass, which grows to a height of 1 m. It is an introduced species in Britain, and used to be a common weed of cereal crops. This grass can be distinguished from perennial and Italian ryegrasses by its longer, outer, empty glume and by the long awns on many of the other glumes.

The nature of the toxicity of darnel has not been elucidated satisfactorily. No recent work on the poisonous principles has been traced, its toxicity still being attributed to substances usually referred to as alkaloids,[6] including temuline, temulentine, and loliin(e). Fungi in or on the seeds have, for many years, been implicated in the toxic reaction but the situation is still 'shrouded in uncertainty'.[7,8] It has been known from ancient times that people can be poisoned by eating flour or baked products contaminated with ground darnel seed.[6,7,9] Occasional cases of poisoning of livestock have been reported in this country and in Europe, but they are not well authenticated. No cases of darnel poisoning have been reported from the USA or New Zealand, where the plant is locally common. In South Africa, darnel is common and bread made with flour containing appreciable quantities of darnel seed is eaten regularly without producing any obvious toxic effects. In feeding experiments in South Africa[10] and New Zealand[11] with laboratory and farm animals, darnel had no toxic effects, whether fungus-infected or not. There was an incident of poisoning among reindeer (*Rangifer tarandus*), addax (*Addax nasomaculatus*), and gazelle (*Gazella soemmeringa*) kept in captivity, when fed oats contaminated with seeds of various plants, including 5% darnel.[12]

• FACIAL ECZEMA   This is a photosensitization reaction of the secondary (hepatogenous) type that is characterized by lesions on unpigmented areas of skin exposed to sunlight; the liver damage can also give rise to jaundice. It occurs mainly in sheep, but also in cattle and deer, after ingestion of sporidesmins, which are mycotoxins present in spores of *Pithomyces chartarum*. This fungus grows on the dead leaves of pasture grasses, generally ryegrass. (For more information on mycotoxins, see pp. 261–264.) Most reports of facial eczema have been from New Zealand and Australia, but it has been diagnosed in sheep in south-west France and suspected in southern England.[13]

• FOG FEVER This is an acute respiratory disorder (pulmonary emphysema) of grazing cattle, particularly beef cows two or more years old; it usually occurs within two weeks of a change from poor to better pasture in autumn.[14] At this time, cattle often become hungry and may consume large amounts of tryptophan-containing herbage. In a survey of over 800 cases in Wales in 1971,[15] it was found that about 10% of the cows at risk were affected in each herd investigated, and 5–20% of them died. In another survey of 30 outbreaks over four years,[16] between 6 and 21% of the cows were affected, and 28 (2.9%) of 965 adult cows at risk died. Clinical signs include apathy, increased breathing rate (50–80 per minute), and increased depth of breathing. Difficult or laboured breathing occurs only in severe cases. Post-mortem findings in the lungs are congestion of blood vessels, oedema, and alveolar changes (formation of hyaline membranes, interstitial emphysema, and epithelial hyperplasia). Fog fever can be avoided by preventing sudden transition from poor to lush pastures, and by reducing stress factors (such as removal of calf from cow) at this time. It has been reported that the frequency of fog fever declines when some dry, mature hay is given to cattle grazing lush forage. The hay decreases the formation of 3-methylindole in the rumen; 3-methylindole formation has also been reduced by giving monensin (200 mg per animal daily) in a pelleted barley supplement. Feeding hay and monensin together reduced 3-methylindole formation in an additive fashion.[17]

• RYEGRASS STAGGERS   Under certain conditions, some grasses become infected with fungi that can have adverse effects on animals; in the past these effects were attributed to the plants themselves, but they are now known to be caused by mycotoxins (for more information on mycotoxins, see pp. 261–264). The fungi involved in ryegrass staggers are endophytes, that is they grow entirely within the host grass and are dispersed in the seed. These endophyte infections do not produce any changes in their hosts that can be detected with the naked eye. They do confer some benefits on their hosts and provide protection against various environmental stresses (heat, drought, insects), and in New Zealand endophyte-infected cultivars have even been preferred.

Ryegrass staggers is a nervous disorder that most commonly affects sheep but also occurs in cattle, horses, and deer eating perennial ryegrass (*Lolium perenne*) infected with the fungal endophyte *Acremonium lolii*. The major neurotoxin in endophyte-infected ryegrass is lolitrem B, a complex substituted indole; the highest concentrations of this mycotoxin are found in the basal leaf sheath and so are most likely to be consumed in toxic amounts when animals are grazing close to the ground.[18] Generally between 15 and 80% of animals in a group show clinical signs, which develop mainly when the animals are disturbed. Affected animals lag behind others, tend to stand with their legs apart, become uncoordinated, walk with a characteristic high-stepping gait, and collapse in a tetanic spasm that usually lasts only a few minutes. Few animals die and outbreaks cease when animals are removed from infected pasture.

In Britain the commercial ryegrass seed presently used by farmers is largely endophyte-free, but the infection is considered widespread in long-established pastures, even when ryegrass is only a minor component, and can lead to outbreaks of ryegrass staggers at the end of August and the beginning of September when there are heavy dews and rainfall after a drought (as in 1976 and 1995).[19]

The ergopeptide alkaloid ergovaline has also been found in endophyte-infected perennial ryegrass, and it has been suggested that this alkaloid causes constriction of peripheral blood vessels that leads to heat stress in high environmental temperatures. This stimulates the animals to move into water, and, in combination with lolitrem-induced incoordination, can result in drowning.[18, 20]

• SWEET VERNAL GRASS POISONING   Some fungi that grow on poorly prepared hay or silage made from sweet vernal grass (*Anthoxanthum odoratum*) can break down natural coumarins in the plant to 4-hydroxycoumarin. This can be broken down further, in the presence of formaldehyde in the atmosphere, to dicoumarol (3,3' methylene-bis-4-hydroxycoumarin), which interferes with blood clotting and leads to haemorrhage in

114

animals that eat it.[21, 22] This effect is usually associated with *Melilotus* species, when it is known as sweet clover disease. Sweet vernal grass grows in Britain, but has not, until recently, been associated with animal disease in this country; most reports are from North America. The circumstances of an outbreak that occurred in cattle on a hill farm in south-west England in 1980,[23] were unusual in that the hay contained 80–90% of sweet vernal grass, whereas the level in permanent pastures in this country is usually only 5–10%. Coumarin, *o*-coumaric acid, and melilotic acid were identified in the hay, and *Aspergillus fumigatus* and *Aspergillus flavus*, fungi known to be capable of converting these to 4-hydroxycoumarin, were also present. As cattle and sheep that grazed the pasture did not develop haemorrhages, it was assumed that the dicoumarol had been produced in the hay. Clinical signs typical of dicoumarol poisoning developed in the cattle. Some animals died suddenly and post-mortem examination revealed extensive haemorrhages. The condition was reproduced experimentally when the hay was fed to calves; an increased blood clotting (prothrombin) time was recorded in three calves. Oral administration of vitamin K_1 reduced the prothrombin time, but the prophylactic use of the vitamin while giving feed containing dicoumarol would not be cost-effective. A similar, acute, fatal haemorrhagic syndrome has been reported in dairy cows given silage containing abundant sweet vernal grass.[24]

• TALL FESCUE POISONING   Tall fescue (*Festuca arundinacea*) is associated with several problems in grazing animals: fescue foot, the summer syndrome (reduced feed intake, milk-yield drop, hyperthermia), fat necrosis, and agalactia (lack of milk production). These are caused by ergovaline, a mycotoxin produced by the tall fescue endophyte *Acremonium coenophialum* (for more information on mycotoxins, see pp. 261–264). The condition that results is dependent on the season. Fescue foot is seen primarily in cattle in the colder months in the USA, Australia, and New Zealand; it has not been reported in Britain. It is manifested by severe lameness, followed in a few weeks by peripheral necrosis of affected limbs, with sloughing of the hooves, and loss of the tail and sometimes the ears.[25, 26]

Poisoning by cereal grains

Any toxicity or serious digestive disturbances occurring in grain-fed animals are usually the result of feeding poor-quality grain, which may have been badly harvested or stored or contaminated in some way, or are the result of overfeeding. Grain is generally processed (ground, rolled, or pelleted) before feeding to animals, but processing is justified economically only if it aids digestion. For sheep, processing is not required, and may have adverse effects on carcass quality and on the rumen. In addition, processing interferes with cellulose digestion when cereals supplement forage. For cattle, processing of grain is usually required, but only to the extent necessary to improve digestibility; fine grinding (rather than just light rolling to crush the grains) may lead to rumenitis, parakeratosis, and inefficient utilization of roughage.[27]

With the current increase in intensive husbandry, large amounts of home-grown and imported cereal grains are fed to farm animals in Britain. They sometimes cause digestive disorders and other problems that, although not strictly regarded as poisoning, will be described briefly, under the appropriate cereal.

• BARLEY   The barley beef system of rearing calves quickly to slaughter weight by giving 85% rolled barley (*Hordeum vulgare*) in the ration was widely adopted by British farmers in the 1960s. This led to digestive disorders and other problems including vitamin deficiencies, allergic reactions (with clinical signs of acute respiratory distress and increased heart rate), liver abscesses, kidney necrosis, laminitis, rumenitis, overeating, and bloat. These troubles largely disappeared when the ration was modified slightly to include 87% rolled barley of 17.5% moisture content (compared with 16% moisture in the former ration), 10% (instead of 15%) additional protein (soya and fish meal) and additional roughage (hay with feed, and straw instead of sawdust for bedding).[28] The best grain feed for pigs is barley, since its low oil content leads to a high-quality carcass, and its fibre content is optimum, although feeding finely ground wheat or barley may cause stomach ulcers.[29, 30]

• MAIZE In Britain maize (*Zea mays*), called corn in the USA, is becoming increasingly popular as a valuable silage, forage, and grain crop. Although it has a high nutritive value, problems can arise from its use. Under certain conditions, particularly in drought or frost and in young plants, nitrates accumulate from which toxic levels of nitrites can be formed. High concentrations of cyanogenic compounds can be found during early growth (12–35 days).[31] Digestive disorders that may result from feeding maize are ruminal acidosis (production of large amounts of lactic acid from the easily digestible carbohydrate) and, from feeding poor-quality silage, ruminal alkalosis (production of large amounts of ammonia and simultaneous depression in the ruminal synthesis of amino acids). Both of these conditions can be accompanied by diarrhoea. Lactic acidosis has also been reported in cattle grazing unripe green maize standing in the field.[32]

• OATS The most suitable grains for feeding to horses are oats (*Avena sativa*); other grains need more processing. Quite small amounts of uncooked wheat, barley, or rye, if fed whole or ground into a meal, may lead to digestive disorders with the release of bacterial toxins that are absorbed rapidly into the blood stream and can lead to laminitis (inflammation of the sensitive laminae or layers by which the horny hoof is attached to the foot).

• RYE No toxic substances are produced by any grain crop grown in this country, except rye (*Secale cereale*). Rye grains contain antinutritional factors that affect digestion and absorption of all nutrients, particularly fats, cholesterol, and vitamin D in chickens. These factors are viscous pentosans.[33] Their intake by chicks can result in depression of both growth and bone mineralization. Chicks fed rye grains produce sticky, black droppings, but this is not necessarily associated with the growth depression.

• WHEAT Large amounts of grain, rich in readily available carbohydrates, can lead to acidosis in cattle and sheep through the accumulation of lactic acid in the rumen. Lactic acidosis occurs among feedlot cattle in the USA, and among sheep in Australia, where 'wheat poisoning' or 'wheat sickness' is seen after giving too much grain feed. Wheat (*Triticum aestivum*) seems to produce acidosis more often than other cereals. Acidosis is characterized by loss of appetite, diarrhoea, mucus in faeces, dehydration, incoordination, and sometimes death. Rumen motility is inhibited, and salivation and intestinal motility are reduced. Acidosis affects the redistribution of water in the body and the elimination of toxic substances. Tissues of the rumen, liver, and other organs may be damaged.[34, 35] In sheep, rumenitis (inflammation of the rumen) may develop after feeding wheat grain,[36] and overfeeding can upset the lower digestive system and lead to diarrhoea as a result of reduced net absorption of water in the colon.[37] The rumen fluid of animals with acidosis also contains endotoxin released from gram-negative bacteria normally present in the rumen. This endotoxin depresses blood pressure and motility of the rumen and intestines, and causes a pronounced drop in the number of white blood cells.[38] Livestock that break into fields of wheat before the grain has ripened are liable to develop severe digestive disorders, which may be fatal.

• OTHER TYPES OF POISONING Some other problems that have occurred as the result of feeding cereals are: nervous disorders and diarrhoea among geese and cattle fed brewers' grains (a by-product of malting barley used for beer-making);[39] rickets in lambs grazing on green oats;[39] nitrate poisoning in cattle fed on oat straw;[39] and biotin deficiency in chicks fed a wheat-based diet.[40]

GUTTIFERAE

Hypericum species

This large genus contains over 300 species, 10–15 of which are native in Britain, although some are rare or have very limited distribution. Several other species have been introduced and are common garden plants, and some of these have escaped and become naturalized.

Hypericum perforatum Common St John's Wort (Plate 39)

This is by far the most frequent *Hypericum* in Britain, being found throughout the country except for some parts of Ireland and northern Scotland. The plant readily established itself in parts of the world to which it was introduced (e.g. Australia, New Zealand, USA), and has become a serious agricultural problem, not only because of its harmful effect on livestock, but because its thick growth eliminates valuable pasture.

It is a perennial plant, usually 30–50 cm high but sometimes growing up to 90 cm. A smooth erect stem, with a woody base and two longitudinal ridges, grows from a thin underground rhizome. The leaves have no stalks and are in opposite pairs on the stem. They are elongated and elliptical, with pointed tips and 1–2 cm long. A characteristic feature is the presence of large numbers of translucent dots on the leaves, these being particularly clear when viewed against the light. Terminal and axillary clusters of flowers appear towards the top of the plant in mid to late summer. The flowers are up to 2 cm across and have yellow petals (usually five) and numerous prominent yellow stamens. The flowers turn brown and dry but remain on the capsule which contains numerous cylindrical pitted seeds.

Poisonous principle

St John's wort and most other *Hypericum* species contain a red, fluorescent pigment called hypericin (hexahydroxy-2,2-dimethylnaphthodianthrone), a polyphenolic compound structurally similar to fagopyrin, the photosensitizing agent found in buckwheat (*Fagopyrum esculentum*). Recent studies have shown that hypericin has antiviral[1] and antidepressant properties.

Animal poisoning

If plants containing hypericin are eaten, lesions may develop on unpigmented areas of skin exposed to bright sunlight. This effect, known as photosensitization, occurs less frequently in Britain than in other countries where the sunlight is more intense, but may well be more common here than is generally supposed, and could be responsible for minor lesions on hairless parts of the skin, such as eyelids, muzzles, and udders. Once an animal has developed a reaction to *Hypericum*, it remains sensitized, so that further eating of the plant and exposure to sunlight rapidly produces photosensitization of increasing severity. The reaction produced by *Hypericum* is primary photosensitization as it affects only the skin, on which the ultraviolet rays of the sun act directly, and does not involve metabolism of the pigment in the liver, in which case the skin lesions would be secondary. The reaction is most severe if the fresh plant is eaten, but photosensitivity can also result from eating the dried plant, although about 80% of the hypericin is lost with drying.[2] In severe cases the unpigmented areas of skin become oedematous and necrotic and may slough off, leaving painful lesions which are slow to heal.

The harmful effects of eating St John's wort have been known for hundreds of years[3] and it is reported that the Arabs used to apply extracts of tobacco and henna to unpigmented areas of the skin of their animals to protect them from sunlight.[4] Under normal grazing conditions in bright sunlight, the skin reaction caused by eating *Hypericum* usually develops in 1–2 weeks.

Hypericum photosensitivity has caused serious illness and economic losses in New Zealand[5] and Australia[6] among sheep (affecting wool quality), cows (reducing milk yield), and horses. The carcasses of affected animals killed for meat are usually of poor quality. In addition to the skin lesions, affected sheep appear distressed, often shaking their heads, and may react to contact with water, so that crossing a stream or being dipped to remove parasites results in wild thrashing of limbs, and convulsions.[5] This occurs only during the active phase of photosensitization and not during the recovery period. In feeding experiments,[5] sheep given 100 g of the fresh plant daily developed the characteristic sensitivity to light, the effect being more severe when freshly extracted juice of the plants was given. In Germany the skin lesions occurred every summer in a flock of sheep on pasture infested with St John's wort.[7]

In cattle, feeding 0.5–0.6% of their body weight of the fresh plant (less than average daily consumption at grazing) was sufficient to induce photosensitivity.[8] When a single dose of an aqueous suspension of the finely ground dried plant (3 g per kg body weight), or an extract containing hypericin, was given by stomach tube to calves,[2] which were then exposed to sunlight, their temperature and respiration rate began to rise 3–4 hours later. They passed soft faeces, became restless, and licked the white areas of their body which became reddened. Calves given a single dose of 5 g per kg body weight of the dried plant had a more severe reaction. They shook their heads vigorously, and exudation and scabbing of the skin around the eyes and muzzle and on white areas of the body developed. The scabs subsequently dried and peeled off, but recovery was not complete for 30–40 days. Similar calves, given dried *Hypericum* but not exposed to sunlight, also passed soft faeces but there was no skin reaction.

Photosensitivity was described in 17 pigs in Britain.[9] After being moved to rough ground where St John's wort was growing in profusion, the white pigs and the white areas of Wessex pigs developed red patches which irritated; rubbing led to abrasions. A black sow was unaffected. In the shade of their sties the animals recovered.

Horses react in much the same way as sheep and cattle, but the effects tend to be more severe. The affected areas of skin irritate, and abrasion by the animals results in open lesions that may become infected. Loss of appetite, debility, staggering gait, and coma have also been reported in horses.[6]

After feeding rabbits with fresh or dried *Hypericum*, some of the white ones died, while grey ones survived. In addition to skin lesions and necrosis of the ears, post-mortem examination revealed enlargement and cirrhosis of the liver and inflammation and necrosis of the kidneys.[10] Liver and kidney damage has also been reported in sheep given large amounts of fresh plant material (4–16 g per kg body weight daily for 14 days).[11]

Human poisoning

Hypericin present in herbal preparations of *Hypericum* species has caused photosensitization,[12] but no reports of poisoning by ingestion of plant material have been found.

HIPPOCASTANACEAE

Aesculus hippocastanum Horse Chestnut (Plate 40)

This large tree is not a native of Britain, but has become well established in the country since its introduction. It is often planted in parks, gardens, streets, and greens. It is a broad-crowned deciduous tree, up to 30 m tall. The bark is dark greyish-brown and somewhat scaly on the trunk and older branches. The large oval buds, pointed at the tip, are often more than 2 cm long and are covered with characteristic, deep red-brown sticky bud scales. The leaves are compound with 5–7 coarsely veined leaflets (8–20 cm long) radiating from the stalk and broadening before terminating in a usually blunt point. When first emerging from the bud they are densely covered with woolly hairs. The white or cream flowers appear in spring in elongated upright clusters. At the base of each flower is a yellow patch that later turns red. The fruits are up to 6 cm across, green, tough, and sparsely covered with coarse spines. They contain one or occasionally two shiny brown seeds (conkers), which have a large, prominent, pale buff scar. Another similar tree, *Aesculus carnea*, a hybrid arising from the common horse chestnut and the American red buckeye tree (*Aesculus pavia*), has red flowers. The buds are not, or only very slightly, sticky, and the fruits are almost smooth.

Poisonous principles

It is generally agreed that the poisonous principle of *Aesculus* is a saponic glycoside (6,7-dihydroxycoumarin 6-glucoside) named esculin (aesculin), although it has been suggested that the tree also contains alkaloids. Esculin yields esculetin (6,7-dihydroxycoumarin) on hydrolysis.[1] Esculin is closely related to the hydroxycoumarin found in spoiled sweet clover hay from which the anticoagulant rodenticides were originally developed.[2] The young leaves and flowers of the tree are usually considered the most toxic parts; the bark is said to contain more esculin, but is probably rarely eaten. Aescin, a mixture of saponins, is also present in horse chestnut seeds.

Animal poisoning

Despite its availability in certain habitats (e.g. to cattle and deer in parkland), horse chestnut rarely causes problems in Britain. In outbreaks in Maryland, USA, the leaves and fruits of the tree caused illness in cattle, some of which died.[3] The seeds of buckeye trees (other *Aesculus* species) have also caused problems among livestock in the USA,[4,5]

119

where poisoning has been reported in cattle, horses, and pigs, with clinical signs including inflammation of mucous membranes, vomiting (where possible), weakness, incoordination, muscular twitching, stupor, and paralysis.[6] In Britain the ingestion of conkers by a donkey[7] resulted in depression, signs of abdominal pain, intestinal impaction, and weight loss; treatment with purgatives was unsuccessful. Cases have also been reported in dogs,[7] in which the clinical signs included vomiting, diarrhoea, abdominal tenderness, dehydration, muscular tremors, and incoordination; of seven cases reported between 1992 and 1995, six recovered within four days and one died. An extract of the seeds of three *Aesculus* species has been shown to be toxic to hamsters and chicks.[8]

Human poisoning

This can occur when conkers are eaten in mistake for sweet chestnuts, and is most common in children. The likelihood of such poisoning is often mentioned, but there are few authenticated cases, and the bitter taste is likely to prevent large quantities being eaten. Gastrointestinal symptoms (vomiting, diarrhoea, abdominal pain) can occur. A fatal case was reported in the USA.[9] A four-year-old boy became restless then slept deeply after eating horse chestnuts. When, two days later, he ate a further quantity, he became unconscious and died in hospital from respiratory paralysis.

HYDRANGEACEAE

Hydrangea macrophylla Hydrangea

In Britain hydrangeas are commonly cultivated as garden shrubs, those found apparently growing wild being garden escapes. Hydrangeas are deciduous shrubs, up to 2 m high. The leaves are broad, stalked, and taper to a point at the tip; the edges are sometimes toothed. The flowers develop in large, showy, flat-topped or domed inflorescences that are up to 20 cm across. The individual flowers usually have four petals; they are white, or shades of pink or blue, depending on the nature of the soil.

Poisonous principles

The plants contain a cyanogenic glycoside called hydrangin, the allergen hydrangenol (an isocoumarin), and also saponins.

Animal poisoning

There have been no recent reports of poisoning in animals, but diarrhoea (with blood), contraction of abdominal muscles, and stiffness of limbs occurred in a horse,[1] and abdominal pain, diarrhoea, and shortness of breath in a cow[2] have been reported.

Human poisoning

Ingestion of the leaves and buds, or smoking the leaves, has caused symptoms including nausea, vomiting, and diarrhoea.[3] Flower buds added to a salad caused nausea and gastroenteritis in a family in Florida.[4] Repeated exposure to hydrangeas can occasionally give rise to allergic contact dermatitis.[5]

IRIDACEAE

This family contains two wild *Iris* species that are poisonous, and also many cultivated irises, crocuses, and gladioli; the toxicity of the individual species and varieties of the garden plants is not known.

Iris foetidissima Stinking Iris

Other common name: Gladdon

This plant is native in Britain and grows on cliffs and in hedgerows and woods on dry calcareous soils in southern England and Wales. It is a perennial, 30–90 cm tall, with long, narrow, dark green leaves and an unpleasant smell. The flower stalk, which is leafless, unbranched, and angled on one side, bears 1–3 purplish flowers, often with darker veins. The outer perianth segments are reflexed, broad, and oval, but narrow towards the base; the inner ones are more erect and are uniformly narrow. The seed capsules split open when dry to reveal bright reddish-orange seeds. Details of poisoning follow the description of *Iris pseudacorus* (see below).

Iris pseudacorus Yellow Flag (Plate 41)

Yellow flag is found throughout Britain in marshes and wet ground at the edge of rivers, ditches, and lakes. The plant is an erect, slightly bluish-green perennial with long, narrow leaves in two opposite ranks sheathing the stem at the base, becoming flattened vertically in one plane and terminating in a point. They may be up to 50 mm wide and as long as, or longer than, the stem (up to 150 cm), which is stiff and bears 2–3 bright yellow flowers in early summer. The flowers are 8–10 cm across and variable in shape, although all have outer segments (usually three), which are narrow at the base, but broaden before terminating in a point directed slightly downwards and away from the flower, revealing the inner segments and stamens and style, which are also yellow. The fruit is a green, elliptical capsule with a broad point at the tip and contains numerous light brown seeds.

Poisonous principles
The nature of these is not clear. In both species they have been described as a resin, a glycoside (iridin, irisin, or irisine), myristic acid, and an acrid compound. All parts of both wild and cultivated *Iris*, but especially the rhizomes, are poisonous. The plant material remains toxic after drying.

Animal poisoning
The unpleasant odour of *Iris foetidissima* makes it less likely to be eaten than *Iris pseudacorus*, but, although potentially poisonous, neither plant is eaten readily when growing undisturbed. Both species have long been regarded as poisonous[1,2] and are still widely referred to as such,[3,4] although no recent cases of poisoning have been attributed to the plants.

The chief clinical signs of *Iris* poisoning are irritation of the stomach and intestines, causing vomiting and diarrhoea, sometimes with bleeding.[5] Elevation of body temperature usually occurs. Linnaeus, in the 18th century, referred to *Iris* as being dangerous to cattle. Early this century, in the USA, a blue-flowered garden *Iris* was eaten by calves pastured on land where there was a flower border.[6] The animals became quiet and recumbent, with salivation and enlargement of glands in the head and throat. Irritating, encrusted lesions developed on the lips and muzzle. In two calves that died, there was acute abdominal pain, and blood-stained faeces were produced. Post-mortem examination revealed inflammation of the stomach, and black areas, 1–15 cm across, in the intestines. The kidneys, liver, and spleen were very dark. There were no further cases of illness when the *Iris* plants were removed. An outbreak of diarrhoea, with faeces containing blood in some cases, occurred in cattle in the West Highlands of Scotland[7] and was attributed to eating the underground parts of *Iris pseudacorus* exposed during drainage operations. The animals recovered when access to the plants was prevented. In the same area, hay often contains *Iris* leaves and it is suggested that the outbreaks of diarrhoea, common in housed cattle, may be caused by ingestion of the plant. Eating the rhizomes of *Iris pseudacorus* left on a canal bank after dredging caused diarrhoea, with haemorrhage, in eight pigs, two of which died. One sow aborted a few days after eating the plant.[8] Poisoning of horses, with recovery in a few days, has been reported.[5]

Human poisoning
Iris species are unlikely to be eaten, except mistakenly; symptoms similar to those reported in animals may occur (abdominal pain, nausea, vomiting, and diarrhoea).[9] The plants have been used medicinally as a strong purgative.[10] The sap can irritate the skin, sometimes causing blistering.[11] A bracelet made from the seeds gave rise to dermatitis.[10]

Other members of the Iridaceae family

The spring-flowering crocus (*Crocus* species) appears to be poisonous. After eating some corms, a four-month-old dog lost its appetite, became lethargic and depressed, showed signs of abdominal pain, and had diarrhoea and an increase in body temperature;[12] it had recovered in 48 hours. In Sicily, poisoning occurred in cattle that ate gladioli (*Gladiolus segetum*).[13]

JUNCACEAE

Juncus species Rushes

Several species of rush occur in Britain in marshy or muddy places on poorly drained soils, where some areas, including pastures, may be dominated by the plants. Rushes are erect plants with long, stiff, narrow leaves that are round in section or grass-like, and grow in tufts or from a creeping rhizome. In different species the leaves appear smooth, ridged, or jointed and may be hollow or completely or partially filled with pith; some species have a sheathing leaf base. The inflorescence is terminal or lateral and composed of small, greenish, or brown flowers in a compact or loose cluster.

Poisonous principles

Some species of *Juncus* are said to have a high cyanide content, probably in the form of cyanogenic glycosides. However, there is very little recent information on the toxicity of rushes.

Animal poisoning

Poisoning of cattle by the joint leaf rush (*Juncus holoschoenus*) has been reported from Australia.[1] The incident involved three calves that ate rushes from a corner of a field and died a few hours later. Post-mortem examination revealed plants in the stomach. Rushes from the field were found to have a high cyanide content, but when tested again later, at the flowering stage, the concentration was much lower.

Species of *Juncus* have been incriminated in outbreaks of poisoning in South Africa in animals grazing areas of land that are sometimes waterlogged and may contain small streams or springs. Such areas are called 'vlei' and the term 'vlei poisoning' is sometimes used.[2] Various vlei plants have been tested for toxicity by feeding to experimental animals. The soft rush (*Juncus effusus*), which dominates some areas of vlei, is considered a likely cause of the condition, in which rapid development of clinical signs and sudden death, consistent with cyanide poisoning, were reported. Rapid death is typical of acute cyanide poisoning, in which oxygen starvation of the central nervous system occurs as a result of inactivation of enzymes involved in tissue respiration.

There is very little known about the effects of eating *Juncus* in Britain. However, the heath rush (*Juncus squarrosus*) is said to be grazed eagerly at times when the pasture is poor,[3] whereas the hard rush (*Juncus inflexus*), which is widespread on heavy soils, has been responsible for the loss of animals, which sometimes appear to develop a taste for it, and eat it to the exclusion of other plants. It is said that its poisonous nature is not generally recognized,[4] although severe clinical signs have been reported in cattle after eating the plant.[5] Irritation of the digestive tract, sometimes accompanied by diarrhoea, developed initially, after which the animals lost condition rapidly and became nervous and partially blind. The disease was progressive, some animals becoming totally blind and developing convulsions; death from brain haemorrhages occurred in some cases. Although similar in some respects to magnesium deficiency, this condition was not improved by the injection of magnesium salts. Animals that recover remain nervous for several days, until their sight returns; they must be housed or kept away from pastures containing rushes or they will seek and eat the plants again and repeat the process. It is not stated which toxic constituents of the rushes are responsible for this syndrome.

JUNCAGINACEAE

The only two plants in this family that grow wild in Britain are the sea and marsh arrow grasses (*Triglochin* species).

Triglochin maritima Sea Arrow Grass

This robust, erect plant grows on salt marshes and grassy places on rocky shores wherever conditions are suitable around the coast of Britain. The leaves, which grow from a stout rhizome, are long, narrow, and thick, not flat as in true grasses. They are erect and, in Britain, may grow up to 30 cm long. The plant flowers from mid to late summer, the inflorescence being borne on a rather stiff stalk, often exceeding the height of the leaves. The flowers are small, green, and crowded close to each other and to the stem. They develop into golden-brown fruits. Details of poisoning follow the description of *Triglochin palustris* (see below).

Triglochin palustris Marsh Arrow Grass

Although distributed throughout Britain, this species is found only very locally in marshy places. It is much more slender than sea arrow grass, having fine, almost thread-like leaves, often cylindrical almost to the tip, and a more delicate inflorescence on which the small flowers are not densely crowded together on the spike.

Poisonous principles

Although both of these plants are readily eaten by animals, they can cause poisoning as hydrocyanic acid is released from them under certain conditions. A cyanogenic glycoside, tentatively named triglochinin, is thought to be the poisonous principle, although its exact nature has yet to be elucidated. The amount of the cyanogenic glycoside in the plant (sometimes called the cyanogenic potential) is variable; it is highest in the period of rapid growth that follows a retardation, such as wilting during drought, or frosting. In the USA, where drought can be severe, *Triglochin* is well known as a potentially poisonous plant. In actively growing plants the green leaves are the most poisonous. Ensiling reduces, but does not eliminate, the toxicity of arrow grass. Hydrocyanic acid is released by the hydrolytic action of enzymes liberated in the plant itself when crushed, and also in the stomach of animals that eat it.[1,2] A cyanogenic glycoside content of 50 mg per 100 g of green arrow grass is considered lethal, even if an amount as small as 0.5% of the body weight of the animal is consumed.[3]

Animal poisoning

There are no recent reports of poisoning by these plants in Britain, but clinical signs have been described for both sheep and cattle in the USA.[4,5] These include nervousness, trembling or jerking, erratic breathing, and excess salivation. The blood is bright red (this may be seen at the nostrils) as it remains highly oxygenated, while the tissues lack oxygen, and the mucous membranes appear bluish (cyanosed). Recumbency and convulsions may precede death, which frequently occurs within an hour of eating the plants. In cases that survive for a longer period there may be vomiting, especially in pigs, and the blood later becomes dark,[6] because of lack of oxygen; blood clotting may be impaired. The conditions under which poisoning may occur and the clinical signs in sheep have been examined in detail in animals fed experimentally with sea arrow grass.[7]

The post-mortem findings are similar in all animals. The bright red blood (especially in animals that die within an hour or two of poisoning) is characteristic, as is the smell of bitter almonds of the stomach contents. The muscles are usually dark and haemorrhages are common.

The action of hydrocyanic acid is so rapid that it is often too late to treat a poisoned animal once the signs have been recognized. Several compounds have been tested as antidotes for cyanide poisoning,[8] but the classical method of injecting an aqueous solution of sodium thiosulphate and sodium nitrite is still the preferred treatment. Intravenous injection gives quicker results, but intraperitoneal or subcutaneous injection may also be effective in saving an animal. Variations exist in the recommended concentrations of the sodium salts, but it is usual to inject a volume of a solution (usually 10–20%) that will give 0.5 g per kg body weight of sodium thiosulphate and 10–20 g per kg of sodium nitrite.[8] Sodium thiosulphate may be used alone, or in larger doses, but high doses of sodium nitrite should be avoided because of the risk of nitrite poisoning.

LABIATAE

Galeopsis species Hemp Nettles

Several hemp nettles grow in Britain, mainly on waste or arable ground. Some can be found throughout the country, while others are more limited in distribution. These are annual plants that grow up to about 20 cm in height. The leaves are produced in pairs on the stem; they have serrated edges, and taper into a point at the tip. The flowers develop in tight clusters at the nodes, where the spiny, pointed teeth of the calyx form a ring from which the individual flowers project. The colour of the flowers varies according to the species, but each has a hooded upper lip, and a smaller lower lip with three lobes.

Poisonous principles
The nature of these is not known, but from the clinical signs described in animals it seems probable that the plants contain irritants similar to those in other members of the family.

Animal poisoning
Hemp nettle is said to have caused poisoning of horses in Europe,[1] but no recent case reports have been found, except in Russia where 1.1–2.5% of seeds of *Galeopsis ladanum* were present as contaminants of feed given to horses and pigs.[2] Of 18 horses, two foals died and two adults had to be killed. The affected animals were weak and refused feed and water; sweating and muscle tremors occurred. Post-mortem examination revealed haemorrhagic inflammation of the stomach and small intestines. On a pig farm, 79 of 150 newly weaned piglets died. They refused feed, did not respond to touch, developed oedematous eyelids, red patches on the skin, and were comatose before death. Jaundice, infiltration of gelatinous material beneath the skin, congestion of the liver and kidneys, and dark red coloration of the mucous membranes of the stomach and intestines were seen at post-mortem examination.

Glechoma hederacea Ground Ivy

This plant is native in Britain, where it grows throughout the country in grassland, waste places and woods. The plant has long trailing stems from which the erect flowering stems grow to about 30 cm (usually less). The leaves arise in pairs on the stem, and are stalked; the leaf blade is rounded, with scalloped edges. The flowers develop in the axils of the leaves, and are bluish purple. Each has a basal tubular portion that opens into unequal lobes at the mouth. Some of the flowers are small and unisexual (female), while the larger ones are bisexual.

Poisonous principles
Ground ivy contains poorly characterized oils and a bitter substance.

Animal poisoning
The plant does not appear to have caused poisoning in Britain, but illness and death among horses and cattle that ate it have been reported in Eastern Europe. After being fed with freshly cut lucerne from a field where clumps of *Glechoma hederacea* were growing, seven horses developed an accelerated weak pulse, difficulty in breathing, conjunctival haemorrhage, elevated temperature, and dizziness.[3] Post-mortem examination of one old horse that died revealed enlargement of the spleen, dilatation of the caecum, and gastroenteritis. The disease was reproduced experimentally by feeding fresh or slightly wilted ground ivy to other horses. Poisoning in cattle was also recorded. In another outbreak, horses given freshly mown lucerne containing a high proportion of *Glechoma* developed forced, rapid breathing, and 15% mortality was recorded.[4] There was dilatation of the air spaces in the lungs. With a change of feed and symptomatic treatment the other animals recovered.

Mentha species Mints

The mints are a fairly large group of plants that are characterized by their pleasant, fresh smell when cut or bruised. The individual species are sometimes difficult to identify as they hybridize, and are very variable in form. There are several wild mints in Britain, and others are grown as garden herbs and used fresh or dried for flavouring food.

    The plants are perennial, and have long stems that grow for considerable distances along or beneath the surface of the ground. The leaves arise in pairs on the stem and may have toothed or smooth edges; in some species they have soft hairs. The flowers are usually shades of pink or pale purple, and develop in tightly packed rings in the axils of the leaves. Each flower has a basal tubular portion that opens at the mouth into four unequal lobes.

Poisonous principles
Irritant oils are present in the plants.

Animal poisoning
Poisoning by mint rarely occurs, but the plants are reputed to cause inflammation, blistering and necrosis of the skin, cramps, increased urine production, and damage to the central nervous system. Abortion has been induced experimentally by feeding mint, and occurred spontaneously in two cows in Austria after they had eaten large quantities of horse mint (*Mentha longifolia*).[5]

Human poisoning

No cases of poisoning by ingestion of mint have been found; the leaves and the oil (derived from the flower stems of some *Mentha* species) are often used for flavouring food. Peppermint oil is irritant, and occasionally causes allergic contact dermatitis.[6]

Other members of the Labiatae family

Henbit (*Lamium amplexicaule*) and other dead nettles (*Lamium* species) have been incriminated as the cause of poisoning among livestock, but no recent cases have been recorded, although the plants are widely distributed throughout Britain and many other parts of the world.

LEGUMINOSAE

Several taxonomists recognize three subdivisions of this large family, while others place almost all of the plants into a family called Fabaceae, for which the older name Papilionaceae is still sometimes used. The family contains trees, shrubs, and herbaceous plants; members of about 20 genera in Britain are potentially poisonous. These include wild plants, garden plants, and various cultivated plants that are fed to animals or used as human food.

Arachis hypogaea Groundnut

Other common names: Peanut; Earthnut; Monkeynut

This plant is occasionally found growing apparently wild on rubbish tips and waste ground in Britain, but it does not usually flower here. The edible groundnuts are the seeds of the plant that become buried, within their fibrous shells, below the surface of the ground. Groundnuts are not grown commercially in Britain, but are imported, either as whole nuts (often for human consumption), or after oil extraction, when the residues are used as meal or cake for animal feeds.

Poisonous principles
The nuts themselves are not poisonous, but if infected with some fungi that produce toxic metabolites (mycotoxins) they can cause poisoning. Mycotoxin production can occur without visible signs of moulding, but moulding of feed does not necessarily indicate mycotoxin production, as only certain strains of fungi are involved.

Animal poisoning
For details of this type of poisoning, see the section on mycotoxins (pp. 261–264).

Human poisoning
In addition to problems associated with mycotoxins, some individuals can have a severe, acute allergic reaction to proteins in peanuts. This is characterized by swelling of the mouth and throat, and may be accompanied by gastrointestinal disturbances; these effects are thought to be due to a reaction between peanut proteins and immunoglobulin E antibodies.

Astragalus species Milk Vetches

Other common names: Locoweed; Poison Vetch

There are many species and varieties of *Astragalus* and the taxonomy of the genus is confused. Although milk vetches occur in Britain they are rare or local in distribution. Most milk vetches are stout perennial plants or shrubs having compound leaves with elongated, round-tipped leaflets arranged in opposite pairs on the stalk. The flowers arise in compact spikes from the axils of the leaves, and are usually white, cream, or pale purple. The fruit is a pod, often divided longitudinally into two compartments.

Poisonous principles

Some *Astragalus* species contain organic nitrogen compounds: the glycoside of nitropropanol, called miserotoxin as it occurs in *Astragalus miser*, or glycosides of nitropropionic acid.[1] Another type of toxin has also been isolated from *Astragalus*, *Oxytropis*, and the related *Swainsona* species; this is the indolizidine alkaloid swainsonine. Some *Astragalus* species accumulate selenium.

Animal poisoning

It is unlikely that animals will be poisoned by eating milk vetches in this country. Some species of *Astragalus*, and the closely related *Oxytropis* (which occurs, although rarely, in Scotland), are considered to be among the most poisonous plants available to livestock in the USA, although several other species appear to be harmless.

The organic nitrogen compounds can lead to acute or chronic poisoning. The acute form is characterized by agitation, laboured respiration, cardiovascular collapse, terminal coma, and occasional episodes of paddling, and the chronic form by weight loss and paralysis of the hind legs.[2]

Swainsonine induces a lysosomal storage disease, with vacuolation in the cytoplasm of nerve cells and the cells of various organs. Affected animals show loss of condition, depression, locomotory disorders, and excitement when disturbed (locoism). Abortion has occurred in cattle and sheep, and the birth of small, weak, and malformed lambs and calves has also been reported; it is not clear whether swainsonine is responsible for the malformations.[3]

The accumulation of selenium in animals eating certain *Astragalus* species can lead to the development of hoof and hair lesions, myocardial necrosis, and mild spongiform changes in the spinal cord and brain stem.[4]

Coronilla varia Crown Vetch

Crown vetch is not native in Britain, but has become well established, after its introduction, in several places scattered throughout the country. It is a straggling perennial plant with stems up to 60 cm long. The compound leaves have elongated, elliptical leaflets arranged in pairs on the stalk. The inflorescence arises from the leaf axil and consists of 10–20 white, pink, or purple flowers. The fruit is a slender pod which breaks up, on ripening, into one-seeded sections.

Poisonous principles

Although it is used occasionally as a forage plant (not in Britain), *Coronilla* contains various poisonous principles, including several flavone C-glycosides[5] and also β-nitropropionic acid, which is a hydrolysis product of nitropropanoyl glucopyranoses.

Animal poisoning

Experimental feeding of meadow voles, young pigs, and chicks with crown vetch forage led to reduced feed intake, reduced activity, a hunched-up appearance, incoordination and, in some cases, death.[6] The glucopyranoses are detoxified by the action of rumen microorganisms, and crown vetch is therefore considered to be a suitable feed for ruminants.[7] The plant is not suitable for feeding to all animals, however, as was found in Hungary when large numbers of coypu died after being given forage containing wild crown vetch.[8] The clinical signs included incoordination, recumbency, muscular spasms, paralysis, and difficulty with breathing. Post-mortem examination showed accumulation of fluid in various organs and in the abdominal cavity. The cause of the poisoning was confirmed by feeding three coypu experimentally with the plants; all died within 26 hours.

Cytisus scoparius Broom

This plant is generally distributed throughout Britain on heaths and waste land, but is restricted to acid soils. It is a much branched shrub, with branches that are flexible, angled, and green throughout the year. The leaves consist of 1–3 elongated leaflets usually less than 1 cm long. The flowers are bright yellow and the fruits are pods, which become dry and dark brownish grey when ripe. The seeds are blackish brown and are shed explosively as the pods open with a characteristic snap.

Poisonous principles

Broom contains small amounts of the toxic quinolizidine alkaloids sparteine and isosparteine. Cytisine, genistein, lupinidine, and sarothamnine are also said to be present,[9] although some of these names may refer to the same compound. The alkaloids can depress the heart and nervous system, sometimes with paralysis of motor nerve endings. Sparteine sulphate has been used medicinally[10] in small doses, and acts as an antidote to some poisons, including snake venom.

Animal poisoning

It is unlikely that this plant would cause poisoning, except in very unusual circumstances, as insufficient amounts of the alkaloids are present, and the small leaves and somewhat wiry stems make it unattractive as a food plant. No reports of specific cases have been traced, but reference is still made to broom as a poisonous plant and a statement that the average poisonous dose for a horse would be over 11 kg (25 lb)[11] is widely quoted.

Galega officinalis Goat's Rue

Other common names: French Lilac; French Honeysuckle

Goat's rue is not native in Britain, but has become naturalized and established in some places. It is an erect, branched plant, which may grow as a woody shrub up to 1.5 m high. The compound leaves have 4–8 pairs of leaflets that are elongated but rounded at the base and tip, which terminates in a small point. The flowers are pale bluish purple (sometimes pink or white) and are borne on short stalks in an erect spike.

Poisonous principles

Several are said to be present in *Galega*. Toxicity varies with different plant populations, parts of the plant, and stages of growth. Galegine (isoamyleneguanidine) and hydroxygalegine are usually considered the most important toxins. Subcutaneous injection of mice with alcoholic extracts of *Galega officinalis*[12] revealed that the leaves are more poisonous than the seeds, although the seeds contain more galegine. It is assumed, therefore, that other toxic substances besides galegine are present; the plant is especially poisonous at the flowering and fruiting stages (usually from mid to late summer). The poisonous principles are not destroyed by drying, so hay containing the plant is also poisonous.

Animal poisoning

There have been sporadic outbreaks of poisoning by *Galega officinalis* reported since last century.[13] Poisoning has occurred in France,[14, 15] Romania,[16] New Zealand,[17, 18] and more recently in Britain.[19] Sheep eat goat's rue readily and are involved in most of the outbreaks of poisoning reported. In four separate outbreaks in 1979–1982 in France, many sheep died after eating *Galega* at pasture or in cut forage or hay.[13, 15] In the outbreak in Britain,[19] sheep grazed *Galega*, which had become established on an embankment that had been constructed and seeded with grass in the course of road works. On this site 12 of 200 ewes died (eight of them within 12 hours) during the summer of 1989, and the remaining animals were removed to another pasture. In spring the following year 9.6% of another group of ewes died on the same site; there was evidence of the *Galega* plants being eaten. It was of interest that rams put on the *Galega*-infested pasture during the winter, between the two outbreaks in ewes, were unaffected. Occasionally cattle are also poisoned,[20] sometimes fatally, although they usually avoid the plant, possibly on account of its bitter taste. It has been found, however, that feeding dried *Galega* to lactating cows at 0.74 kg daily increased their milk yield.[21] In New Zealand a goat was found dead within 36 hours of being introduced to a pasture where goat's rue was growing.[18] Clinical signs of *Galega* poisoning usually appear 18–24 hours after eating the plant, but may develop more rapidly and last for only a few hours. The signs may therefore not be noticed, affected animals sometimes being found dead. Accounts of the clinical and post-mortem signs associated with *Galega* poisoning in animals poisoned naturally or experimentally are very consistent.[22] Laboured breathing, oedema of the neck, frothy discharge from the nostrils, loss of balance, muscular spasms with the head thrown back, and convulsions are reported in poisoned sheep. Fluid accumulation in the thorax and abdomen and beneath the skin, congestion of blood vessels in the lungs and intestines, and haemorrhages beneath the skin, around the heart, and in mucous membranes are typical post-mortem findings. If possible, microscopic examination of plant remains in the stomach should be made to confirm the diagnosis.[14] From feeding experiments in Utah, USA, where the plant has spread on agricultural land after its introduction late last century as a potential fodder crop, it appeared that animals can become adapted to eating *Galega*.[23] However, later work there suggested that great variation in the susceptibility of individual animals may be the explanation for the apparent adaptation.[24]

Glycine max Soya Bean

Climatic conditions in Britain are not suitable for growing soya beans, although some varieties are being produced, which could give fairly good crops in this country, and may be available commercially in the future. Because of their high protein content, soya beans are imported for incorporation into many animal feed mixes, and are used in human diets to replace, or supplement, animal proteins.

Poisonous principles

Soya beans or meal (the residue after extraction of oil) should not be used untreated as, in common with other legume seeds, they contain various toxins. Among these are lectins (phytohaemagglutinins),[25] trypsin inhibitors (the Bowman–Birk and Kunitz inhibitors), saponic glycosides,[25] oestrogenic substances,[26] and anti-thyroid factors.[27, 28] The presence of these antinutritional factors[29] is thought to account, at least partly, for the poor performance of animals on a diet containing soya beans. After heat treatment they are such a good source of vegetable protein that they are used as a reference with which other legume seeds are compared.[30]

Animal poisoning

Lectins (phytohaemagglutinins) that are responsible for the digestive system damage that follows the consumption of some beans (*Phaseolus vulgaris*) are also present in soya beans, but at too low a concentration to cause more than minor problems. Trypsin inhibitors, associated with enlargement and degeneration of the pancreas, are often considered the main cause of death in experimental animals fed raw soya beans.[25] There are conflicting reports on the mechanism involving amino acid loss in this reaction.[31, 32] The possibility of interaction between the toxins has been suggested.[25] A commercial extraction method, now largely discontinued, using the solvent trichloroethylene, has been responsible for numerous outbreaks of poisoning.[33, 34] Although the solvent itself is of low or doubtful toxicity to animals, even above the concentration used in the extraction process, the toxicity of soya bean residues after extraction is enhanced greatly. The extracted oil is usually considered harmless and useful for adding to animal feeds and for culinary use, but a toxic factor (chlorinated dibenzo-*p*-dioxin) released during some processing procedures has caused oedema, particularly around the heart, in chicks.[35] Since the most serious outbreaks of soya bean poisoning have involved residues from trichloroethylene-extracted seeds,[36] it has even been stated that soya beans themselves are not toxic.[36] This opinion is, however, not generally held. The apparent clinical signs of poisoning by raw soya beans are confined mainly to depression of growth rate, which varies in different animal species and stages of their growth,[37] and may not readily be recognized in live animals. Post-mortem examination, however, often reveals changes in the liver, pancreas, and thyroid gland. Congenital blindness in chicks hatched from eggs of hens fed raw soya bean meal has been reported.[38]

Human poisoning

Although soya beans are potentially toxic, it should be emphasized that, when properly prepared (by commercial procedures or by household cooking involving boiling for at least 30 minutes, or pressure cooking), soya beans and food prepared from them are safe and nutritious.

Laburnum anagyroides Laburnum (Plates 42 and 43)

Other common names: Golden Chain; Golden Rain

Laburnum does not grow wild in Britain, except occasionally in waste places as an escape from cultivation, but is often planted as an ornamental tree in gardens throughout the country. It usually grows as a tree, 7–9 m high, with a trunk rarely exceeding 20 cm in diameter, but Scotch laburnum (*Laburnum alpinum*) is smaller and branches from near the base. Hybrids of the two species also occur and there are several commercial varieties recognized. The leaves have long stalks and bear three terminal leaflets, which are elliptical in shape, light green and minutely downy beneath. The conspicuous inflorescences develop in early summer and consist of long (up to 20 cm) pendulous clusters of bright yellow, pea-type flowers usually about 2 cm across. The fruits are pods, 3–8 cm long, depending on the variety. These are green and contain green seeds when first formed, but become pale brown and dry as they mature. When ripe, the pods open explosively to reveal dark brown or black rounded seeds, usually about 0.5 cm in diameter. In most varieties the dry pods remain hanging on the tree throughout the winter.

Poisonous principles

All parts of the tree, but particularly the bark and seeds, contain a quinolizidine alkaloid, named cytisine, after the old name of the plant, *Cytisus laburnum*. It is said that the leaves become less toxic and the flowers and fruits more so as the latter develop.[39] The quantities of cytisine found in laburnum and said to be dangerous (or even fatal) vary greatly.

Animal poisoning

In general, laburnum poisoning in animals is rare, but a few fatal cases have been reported. One horse fed with oats that had been spilled and then gathered up with a considerable amount of laburnum seeds and pods, and two others that ate leaves and pods of laburnum trees to which they had been tied, became uncoordinated, developed muscular tremors and slight abdominal pain, became comatose, and died within four hours.[40] A pig became severely ill, with profuse diarrhoea, after eating lawn mowings containing laburnum leaves,[41] and a cow that ate parts of an uprooted laburnum lost condition, its milk yield fell, and the milk contained large yellow clots.[41] Other cattle that ate laburnum from a felled tree or branches left in their field during winter developed a stiff, unsteady gait and violent tremors.[42] Several animals went down and were unwilling to rise. If forced to do so they walked reluctantly, as if with sore feet. One animal died and twigs and pods of laburnum were found in the rumen. Experimentally, an extract of *Laburnum* seeds and pods given to heifers daily for 2–3 days caused frothing of the mouth, and an irregular gait. The alkaloid in the extract was confirmed chromatographically to be cytisine.[43] Laburnum poisoning has also been reported in dogs. One animal died in convulsions about 30 minutes after chewing a stick, subsequently found to be from a laburnum tree,[44] and two bitches were poisoned (one fatally) after chewing low branches of a laburnum.[45] Post-mortem examination of stomach and intestinal contents of the dogs that died revealed bark of the tree in the first case, and a large quantity of pods in the second. In 1993–1995 the Veterinary Poisons Information Service (VPIS) in London received enquiries concerning 11 cases of poisoning in dogs by laburnum leaves, flowers, or seed pods.[46] The clinical signs included vomiting, diarrhoea, listlessness, abdominal pain, muscular spasms and rigidity, salivation, incoordination, and shock; all recovered in 2–3 days, after symptomatic treatment. The two cats affected in this period vomited and showed signs of intense abdominal pain.

Human poisoning
There are many alarming and sometimes dramatic references to laburnum poisoning, but these appear to be based more on old accounts, with their descriptions of severe symptoms,[47] rather than on specific cases, in which the course of poisoning, albeit very unpleasant, is rarely serious.[48, 49] Most cases of laburnum poisoning occur in children who eat the green pods whole, or open them and eat the pea-like seeds. The symptoms, which usually develop in less than an hour, include burning of the mouth and throat, nausea, vomiting, abdominal pain, drowsiness, headache, dizziness, elevated body temperature, rapid pulse, mental confusion, cold clammy skin, difficult breathing, and dilated pupils;[48, 50, 51] diarrhoea is not a typical symptom, but is recorded occasionally. It is even possible that, in cases involving children, some of the symptoms may be those of fear, induced by parental anxiety. In many cases the symptoms are limited to nausea, vomiting, and mild abdominal pain and recovery is complete in 12–24 hours. Nine people who ate fritters that incorporated laburnum flowers, mistaken for those of false acacia, developed signs of poisoning in 2–3 hours; these included nausea, vomiting, abdominal pain, headache, muscular tremors, dilatation of pupils, and dizziness.[52] The only treatment was a stomach washout and all recovered within 48 hours. Cytisine was detected in their urine. The more severe symptoms attributed to laburnum, including hallucinations, convulsions, respiratory failure, and coma, sometimes followed by death, are likely to occur only under exceptional circumstances, and no actual account of such poisoning involving laburnum alone has been found. An unusual case is that of a paranoid schizophrenic man who died, apparently with no clinical symptoms; no abnormalities were revealed by post-mortem examination, except the presence of 23 laburnum pods in the stomach. Laburnum trees were growing in the hospital grounds. A diagnosis of cytisine poisoning was made,[53] based on toxicological analysis. The man had also taken chlorpromazine, which may have prevented the vomiting that usually occurs and reduces the amount of toxic material present thus helping to prevent serious poisoning. It appeared that 35–50 mg of the alkaloid had been absorbed, but no precise figures are available for the fatal dose of cytisine.

Treatment is considered necessary if more than five seeds have been ingested by a child, or 15 by an adult.[50] Within two hours of ingestion the administration of activated charcoal (1 g per kg body weight for a child, and a dose of 50 g for an adult) is recommended. If a large number of seeds has been taken, stomach lavage should be carried out before giving charcoal. Hospital admission is sometimes suggested, but is rarely necessary. Fluids (especially milk) should be given during the six hours after ingestion. Discharge for observation by parents would seem sufficient for most cases in children.[54] Symptoms generally subside within 24 hours.

Lathyrus species Vetchlings; Chickling Peas; Sweet Peas; Wild Peas

With the exception of the meadow vetchling (*Lathyrus pratensis*), which is common throughout Britain in hedges, field borders, and grassy places, *Lathyrus* species have only a limited distribution in this country, and are not grown here as a fodder crop. The sweet pea (*Lathyrus odoratus*) is cultivated extensively in gardens.

Members of the genus differ in their growth habit, some being erect while others are scrambling plants with tendrils. The stems of most species are winged or angled and bear compound leaves with rounded or elongated leaflets, with or without prominent stipules. The pea-type flowers of most *Lathyrus* species in Britain are shades of pink or purple, but the meadow vetchling (*Lathyrus pratensis*) and the yellow vetchling (*Lathyrus aphaca*) have yellow flowers. Cultivated varieties of the sweet pea (*Lathyrus odoratus*) have large flowers, up to 4 cm long, of many different colours. The fruits of the plants are pods containing up to 20 seeds (usually less than 10), which are compressed or rounded, according to the species. The species whose seeds are used most frequently for food is the chickling pea (*Lathyrus sativus*). This has many other common names including chick pea, Indian pea, mutter pea, grass pea, and chickling vetch. These names may cause confusion as some of them are also used for other leguminous plants, e.g. the chick pea (*Cicer arietinum*) that is frequently used for food.

Poisonous principles

These are numerous toxic amino acids (lathyrogens)[55] and their derivatives. They occur in all parts of the plants but are present in highest concentration in the seedlings, pods and, particularly, the seeds. The amino acids include L-α-γ-diaminobutyric acid, L-α-amino-β-oxalylaminopropionic acid and L-α-amino-γ-oxalylaminobutyric acid, which are found in several *Lathyrus* species including the chickling pea (*Lathyrus sativus*), and β-N-(γ-L-glutamyl) aminopropionitrile found in other species, including the sweet pea (*Lathyrus odoratus*), the caley (or kaley) pea or hairy vetchling (*Lathyrus hirsutus*), and the everlasting or wild pea (*Lathyrus sylvestris*). Sweet pea seedlings are said to be more toxic than dry seeds because of the presence of isoxazolin-5-one derivatives,[56] as well as aminopropionitrile. Toxic amino acids have been found in several species of *Lathyrus* in many parts of the world, but the meadow vetchling (*Lathyrus pratensis*), the only common British member of the genus, has not been recorded specifically as containing poisonous substances. There is confusion, particularly in older literature, over many aspects of *Lathyrus* poisoning including the precise nature of the toxic principles, the plant species involved, the type of toxic reaction, and the possibility of contamination of *Lathyrus* seeds with those of other plants, e.g. the common vetch (*Vicia sativa*), which are known to be toxic.

Animal poisoning

The human disease complex to which the name 'lathyrism'[57] was given in Italy in 1873,[55] was mentioned in works attributed to Hippocrates as early as 300 BC; the disease also occurs in animals. The complex has now been separated into two syndromes, osteolathyrism and neurolathyrism. Osteolathyrism, characterized by severe skeletal abnormalities and, in some animals, dilatation and rupture of arteries, and damage to connective tissue, has been produced experimentally by feeding animals with β-aminopropionitrile or seeds of sweet pea (*Lathyrus odoratus*).[58, 59] A separate name, 'odoratism' was suggested for this condition in 1951,[59] but has not come into general use, and has caused some confusion.[60, 61] Osteolathyrism has not occurred as a human disease and there are no conclusive reports of the condition in animals except as a result of experimental feeding. The syndrome called neurolathyrism, since the principal symptoms involve the nervous system, is the condition usually referred to simply as lathyrism.

As the seeds of the chickling pea (*Lathyrus sativus*) are used for animal feed and human consumption more than those of other species of *Lathyrus*, they are the most frequently reported cause of lathyrism. However, the pods and seeds of several related plants also contain toxic amino acids[58] and some have been implicated in outbreaks of the disease.[58] Some of the *Lathyrus* species that induce osteolathyrism experimentally are also responsible for natural outbreaks of the paralytic condition, neurolathyrism. This disease is most likely to occur after a period of eating large quantities of chickling peas, often when other feed is scarce. Neurolathyrism is characterized by weakness and paralysis of the hind legs and difficulty in breathing. The onset of clinical signs may be rapid, the animals falling and being unable to rise. This effect can occur soon after eating *Lathyrus* seeds or may not develop for several weeks. Most animals recover within a few days, after a change of diet, but in others the disease may be progressive, with the forelimbs also becoming affected, and the respiratory problems leading to death. Horses are particularly susceptible to this condition,[62] although cattle[63–65] and sheep[66] can also be affected. An outbreak in which 60 of 600 lambs died has been reported from New Zealand,[66] where *Lathyrus* does not usually cause poisoning.[67] The condition arose when the lambs were moved to a paddock, the edges of which contained a lot of everlasting or wild pea (*Lathyrus sylvestris*). Because of the potential use of *Lathyrus sylvestris* varieties as forage legumes the air-dried mature plant was fed to sheep in experiments in the USA.[68, 69] The results indicated that there was not yet enough information on the variations in toxicity of the plant or on its detoxification in ruminants. When hens were given β-aminopropionitrile in their feed, the activity of their ovaries was impaired, with a reduction in egg production.[70]

Lathyrism occurred in Britain in the latter half of the 19th century[62] as a result of feeding imported chickling peas to domestic animals, but more recently, in 1963, some horses were poisoned and temporarily paralysed after eating hay containing a high proportion of grass vetchling (*Lathyrus nissolia*).[71] In Germany, two horses that were on a heavily grazed meadow in October ate broad-leaved everlasting pea (*Lathyrus latifolius*) growing over a fence.[72] They developed incoordination, ascending flaccid paralysis of muscles, and laryngeal paralysis. They assumed a dog-sitting position before complete paralysis took place and the animals were killed; the course of the disease was 67 days.

Human poisoning

This can result from eating large quantities of chickling peas raw, cooked, or ground into flour. This is most likely to occur in times of food shortage, such as during drought conditions in India, when these peas still grow while few other plants survive.[55] The neurotoxic symptoms are similar to those in animals, with paralysis usually confined to the legs but sometimes extending to the arms, bladder, and bowel. There may be muscle tremors or rigidity of leg muscles. A variety of secondary symptoms may also occur, but these are resolved if the diet is corrected, whereas the paralysis is often permanent.[73] Lathyrism affects adults more than children and young men more than older men or women. Several theories have been put forward to explain this, but none of them is conclusive. In the past, human lathyrism has occurred in several countries, including Britain, but it is now restricted to poorer parts of the world where famine conditions prevail. From time to time a ban has been placed on the sale of *Lathyrus sativus* seed because of its poisonous nature, but despite this, farmers continue to grow the plant when they lack alternative food sources.

Several methods for removing the toxins have been tried on both whole and dehusked *Lathyrus* seeds.[55] Hot water treatment of seeds, particularly when dehusked, greatly reduces the concentration of toxic amino acids but, in common with other water treatments, there is substantial loss of essential water-soluble nutrients, including vitamins. Attempts to produce a hybrid variety of *Lathyrus*, free of the toxic amino acids, are in progress. It should be emphasized that when only relatively small quantities of chickling peas are eaten, constituting part of a mixed diet, they are harmless and nutritious.

Lotus corniculatus Bird's Foot Trefoil

Other common name: Bacon and Eggs

Bird's foot trefoil grows throughout Britain in pastures and grassy places where it sometimes forms a dense mat. The stems of the plant, which are up to 40 cm long, lie along the ground but often become erect near the tip. The compound leaves are usually less than 1 cm long, with paired oval leaflets that often have a blunt point at the apex. The flower stalks are less than 10 cm long and bear 2–6 pea-type flowers, which are approximately 15 mm across and bright yellow, often streaked or tipped with red. The fruit is a pod that elongates up to 3 cm as it matures.

Poisonous principles

Lotus corniculatus contains a cyanogenic glycoside, sometimes called lotusin(e), which is considered by some to be the same as linamarin, a cyanogenic glycoside also found in some other plants including linseed (*Linum usitatissimum*). Hydrocyanic acid is released when the glycoside comes into contact with hydrolysing enzymes present in the plant. This can occur when the plant is crushed or when broken down during digestion in the rumen. Natural populations of the plant contain both cyanogenic and non-cyanogenic plants, the difference being genetically determined. In some non-poisonous plants the glycoside may be present but the enzyme absent. The amount of glycoside in the plant (cyanogenic potential) varies with climatic conditions, stage of growth, and the part of the plant. Concentrations ranging from 5 to 51.5 mg % have been recorded.[74] These variations may well account for the contradictory reports that exist on the toxicity of this plant. It has a long-standing reputation for being poisonous, although there are few actual outbreaks reported, and it is also claimed to be a harmless and useful fodder crop. In general, the seed pods contain the least and the leaves the most glycoside, the amount increasing with the age of the leaves.[75] The glycoside is not destroyed by drying, so hay containing the plant is still toxic.[74] The seeds of the plant also contain saponins.[76]

Animal poisoning

Evidence that hydrocyanic acid is a poisonous constituent of bird's foot trefoil was obtained when sap pressed from freshly cut plants was introduced experimentally into the stomachs of sheep, which died in a few hours. No clinical signs were produced in other sheep given sap from which the hydrocyanic acid had been removed.[77] Poisoning by *Lotus corniculatus*, in which the presence of hydrocyanic acid was confirmed, occurred in Russia[78] in goats on pasture, and in sheep given hay, containing the plant. The animals became restless, and muscular spasms, unsteady gait, progressive weakness, and difficulty in breathing were reported. The milk from cows with signs of poisoning by the plant is reported to have a bitter taste and a yellow colour.[79]

Lupinus species Lupins (Plate 44)

Lupins are not native in Britain, but the tree lupin (*Lupinus arboreus*) has become naturalized in a few waste places, and another species (*Lupinus nootkatensis*) is found beside rivers in some parts of Scotland. In other parts of Europe and in the USA and Australia, several varieties of lupin are grown as green forage or for their protein-rich seeds that can be used in compound feeds. Past attempts to grow lupins as crop plants in Britain were unsuccessful,[80] but new varieties are now being cultivated for their seeds, to incorporate in animal feeds. Many lupins (often referred to as Russell lupins) with a wide range of attractively coloured flowers are grown in gardens. These are hybrids whose parentage is not clear, although they may be crosses with *Lupinus polyphyllus;* they sometimes persist for a time in a semi-wild state after being discarded.

Lupins are perennial plants, often 1 m high, with compound leaves, the elongated pointed leaflets radiating from the end of the stalk. The inflorescence is a terminal spike of closely packed flowers of a wide range of colours, those of wild lupins usually being white or shades of blue. The pods are elongated, constricted between the seeds, and greyish brown and silky when ripe.

Poisonous principles

Lupins contain several toxic constituents, present in all parts of the plants, particularly the seeds; drying and storage do not eliminate the toxins. The most important toxins are quinolizidine alkaloids, some of which are named after the plant (lupinine, lupanine); others are named after different plants in the same family (anagyrine, sparteine). Other potentially damaging constituents of some species of lupin are enzyme (trypsin) inhibitors[81] and a substance called biochanin A, which has oestrogenic activity[82] and can give rise to reproductive disorders. Toxic metabolites (mycotoxins) produced by the fungus *Phomopsis leptostromiformis* that may infect lupin plants can have adverse effects on animals.

Animal poisoning

Lupin poisoning can affect several animal species, but is of economic importance only in sheep and cattle. The so-called bitter varieties contain at least five toxic alkaloids.[83] To some extent animals are protected from eating these varieties by their bitter taste, but when they are eaten, nervous signs develop, including staggering, falling, and convulsions. Affected animals may also have difficulty in breathing, and may froth at the mouth. Plants with low alkaloid content, known as 'sweet' lupins (including *Lupinus luteus*), have been developed,[80] and the cultivation of bitter lupins is therefore declining. At least one alkaloid found in lupins (anagyrine) is teratogenic[84] and is the cause of a congenital condition in the USA called 'crooked calf disease'.[85, 86] It has been suggested that cattle convert anagyrine to a complex α-substituted piperidine alkaloid with structural similarities to the teratogens of *Conium maculatum* and *Nicotiana glauca*.[87] Calves with leg deformities, spinal curvatures, and sometimes cleft palate are most likely to occur if cows have eaten lupins containing the alkaloid between 40 and 70 days of pregnancy. The presence of anagyrine was reported in milk 10 and 24 hours after feeding a goat with 2–3 g of toxic lupin.[88] Anagyrine is not present in the major cultivated species.[89]

Another type of poisoning that may result from eating lupins is called lupinosis. In the past this condition was also usually attributed to alkaloids, although it occurred after eating both sweet and bitter lupins. Lupinosis is now known to result from fungal infection of the plants, and several fungi have been suspected. The original toxic fungal isolate, from lupins involved in an outbreak of lupinosis in the Cape Province of South Africa in 1969, was tentatively named *Cryptosporium leptostromiforme*. It has also been referred to as a *Cytospora* species,[90] but further taxonomic work has established that the fungus is *Phomopsis leptostromiformis*;[91] *Phomopsis russiana*[92] is one of several synonyms under which this fungus is described. A linear hexapeptide mycotoxin (phomopsin A) produced by the fungus is the main toxic principle; phomopsins B, C, D, and E have also been identified.[89, 93] It is of interest that more than 100 years ago a possible connection between fungal infection and lupin poisoning was suggested.[94] Detailed clinical signs and post-mortem findings in affected sheep were described in Germany in 1879, as were various fungi seen on the plants. However, experimental feeding of sheep with lupins infected with fungi failed to reproduce the condition. It has been suggested subsequently that the lupins may have been infected with fungi other than those that produce the mycotoxins responsible for lupinosis. The disease is characterized by damage to the liver and is accompanied by jaundice, depression, and loss of weight and condition. In Australia, two distinct forms of liver disease are seen in cattle affected by lupinosis.[95] The commoner form occurs in late pregnant or recently calved cows, and is characterized by fatty liver. This may be a nutritional disorder, secondary to loss of appetite resulting from lupinosis toxin. The other form of the disease affects all classes of cattle and appears to be a direct result of lupinosis toxin. Mortality from this form is lower and the livers are not fatty but cirrhotic, with extensive damage to cells and development of fibrous tissue. Sensitivity of the skin to light (photosensitivity) may also occur and give rise to skin lesions. In a severe outbreak of poisoning in a sheep flock in Romania there were abortions in addition to signs of photosensitization.[96] Sudden death has been reported in pigs in Hungary[97] and produced experimentally in canaries given 120 mg of ground leaves in water.[98]

Human poisoning
The most likely cause is the consumption of green, unripe seeds or pods of garden lupins, mistaken for peas or beans, or of ripe seeds, the pods of which are attractive to children because of their covering of silky hairs. The effects are similar to those of laburnum, but not as severe, and include nausea, vomiting, dizziness, headache, and abdominal pain.[99] There may be respiratory depression and slowing of the heart.[100] In southern Spain lupin seeds are consumed as appetizers after their bitter taste has been

removed by maceration and boiling in water. An hour after a man drank half a litre of the debittering water he became weak and his short-range sight was impaired.[101] Later he developed a dry mouth, palpitations, and urine retention; he recovered in 48 hours. The atropine-like effects in this patient were attributed to lupanine detected in the debittering water and in the patient's blood and urine.

Medicago species

Lucerne (*Medicago sativa*) is the plant in this genus that is mainly associated with poisoning, but other species have also caused problems.

Medicago sativa Lucerne

Other common name: Alfalfa

This plant is not native in Britain, but has become naturalized and is fairly common, especially on calcareous soils in some areas of south-east England. It is an important forage crop in many parts of the world, including Britain,[102] where it is often sown with a grass.

Lucerne is a deep-rooted perennial plant, the forage varieties of which are mainly erect in habit and up to 1 m high. The leaves are compound and composed of three radiating, elongated oval leaflets all attached to the end of the stalk. The flowers are purple, and borne in the axils of the leaves. The fruit is a pod that splits longitudinally, on ripening, into two spirally twisting portions.

Poisonous principles
Like clovers, lucerne contains oestrogenic compounds, but in contrast to the clovers, in which the oestrogenic compounds are isoflavones, those in lucerne are coumestans, mainly coumestrol. The coumestrol content increases when lucerne is being attacked by plant pathogens.[103] A substance that causes liver damage is also thought to be present in lucerne as secondary photosensitization can result from eating it.

Animal poisoning
Some of the conditions that occur in animals fed lucerne are the same as those that result from eating clovers (*Trifolium* species). These include reproductive failure, due to the oestrogenic substances in the plant, and photosensitivity, with consequent dermatitis. In general, coumestrol has one-hundredth and isoflavones one-ten-thousandth of the activity of oestradiol when given orally to sheep.[104] In lambs grazing lucerne in spring to autumn and given lucerne hay in winter the size of the uterus, cervix, and vagina was increased, while that of the ovaries was decreased.[105] The photosensitization associated with lucerne hay is apparently due to liver damage, but what causes the liver damage is not clear; mycotoxins have been suspected but not detected.[106, 107] Loss of condition and reluctance to move were associated with soreness of the skin in young pigs that ate lucerne and medick.[108] Other species of *Medicago*, including the hairy medick (*Medicago hispida*) and burr trefoil (*Medicago denticulata*) that are both now placed in the *Medicago polymorpha* group, have also caused photosensitization reactions. All animal species are said to be susceptible to this type of poisoning, but there are few reported cases. Prolonged blood coagulation time has

been recorded during experiments on calves grazing lucerne.[109] As with other legume pastures, frothy bloat can also occur with lucerne.

Melilotus species Sweet Clovers

Other common name: Melilots

The white melilot (*Melilotus alba*), the small-flowered melilot (*Melilotus indica*), the common or ribbed melilot (*Melilotus officinalis*), and the tall melilot (*Melilotus altissima*) are not native to Britain, but have become naturalized in fields and waste places, particularly in southern England.

The four plants are similar in appearance, being branched, usually erect, biennials (sometimes annual) with compound leaves that have elongated, elliptical leaflets, pointed at both ends. The inflorescences are loose, slender clusters of small pea-type flowers; those of the common, small-flowered, and tall melilots are yellow, and those of the white melilot are white. The pods are up to 5 mm long and brown when ripe in *Melilotus alba* and *Melilotus officinalis*, black in *Melilotus altissima* and olive green in *Melilotus indica*.

Poisonous principles

Melilots are safe for grazing, but in hay or silage, natural constituents of the plants (coumarins) may be changed by the action of mould fungi into dicoumarol (3,3'-methylene-bis-4-hydroxycoumarin), which impairs blood clotting.[110, 111] This characteristic has been utilized in the development of anticoagulant preparations, used extensively as rodenticides. The conversion of coumarins to dicoumarol is not associated with any particular fungus, and a variety of fungi (that are almost inevitably present) can render the plants toxic. The concentration of coumarins varies in different strains of the plants, and the toxicity of a sample is not related to the extent of spoilage by moulds.

Animal poisoning

Sweet clover poisoning is unlikely to occur in Britain, because *Melilotus* is not grown as a fodder crop, but it is a problem, particularly in North America. Primarily it affects cattle,[111] but it has occurred very occasionally in horses and sheep. Haemorrhages, resulting from failure of blood to clot, may be internal or external, and are extensive and often fatal. The course of the disease is rapid, with subcutaneous haemorrhages being visible as swellings, usually on the back of the animals. This is associated with pale mucous membranes, weakness and rapid heartbeat just before death, which usually occurs after about three days. At post-mortem examination, the tissues appear bruised and there are haemorrhages of varying severity throughout the body.[110,112] Vitamin K_1 (phytomenadione) is recommended for treating sweet clover disease in cattle; menadione is reported to be ineffective.[113]

The small-flowered melilot (*Melilotus indica*) is said to taint milk and dairy products if eaten by cows, and flour if harvested with wheat. There are sporadic reports in old literature of poisoning in animals after eating the plant, but no reports of recent outbreaks have been found.[114]

Phaseolus vulgaris Beans

Other common names: Black Bean; French Bean; Haricot Bean; Navy Bean; Pinto Bean; Red Kidney Bean; Wax Bean; White Bean; and many others

In this diverse species there are many varieties, distinguishable morphologically and varying considerably in the constituents of their seeds. As legume seeds are currently assuming an important place as a protein source in both animal and human diets, there is a considerable amount of work in progress on both their nutritional and toxic constituents.

Poisonous principles

It has long been known that raw legume seeds (beans, peas, etc.) can cause poisoning. A variety of constituents (often referred to as 'antinutritional factors' rather than toxins) have been claimed to be at least partly responsible. These include enzyme inhibitors, lectins (phytohaemagglutinins), tannins, antigenic proteins, cyanogenic glycosides, saponins, oestrogens, goitrogens, anti-vitamins, phytates, and flatulence factors.[58, 115-117] Most are present at very low levels, but the enzyme (chiefly trypsin) inhibitors,[58, 117,118] tannins[117] and, in particular, the lectins[116, 117, 119-121,] are considered to be the main toxic constituents. The effects of these constituents may be due to their combined effects;[117] possible interaction among them has been investigated specifically in the lima bean (*Phaseolus lunatus*).[122] Concern has been expressed that, by selective breeding to eliminate toxic constituents for the food industry, the natural defences of the plant against attack by insects, fungi, bacteria and viruses will be undermined.[115, 117] The toxins of legumes have been utilized medically to destroy malignant cells and also as pesticides in agriculture.

• LECTINS Many plants contain lectins, which are glycoproteins that have the ability to agglutinate red blood cells, hence they are called phytohaemagglutinins. This ability to agglutinate blood cells is used in laboratory tests to detect the haemagglutinins[116, 117] and classify the beans that contain them,[123] but it should be noted that they agglutinate the blood of some animal species more readily than that of others. Several different lectins have been described in beans; they often occur together, and not all are poisonous. The lectin content of different varieties of beans also varies considerably and could account for the conflicting reports on the toxicity of these seeds. Red kidney beans have been considered as having a particularly high content of phytohaemagglutinins; because of their potential human toxicity the importation of the beans for cultivation or consumption was prohibited in South Africa.[124] However, in a recent study in that country, the haemagglutinating activity of red kidney beans was found to be no higher than that in 50% of the other bean varieties.[124] The mechanisms of lectin toxicity are very complex. The lectins are very resistant to breakdown by enzymes that digest proteins, and therefore remain at a high concentration as the food passes through the intestines; they bind to some enzymes, thus inhibiting their action. The lectins also bind to the intestinal walls, the cells of which become damaged and the processes of digestion and absorption (particularly of proteins) are impaired. The cells lining the intestines produce excess mucus in response to the cell damage and this, combined with the presence of undigested food and the sloughed-off, damaged cells themselves, encourages the growth of undesirable bacteria in the intestines.[121] As a result of the disturbances in protein digestion, nitrogen is present in abnormally large amounts in the faeces and urine (as urea) of

141

animals poisoned by legume seeds, or, experimentally, by pure lectin. An excess of nitrogen may also result from a systemic effect of lectin toxicity involving increased tissue catabolism (chemical breakdown of complex compounds). The increased permeability of the damaged intestinal walls allows lectins to pass into the circulation and cause disturbances to the immune system; this is sometimes associated with a decrease in the size of the thymus.

• TRYPSIN INHIBITORS These act primarily by interfering with digestion by inactivating trypsin (mainly chymotrypsin), thus reducing the digestibility of protein. A second effect is that, under conditions of trypsin inhibition, the production of pancreatic enzymes is increased and, at least in some animal species, the pancreas becomes enlarged.

• TANNINS These are present in significant quantities in the seed coats of coloured (not white) beans, and can also damage the intestinal walls and decrease the activity of enzymes, thus causing additional interference with digestion.

Animal poisoning
Soaking and heating beans before they are eaten reduces their toxicity, but, in general, the trouble and expense of treating adequately the large quantities of beans that would be needed for animal feed preclude their use. However, beans of low quality, culled from among those intended for human consumption, are sometimes used. In feeding experiments in pigs the incorporation of raw beans in as low a concentration as 5% of the diet had adverse effects.[125] In three large pig farms in Germany, feed intake was reduced when a mixed feed that included beans was given.[126] The feed had been heat-treated, but on two farms, where the pigs developed diarrhoea, it was not known if the heating had been sufficient to destroy the toxins. Mice, rats, chicks, and quails have been poisoned experimentally by beans or their extracts,[127] the severity of the toxic reaction varying with the type and strain of animal used. Much of the recent experimental work on the toxicity of beans in animals has been done on pigs.[125, 128-130] Loss of appetite, reduced growth rate, and intermittent diarrhoea were the most common clinical signs. The effects of raw beans and lectins purified from them on the intestines of the pigs were studied, and damage to the cells of the lining of the walls was apparent.[128, 129]

Human poisoning
From last century onwards there have been sporadic references to poisoning by legume seeds. The current trend in increased production of plant protein to supplement (or replace) the more expensive animal protein in the human diet could lead to an increase in poisoning by legume seeds. It should, however, be emphasized that legume seeds are safe and highly nutritious foods when properly heat-treated. Reports in medical journals and the press,[131, 132] concerning raw and inadequately cooked red kidney beans, have received considerable attention. In the period July 1976 to February 1989, there were 50 incidents (over 200 cases) of suspected poisoning by red kidney beans reported in Britain.[133] In response to an appeal, a further 870 suspected cases were recorded; in many of the incidents the beans had been eaten raw or inadequately cooked. Typical symptoms (nausea, vomiting, and diarrhoea) developed within 1–7 hours.[131, 134] The diarrhoea is usually very watery and may contain blood. The body temperature is often low, the heart rate high, and there may be

abdominal pain. Poisoning can be more severe, however, as in the case of two people in Denmark[135] who, in addition to these usual symptons, had muscular pains and evidence of damage to muscles, including those of the heart. Recovery is usually rapid and treatment is rarely necessary, although attention should be given to replacing lost fluids. This type of poisoning is avoidable if the beans are prepared appropriately before they are eaten.

Another problem associated with beans is that, if they are badly stored and allowed to become damp, they may become contaminated by mould fungi and therefore be poisonous, because of the presence of mycotoxins produced by the fungi.

The flatulence experienced by some individuals after eating beans can be a deterrent to their inclusion in the diet. The 'flatulence factors' are associated with carbohydrates (oligosaccharides) that are fermented by bacteria in the large intestine, with the production of gases.

Detoxification of beans
The disturbances to normal body (especially digestive) function caused by eating raw beans indicate that they are highly undesirable as a main food ingredient. The threshold level at which raw beans can be incorporated safely into animal feeds or human food is not known.[117] Soaking in water reduces, but does not eliminate, their toxicity, and both the trypsin inhibitors and the lectins are destroyed by heat; properly pre-treated beans are an excellent source of nutrition. It was found in some recent experiments[124] that high levels of haemagglutinating activity remain in some varieties after cooking unsoaked beans at 100°C for 30 minutes; after 60 minutes the activity had been destroyed in all but one sample (in which only 2% of the original level of activity remained). After overnight soaking, however, almost all agglutinating activity was lost after cooking for 15 minutes at 100°C. It is recommended, therefore, that beans are soaked in plenty of water (which should be discarded afterwards) for at least five hours, then boiled in fresh water for at least 15 minutes. It is essential that sufficient heat be applied to denature the lectins,[136] as undercooked beans (for example those simmered below 100°C, cooked in an electric slow cooker, or inadequately baked in an oven for human consumption)[131] retain at least some of their toxicity; it has even been reported that such preparation may activate the lectins. Canned beans are safe to eat as the heating involved in their processing is adequate to destroy the lectins.

Pisum species Peas

Pea plants (*Pisum sativum*) are grown on a large scale in many countries, including Britain, for the production of their fresh green seeds that are used mainly for human consumption. Field peas (*Pisum arvense*) are grown, chiefly on light calcareous soils in this country, and are cut green for direct feeding to animals or for silage.

Poisonous principles
The presence of heat-labile growth inhibitors or toxic factors in peas has been suspected for many years. It is now known that peas contain many similar toxins (antinutritional factors) to those of beans (*Phaseolus* species, see above),[117] but less experimental work has been done on peas. They are said to be utilized effectively by

143

animals, but lectins isolated from them caused growth retardation and a reduction in the activity of some digestive enzymes in rats.[137] The lectins themselves were not broken down in digestion, but did not appear to bind to the intestinal walls as do those of beans.

Animal poisoning

According to old reports both the seeds (peas) and the plants (vines) have had adverse effects when fed to pigs and sheep. In the USA, lameness occurred in pigs that ate field peas (*Pisum arvense*);[138] when ten experimental pigs were placed in the pea pasture, the plants were refused initially, then eaten readily. Muscular incoordination and weakness, particularly of the hind legs, developed, with varying severity, in all of the animals. A staggering gait was observed and eventually two of the animals were unable to stand. Incoordination also occurred in the lambs of ewes fed pea vine silage and pods from canning peas (*Pisum sativum*).[139] Affected animals were tense and tended to run, walk backwards, then collapse. This was repeated after rest or if forced to move. Pea vine silage is a good cattle feed, but has a strong odour. If fed to cows after milking, however, there is no taint in the milk.[140] Depression of growth occurred in chicks fed raw peas, but not when they were given heat-treated (autoclaved) peas.[141]

Robinia pseudoacacia False Acacia (Plate 45)

Other common names: Black Acacia; Black Locust

This tree is not native in Britain but has become established after its introduction from North America; it is often planted as an ornamental tree or in thickets. It is a large, deciduous tree that often grows 25–30 m high. The trunk and older branches have deeply fissured bark. The leaves are compound, consisting of elliptical leaflets arranged in pairs in one plane on the stalk, at the base of which there are often persistent spines. The fragrant flowers are white (occasionally pink) and hang in drooping clusters. The fruits are flat pods containing numerous seeds.

Poisonous principles

These are not fully known but are thought to include toxic proteins (lectins) that are similar to ricin in the castor oil plant (*Ricinus communis*), but far less toxic. The proteins are sometimes called robin or phasin. A glycoprotein that agglutinates red blood cells (a phytohaemagglutinin) has also been extracted from the tree, but it is not clear whether this is robin, phasin, or another substance. All parts of the tree, except perhaps the flowers, are said to be poisonous; the bark is usually considered the most toxic.

Animal poisoning

This has not been reported in Britain, but the tree should be regarded as potentially poisonous as it has caused illness and sometimes death in horses, cattle, sheep, and poultry.[142] Clinical signs are similar in all animal species and include staggering, incoordination, paralysis, and gastrointestinal disturbances, which may be severe. In addition, laminitis was recorded in one of nine horses that suffered severe colic after chewing bark from acacia fence posts.[143] Post-mortem examination revealed intense irritation and inflammation of the mucous membranes of the digestive tract. A phytohaemagglutinin extracted from the plant caused fatty degeneration of the liver and death in chick embryos[144] at doses of 0.25–2.0 mg per egg.

Human poisoning

This is characterized by lassitude, nausea, vomiting, dilatation of pupils, and, in severe cases, stupor.[145] When 19 school children of 4–11 years of age sucked or chewed pieces of the bark of *Robinia pseudoacacia*, six of the younger ones showed clinical signs that included thirst, dry throat, abdominal pain, nausea, vomiting, muscle weakness, dilated pupils, and headache.[146] Of seven schoolboys who ate the roots and stems and had abdominal pain and repeated vomiting, four recovered in about two hours but three developed stupor and took 7–8 hours to recover.[147] Other similar cases in young children have also been reported.[148, 149]

Spartium junceum Spanish Broom

This cultivated broom is common in gardens throughout the country and sometimes grows wild, as a garden escape. The shrub is very similar to, although usually larger than, the wild, yellow-flowered, common broom (*Cytisus scoparius*), but the flowers are of various colours (often shades of pink, or red with yellow).

Poisonous principles

Little has been found about these, but they are thought to be quinolizidine alkaloids similar to those found in the common broom and in laburnum.

Animal poisoning

This is often mentioned in general texts, but no specific cases have been reported.

Human poisoning

It is unlikely that the wiry foliage of this plant would be eaten, but ingestion of the pods caused poisoning in a seven-year-old girl[46] who ate about 20 of them because she thought they looked like runner beans. The symptoms included vomiting, abdominal pain, unsteadiness, and numbness and tingling in the feet; a transient rash was also observed.

Trifolium species Clovers

Several clovers are native and widely distributed as wild plants in Britain, and a range of cultivated varieties is grown for grazing or hay or to be ploughed in, to increase soil nitrogen.

Trifolium hybridum Alsike Clover

This clover is probably not a native British plant, but has become naturalized, often beside roads, throughout the country. Alsike clover is a white-flowered perennial similar to white clover (*Trifolium repens*) but it is not creeping. Details of poisoning follow the description of *Trifolium subterraneum* (see below).

Trifolium pratense Red Clover

This plant is generally distributed in grassy places throughout Britain. It is perennial and may be erect or prostrate in habit. The leaves are formed of three radiating leaflets, all attached at the end of the stalk. The leaflets may be slightly toothed at the edges and, with the exception of some uniformly green cultivated forms, have a whitish crescent-shaped area near the base. The pinkish-purple flowers form in a dense terminal head, which is spherical at first but elongates slightly to become ovoid. Details of poisoning follow the description of *Trifolium subterraneum* (see below).

Trifolium repens White Clover

Other common names: Dutch Clover; Ladino Clover (a large-leaved cultivated form).

White clover is a perennial plant that grows in grassy places throughout Britain. It is similar to red clover (*Trifolium pratense*) but is a creeping plant, rooting at the nodes. The leaflets have a whitish band towards the base and the flowers are white (occasionally pale pink). Details of poisoning follow the description of *Trifolium subterraneum* (see below).

Trifolium subterraneum Subterranean Clover

Other common name: Subterranean Trefoil

This plant is native in Britain, but occurs only locally in sandy and gravelly pastures in the southern part of the country. It is a hairy, prostrate annual, with sparsely flowered heads bearing both fertile cream-coloured flowers and sterile flowers. The calyx enlarges to cover the seed pod, whose stalk bends over so that the pod becomes buried in the soil as it matures.

Poisonous principles
Clovers may contain a number of compounds that can have adverse effects on animals. These include oestrogens, cyanogenic glycosides, goitrogens, nitrates, and substances that can cause bloat, laminitis, blood coagulation disorders, or photosensitivity. Diseases can also arise from ingestion of toxic metabolites (mycotoxins) of fungi that infect clovers.

Animal poisoning
Clovers have poisoned animals in many parts of the world and should therefore be regarded as potentially poisonous in Britain, although, for a variety of reasons including climate, agricultural methods[150, 151] and possibly the strains of the plant present, they cause few problems in this country.

• OESTROGEN-RELATED CONDITIONS   Many clovers contain oestrogenic substances called phyto-oestrogens (isoflavones) such as genistein and formononetin, that can cause reproductive problems in animals that eat them. Female animals may develop swelling of the external genital organs, milk production without pregnancy, temporary or permanent infertility, and abortion; wethers (castrated male sheep) may develop swelling of the teats and the rudimentary mammary glands may be stimulated to produce milk. These conditions are associated particularly with subterranean clover

(*Trifolium subterraneum*) in Australia.[152, 153] Red clover silage has been reported to have an oestrogenic effect on heifers[154] and to cause infertility problems in cows in Scandinavia.[155] White clover (*Trifolium repens*) can become oestrogenic[156] if infected with various fungi that cause leaf-spot diseases in the plants. It has been suggested that 'ringwomb', a condition occurring in ewes in Britain, and associated with difficult birth due to incomplete dilatation of the cervix, may be caused by clover oestrogens.[157, 158] Ruminants can detoxify some phyto-oestrogens, but not others.

• CYANIDE POISONING   Some strains of white clover (*Trifolium repens*) can cause hydrocyanic acid poisoning as they contain both cyanogenic glycosides and an enzyme (β-glucosidase) that releases the toxin from the glycosides. These glycosides include lotaustralin and linamarin, and the enzyme is sometimes called linamarase. Cyanogenic potential may be linked to plant damage caused by heavy grazing,[159] possibly indicating that the cyanide toxicity of clover is a natural defence mechanism of the plant. In general, clovers do not contain enough cyanogenic glycosides to cause severe poisoning, but typical clinical signs, including shortness of breath, muscular contractions, and, initially, bright red mucous membranes, have been seen occasionally in cattle as a result of eating white clover. The condition has been reproduced experimentally in cattle given minced white clover through a stomach tube.[160] The animals become prostrate, with rigid limbs, distressed breathing, increased heart rate, and, finally, cyanosis of the mucous membranes, indicating oxygen shortage in the tissues, which occurs when death from cyanide poisoning is delayed.

• GOITRE   Consumption of some clovers by pregnant ewes has led to goitre in their lambs. This goitrogenic activity has been attributed to oestrogens, cyanogenic glycosides, and another, as yet unidentified, substance.

• NITRATE POISONING   Bacterial action in the root nodules of leguminous plants results in their having a high nitrogen content. Nitrates eaten in forage are converted in the rumen to nitrites; these combine with haemoglobin in the blood to form methaemoglobin, a stable substance that does not combine with oxygen. Typical clinical signs are bluish mucous membranes, laboured breathing, staggering, and vomiting (where possible). Nitrite poisoning may occur, with or without other types of poisoning attributable to clovers.

• BLOAT   Excessive intake of clovers may result in bloat, a condition in which the rumen is distended because the gases resulting from ruminal digestion become trapped in a stable foam produced by foaming agents from the plants. The various factors that lead to bloat are still not fully understood, but it is considered to be a metabolic disorder rather than poisoning.

• LAMINITIS   This condition, characterized by tenderness, swelling, and inflammation around the hooves, is seen most frequently in horses and usually results from overfeeding with grain. However, severe laminitis has been reported in Britain among cattle pastured on white clover that had seeded, the seeds having sprouted again in the seed heads.[161] The feet of affected animals developed bony outgrowths and there was separation and sloughing of skin.

• BLOOD COAGULATION DISORDERS   Preliminary studies have revealed that the clotting time of blood is prolonged in animals fed legume forage.[162] This has been demonstrated experimentally in calves grazing lucerne and in sheep fed white clover.

No haemorrhagic disease or other adverse effects have been described in live animals, but this condition is of importance in the meat industry where undesirable 'blood splash' from the meat of such animals is encountered.

• PHOTOSENSITIVITY Some species of *Trifolium*, particularly white and Alsike clover, can, under certain weather conditions, lead to photosensitive reactions with severe necrosis of unpigmented skin of animals that eat them.[163, 164] This condition, sometimes called 'trifoliosis' or clover disease, may be primary photosensitivity (a direct effect on the skin, without involvement of the liver), but secondary photosensitivity resulting from liver damage may also result from eating these plants; a mycotoxin may be involved. In addition to this skin reaction, other clinical signs including dullness, staggering, blindness, jaundice, and gross enlargement of the liver have been attributed to the consumption of clover. There may also be gastrointestinal disturbances and, in cows, a fall in milk yield. Alsike clover has caused photosensitivity in horses,[165] but a fatal condition, known as 'Alsike clover poisoning' (big liver disease, chronic hypertrophic cirrhosis) has also been recognized in Canada since the 1920s and been reproduced experimentally by feeding alsike clover.[166] An acute nervous form and a chronic wasting condition occur.[167] The clinical signs do not appear until horses have been exposed to alsike clover in pasture or in hay for a year or more. The toxin responsible for the liver changes that are found (bile duct proliferation and perilobular fibrosis) has not been identified.[168]

• MYCOTOXICOSES It is possible that some of the cases of 'trifoliosis' reported in older literature (mainly from Australia and the USA) were mycotoxicoses. Some of these old reports, particularly those in which the skin reaction is limited to the muzzle of the animal, probably refer to conditions resembling facial eczema,[169] a sheep disease occurring in New Zealand and to a limited extent in Australia and South Africa. Facial eczema is now known to be caused by contamination of pasture plants with spores of the fungus *Pithomyces chartarum*, which produces the mycotoxin sporidesmin. From descriptions of clinical signs, it seems possible that some other skin conditions, perhaps including those attributed to photosensitivity, may also result from toxins produced by fungi infecting clovers rather than from the plants themselves. In the USA, red clover (*Trifolium pratense*) pasture and hay have given rise to excessive salivation ('slobbers') in cattle, horses, and sheep. The causal factor is the mycotoxin slaframine, a metabolite of the fungus *Rhizoctonia leguminicola*, that causes black patch disease, mainly in red clover.[170] (For more information on mycotoxins, see pp. 261–264.)

Vicia faba Broad Bean

Other common names: Horse Bean; Fava Bean

This plant has been cultivated since prehistoric times in the Mediterranean area[171] and its large seeds are used in many countries for animal and human consumption. The plant is an erect, pale green, square-stemmed annual, ranging from about 50 cm to over 1 m in height, according to the variety. Occasional plants may persist in a semi-wild state for some years after planting. The compound leaves have several pairs of oval leaflets. The inflorescences are axillary clusters of white, pea-type flowers with a blackish-purple blotch. The fruit is a fleshy pod, up to 20 cm long, containing large flat seeds, 2–3 cm long. Both the pod and the seeds become light brown and hard when dry; the seeds usually have a prominent black scar.

Poisonous principles

The glycosides vicine and convicine are found in these beans, their concentrations being affected by various environmental and genetic factors. Vicine and convicine are hydrolysed by microflora in the intestines to their respective aglycones divicine and isouramil.[172] Tannins, particularly in the seeds and husks,[173] and other antinutritional factors[174] that affect the activity of digestive enzymes, are also present. Polyphenols that have been shown to affect digestion in rats are found in varying quantities in some varieties of the beans.[175]

Animal poisoning

Broad beans are not usually considered poisonous to animals, and many varieties are used for animal feed, either in silage, when the whole plant is eaten, or when the beans are added to mixed feed. In experimental work with pigs, a slight reduction in growth rate occurred with increasing proportions (up to 25%) of broad beans in the diet,[176] compared with similar pigs given other sources of protein, but there was no evidence of toxicity. However, during an economic crisis in Poland, poisoning occurred in pigs given broad beans at approximately one-third of their diet.[177] In this outbreak, 25% of the animals died and a further 25% had to be slaughtered. The clinical signs appeared in three to five days and included depression, reduced activity, loss of appetite, flatulence, constipation, and a hunched appearance indicative of abdominal pain. Post-mortem examination revealed inflammation of the alimentary tract, and pale yellow liver and kidneys. The blood vessels of the intestinal mucous membranes, lungs, and urinary bladder were congested. It was noted that the feed had not been mixed thoroughly, so that some animals would have eaten more beans than others. In experiments on pigs fed varieties of *Vicia faba* with low or high tannin content, there was lower activity of trypsin in the contents of the small intestine of those on the high tannin diet.[173] There is some evidence that vicine and convicine (and their hydrolysis products) can have an adverse effect on the reproductive performance of hens,[178] and that the tannins in the beans can inhibit the actions of some of their digestive enzymes.[179]

Human poisoning

Broad beans are not poisonous, in the conventional sense, but they may cause favism in susceptible individuals. This disease, also called fabism or fabismus,[180] is characterized by haemolytic anaemia of varying severity, and occurs after eating the seeds (beans) of the plant, particularly when raw or partially cooked. It was thought that the disease could also arise from inhaling the pollen of the plants, but this now appears not to be the case.[172] There is a seasonal incidence of favism at the time of the bean harvest. Favism is most prevalent in some islands and coastal regions of the Mediterranean, with its highest frequency in Sardinia; it also occurs in China. Susceptibility to the condition is dependent on a genetically transmitted, male sex-linked deficiency of the enzyme glucose-6-phosphate dehydrogenase that is found in some human populations. It is, therefore, determined racially rather than geographically, and cases that occur outside the endemic regions involve individuals who originated there.[181] Deficiency of the enzyme alone is not necessarily the only predisposing factor for the development of favism, which appears also to depend on the condition of the red blood cells and possibly on vitamin E deficiency.[172]

The glycosides vicine and convicine[180] and their respective hydrolysis products (aglycones), divicine and isouramil, are strongly suspected of being the causative agents of favism.[172] It was suggested in the past[182, 183] that beans that have caused poisoning may have been contaminated with fungi, but this has not been proved.

The symptoms of favism include vomiting, abdominal pain, dizziness, headache, back pain, and elevated body temperature. These symptoms start 5–24 hours after eating the beans; this is presumably the time taken for the glycosides to reach the small intestine where hydrolysis by the bacterial flora occurs. In more serious cases there may be severe anaemia with associated jaundice and dark or apparently blood-stained urine (haemoglobinuria) for up to six days; in severe cases collapse and death may occur. Environmental conditions and variations in the toxicity of different samples of beans can also influence the severity of the disease. Except for individuals of susceptible races, broad beans are generally safe and good to eat.

Vicia (other species) Vetches

Other common name: Tares

Several vetches have caused poisoning in animals under natural conditions and in experimental work. These include the common vetch (*Vicia sativa*) and *Vicia sativa* subspecies *sativa* (the form that was formerly cultivated in Britain), the narrow-leaved vetch (*Vicia sativa* subspecies *nigra*), the hairy tare (*Vicia hirsuta*), and the hairy or fodder vetch (*Vicia villosa*). There have been changes in the classification of vetches and there are several synonyms in use; some plants previously given the rank of species are now considered varieties or subspecies. There is considerable variation even among these, and there are many intermediate forms. Details of poisoning follow the description of *Vicia sativa* (see below).

Vicia sativa Common Vetch

This vetch is generally distributed as a wild plant in hedges and grassy places throughout Britain. Its cultivated form was grown in this country, usually on moderately calcareous soils, for animal feeding, either freshly cut or as hay or silage;[184] it is still found on field borders and waste ground.

Common vetch is a trailing or climbing plant; it climbs by means of fine tendrils and the stems of wild plants may be up to 120 cm long. The leaves have paired, elongated oval leaflets 1–2 cm long, and pointed stipules that often have a dark spot. The pale purple flowers are borne singly or in pairs and are up to 2 cm long. The fruit is a beaked pod, up to 7 cm long, and contains 4–10 seeds.

Poisonous principles

There is confusion over the nature of these in vetches. They contain cyanogenic glycosides, including vicianin, but do not necessarily cause cyanide poisoning. The release of hydrocyanic acid from the glycosides is dependent on the action of enzymes in the plant (when crushed) or, to a smaller extent, in the digestive system of animals. The apparently contradictory reports on the toxicity of vetch plants and their seeds under natural conditions and in experimental work[185] may relate to the presence or absence (in toxicologically significant quantities) of the glycosides or the enzyme in different species, varieties or plant populations. It has been reported, for example, that the common vetch (*Vicia sativa*) does not contain cyanogenic glycosides, but that they are present in the narrow-leaved vetch.[186] It is also stated, however, that the seed of *Vicia sativa* has cyanogenic potential.[187] No conclusive reports typical of hydrocyanic acid poisoning of animals after eating vetches have been found.

Some vetches contain the toxic amino acid L-β-cyanoalanine[188] that may be at least partially responsible for a form of the paralytic disease, neurolathyrism, usually associated with species of *Lathyrus*. It has even been suggested that neurolathyrism occurs, or is more severe, when *Lathyrus* seeds are contaminated by those of vetches. However, some species of *Lathyrus* are poisonous alone, and no reports of poisoning by vetches involving the nervous system and definitely attributed to this amino acid have been traced. Other glycosides, vicine and convicine, are also present, particularly in the seeds of *Vicia sativa*, but their effects are more pronounced in *Vicia faba* (see above).

Animal poisoning
Various vetches have undoubtedly caused poisoning, although this has not necessarily been linked with any specific poisonous substances present in the plants. No reports have been found of poisoning of animals by vetches in Britain, but as they grow in this country, and can be toxic, they are included. In the old literature, poisoning by the common vetch has been described in horses, pigs, and cattle,[189] with clinical signs that include skin lesions with hair loss, digestive disturbances and weakness, and sometimes loss of use of hindquarters. Post-mortem examination often revealed enlargement of the liver. Experiments on poultry given feed containing 30–80% of seeds of *Vicia sativa* and/or *Vicia villosa*[190, 191] resulted in 20–40% mortality in chicks. Clinical signs included loss of weight and condition, excitability, incoordination, difficulty in breathing, and sometimes violent convulsions. The signs were more severe, and death was more rapid, with common vetch seeds.

In cattle, three apparently different disease syndromes have been recognized after eating *Vicia villosa*. The first involves the nervous system, as in the case, described in the USA, in which acute illness and death occurred in five of six cattle that ate hairy vetch seed from a sack.[192] The animals were extremely restless, appeared to be in severe pain, and convulsions occurred when handling was attempted. The second type involves skin lesions, cough and respiratory distress, and general weakness, followed by death in some animals after about two weeks.[189] Post-mortem examination reveals inflammation of the forestomachs, severe bronchitis with pneumonia, and a yellowish-brown liver. The third type is also characterized by a rough coat and necrotic skin lesions on both pigmented and non-pigmented skin, but is otherwise similar to a photosensitization reaction. Soreness of the eyes (conjunctivitis) and severe diarrhoea, accompanied by progressive weight loss and 50% mortality, were recorded among the clinically ill cattle in 23 herds in the USA.[193] Similar clinical signs, with dermatitis spreading from the tail and neck to the whole body of black-coated (Angus) cattle were recorded in the USA;[194] some animals became emaciated and died. In two incidents in South Africa, groups of cattle developed very severe skin lesions and had diarrhoea, often containing blood, when grazing a pasture containing a hybrid vetch (*Vicia villosa* × *Vicia dasycarpa*).[195] The clinical signs began after about a month on the pasture; several animals died. In a horse in the USA, corneal ulceration and oedema, eventually involving the whole body, was attributed to grazing a pasture containing *Vicia villosa*.[196] The post-mortem findings of thromboses, enlarged lymph nodes, and extensive granulomatous inflammation were similar to those described for the third syndrome in cattle. Attempts to reproduce the disease by feeding hairy vetch to cattle[193] were not successful, indicating that other factors may also be involved.

Wisteria species Wisteria (Plate 46)

Wisteria occurs in Britain only as an ornamental plant in gardens. It is grown occasionally as a specimen tree, but is more often trained on walls. It usually grows as a woody climber, with intertwining branches. The leaves have paired, oval leaflets, pointed at both ends. The inflorescences are pendulous clusters of fragrant, pea-type flowers that are usually bluish or purple, but may be pink or white according to the variety. The fruit is a flat pod, which dries on ripening and splits open to reveal dark, rounded seeds.

Poisonous principles
Little work appears to have been done on the nature of the poisonous principles of *Wisteria*, but these are generally thought to be a glycoside (wistarin) and a resin.

Animal poisoning
It is sometimes stated that wisteria has been found only recently to be poisonous, but its toxic nature was known in the 1880s,[197] although experimental feeding of animals at about that time failed to produce clinical signs.[198] It appears that reports claiming the plant is not poisonous are based largely on these old experiments, and the toxicity of *Wisteria* in animals is still not proven.

Human poisoning
The clinical signs produced by *Wisteria* poisoning are well documented, and were described in detail last century.[197] Poisoning has resulted from chewing wisteria twigs,[197] but is most common in children who have eaten the pods and seeds, mistaking them for peas. Even one or two seeds may give rise to a reaction.[199] *Wisteria* acts as a digestive system irritant and can cause nausea, abdominal pain, vomiting, and, sometimes, diarrhoea,[200] but even in severe cases, recovery is usually complete in 24 hours.[201] In addition to abdominal pain, nausea, and repeated vomiting, two teenage boys who each ate 5–6 seeds experienced drowsiness for the following 24 hours,[202] while a 50-year old woman who ate seeds from ten pods also developed a severe headache, dizziness, confusion, perspiration, and fatigue that persisted for 5–7 days.[203]

Other members of the Leguminosae family

Some of the many garden shrubs in this family, including the bird of paradise (*Caesalpinia gilliesii*) and some other *Caesalpinia* species that may still be referred to by their old name, *Poinciana*, are poisonous. The leaves and seeds can cause vomiting and diarrhoea. Jequirity beans, which are the attractive seeds of *Abrus precatorius*, are bright red with a black area at the hilum (the point of attachment to the fruit); they are sometimes threaded to make necklaces. They contain lectins that are dangerously poisonous. If the beans are chewed, very severe gastrointestinal symptoms develop and death may result.

LILIACEAE

This large family is split by some taxonomists into several smaller families. It contains many poisonous plants, whose toxicity is due to a range of different compounds.

Colchicum autumnale Meadow Saffron (Plate 47)

Other common names: Autumn Crocus; Naked Ladies

Meadow saffron grows in damp meadows and woods in several isolated areas of England and Wales. The plant has been introduced to some parts of Scotland. Although it is sometimes very common within these areas, it is most often seen elsewhere as a garden plant. The alternative common name, autumn crocus, sometimes causes confusion with *Crocus nudiflorus* which is also called autumn, or autumnal crocus, but which belongs to a different family (Iridaceae).

Colchicum is a perennial that grows from a corm 3–5 cm in diameter. The plant has glossy, bright green, parallel-veined leaves, which grow up to 30 cm long and 4 cm wide. These are produced at the base of the plant in spring and die before the flowers appear. The flowers which, when open, resemble superficially a spring-flowering crocus, are pale purple (sometimes almost white) and appear, one or more from each corm, in late summer or autumn. The basal part of the flower is narrow, tubular and up to 20 cm long. The flowers die down soon after they have opened, and an oval fruit, 3–5 cm long, is formed at the base of the flower tube, close to the soil, where it remains until the following spring, when the flower stalk elongates so that the fruit appears above the leaves and opens when ripe, to reveal numerous small seeds.

Poisonous principles

These are two structurally similar alkaloids, colchicine and colchiceine, of which the former is the more toxic. Both are able to withstand drying, storage, and boiling without losing their toxic properties. In addition to its effects on the gastrointestinal system, colchicine affects the nervous system, paralysing peripheral nerve endings and blocking neuromuscular connections; it also prevents normal cell division. Because of the last property, colchicine has been used in experiments on plant genetics, and the possibility of its use against cancer has been investigated. Colchicine has been used medicinally in the treatment of gout and rheumatism.

All parts of the plant are poisonous, particularly the corm (colchicine content up to 0.6%) and the seeds (colchicine content up to 0.8%). The highest concentration is present in the plant during the summer.[1,2] The lethal dose has been estimated as 8–16 g of fresh leaves per kg body weight for cattle,[2] 6.4 g per kg for lambs aged 2–3 months, and 12 g per kg for adult guinea pigs.[3]

Animal poisoning

As the plant grows in meadows, the domestic animals most likely to be poisoned by *Colchicum* are cattle and sheep. Poisoning has been reported in cattle,[2–6] sheep,[2, 3, 6–8] horses,[2, 6, 9] pigs,[6, 10] and goats.[6] Poisoning due to colchicine has also been reported in dogs,[6, 11] and a hyena in a zoo;[12] laboratory animals have been poisoned when given either colchicine or *Colchicum*.[6, 7]

Colchicine is absorbed slowly into the body, and signs of poisoning may be delayed for 12–48 hours.[2] Excretion of colchicine by the kidneys and in the milk of lactating animals is also said to be very slow, with a gradual increase in concentration that may reach a toxic level. However, in experimental work in a sheep,[13] a single oral dose of 10 mg colchicine did not give rise to any clinical signs of poisoning, but colchicine was detectable in milk, by thin layer chromatography, six hours after administration, with maximum concentration being reached three hours later. It was no longer detectable in milk 40 hours after administration. As colchicine is excreted in milk, young animals and people that drink the milk are liable to be poisoned.[14] Cattle, and to a lesser extent sheep and goats, can develop a tolerance and even complete resistance to *Colchicum*.[14] In most animals *Colchicum* poisoning causes abdominal pain, salivation, severe diarrhoea (often containing blood), grinding of teeth, coldness of the extremities, depression, apathy, incoordination, decreased milk production, collapse, and death through respiratory or circulatory failure. Colchicine given to dogs (4 mg daily for 14 days) interfered with gastrointestinal absorption of some sugars and fat.[12]

Colchicum poisoning is unlikely in Britain, but could occur in areas where the plant is plentiful. Colchicine poisoning was diagnosed in northern Germany in horses[10] that developed colic within a few days of being fed hay found to contain about 1.5% of meadow saffron; one horse died. Also in Germany an outbreak was recorded which affected 30 of a herd of 96 cattle[4] after their first introduction to spring pasture. They developed salivation, depression, unsteady gait, abdominal pain, greenish diarrhoea with mucus, and a sudden decrease in milk production; three of the cows died. In a similar incident in France, five of seven cows died within two days of eating the plant, which was abundant in their pasture.[6] A high annual incidence of poisoning has been reported among lambs during May–July in the highlands of central Tien-Shan in Kirghizstan.[3] Clinical signs in the lambs were abdominal pain, followed by salivation, diarrhoea, and later depression, apathy, and collapse. Post-mortem examination revealed acute gastrointestinal inflammation. The heart appeared flabby, with small haemorrhages; the liver and spleen were congested and enlarged, the lymph nodes were oedematous and haemorrhagic, the lungs and kidneys were congested, and the mucous membranes of the intestine were thickened and covered with mucus. The main histological changes were congestion of organs, haemorrhages, and destruction of lymphocytes in the lymph nodes, spleen, and lymphoid follicles of the large intestine.[8] Similar clinical signs and post-mortem findings were reported in pigs in Germany;[11] 25 of 70 animals died after being given green feed containing meadow saffron. In four pigs examined post mortem a concentration of 0.15 mg colchicine per kg of stomach contents was measured.

Colchicum poisoning can be diagnosed by identifying leaves or seeds in stomach contents, although it is difficult to recognize flowers ingested in autumn. The presence of colchicine in ruminal fluid can be detected by thin layer chromatography.[9, 15]

Human poisoning

This can occur if children eat the flowers, or if the leaves are mistaken for those of an edible plant, or the corms for onions. Drinking milk from poisoned animals can also cause poisoning.[14] A latent period of up to six hours is typical for colchicine poisoning. Clinical signs are burning of the mouth and throat, nausea, abdominal pain, violent vomiting, diarrhoea (often with blood), shock due to fluid loss, and collapse. Scanty and blood-stained urine indicates kidney damage. There may be paralysis and convulsions, and (rarely) death may follow. The excessive medicinal use of colchicine (e.g. to treat gout) has also caused poisoning, and even death when large amounts have been taken.[16, 17]

Fluid therapy, and analgesics to relieve pain, are recommended for treatment.[18] Colchicine-specific Fab antibody fragments were used successfully to treat a woman with colchicine poisoning.[19]

Convallaria majalis Lily of the Valley (Plate 48)

This spring-flowering woodland plant is native in Britain, especially in eastern parts of the country, where it is widespread, but local in its distribution. It is widely cultivated and often occurs as a garden escape. The plant is a perennial with a creeping rhizome, and leaves 8–20 cm long, pointed at the tip, widening up to 5 cm then narrowing into a stalk that sheaths the stem at the base. The flower stalk rarely exceeds 10 cm in height, has no leaves, and bears a terminal cluster of 6–12 fragrant, white, bell-shaped flowers about 8 mm across.

Poisonous principles
All parts of the plant (but especially the flowers and seeds) are poisonous, as they contain various cardioactive glycosides. The three most frequently named are convallarin, convallamarin, and convallotoxin, the last being one of the most toxic naturally occurring substances that affect the heart. All *Convallaria* glycosides cause irregularities of the action of the heart, and some of them are saponins which, together with volatile oils also present in the plant, act as gastrointestinal irritants.

Animal poisoning
The nature of the toxic constituents of lily of the valley indicates that it should be regarded as potentially poisonous to animals. There are, however, few actual reports, probably because animals rarely eat the plant. In the USA, a previously healthy dog developed 'seizures', then collapsed and died;[20] fragments of lily of the valley leaves (most over 4 cm in length) were found in the contents of the small intestine. This evidence, as well as the post-mortem findings of extensive congestion of blood vessels that was particularly severe in the liver, was consistent with poisoning by a cardiac glycoside. Poisoning by the seeds has also been mentioned in poultry in the older literature, but no details are available.

Human poisoning
Lily of the valley has a long-standing reputation as a poisonous plant, but the highly toxic cardiac glycosides it contains are not readily absorbed from the digestive tract, and the vomiting that commonly follows ingestion reduces the amount of toxin available for absorption. Few well-authenticated cases have been reported. It is often stated that children have been poisoned, some fatally, by chewing the growing plant or eating the berries. Even drinking water from a vase that had contained lily of the valley was assumed to have poisoned a child.[21] In the USA in 1959–1960, cases reported of lily of the valley being eaten included those relating to four children, aged eight months to two years, who ate the fruit (berry) or seeds of the plant.[21, 22] When lily of the valley leaves were mistaken for those of wild garlic, and made into soup, those eating it became hot, flushed, and tense, and developed headache and hallucinations; red skin patches also occurred.[23] Symptoms of *Convallaria* poisoning include excess salivation, nausea, stomach pains, vomiting, headache, dilated pupils, cold clammy skin, and slow irregular heartbeat. There have been no recent reports of serious cases of poisoning.[16]

If spontaneous vomiting has not occurred, stomach lavage is recommended, in addition to the administration of a cardiac depressant, such as quinidine, to control cardiac rhythm.

Hyacinthoides non-scripta Bluebell (Plate 49)

Other common name: Wild Hyacinth

Bluebells are common throughout Britain in woods and shady places, but rarely grow in pastures. Linear leaves, 20–45 cm long and about 1 cm wide, develop in early spring from the white, oval bulb. The single flower stalk appears a few weeks later and bears 4–16 drooping, blue, bell-shaped flowers.

Poisonous principles
All parts of the plant contain glycosides, generally termed scillarens, which are similar in chemical structure to the cardiac glycosides of *Digitalis*.

Animal poisoning
In a horse that had eaten bluebell bulbs,[24] clinical signs appeared after about six hours, when the animal appeared to be choking. There was some abdominal pain and intermittent attempts at vomiting; the pulse was slow and weak and the temperature low, the skin was cold and clammy. About ten hours later there was dark-coloured diarrhoea with a considerable amount of blood; urination ceased altogether. The horse was acutely ill for two days, then slowly recovered but continued to pass blood-stained urine for several days. In early spring in Britain, when feed was scarce, an area of bluebells with closely cropped leaves was seen adjacent to pasture where a group of Hereford cows and calves were grazing. Within the next few days, the animals became dull and lethargic, chewed only intermittently, and produced hard, dry faeces. Body temperature and respiration rate decreased, heart beat was erratic, and lactating cows became dry. The animals recovered slowly when removed from the area and given extra feed. Bluebell poisoning was considered to be the cause of the condition.[25] In another incident in Britain, 19 of 76 beef cattle developed bloat and one died after eating bluebell leaves in a hedgerow when their pasture had been manured and harrowed.[26]

Human poisoning
Bluebell bulbs have caused poisoning when eaten mistakenly instead of onions. The fruits of bluebell have also caused poisoning; an 18-month-old child developed diarrhoea after eating 6–10 pods with seeds.[23] The sap of the plant can cause dermatitis.[27]

Hyacinthus orientalis Hyacinth

This cultivated plant is similar to, but larger than, the bluebell (*Hyacinthoides non-scripta*), and has white, blue, pink, or occasionally yellow flowers.

Poisonous principles

The scales on hyacinth bulbs contain calcium oxalate, but no definite information has been found on any other possible toxins.

Animal poisoning

Feeding of bulbs during feed shortage in the Netherlands in the Second World War was suspected to be the cause of severe purgation in cattle.[28] Vomiting and diarrhoea were reported in a dog that ate six bulbs.[23]

Human poisoning

Hyacinth bulbs have caused human poisoning when mistaken for onions; if eaten, they can cause stomach cramps, vomiting, and diarrhoea.[29] The sap can cause dermatitis.[30]

Narthecium ossifragum   Bog Asphodel (Plate 50)

Bog asphodel is found throughout most of Britain in wet acid bogs, and on moors, mountains, and heaths; it is absent from some central and eastern areas. It is a summer-flowering plant with a creeping underground stem (rhizome) and many fibrous roots. Stiff, narrow leaves (5–30 cm long and 2–5 mm wide) arise at ground level. Their basal sheaths are flattened in one plane, and the tips of the leaves tend to curve downwards. The flower stalk is stiff and erect (5–40 cm high) and bears a few leaf-like bracts that clasp the stalk and rarely exceed 4 cm in length. The inflorescence is a terminal cluster of yellow flowers with prominent, bright orange centres. After flowering, the ovaries and top of the stem become uniformly orange.

Poisonous principles

For many years saponins present in the plant, in particular the spirostanol forms of two saponins (one was named narthecin),[31] were thought to be responsible for the toxicity (hepatogenous photosensitization) associated with *Narthecium ossifragum* in sheep. The disease, named 'alveld' in Norway, can be reproduced in lambs placed on pastures containing *Narthecium*.[32] Experimental reproduction of the disease by administration of saponin extracts from the plant was reported,[33] but later it was suggested that saponins alone are not responsible,[34] and recent work, particularly in Norway in the 1990s, has indicated a more complex picture. Enzyme differences in the liver of lambs (that are more susceptible) and adult sheep were studied[35, 36] as were differences in susceptibility among sheep breeds.[36, 37] The role of fungi on the plants was also investigated. The fungus *Pithomyces chartarum*, which produces the mycotoxin sporidesmin that causes the photosensitization reaction known as facial eczema in sheep (see p. 113), was suspected,[38, 39] and similarities were found in the liver damage associated with *Narthecium* photosensitization and experimental sporidesmin poisoning.[40] In areas of Norway where the disease occurred, however, the fungus was found only sporadically, and from further work it was considered that sporidesmin was not involved.[41] The possibility that another fungus, *Cladosporium magnusianum*, which was found frequently on *Narthecium*, may produce a toxin and be involved with the photosensitization reaction was also considered,[39] but later work did not confirm this.[42] Thus the exact nature of the toxins involved in the photosensitization reaction induced by *Narthecium* remains unclear; it seems probable that the saponins, in combination with another toxic substance (or substances), are responsible.

157

Bog asphodel also contains an unidentified toxin (or toxins) that has been implicated in a disease of the kidneys and liver of cattle.[43, 44] It is not clear if the nephrotoxin and the hepatotoxin are the same, but an agent other than the steroidal saponin associated with alveld is thought to be involved.[45] Ergot (*Claviceps purpurea*) found on grasses growing with *Narthecium* was considered, but eliminated as a cause of this disease.[46] Tannins are also present in the plant, and it has been suggested that they may also be toxic factors.[43]

Animal poisoning

The specific name '*ossifragum*' refers to the old idea that eating the plant predisposed animals to fractures. There may, however, be a sound basis for this idea; it has been suggested that the kidney lesions that develop in cattle after eating *Narthecium* may lead to renal osteodystrophy and decreased levels of calcium in the blood, and hence to brittle bones.[43] Although *Narthecium* has long had the reputation of being poisonous,[47] references to its toxicity were rarely seen until the 1950s. Since then, increasing numbers of reports of liver dysfunction and photosensitization associated with sheep grazing *Narthecium* have been recorded, chiefly from Norway,[48] where the disease was first described in the veterinary literature in 1891.[47] The Norwegian name 'alveld' (elf fire) refers to the belief of former times that wicked elves came at night and threw fire over the sheep,[49] or shot them with their arrows.[48] The disease occurs mainly in lambs up to about five months of age, but is also seen occasionally in adult sheep, particularly when other green plants are scarce.[50] Lambs grazing pasture containing *Narthecium* do not, however, necessarily develop the disease.[48]

The photosensitization is of the secondary (hepatogenous) type, the toxins in the plant causing liver damage and interfering with the excretion in bile of the photosensitive substance phylloerythrin, a normal breakdown product of chlorophyll. The phylloerythrin accumulates in the circulating blood of animals that have eaten *Narthecium*.[49] When exposed to bright sunlight the poorly pigmented areas of skin, particularly those with least wool, develop clinical signs of photosensitization. These include oedema and reddening of the skin, initially of the ears, which become hot and drooping. The whole head is usually involved and the effects sometimes extend along the back and to the forelegs. This is followed by itching (with restlessness and scratching), pain, exudation of fluid from broken skin that may become infected, and sloughing of dead tissues, sometimes including the tips of the ears; in severe cases there may be blindness.[33] It has been noticed that affected animals often seek shade. Mortality rates of 25–50% have been recorded in lambs in Norway.[33] Jaundice, resulting from damage to the liver, is often, though not necessarily seen. This may occur in black lambs that do not suffer from photosensitization.[33] Although the association between *Narthecium* ingestion and these clinical signs has been studied extensively in Norway, some outbreaks of a similar disease of sheep have been reported in Britain[51–53] in areas where the plant is abundant. Loss of ears and death in lambs on Dartmoor have been attributed to bog asphodel.[51] It appears that only white-faced lambs in their first year on moorland pasture are affected. A similar condition, known locally as 'heddles' or 'hard lug' has been known for many years to farmers in the Antrim Hills in Ireland;[52] photosensitization after eating *Narthecium* has been suspected as the cause. In this area feeding lambs exclusively on bog asphodel failed to reproduce the disease, but there were no alternating periods of showers and bright sunlight (weather conditions associated with the disease) during the four days of the experiment; the animals may have had some reaction, however, as they remained in the shade. Photosensitization, with skin lesions developing particularly on the ears but also on other white areas of the head and legs, has occurred annually in sheep of the Blackface breed on farms in Perthshire in Scotland.[53] Swelling of eyelids and consequent closure of the eyes led to the death of some animals that wandered aimlessly into bogs and streams. Known locally as 'plochteach', the disease affects up to 10% of young lambs in May and June; severe jaundice is also present in some cases. Lambs with this condition were studied over three consecutive years[53] and high phylloerythrin levels in blood were found consistently. It was suggested that *Narthecium* may be involved, mainly because of the similarities to alveld in Norway. Diseases in sheep described as 'yellowses' or 'head greet' in Scotland and 'saut' in Cumbria have been recognized for many years,[53] and bog asphodel was thought to be the cause.

A disease of cattle associated with grazing *Narthecium asiaticum* was reported in Japan in 1984,[54] and evidence that *Narthecium ossifragum* can also cause poisoning (kidney failure and liver damage) in cattle has been accumulating in recent years. In Northern Ireland in 1989, loss of condition and appetite, leading in severe cases to recumbency and death, occurred among cows on a pasture containing bog asphodel.[41] Similar clinical signs, as well as dehydration, erosions in the mouth, diarrhoea, and blood in the faeces, were reported in cattle in Norway,[42] where a survey for the disease was carried out in 1992.[44, 55] There were more cases than usual that year, when the summer was uncharacteristically warm and dry. Post-mortem examination showed erosions in the digestive tract as well as in the mouth, but the most significant findings, that were consistently found, were indicative of kidney damage (renal tubular necrosis); there was also fatty infiltration of the liver, with some necrosis. Both kidney and liver damage were produced experimentally in calves[43] by feeding a mixture of bog plants, including bog asphodel, for two days (after which the calves refused the feed). Lambs given the same feed for ten days showed no signs of illness and did not reject the feed,[56] but histological studies of kidney tissue showed that degeneration and necrosis had occurred; there was no liver damage.

It was suggested, although not verified, that bog asphodel caused the death of 15 ponies on Dartmoor in 1977.[57]

Ornithogalum umbellatum Star of Bethlehem

This plant is thought to be native in eastern England, but is found throughout Britain, where it and other *Ornithogalum* species have become naturalized locally. Characteristics of the plant are the pale green or white midribs of the long narrow leaves and the 6-pointed, star-like flowers that have a green stripe on the back of each segment. Other species of *Ornithogalum*, several of which share the common name chincherinchee, are grown only as ornamentals and used as cut flowers in Britain.

Poisonous principles

It is stated that alkaloids found in the bulbs and above-ground parts can cause nausea and intestinal disorders;[29] colchicine and a haemolytic sapogenin are also said to be present in *Ornithogalum*.[58]

Animal poisoning

Although there are variations in toxicity, some *Ornithogalum* species are highly toxic and are responsible for poisoning in sheep, and for permanent blindness and sometimes death in cattle in South Africa.[59] Horses rarely eat the growing plants, but have been poisoned by hay containing them.[59]

Human poisoning

Children have been poisoned by eating the flowers and bulbs. The plants can cause dermatitis; this is a potential hazard in the cut-flower trade in Britain, as chincherinchees are imported from South Africa for sale here.

Paris quadrifolia Herb Paris

Herb paris grows in damp woods, chiefly on calcareous soils. It is a native British plant, local in distribution, being absent from most western areas of the country and from Ireland. The plant is perennial and has a creeping rhizome and a stem up to 40 cm high, with four (occasionally more) leaves 6–12 cm long arranged in a whorl around it. The leaves are oval in shape, pointed at the tip and narrowing where they join the stem. A single yellowish-green flower appears in spring, and in midsummer the fruit, a single blue-black berry, develops.

Poisonous principles

Published information on the nature of these is confusing. They have been referred to as saponins or glycosides, and the names most often quoted are paristyphin and paridin. All parts of the plant are said to be poisonous, but it appears to be very unpalatable, and few authenticated cases of poisoning in livestock have been reported.

Animal poisoning

Ingestion of berries by dogs and poultry, resulting in unsteadiness, vomiting, or regurgitation and abdominal pain has been recorded.[60] Horses fed experimentally with the plant (1.3 kg) at the ripe berry stage[61] showed, on the first evening, increased excitability, elevation of the head, muscular twitching, constant licking of the lips and increased pulse rate. The following day the pulse was still rapid (54 per minute); yellowing of the mucous membranes was apparent and persisted for three days. When 2 kg were fed, there was general weakness and yellowing of mucous membranes. The horses refused to eat the plant unless it was sweetened.

Human poisoning

Reported cases refer to children, who sometimes eat the berries, thinking them to be bilberries (*Vaccinium myrtillus*). Symptoms including vomiting, diarrhoea, abdominal pain, and pain during micturition and bowel movements develop initially. Headache, dizziness, difficulty in breathing, and narrowing of the pupils occur later.[62] Because of its unpleasant taste, the plant is not normally eaten in sufficient quantity to cause severe poisoning.

Polygonatum multiflorum Solomon's Seal

Solomon's seal is occasionally found growing apparently wild, but this and other *Polygonatum* species are more usually known as garden plants.They have arching stems bearing pale green leaves and pendulous, white, elongated, bell-shaped flowers with green tips. The fruits are blue-black berries.

Poisonous principles
Polygonatum species contain saponins and also convallamarin, a cardioactive glycoside present in *Convallaria.*

Animal poisoning
Vomiting that persisted for three days and did not respond to treatment was reported in a puppy that had chewed the leaves of the plant over a few days;[63] it was also noticed that the dog's heart rate was slow.

Human poisoning
The berries are said to have caused poisoning in children, but no details are available.

Tulipa species Tulip

Tulips are not native in Britain, but many species and varieties are cultivated. Most garden varieties have been derived from *Tulipa gesneriana*, although some have been given other species names. Tulips vary in size, and there is a wide range of flower colours. The plants grow in spring from a bulb with a thin, brown, papery skin. The leaves are smooth, broad, somewhat fleshy, and taper to a point; the flowers are borne singly on a cylindrical stalk, the coloured flower segments overlapping each other to form a straight-sided, cup-shaped flower held vertically on the plant.

Poisonous principles
Tulips contain glycosides named tuliposide A and B. On hydrolysis these yield the lactones tulipalin A and B. These have not been linked with the oral toxicity of the plant, but are allergens, of which tulipalin A is the more active. The allergens are present mainly in the outer layers of the bulbs.[64]

Animal poisoning
There are few reports of poisoning in animals by tulips, but a dog given goulash prepared with tulips instead of onions vomited many times and thereafter ate nothing for three days.[65] Tulip bulbs were fed to eight cattle in a beef herd in the Netherlands at 5–15 kg daily without any ill effects, but one lot of tulip bulbs that was mouldy caused the sudden death of five of the cattle.[66] It was assumed that a mycotoxin produced by the moulds was the cause of the poisoning.

Human poisoning
The few outbreaks reported all refer to the ingestion of tulip bulbs either to supplement food, as occurred in the Netherlands in the Second World War,[29, 65] or when used in mistake for onions.[23] In an incident in Yugoslavia[65] five tulip bulbs were used in place of onions in a goulash eaten by all six members of a family and their dog (see above). The dish had a bitter taste and within ten minutes, symptoms including

nausea, sweating, increased salivation, difficult breathing, and palpitations were experienced. Vomiting occurred in some, and weakness persisted for several days in all cases.

There are numerous reports of allergic reactions in people handling tulip bulbs. Both respiratory allergy[67] and contact dermatitis[68] ('tulip fingers') are common; the eyes may also be affected.[69] In one case eczema, eventually involving the skin of the whole body, developed in an employee in a seed shop that sold bulbs.[70] Skin tests and tests on dust from the environment were strongly positive for tuliposide A.

Veratrum species False Hellebores

Other common name: False Helleborines

The common names of these plants can cause confusion with the 'true' hellebores (*Helleborus* species) that are also poisonous; they belong to the Ranunculaceae family. *Veratrum* species do not grow wild in Britain, but are cultivated here as garden plants. They grow from underground rhizomes and have large leaves (up to 30 cm long and 20 cm broad) that are pointed at the tip and prominently grooved along their (parallel) veins. Numerous small, star-like flowers develop in plumes on stalks that grow up to 1.5 m tall. Depending on the species, the flowers are yellowish- or whitish-green or dark red.

Poisonous principles
The whole plants (especially the roots) are a potential source of severe poisoning as they contain at least 20 steroidal alkaloids (including proveratrine, protoveratrine, veratramine, and jervine) that are closely related chemically, and can affect the heart and paralyse the nervous system.

Animal poisoning
There are few reports of this (none in Britain), possibly because the plant is well known for its toxicity in the areas where it grows, and is eradicated from pasture. Sheep have been poisoned when given green feed containing *Veratrum album*.[71] It was found that 200 g would produce signs of poisoning, and that 400 g was a fatal amount. Clinical signs developed in 5–6 hours and included gastrointestinal disturbances, salivation, trembling, initial stimulation and then depression of the nervous system. In Slovakia, five heifers died suddenly at pasture. *Veratrum album* was found on the pasture, and veratrine demonstrated in the ruminal contents of the animals.[72]

Human poisoning
Several cases of severe poisoning by *Veratrum* species (including *Veratrum album* and *Veratrum viride*) have been recorded in the medical literature. Most have resulted from eating parts of the plants[73–76] (usually mistaken for edible plants) or drinking home-made wine or tea prepared from them.[77, 78] The symptoms are similar in most cases, and include vomiting, diarrhoea (sometimes with blood), muscle tremors, slow heart rate, low blood pressure, sweating, and loss of consciousness. Children have been poisoned by sneezing powder containing *Veratrum*,[79, 80] which is highly irritant to mucous membranes. In addition to sneezing, they have shown symptoms similar to those of poisoning by ingestion. Atropine has been used successfully in treatment.

Other members of the Liliaceae family

Some members of this family that are grown as house plants or in gardens in Britain are also poisonous. They contain substances known to be plant toxins, and some have been involved in cases of poisoning in other countries. The plants included in this group, with their toxins, are: aloes (*Aloe* species), an irritant purgative anthraquinone glycoside; asparagus (*Asparagus* species), saponins; spider plants (*Chlorophytum* species), toxins similar to those in tulips; fritillaries (*Fritillaria* species), alkaloids similar to those in *Veratrum*; gloriosa lilies (*Gloriosa* species, including *Gloriosa superba*), colchicine and a glycoside called superbine; day lilies (*Hemerocallis* species), a neurotoxin called hemerocallin; the Easter lily (*Lilium longiflorum*), a toxin that has caused kidney failure in cats; scillas (*Scilla* species), toxins similar to those in bluebells; death camas (*Zigadenus* species), alkaloids similar to those in *Veratrum* and causing both animal and human poisoning.

LINACEAE

Linum usitatissimum Linseed

Other common name: Flax

This plant was cultivated formerly in this country, mainly for linen production from the fibre in its stem, but after that time it was found here only very occasionally, sometimes growing from discarded bird seed. In recent years, however, varieties with shorter stems have been developed for oilseed production, and the plant can be seen again as a crop in Britain. It is an annual, usually with a single stem 60–80 cm tall. The leaves are narrow, and the flowers delicate; each has five pale blue or white petals.

Poisonous principles
Linseed contains the cyanogenic glycosides, linamarin and lotaustralin, from which hydrocyanic acid is released by hydrolysis involving the enzyme, β-glucosidase, sometimes called linamarase. Hydrolysis may take place in the plant itself, if crushed or bruised, or in the stomach of animals after ingestion of the seeds.[1] The severity of poisoning depends on the cyanogenic glycoside content of the plant (which varies considerably with genetic strain, climate, season, and soil type), the activity of the enzyme, and the rate of release of the hydrocyanic acid (which is influenced by the amount of water present; drinking water results in rapid release of the toxic substance).[2] If the toxic material is eaten slowly, enzymatic detoxification of the cyanide occurs. Another component of linseed, a dipeptide named linatine (or linatene) is a vitamin B_6 antagonist. Marginal deficiency of the vitamin developed in pigs fed 300 g per kg body weight of linseed meal.[3]

Animal poisoning
Hydrocyanic acid prevents the utilization of oxygen by cells. The blood, therefore, retains oxygen and remains bright red, and it is oxygen deficiency in brain cells that leads to death. Most cases of hydrocyanic acid poisoning after consumption of linseed

cake or meal are reported in older literature. Modern methods of extraction of linseed oil involve heat treatment, during which the enzyme responsible for the release of hydrocyanic acid from the glycoside is inactivated.

Poisoning has been reported in cattle given linseed cake containing 0.4% hydrocyanic acid or a hot-water extract of cake which contained 0.8% hydrocyanic acid.[4] Salivation, staggering, and somnolence resulted from eating the cake, while drinking the extract produced more severe clinical signs, the animals trembling, gasping, falling, and having convulsions before death, which occurred within an hour. In other cases of linseed cake poisoning in cattle,[5] prostration, depression, dilated pupils, and rapid pulse were reported. Similar signs and some deaths were reported in sheep[6,7] given linseed cake, and in lambs as a result of being suckled by poisoned ewes. Occasionally animals die so quickly that no clinical signs are seen. Reference is often made to the laxative effect of linseed oil feeds,[8] and gastrointestinal inflammation has been found at post-mortem examination. No reference to the substance(s) responsible for this effect has been found. Linseed is generally not recommended for inclusion in poultry feed because of the reported growth-inhibiting effect of linatine.[9] However, when one-week-old chicks were given a feed containing 2 or 10% *Linum usitatissimum* seed for six weeks, their growth rate was increased, but some pathological changes were found in the liver, kidneys, and intestines.[10] Water in which flax has been steeped is poisonous to cattle and fish.[11]

For poisoning by hydrocyanic acid, intravenous injections of sodium thiosulphate and sodium nitrite are recommended.

Other members of the Linaceae family

Purging (or fairy) flax (*Linum catharticum*) is a common annual plant found throughout Britain, often as a weed of cultivation. Purging flax also contains linamarin, but the plant has not been incriminated in cases of poisoning; it has been suggested, however, that, if eaten in sufficient quantity, it could cause diarrhoea.[12]

MALVACEAE

Malva species Mallows

There are several native species of mallow in Britain, including the musk mallow (*Malva moschata*), the dwarf mallow (*Malva neglecta*), and the common mallow (*Malva sylvestris*). The marsh mallow (*Malva parviflora*) has been introduced to this country and has become established locally. Other mallows are cultivated in gardens.

They are annual or perennial herbaceous plants that rarely exceed 50 cm on height. The leaves near the base are rounded or lobed, often with scalloped edges, while those of the flowering stems are usually more finely divided. The flowers are usually pink (some are white) and 2–4 cm across, depending on the species; each flower has five petals that broaden from the base to the irregularly indented distal edge.

Poisonous principles
The plants contain nitrates (readily converted to nitrites that combine with haemoglobin to form methaemoglobin, thus preventing adequate uptake of oxygen). A fatty acid now often called malvalic acid, but referred to previously as Halphen acid, is also present.

Animal poisoning
Malva parviflora is recognized as a poisonous plant abroad, mainly in Australia[1, 2] and South Africa,[3] but also in the USA. Even in these countries, however, outbreaks of poisoning are recorded only in older literature. Sheep are most often affected and develop clinical signs including staggering, incoordination, trembling, arched back, extended head, and laboured breathing;[1, 2] severely affected animals may fall and die. It has been noted on several occasions, and verified experimentally, that staggers develop when the sheep are driven.[1] Staggers in lambs has resulted from sucking the milk of ewes that have eaten mallow.[1] The conditions under which poisoning occurs in different countries appear to vary as, in the USA, a sheep fed experimentally with cut, dried mallow for 11 days increased in weight and was apparently unaffected.[4] A condition similar to that in sheep occurs in horses and cattle, although much less frequently.[5] In addition to the staggering characteristic of mallow poisoning, profuse sweating and rapid breathing have been seen in horses.[1] It is unlikely that sufficient mallow would be found and eaten by animals in Britain for such severe poisoning to occur, although the plant appears to be increasing in some waste places and areas previously kept weed-free by herbicides.

Later reports on the adverse effects of mallow have been in poultry, the biologically active fatty acid in the plants[6] having been implicated as the cause of a pinkish coloration of the whites of eggs[7] particularly after storage.[8] There have been no reports of this occurring in Britain.

OLEACEAE

Fraxinus excelsior Ash (Plate 51)

Ash can be found in mixed woodland, scrub, and hedges throughout Britain, but especially in wetter parts of the country on calcareous soils. It is a tall, deciduous tree with spreading branches, growing up to 25 m high. The trunk of the tree is grey and sometimes fissured, the buds are large (up to 10 mm) and have a sooty appearance. The leaves are compound, bearing 7–13 oval leaflets that have slightly serrated edges and are pointed at the tip. The small flowers that appear in bunches, before the leaves, have no sepals or petals; the stamens, however, give the flowers a reddish-purple colour. The winged fruits (keys) are 3–4 cm long and hang in clusters in late summer and autumn, often persisting into the winter after the leaves have fallen.

Poisonous principles
These have not been determined fully, but are probably glycosides, including the lactone glycoside esculin (aesculin), which also occurs in *Aesculus* species (see pp. 119–120).

165

Animal poisoning

Although a rare occurrence, ash poisoning is a potential problem where animals graze near these trees. The leaves of ash often fall in large quantities (while still green) after an early, sharp frost in autumn, and eating these can cause impaction of the rumen in cattle, a condition formerly known in the Midlands as 'wood evil'. The clinical signs are acute indigestion with cessation of rumination, distension and hardness of the rumen, the passage of small amounts of hard faeces or no defaecation, grunting, and reduced milk yield.[1] Drowsiness, abdominal pain, incoordination, and collapse were also seen in two cows,[2] which stripped leaves and fruits from a branch of ash that fell in a storm. In these animals there was pronounced oedema of the rib region, flanks, and udder, and purple discoloration of the perineum. It has been suggested that fungi present on the leaves may be implicated in poisoning attributed to ash.[3] There is historical and current evidence of ash being used as fodder,[4] and it may be that the quantity eaten determines whether ash has adverse or beneficial effects.

Treatment should include attempts to stimulate resumption of rumination, but may necessitate rumenotomy.

Human poisoning

There are no reports of poisoning by ingestion, but ash has caused dermatitis.[5]

Ligustrum species Privet (Plates 52 and 53)

Common privet (*Ligustrum vulgare*) is a native shrub of southern England, where it is found chiefly on calcareous soils. An introduced species, oval-leaved privet (*Ligustrum ovalifolium*), is common throughout the country as a cultivated hedging plant, and many yellow and variegated types are grown as ornamentals. Common privet is deciduous, but the cultivated varieties may keep some of their leaves throughout the winter and be classified as evergreen.

Common privet can grow up to 5 m in height, has smooth bark, slender branches, and young shoots with a light covering of soft hairs. The leaves are 3–6 cm long, have short stalks, and are bright green and shiny when young, becoming dull and darker green later. They are 1–2 cm wide and taper gradually to a point at the tip and towards the stalk. Clusters of small, creamy-white flowers appear in summer. They have a tubular base, extending into a flattened expanded portion, 4–5 mm in diameter. The fruits are black, shining berries, 6–8 mm in diameter. Oval-leaved privet is very similar except that the shoots are hairless, the leaves more oval or elliptical in shape, and the flowers longer.

Poisonous principle

The precise nature of this is not known, but it is generally referred to as a glycoside, ligustrin. The berries are usually considered the most toxic, but all aerial parts of the plant have been involved in poisoning.

Animal poisoning

Poisoning by privet is rare, but when it does occur it is often severe or even fatal, and the plant should be considered potentially dangerous. Most cases involve hedges or their trimmings rather than the wild plants. Death has occurred in horses 4–48 hours after eating the plant. Clinical signs of colic and unsteady gait preceded death in two horses, which had eaten material from a neglected hedge that was in flower;[1] five horses died after eating twigs with leaves from an untrimmed hedge in an earlier incident in Britain.[6] Some animals were staggering, while others were down and unable to rise and appeared to have paralysis of the hindquarters. The pulse was rapid, the visible mucous membranes were congested, and the pupils dilated. In New Zealand, five heifers died and others became ill after grazing a privet hedge at the berry stage.[7] Eating trimmings from a privet hedge caused the death of sheep in Maryland, USA,[8] and were implicated in a case of suspected poisoning in a lamb in Britain.[9] Congestion of the mucous membranes and hind limb paralysis were still apparent after 12 hours, but the lamb recovered after a further 24 hours.

In all of the post-mortem examinations described, the presence of privet in the stomach and intense gastrointestinal irritation and inflammation were the only findings.

Human poisoning

Privet berries are often stated to be a cause of poisoning, particularly in children, but cases are recorded only sporadically. Vomiting and diarrhoea were reported in two children[10] who ate privet berries, and in an intoxicated man[10] who ate the leaves. The toxicity of the plant should not, however, be underestimated, as a two-year-old boy in Germany[11] and two of four children in Russia[12] died 3–4 hours after eating privet berries. Convulsions and irregular heart beats preceded death. Privet can cause dermatitis,[13] and in one case a severe skin reaction occurred in a boy working on a privet hedge.[8]

OXALIDACEAE

Oxalis acetosella Wood Sorrel (Plate 54)

Other common name: Sleeping Beauty

The common name of this plant can cause confusion with other sorrels, which are *Rumex* species and in a different family (Polygonaceae). *Oxalis acetosella*, the only member of this large genus native in Britain, grows in woods and shady places where it may be the dominant ground cover plant. It has yellowish-green, compound leaves divided into three more or less equal, bluntly rounded leaflets (similar to clovers) with indented tips, and bears white or pinkish flowers, veined with lilac, on slender stalks up to 15 cm long.

Poisonous principles

Oxalis species contain oxalic acid and oxalates that can cause poisoning. It is unlikely that enough of the plant would be eaten to cause poisoning in Britain, but procumbent yellow sorrel (*Oxalis corniculata*), an introduced species in this country, has caused poisoning, particularly of sheep in Australia, where it is a troublesome weed. A total oxalate content of 7% has been estimated in air-dried plants.[1]

Animal poisoning

Sheep and other ruminants can detoxify considerable quantities of ingested oxalates. The nutritional status of the animals before eating plants containing oxalates is an important factor in determining the severity of the toxic reaction. If eaten in sufficiently large quantities over a relatively short period, plants containing oxalates can cause severe calcium deficiency (hypocalcaemia), as the oxalates ingested combine with blood calcium to produce insoluble calcium oxalate. As little as 600 g of the plant fed to sheep can cause hypocalcaemia.[1] Severely affected animals develop muscular twitching, trembling, and staggering, and may die suddenly. Ingestion of smaller quantities of the plant over a long period results in the formation of calcium oxalate deposits in the kidney tubules, sometimes leading to kidney failure and death. In one outbreak of poisoning by *Oxalis corniculata*, sheep walked with a stiff gait, paralysis of the hind limbs developed, and the animals dragged themselves along on their knees.[2] In Australia, more than 10% of nearly 3000 sheep died after eating *Oxalis*, which grew in abundance on the route along which they were being driven; affected animals lay down, with outstretched necks.[3] Post-mortem examination showed congestion of the intestines and kidney degeneration. In the Mediterranean region *Oxalis pes-caprae*[4] and *Oxalis cernua*[5] have caused poisoning of sheep in Sardinia, and sheep and goats have been poisoned by *Oxalis cernua* in Tunisia.[6] Experimental feeding of *Oxalis cernua* to sheep in Italy produced signs of oxalic acid poisoning.[7] Changes in blood[8,9] and urine[5,9] constituents were reported; serum calcium levels were reduced, urine pH increased, and calcium oxalate deposited in the kidneys. Injection of calcium borogluconate may prevent death if given in the early stages of poisoning.

Early this century it was stated that milk from cows poisoned by *Oxalis* is difficult to churn into butter,[10] but there is no recent report of this.

PAEONIACEAE

Paeonia species Peonies

Peonies are not native British plants, but an introduced species has become naturalized locally in an area of south-east England. There are many species and varieties cultivated in gardens. Simple, leafy shoots grow annually from the perennial tuberous stock of the plants. The leaves are smooth, dark green, and divided into pointed leaflets; the flowers are produced terminally and are large (up to 10 cm across) and conspicuous, having many slightly incurved, dark red, pink, or white petals. The fruits, which grow up to 2 cm long, are pale green at first and covered with downy hairs. They contain smooth round seeds, which change from red to dark blue and finally black as they ripen.

Poisonous principles
Information on the nature of these is confusing. A glycoside, peonin, is present throughout the plant and said by some to be toxic, while others state that alkaloids are the toxic factors.

Human poisoning
Species of *Paeonia* have long been suspected of being poisonous plants and are included in lists of such plants from the 18th century. There is, however, little evidence to substantiate this, although it seems likely that the plant does contain at least a gastrointestinal irritant. A case is reported of an eight-month-old girl who vomited an hour after eating 3–4 peony flower petals.[1] An unidentified substance isolated from

peonies is said to cause difficulty in swallowing, coldness and loss of sensitivity of extremities, constriction of blood vessels in the kidneys, and inflammation of intestines and kidneys.[2]

PAPAVERACEAE

The members of this family said to be poisonous include greater celandine (*Chelidonium majus*) and several wild and cultivated poppies (mainly *Papaver* species).

Chelidonium majus Greater Celandine (Plate 55)

Other common names: Celandine Poppy; Wart Wort

Although implied by the common name, this plant is not related to lesser celandine (*Ranunculus ficaria*), which belongs to a different family (Ranunculaceae). Greater celandine grows throughout most of Britain, except parts of Scotland, in banks and hedgerows, but is often found near old buildings, where it has probably survived from earlier times when it was grown as a medicinal plant. It was applied to corns and warts or taken internally to treat liver, lung, and gastrointestinal disorders, and rheumatism.

The plant has erect, branched, smooth or slightly hairy stems and grows up to 60 cm high. The basal leaves have long stalks and the upper ones short stalks. The leaves, which are bluish green below, are deeply divided into distinct oval segments that have irregularly scalloped edges. The flowers, borne in loose terminal clusters throughout the summer, are 2.0–2.5 cm across and have bright yellow petals and greenish-yellow stamens. The fruit is an elongated pod-like capsule that contains white-tipped black seeds. The sap of the plant (latex) is yellowish orange in colour, but turns red on exposure to the air.

Poisonous principles

Greater celandine is said to contain many potentially toxic alkaloids, of which the most frequently named are chelidonine and α-homochelidonine (both chemically related to papaverine, found in *Papaver* species), chelerythrine, sanguinarine, and protopine. However, the plant rarely causes poisoning, possibly because it is unpalatable, having an acrid taste and a pungent, foetid smell.

Animal poisoning

The plant has a long-standing reputation for being poisonous to animals, but this is apparently based largely on adverse effects of its medicinal use and a single report, in 1903, of poisoning of cattle in Britain.[2] Throughout the summer, the herd had been eating, apparently without adverse effects, greater celandine which grew luxuriantly along a hedge. In the autumn, however, when the seed capsules were ripe, many of the animals became poisoned and some died after eating the plant. The clinical signs included excess salivation and urination, thirst, drowsiness, cessation of bowel movement, and staggering gait. Violent convulsions occurred when the animals were approached and touched. Calves suckled by the poisoned cows were unaffected. Post-mortem examination revealed gastrointestinal irritation.

Other, less well-documented, cases refer to the drastic purgative action of the plant, with consequent dehydration from which animals may die. No recent reports have been found. The practice (now largely discontinued) of applying the sap of the plant (or an infusion of it) externally to minor skin injuries, as a wash to remove parasites, or for the treatment of certain eye disorders often resulted in irritation and soreness that required further treatment.[3]

Human poisoning

Reports in older literature state that the sap of the plant can cause irritation and blistering of the skin,[4] and the death of a four-year-old child, who developed haemorrhagic gastroenteritis and circulatory failure after eating the plant, is recorded.[5] Apart from a single case of haemolytic anaemia following long-term oral use of an extract of the plant,[6] no further reports of poisoning have been traced, and the repeated external application of the sap failed to cause skin damage.[5] It appears, therefore, that the reputation of greater celandine as a severely toxic plant is dubious.

Glaucium flavum Yellow Horned Poppy

Other common name: Sea Poppy

This plant, which has large, coarse, deeply serrated, divided leaves, and flowers (6–9 cm across) with rounded, yellow petals, grows chiefly on shingle banks around the coast of England and some parts of Scotland.

No actual cases of poisoning by this plant in its wild state have been recorded, but it should be regarded as potentially toxic as it contains poisonous alkaloids, named as glaucine, protopine, chelerythrine, and sanguinarine.[3]

Papaver nudicaule Iceland Poppy

This plant has leaves in a basal rosette and flowers (3–8 cm across) with yellow, orange, or reddish petals. Iceland poppies are grown only as ornamentals in Britain but are of some importance, as incidents of poisoning have occurred when animals have had access to garden rubbish containing the plants.

Poisonous principles

Iceland poppies contain a variety of toxic alkaloids.

Animal poisoning

This has been recorded in horses,[7] cattle,[8] and sheep.[9-11] In most cases, poisoning has resulted from cut flowers or discarded plants being thrown to animals; there are no records of animals having eaten the growing plant. The clinical signs are similar in all animal species and include initial restlessness and excitation, followed by incoordination, stiffness, muscular twitches and spasms of limbs, falling and inability to rise, and, in some cases, distension of the abdomen (bloat). Iceland poppy poisoning is rarely fatal, but affected animals may take many months to recover and, in lactating animals, milk yield remains depressed.

Papaver rhoeas Field Poppy (Plate 56)

Other common names: Red Poppy; Corn Poppy

This plant, probably the only *Papaver* species that is truly native in Britain, is still common, particularly in the south, where it is often seen in waste places and beside roads and railways. Until recently its occurrence in arable land had been greatly reduced by herbicides, but it is now seen more frequently.

The erect stems of the plant grow up to 60 cm in height and bear stiffly hairy leaves with deeply indented or toothed edges. The flower buds are pendulous, but the flowers, which develop in summer, are erect and have delicate scarlet petals (rarely pink or white) that often have a dark blotch at the base. The fruit is a firm, smooth capsule with a flattened top on which are dark radiating lines (stigma rays). The seeds are very small, numerous, and golden brown. The form of the plant is variable.

Poisonous principles

All parts of the plant are said to be poisonous, and it is generally considered to have an unpleasant taste. Various alkaloids, one of which is rhoeadine, are contained in the plant.

Animal poisoning

Clinical signs described in cattle in early literature[12] are consistent with those described more recently for other *Papaver* species. However, no recent cases of poisoning by this poppy have been described, although the plant should be considered as potentially toxic.

Papaver somniferum Opium Poppy

Other common name: White Poppy

Opium poppies are not native in Britain, but are sometimes grown as ornamentals. They may appear occasionally as wild plants, when they are garden escapes or relics of former cultivation. Legislation to control the growing of opium poppies, in an attempt to limit the availability of the narcotic drug, opium, has been made in some countries.

Papaver somniferum grows up to 100 cm tall, is smooth and uniformly bluish green. The lobed leaves have undulating margins; the flower petals are white or pale lilac, with or without a darker basal blotch. The fruit is a spherical or oval capsule, and the numerous, small seeds are black or white. The plants are very variable in form and numerous subspecies have been defined.

The seeds of the plants are generally considered harmless and are sometimes used as condiments, and for decorating bread and cakes. An edible oil can be obtained by pressing the seeds, and there was a revival of the cultivation of the poppy for this purpose in France during the Second World War.[13] However, the residues left after pressing caused many cases of poisoning when fed to cattle.

Poisonous principles

These are found in the crude resin, opium, which is present in the whole plant but mainly in the unripe seed capsule, the milky sap of which is released by cutting and then allowed to dry before collection. Medicinal drugs, such as morphine and codeine, are constituents of opium, as are many other alkaloids, including papaverine, laudanidine, narcotine, narceine, amurine, nudaurine, and protopine. It is highly probable that individual alkaloids, described over the years, have been referred to by more than one name.

Animal poisoning

This has been recognized for many years.[12] The plant is seldom eaten while growing, but when cattle were given stalks with seed capsules[14] or seed residues after oil extraction,[13] they became restless within a few hours and moved, turned, or ran about constantly. When tied to prevent this, the animals moved their feet continuously, scraping the ground and injuring themselves by abrasion. Continuous lowing was also a characteristic sign. Feeding, rumination, and lactation ceased, and the animals produced excess saliva; their body temperature decreased and the rate of breathing increased. Finally the animals went into a deep sleep. Poisoning by opium poppies is rarely fatal, but affected animals are often an economic loss as they are very slow to recover, and the milk yield of lactating animals rarely returns to normal. Post-mortem examination revealed inflammation of the intestines and kidneys, increased blood in the blood vessels of the brain, and yellowing of the liver. In South Africa two young dogs showed signs reminiscent of opium poisoning, including muscular incoordination and contracted pupils, after playing in a garden where opium poppies were growing;[15] there was evidence that the plants had been chewed.

Human poisoning

The narcotic effects of opium preparations on the central nervous system have been well documented over many years,[16] but acute poisoning can result from the direct ingestion of plant parts or crude extracts. Fatal poisoning occurred in a young man who drank a tea made by boiling dried poppy seed capsules, and in a child who ate fresh capsules.[17] A young baby given poppy capsule tea remained asleep for several hours.[17] No behavioural or sensory changes have followed the consumption of poppy seeds used to decorate or flavour foods, and the concentration of alkaloids in them is usually stated to be very low. However, after eating poppy seed cake, morphine was detected in the urine of five adults[18] at levels that exceeded those considered positive in standard drug tests. The possible implications of this finding in interpreting screening tests should be considered.

Other members of the Papaveraceae family

Some poppies that grow wild in Britain and have been recorded as causing animal poisoning in other countries are the long-headed poppy (*Papaver dubium*) and the rough poppy (*Papaver hybridum*). The cultivated Mexican poppy (*Argemone mexicana*) contains toxic isoquinolone alkaloids that can cause animal as well as human poisoning.

PHYTOLACCACEAE

Phytolacca americana Pokeweed

Other common names: Pokeberry; Pigeonberry; Inkberry; American Nightshade

Pokeweed is not native in Britain but has been introduced from the USA as a garden plant. In a few localized areas it has escaped and become naturalized. It is a perennial shrub which grows up to 3 m high. The leaves are light green, thick, and prominently veined. They are generally oval, but are pointed at the tip and taper towards the stalk. The small, white, or greenish flowers are borne in a spike up to 20 cm long, and the fruit is a purple berry with red, staining juice.

All parts of the plant, but especially the thick, fleshy tap root and the unripe green or reddish berries, are said to be poisonous. The ripe berries appear to be the least poisonous and have been used in making pies.[1] The young shoots are also considered safe to eat as a cooked vegetable if the cooking water is discarded.[1]

Poisonous principles

The precise nature of these in *Phytolacca americana* (and some other *Phytolacca* species) is not known and several old names persist for the supposed toxins. It is known, however, that the plants contain triterpenoid saponins (sometimes referred to as alkaloids), of which the most frequently named are phytolaccin(e) and phytolaccatoxin.

Animal poisoning

Pokeweed is poisonous to cattle, sheep, horses, and pigs.[2] It has an acrid taste and burns the tongue. The clinical signs, which develop 1–2 hours after eating pokeweed, include severe diarrhoea, vomiting (where possible), salivation, muscular cramps, weak breathing, impaired vision, and drowsiness; coma and death may result.[3] Most recorded cases of *Phytolacca* poisoning are in pigs. In one outbreak in the USA, the roots of the plant eaten by pigs caused them to run about aimlessly as though blind. Their eyes were inflamed and they staggered as they moved and were unusually docile.[4] In another, more serious, incident involving mature sows, *Phytolacca* poisoning resulted in paralysis of the hindquarters and death.[5] Another pig fed pieces of root of the plant became unsteady, lay down, and was unable to rise.[5] Jerking movements of the legs were observed. The animal was killed, and post-mortem examination of this pig and the sows showed ulceration with haemorrhages of the stomach and intestines. Dark red coloration and extreme swelling of the liver were recorded for the sows.

Chickens are said to eat the berries of the plant without ill effect and wild birds often feed on them, but turkeys have been poisoned by eating pokeberries.[6] Addition of liquidized fresh pokeberries to the diet of young turkeys reduced weight gain. Hock disorders, sometimes causing inability to stand or walk, developed. Post-mortem examination of birds that died revealed fluid accumulation in the abdominal cavity and gall bladder. There is some evidence that ingestion of the berries has an adverse effect on the immune responses of the birds, but this is inconclusive.[7]

In New Zealand, pokeweed continues to be a potential toxic hazard, particularly to cattle. The plant tends to flourish after the removal of sheep from an area and, although chemical weedkillers are effective against seedlings, the mature shrubs are difficult to eliminate.[8]

Human poisoning

Most cases involve children who may become seriously ill after eating raw berries. In the USA in 1959–1960 there were 97 reported cases of ingestion of pokeberries, mostly by children aged 2–3.[9] Stomach cramps, vomiting, and diarrhoea were reported. An adult man who ate pokeweed root in mistake for horse radish experienced a sore mouth and throat and extreme lassitude, with yawning. Severe vomiting, exhaustion, and dizziness followed and breathing became difficult. The pupils were contracted and the skin cold and clammy. Vomiting persisted for 12 hours and a bitter taste for 48 hours before recovery.[10] In a similar incident in which pokeweed root was mistaken for horse radish and grated in a salad, 32 people had symptoms ranging from a dry throat to severe nausea, vomiting, and diarrhoea; most had extreme thirst.[11] In another episode,[12] a group of campers became ill after eating a salad containing pokeweed leaves that had been boiled twice (a process reputed to make them edible). Headache, dizziness, and gastrointestinal disturbances with stomach cramps were experienced; symptoms lasted for up to 48 hours. Effects on the central and peripheral nervous system were suggested in the case of a man who drank a tea made from leaves and stems of pokeweed,[13] without the necessary preboiling and discarding of the water. After 15 hours he experienced sweating, mental confusion, muscular tremors and weakness, urinary incontinence, and loss of consciousness. In another incident very severe vomiting and watery diarrhoea occurred in two adults[14] within two hours of eating a few uncooked leaves of pokeweed, followed by others that had been adequately cooked. A third person, who ate only the cooked leaves, did not develop symptoms. Cardiac effects noted on the electrocardiogram of the more severely affected adult were thought to be secondary to the severe gastrointestinal signs, and not indicative of the presence of a cardiotoxin in the plant material. There are some old, but no recent reports of inflammation of the skin and eyes following contact with the plant.[15] An extract of the plant (pokeweed mitogen) is used experimentally because of its ability to influence cell division; it affects the division of white blood cells,[16] and induces the proliferation of both B and T lymphocytes.

PINACEAE

Pinus ponderosa Western Yellow Pine

This is not a native tree, but is planted here frequently in parks and large gardens; occasionally it is used in experimental forestry plantations. These pines can exceed 50 m in height. Their needle-like leaves are grouped in threes, and may be up to 25 cm long.

Poisonous principles

The trees are said to contain phenolic compounds, but these have not proved to be the toxic agents. Several other substances have been isolated, including isocupressic acid, which has been shown to be a cause of abortion, and various abietane diterpene acids.

Animal poisoning

In the USA, *Pinus ponderosa* needles are a cause of abortion and placental retention in cattle that eat them in the last three months of pregnancy,[1] calves that survive are often weak. In experimental work, isocupressic acid extracted from the needles has caused abortion when given to pregnant cattle.[2, 3] The precise mechanism that leads to abortion is not known, but it has been shown that consumption of the needles progressively reduces the blood flow to the uterus,[4] and this seems to be the direct cause of the abortions. Consumption of pine needles fed in varying proportions of the diet of experimental pregnant beef cows led to major changes in the ruminal microflora of the animals[5] that may have some influence on abortion.

Other members of the Pinaceae family

The leaves of the pine trees that are native in Britain are unlikely to be eaten by animals because the needles are stiff and sharp, but other *Pinus* species, in addition to the Western yellow pine, have been associated with abortion in cows in the USA.[1] There are no well-documented reports of human poisoning by ingestion, but various pines, including the Scots pine (*Pinus sylvestris*), and some spruces (*Picea* species), such as *Picea abies* that is commonly used as a Christmas tree in Britain, have occasionally given rise to an allergic contact dermatitis.[6]

POLYGONACEAE

Fagopyrum esculentum Buckwheat

Buckwheat is cultivated on a very small scale in Britain, particularly in the Fens. It occurs occasionally on waste ground, but is not a native plant. It is an erect annual with few branches, leaves longer than broad with rounded or slightly pointed lobes at the base, and pink or white flowers borne on a branched inflorescence.

Poisonous principles

A pigment, fagopyrin, that is present in the plant is thought to be the active principle, and clinical signs have been produced in domestic and laboratory animals given the pigment orally. Several attempts have been made to identify it, and various fractions have been separated.[1-3] Fagopyrin is probably a naphthodianthrone derivative.

Animal poisoning

When dehusked, the black, triangular seeds are considered harmless and are often incorporated into animal feeds or seed mixtures for cage birds and poultry.[4] Under certain conditions, however, animals that eat the fresh or dried plant in fairly large quantities develop dermatitis on white or unpigmented areas of the skin if exposed to sunlight. Animals that are housed or have heavily pigmented skin are unaffected. Such photosensitivity has been reported in cattle, sheep, goats, pigs, and chickens.[5] Although pigs are said to be less susceptible,[6] cases have been reported in Russia.[7] It is usually considered to be primary photosensitivity, as the main clinical signs are the direct result of sunlight on the skin, but there may be concurrent jaundice, indicating secondary involvement of the liver and interference with its function.

Affected animals usually develop reddening and blistering of the skin within 24 hours of eating the plant and exposure to strong sunlight, but delayed reactions can also occur.[8] The lesions often became necrotic and are slow to heal. Occasionally nervous signs with agitation, possibly due to intense irritation of the skin,[6] convulsions, somnolence, and prostration may develop. In one outbreak in France,[9] cattle fed on buckwheat plants were unaffected while housed, but when transferred to pasture in sunny weather, they soon became recumbent, moving only when stimulated. Severe skin lesions, thirst, and emaciation were prominent features. In Russia and the Ukraine[8] sheep showed similar signs, with initial excitement followed by paralysis. In addition to an intense skin reaction on the bare parts of the head, incoordination was reported in turkeys that gained access to a field of unripe buckwheat.[4] The term 'fagopyrism' is sometimes used for the condition induced by buckwheat poisoning.

Symptomatic treatment of the skin lesions may be required; a change of diet and removal from sunlight (preferably by housing) are obviously desirable.

Human poisoning

The grain of buckwheat (whole or ground into flour) is used extensively for human food in some countries, and is imported into Britain. As only dehusked grain is offered for sale for human consumption in this country, it is unlikely that poisoning will occur here. Allergic reactions to the plant are far more common than the photosensitization.

Rheum rhabarbarum Rhubarb (Plate 57)

The rhubarb cultivated for culinary use is a hybrid referred to as *Rheum* x *hybridum*, *Rheum* x *cultorum*, or *Rheum rhabarbarum*; one of the parents is *Rheum rhaponticum*. This plant has a perennial rootstock from which the leaves develop each spring. They grow rapidly, and consist of a large, more or less triangular leaf blade (often exceeding 30 cm across) that has broadly wavy margins, and a reddish stalk that is often flattened on the upper surface, and may be up to 50 cm long. A tall flower spike develops later in the season and bears crowded, reddish-cream, small flowers.

Medicinal use of the rhizomes of some types of rhubarb has been recorded for thousands of years; the reddish leaf stalks of the cultivated form are eaten as a dessert after cooking, but the large blades of the leaf are poisonous.

Poisonous principles

All parts of the plant, but particularly the green part of the leaves, contain oxalates (usually of calcium or potassium); these are irritant poisons. There is, however, some doubt that the oxalates are the main toxic constituents of rhubarb. Anthraquinone glycosides present may be at least partly responsible for its toxicity.

Animal poisoning

Animals rarely have access to the plant, but when they do they can be poisoned by it. A goat that ate rhubarb leaves stood with outspread legs, protruding eyes, and an open mouth. The animal was foaming at the mouth and crying, and produced sour-smelling, green vomit and profuse diarrhoea.[10] A sow that ate rhubarb leaves refused all other food thereafter and died two days later.[11] Post-mortem examination revealed severe inflammation of the stomach and intestines, which contained decaying leaves, and smelled strongly of rhubarb. In the USA, nine pigs were poisoned after eating a wheelbarrow full of rhubarb leaves thrown to them as feed.[12] They foamed at the mouth, staggered, and died in convulsions 3–4 hours after the appearance of clinical signs. On another farm, the death of a cow under similar circumstances was reported. Vomiting, diarrhoea, lethargy, and muscular tremors were reported in a cat,[13] and diarrhoea, depression, and apathy in a rabbit[13] after eating rhubarb. Chickens have been poisoned in Australia.

Human poisoning
Many cases of poisoning and some fatalities have resulted from eating cooked green leaves of rhubarb as a vegetable.[14,15] This practice was even recommended in Britain during the First World War, when food was scarce. As with many other poisonous plants, the amount eaten that causes poisoning varies in different individuals. The rhubarb leaves eaten in one fatal case[16] contained only 1.3 g oxalic acid per kg, whereas five or six times this concentration is considered a fatal dose. Symptoms often begin within an hour of eating the leaves and include cramp-like abdominal pains, nausea, vomiting, weakness, and drowsiness; blood clotting is impaired. There may be muscular twitching and convulsions. A woman in early pregnancy aborted before dying from rhubarb poisoning.[14] More recently, two children who ate raw rhubarb leaves and stalks (20–100 g) developed vomiting and jaundice;[17] there was liver and kidney damage. A five-year-old girl who ate 'a large quantity' of raw rhubarb leaves died two days later.[18] In these and other cases[19] it has been thought that the toxic reaction was due to anthraquinone glycosides rather than oxalates. Analysis of the urine for the presence of oxalate crystals may help in the diagnosis of rhubarb poisoning.

Rumex species Docks and Sorrels

There are about 20 species and many hybrids present in Britain. At least some of these are known to be poisonous.

Rumex acetosa Common Sorrel

Other common name: Sour Dock

This plant is widespread in Britain, and is common in grassy places on open land and in clearings in woods. There are various subspecies; *Rumex acetosa* subspecies *acetosa* is the one which is most frequently found here. It is an erect perennial with a furrowed stem that grows up to 100 cm tall. The leaves are up to 10 cm long, and have an irregular edge, with broad points especially near the base, where the two lobes point downwards beside the stalk. The upper leaves have scarcely any stalk and tend to clasp the stem. The inflorescence is up to 40 cm long, branched, and usually leafless. The flowers grow close together on short stalks in early and mid summer; they tend to be pendulous, and have reddish outer segments that turn back after flowering to reveal the capsule. Details of poisoning follow the description of *Rumex crispus* (see below).

Rumex acetosella Sheep's Sorrel (Plate 58)

Other common name: Sour Grass (a misnomer, as the plant is not a true grass)

This common perennial plant is found throughout Britain on rough and cultivated land and heaths on acid soils. It is virtually absent from calcareous soils. Stalked leaves grow from the basal rhizome and also on the erect reddish stem which may be up to 30 cm tall. A small, ragged, transparent sheath is present at the point of attachment of the leaf, the blade of which is elongated, pointed at the tip, and has, at the base, two narrow pointed lobes that are usually directed sideways or slightly forwards. The branched inflorescence may be up to 15 cm long and is usually leafless. The male and female flowers appear in midsummer, closely attached to the stem or on short stalks. They are superficially similar, but are borne on separate plants. The flowers are reddish brown and less than 0.5 cm across. The thin, outer segments tend to curve inwards around the inner ones, which enlarge slightly and harden to form an outer covering for the fruit which is triangular, up to 1.5 mm across, and contains tiny dark seeds. Details of poisoning follow the description of *Rumex crispus* (see below).

Rumex crispus Curled Dock

This is the most common *Rumex* species in Britain and is found throughout the country on cultivated and waste ground, and on coastal sand and shingle. The plant is variable in size and form. It is an erect perennial and grows up to 1.5 m high. The leaves are stalked with elongated blades, several times longer than broad; they are rounded at the base and taper towards the tip. The leaf margins are wavy and crinkled. The flowers are grouped in whorls around the stem. Each flower is small, stalked, and green with red swellings (tubercles) developing at the base as the small woody fruits (2.5–3.0 mm) ripen.

Poisonous principles

All of these *Rumex* species contain oxalates, which have long been regarded as their poisonous principles. However, under certain conditions, sorrels and some docks accumulate nitrates in sufficient concentration for them to cause poisoning. An unidentified substance, tentatively called rumicin, has also been incriminated, and more recently it has been suggested that anthraquinone glycosides present in the plants are the main toxins. In the few recorded cases of severe poisoning attributable to the plants, the clinical signs in affected animals are consistent with oxalate poisoning.

Animal poisoning

The likelihood of poisoning, particularly by *Rumex acetosella*, is reduced in areas where liming of the land is common agricultural practice, as this discourages growth of the plant. The plants have a pleasantly sharp taste and are apparently palatable to animals, which often eat them without any obvious ill effects. The conditions under which poisoning does occur are not clearly defined. The nutritional status of the animal, calcium deficiency, acclimatization to the plant by previous feeding of small quantities, the variable concentration of oxalates in the plants, and the amount eaten are factors that may influence reactions to eating these plants.

Soluble oxalates are detoxified during digestion, particularly in ruminants, but if eaten in large enough quantities they may be absorbed into the blood, where they combine with blood calcium, forming calcium oxalate and causing calcium deficiency (hypocalcaemia). Acute hypocalcaemia can lead to rapid death, but this is unusual. Disturbance of calcium metabolism can interfere with bone formation and milk production in pregnant and lactating animals. The most common effect of oxalate poisoning is accumulation of calcium oxalate crystals in the kidneys, where some tubules may become completely blocked, causing renal failure. Oxalate crystals may form in the brain, causing disorders of the central nervous system and sometimes paralysis, or in the rumen where haemorrhages of the walls may occur.

Most reported cases of poisoning have involved sheep. An outbreak in New Zealand[20] (now attributed to *Rumex acetosella* and not, as originally reported, to *Rumex acetosa*, which is rare in that country) resulted, in one flock, in the death of 10% of the ewes, whereas their 5–8-week-old lambs were unaffected. In other similar outbreaks, 10% of a flock of 240 sheep died, and 25% of another flock of 800 were affected. Clinical signs included staggering and, in severe cases, falling and inability to rise. Some animals developed a nasal discharge and all had muscular spasms and abnormal breathing. Coma usually preceded death. Post-mortem examination revealed oxalate crystals and inflammation of the kidneys. In an outbreak in Britain,[21] five sheep died, and many others in the flock of 90 became ill after being allowed access to a field where a dense crop of sorrel (*Rumex acetosa*) had grown up after seeding with grass had failed. The clinical signs included loss of muscular coordination, falling and inability to rise, frothing at the mouth, dilated pupils, and coma. The severity of the reaction was attributed to the animals having eaten a large quantity of sorrel in a short period. Acute renal tubular necrosis as a result of oxalate poisoning was found in sheep that had eaten curled dock (*Rumex crispus*) in the USA.[22] The clinical signs were similar to those reported in *Rumex acetosa* poisoning; two of ten affected ewes died. In cattle, reports on the effects of eating sorrel are inconsistent. Experimental feeding of housed bullocks[23] with up to 100 kg of sorrel over a six-week period had no adverse effects. Other bullocks, which had previously been pastured, ate sorrel reluctantly. In lactating ewes and cattle the initial signs of oxalate poisoning resemble milk fever, and there may be a favourable response to calcium injection (the standard treatment for milk fever), but this response is only transient, as kidney failure develops later.

Early literature[24] records poisoning in horses, as well as sheep, as a result of eating *Rumex acetosella*. The signs were similar to those already described for sheep, but also included a slow, feeble pulse, sunken eyes, and periods of quiescence followed by redevelopment of the clinical signs.

Chickens are said to be resistant to oxalate poisoning because of the high calcium content of their intestines.

Human poisoning

When a family in Spain ate about 1 kg of curled dock (*Rumex crispus*), severe poisoning developed in one man who died in 72 hours despite emergency treatment.[25, 26] The others, who ate less, recovered in a few days. The initial symptoms were vomiting and diarrhoea; coma preceded death. Oxalate poisoning was confirmed at post-mortem examination when typical liver and kidney damage was seen.

Other members of the Polygonaceae family

There are occasional reports of other members of the family having caused poisoning in animals abroad, but cases have rarely been recorded in Britain, although some of the plants are native to this country. They include wireweed or common knotgrass (*Polygonum aviculare*), water pepper (*Polygonum hydropiper*), and persicaria or redshank (*Polygonum persicaria*).

The plants contain a sharp, acrid juice that is irritant to the skin and, if eaten, they cause gastrointestinal irritation and inflammation.[27] Outbreaks of suspected nitrite poisoning by *Polygonum aviculare* occurred in horses in Australia.[28] The animals, which were observed eating the plant when other pasture plants were scarce, were found lying down unable to rise and with abrasions on their sides acquired by struggling; some of the animals died. In Britain, a goat died after eating Japanese knotweed (*Polygonum cuspidatum*).[29]

PRIMULACEAE

Anagallis arvensis Scarlet Pimpernel (Plate 59)

Other common names: Shepherd's Weatherglass; Poor Man's Weatherglass

This small annual or perennial plant is widely distributed throughout Britain, although it is less common than formerly as a weed of cultivation. It usually lies loosely on the surface of the ground, but some branches are erect. The four-angled, much branched stems grow up to 30 cm long and bear small (usually less than 2 cm), paired, stalkless leaves that are oval, but pointed at the tip. The flowers appear on slender stalks from the leaf axils from mid to late summer and are 10–15 mm across. They are bright orange-red (rarely pink or blue) and have, usually five, minutely toothed lobes, giving a star-like appearance. The fruit is a brown, three-angled capsule about 5 mm across.

Poisonous principles
The nature of these is uncertain, although scarlet pimpernel has a long-standing reputation for being poisonous. Aerial parts of the plant are said to contain a glycosidal saponin, the roots another saponin (cyclamin), and an acrid volatile oil has also been isolated. It appears that the plants are poisonous only for limited periods and under certain unknown conditions, so that it is not surprising that there are conflicting reports on their toxicity. There are, however, sufficient authenticated reports of field cases and feeding experiments to warrant treating the plant as poisonous.

Animal poisoning
Early literature states that scarlet pimpernel irritates the intestines and stupefies the nervous system.[1] The plant is reported to produce gastrointestinal signs in dogs and horses, and to be toxic to rabbits and poultry, and (the seed) to birds.[2] An outbreak of poisoning in Pennsylvania, in which six calves died, was attributed to scarlet pimpernel, which was exposed and heavily grazed when the grass in the pasture had been eaten low.[3] In Iraq, horses and mules suffered severe anaemia, listlessness, and debility,[4] when, owing to lack of rain, their normal food was in short supply and was

supplemented with plant material collected by hand and containing a large quantity of scarlet pimpernel. Respiration was shallow, the pulse weak, and faeces varied from normal to loose. Dark froth formed during urination. Recovery was slow, but complete, in animals given vitamins, iron, and a change of straw. Most other reports involve sheep. In one case in Australia,[5] sheep, pastured on land where a prolific growth (90%) of pimpernel had followed ploughing, developed diarrhoea. Rumination was suppressed and the animals were weak, staggered when forced to move, and some became recumbent and died. Samples of *Anagallis* from this pasture were taken at intervals of 2–3 weeks and fed experimentally to sheep. On the first occasion fatal poisoning developed, but there was evidence of decreasing toxicity in successive samples. The results were similar with fresh or dried plants. More recently in South Africa,[6] poisoning of sheep, all of which died, was attributed to *Anagallis arvensis* after other sheep had been fed experimentally with the plant and developed the same clinical signs. These included difficult breathing, depression, stiffness of gait, leg weakness, recumbency, and, in the terminal stages, coma and a rapid drop in body temperature. Typical post-mortem lesions are haemorrhages of the kidneys, heart, and intestines and congestion of the lungs and liver. In Australia, where *Anagallis arvensis* was thought to have caused the death of ewes,[7] the most significant lesions were in the kidneys.

Human poisoning
Contact with the leaves of this plant can cause dermatitis.[8]

Primula obconica Poison Primrose (Plate 60)

Other common name: German Primrose

This is a popular pot plant, and several varieties and hybrids are cultivated that have different floral characteristics. The plant has stalked leaves arising from the base. They are rounded (up to 8 cm across) with slightly undulating, irregular edges, and have coarse hairs making them rough to touch. The flowers are borne in groups at the top of the stalk, which usually grows above the level of the leaves. Each flower may be 3–4 cm in diameter, with notched petals that are usually shades of pink or purple, but sometimes white.

Poisonous principles
An allergenic factor, primin (2-methoxy-6-pentylbenzoquinone), that was recognized in the early 1900s, is present in the plant, mainly in the glandular hairs on the calyx in the flower head; the leaf hairs do not contain the allergen. The allergenic activity is highest in summer and neglible in winter. Other allergens may also be present.

Human poisoning
This is one of the plants most frequently involved in allergic skin reactions in Britain,[9] and it has even been recommended that the plant should not be grown for retail sale. According to various reports, 5–8% of the population are sensitive to the plant, with a higher proportion in women. The fingers and hands are most commonly affected, although the allergen can be transmitted by them to other parts of the body. Initially the affected areas become red, often in streaks, then numerous small blisters develop;

these may enlarge. Itching, burning, and swelling may also be noticed. Repeated exposure to the plant can lead to folding and thickening of the skin, and the development of thin scales, especially around the eyes.[10] It is claimed that sensitized individuals may react to the presence of a plant,[9] even without touching it.

Other members of the Primulaceae family

Some species of *Cyclamen* contain irritant triterpenoid saponins. A cat that ate ten flower heads vomited and became depressed, but recovered within 24 hours.[11] No recent reports of human poisoning by ingestion have been found, but severe gastrointestinal symptoms (mainly after taking the rhizome as a purgative), and contact skin reactions are often mentioned in the literature.

RANUNCULACEAE

The information available, particularly that relating to specific plants in the family, is confusing and sometimes even contradictory. It has been customary to refer to three groups of plants, classified according to their toxins, but it is more probable that only two groups are of importance in this context: those that contain the volatile, oily, irritant substance protoanemonin, and those that contain highly toxic alkaloids. The *Helleborus* species were once classified as a third group.

PROTOANEMONIN GROUP

This group includes species of *Anemone, Clematis, Helleborus,* and *Ranunculus,* in which protoanemonin, the lactone of γ-hydroxyvinylacrylic acid, is present in variable amounts.[1] The concentration of protoanemonin increases during growth and is at its highest during flowering.[2] It is an unstable compound, derived from the glycoside ranunculin, and is readily converted by polymerization into an inert, non-toxic crystalline substance, anemonin. This occurs during drying of the plant, so that hay containing buttercups (or other plants of the family that contain protoanemonin) is safe to use for animal feeding.

The clinical signs of protoanemonin poisoning are similar in all animal species. In the early stages, salivation, inflammation of the mouth, and abdominal pain occur. They may be followed by severe ulceration of the mouth and damage to the digestive and urinary systems. Dark-coloured diarrhoea and dark or blood-stained urine are produced, and at this stage the animals have an unsteady gait, particularly of the hind legs; vision is often impaired or lost. Convulsions usually precede death, although fatal poisoning is rare.

Human ingestion of species containing protoanemonin and related compounds is unlikely because the plants have an acrid taste and cause burning in the mouth and throat. Symptoms may include abdominal pain and diarrhoea.

Anemone nemorosa Wood Anemone (Plate 61)

This plant grows throughout Britain except on waterlogged soils. It is abundant, and often forms a carpet in deciduous woodland. Wood anemones are perennials with slender, brown rhizomes from which the basal leaves grow after flowering. The basal leaves have three lobes, which are further subdivided. Three other leaves grow in a single ring on the otherwise leafless flower stalk. These leaves appear to be more numerous, because of their subdivision into smaller, pointed lobes. The flowers, which appear in early spring, have (usually 6–7) white or pinkish-white petal-like segments. They are 2–4 cm across and are borne singly at the top of the stalk. The seeds form in a downy, globular cluster of fruits.

Poisonous principle

This and other *Anemone* species contain protoanemonin (see above). *Anemone nemorosa* is reported to contain 333 µg per g (wet weight).[1]

Animal poisoning

No reports of specific cases of poisoning have been found, but this may occur as animals sometimes eat wood anemones in early spring, when other green food is scarce. Clinical signs similar to those caused by other protoanemonin-containing plants could be expected.

Clematis vitalba Traveller's Joy (Plate 62)

Other common name: Old Man's Beard

This perennial plant is a rampant climber that often completely obscures the vegetation over which it climbs. It can hinder the establishment of new hedges, and also threaten older ones. The stems are woody, up to 30 m long and 10 cm in diameter at the base, where they twine strongly round each other or around other trees and shrubs. Longitudinal splitting of the bark, often with peeling, is a characteristic feature. The leaves are compound and have 3–5 stalked leaflets, which are oval but pointed at the tip. The fragrant flowers are borne at the ends of the stems or in the axils of the leaves in loose, stalked clusters. They are up to 2 cm in diameter and have greenish-white, petal-like sepals. The fruits (achenes) form in large heads and have long, whitish, feathery plumes that form the hairy mass from which the plant derives its name of old man's beard.

Poisonous principle

Clematis vitalba, as well as some cultivated *Clematis* species and varieties, contains protoanemonin (see above); there is considerable variation in the protoanemonin content of the different species that have been studied. That of *Clematis vitalba* has been reported as 150 µg per g (wet weight).[1]

Animal poisoning

All parts of the plant are said to be poisonous; animals rarely eat it, possibly because of its acrid taste and its irritant effect on the mouth. If it is eaten, however, it causes gastrointestinal irritation and severe abdominal pain; death may result.[3] Numerous fragments of leaves and stems of *Clematis vitalba* were recovered at post-mortem examination of a cow that died a few hours after first showing clinical signs.[4] Before death the animal was breathing noisily and had inflamed, swollen eyes, ulceration of the muzzle, loss of muscle tone, abdominal pain, and weakness.

Human poisoning
Protoanemonin is an irritant that can damage the lining of the digestive tract and cause vomiting and diarrhoea (sometimes with blood). Contact with the sap of the plants can result in blistering of the skin.[5]

Helleborus species Hellebores

There is confusion over the common names of these plants as some species of *Veratrum* (Liliaceae) are called false, or white hellebore, or simply hellebore. *Veratrum* species are also poisonous, but the plants are not similar in appearance.

In Britain the native species are *Helleborus foetidus* and *Helleborus viridis*. These two plants, subspecies of them, including *Helleborus viridis* subspecies *occidentalis*, and also Christmas and Easter (or Lent) roses (*Helleborus niger*) and their numerous hybrids are grown in gardens throughout the country.

Helleborus foetidus Stinking Hellebore (Plate 63)

Other common name: Bear's Foot

Stinking hellebore is found as a wild plant in only a very few localities, on calcareous soils in Britain. It is a perennial plant that has a robust, branched, overwintering stem, which grows up to 80 cm high and bears stalked leaves, the bases of which sheath the stem. The leaves are light green and tough, and are divided into long narrow segments with toothed edges. The flowers develop in spring in loose clusters. They are drooping, 1–3 cm across, and have insignificant petals but prominent yellowish-green, incurved, petal-like sepals sometimes tinged reddish purple at the tips. The fruits are 2–5 carpels, which are slightly joined near the base and bear the persistent styles of the flower above. They contain smooth, black seeds with a white fleshy ridge. Details of poisoning follow the description of *Helleborus viridis* (see below).

Helleborus niger Christmas Rose and Easter (or Lent) Rose

This plant is sometimes, incorrectly, named *Veratrum nigrum*. The plants in this group are variable in form, but in general the leaf segments are wider and more coarsely toothed than those of the wild species, and the petal-like sepals of the flowers may be white, pinkish, or uniformly dark reddish purple. Details of poisoning follow the description of *Helleborus viridis* (see below).

Helleborus viridis Green Hellebore

Other common name: Bear's Foot

Green hellebores can be found as wild plants on calcareous soils in Britain, but are very local in distribution. They are grown here in gardens and may become naturalized in a few places. They are perennial plants, similar to stinking hellebores, but shorter. They do not have an overwintering stem, the leaves are smaller and less prominently toothed, and the flowers uniformly yellowish green.

Poisonous principles

The plants contain protoanemonin (see above), which seems to be their main toxic constituent. The content of this irritant toxin in *Helleborus foetidus*, *Helleborus niger*, and *Helleborus viridis* has been reported as 672, 5820 and 28 µg per g (wet weight), respectively.[1] Information on the nature of other possible toxins in hellebores is confusing, and sometimes contradictory.[6]

Animal poisoning

Decoctions of hellebores were used formerly as purgatives, local anaesthetics, abortifacients, or to clear parasitic infestations on the skin. It is not clear whether poisoning by application to the skin took place by skin absorption or whether the animals may have licked the treated areas. When applied to the neck of cattle to remove lice, a preparation of green hellebore resulted in prostration, loss of appetite, cessation of rumination, and swelling of the neck. Loss of condition of the coat, muscular tremors, and difficult breathing were also reported.[7] It is now more likely that poisoning by hellebores will occur after animals have had access to growing or discarded garden plants. Bullocks that had eaten green hellebore plants discarded from a garden developed abdominal pain, fluid faeces, and moved with great reluctance.[8] Some animals died within 2–3 days and others after 10–11 days. Similar signs occurred in cattle that ate stinking hellebore (*Helleborus foetidus*); some died.[9] Dark-coloured diarrhoea containing blood and mucus, violent straining alternating with quiet periods, and excessive, frequent urination have also been recorded in cases of hellebore poisoning in cattle and sheep.[3] Post-mortem examination reveals inflammation of the digestive tract, sometimes with ulceration. Haemorrhages occur in the intestines and around the heart.

Human poisoning

In the past, before the medicinal use of hellebore preparations was abandoned because of the risks, there were incidents of poisoning recorded: disturbance of vision and abortion occurred in a pregnant woman who used a decoction of hellebores to remove lice.[7] Drinking milk from poisoned cows has caused diarrhoea and vomiting.[3] No recent case reports have been found, but the possibility of irritation of the gastrointestinal tract and skin is often mentioned.

Ranunculus species Buttercups and Crowfoots (Plate 64)

Because of their abundance and widespread distribution in pastures in Britain, the buttercups and crowfoots are the members of the Ranunculaceae most likely to be eaten by animals in this country. However, grazing animals generally reject these plants, possibly because of their acrid taste, but when other food is scarce or when young animals (particularly calves) are first turned out to pasture they may eat them. The *Ranunculus* species that occur in pastures can be eradicated by the use of hormone weedkillers such as 2,4-D. It is recommended that treated areas should not be grazed for at least 14 days after application because, after treatment, the plants are consumed readily by animals even if they were not grazed before.[10] This may be due to loss of a selective instinct on the part of the animal, increased palatability of the plant during growth disturbances caused by the chemicals, or the development of a taste for the weedkiller itself.

Ranunculus acris Meadow Buttercup

Other common names: Common Buttercup; Field Buttercup; Tall Buttercup; Crowfoot

This plant is widespread in pastures and damp meadows throughout Britain, except on acid soils. Meadow buttercup is a much branched, hairy perennial with stems that are erect or may creep along the ground but do not form roots at the nodes. The basal leaves have long stalks and the upper ones short stalks. The leaf blades are hairy and deeply divided into 2–7 lobes, which are themselves deeply indented and toothed. The flower stalks are also hairy, and may be 15–100 cm tall, depending on the nature of the soil. They terminate in loose, irregular clusters of flowers, each up to 25 mm across. The petals are rounded, glossy, and bright yellow (occasionally pale yellow or white); the sepals are close to the petals and not reflexed; the seeds develop singly in small (2.5–3.0 mm) fruits (achenes), which are smooth, have a short hooked beak and are tightly grouped together. Details of poisoning follow the description of *Ranunculus sceleratus* (see below).

Ranunculus bulbosus Bulbous Buttercup

Other common name: St Anthony's Turnip

This plant occurs throughout Britain on dry pastures, grassy slopes, and garden lawns, but is less common in the north. It is a hairy perennial that grows from a rounded or flattened stem tuber, which bears fleshy roots. The stems are usually erect, up to 40 cm high (usually shorter), and bear deeply cut, three-lobed leaves of which the central lobe is long-stalked. The flowers are 1.5–3.0 cm in diameter and develop in loose clusters on hairy, furrowed stems. The petals are bright yellow (rarely pale yellow or white) and the sepals turn back against the stem. The single-seeded fruits (achenes), which are tightly grouped together, are finely pitted, dark brown with a paler border and have a short beak at the tip. Details of poisoning follow the description of *Ranunculus sceleratus* (see below).

Ranunculus sceleratus Celery-leaved Crowfoot

Other common names: Celery-leaved Buttercup; Cursed Crowfoot

Celery-leaved crowfoot grows throughout Britain, usually in muddy places beside shallow water. It is generally an annual although it occasionally survives a winter. The plant has fibrous roots and a stout, erect stem, which grows up to 60 cm high and is hollow and branched. The lower leaves have long stalks with three deeply segmented, toothed lobes near the top, giving them a superficial resemblance to edible celery, although the stalks are thinner. The stem leaves have short stalks and are divided into narrower segments. The flowering stems are smooth, furrowed, and branched and bear loose clusters of flowers with pale yellow petals and greenish sepals of almost equal size. The single-seeded fruits (achenes) are numerous, about 1 mm across and crowded together in a tight oval group.

Poisonous principles

Protoanemonin (see above) is responsible for the toxicity of *Ranunculus* species. Its content in *Ranunculus acris* and *Ranunculus bulbosus* has been reported as 1372 and 7766 µg per g (wet weight), respectively.[1] The protoanemonin content of *Ranunculus repens*, which has not been found to cause poisoning, is considerably lower (126 µg per g). From the clinical signs described in some reports of poisoning attributed to buttercups, it would appear that not all cases were due to protoanemonin.

Animal poisoning

Ranunculus acris is reputed to cause poisoning in cattle and sheep, but few cases have been reported recently, possibly because pastures contain less of these plants than formerly. In Norway, five cows in late pregnancy were turned out on to pasture where *Ranunculus acris* was abundant.[11] They developed diarrhoea that was sometimes blood-stained, a rapid pulse, and noisy respiration; all died or were killed because of their deteriorating condition. Post-mortem findings in the digestive tract were typical of protoanemonin poisoning; there was also fatty infiltration of the liver and kidneys. When fed at the flowering stage to cattle in increasing amounts up to 25 kg per day for two weeks, the animals gained weight and showed no ill effects, although initially they were reluctant to eat the plant.[12] In other experiments,[13] steers fed an average of 7 kg and sheep 3.5 kg of the green plant daily were unaffected. In Yugoslavia, poisoning occurred in five cattle on a pasture where *Ranunculus acris* and pasque flower (*Anemone pulsatilla*), another member of the Ranunculaceae that contains protoanemonin, were prevalent.[14] The animals developed chocolate-coloured diarrhoea, blood-stained urine, and decreased body temperature. Paralysis of a pig after eating the plant is reported.[15] Severe swelling of the eyes, nose, muzzle, and lips developed in a dog that ate the plant; leaves, stems, and flowers were seen in its vomit.[16]

Ranunculus bulbosus was suspected of poisoning a cow in Britain.[17] The animal salivated and coughed and there was a mucous discharge from the nostrils. Swaying of the hindquarters and uneasy movements of the legs were noticed. A period of noisy breathing preceded recovery. In a case of suspected poisoning by *Ranunculus bulbosus* in a heifer in the USA,[18] there was liver damage, with secondary photosensitization in addition to the usual signs of gastrointestinal irritation.

Ranunculus sceleratus is reputed to be the most poisonous *Ranunculus* species, but it may be that because of its rich, luxuriant growth it is eaten in larger quantities than other species. All classes of livestock are susceptible, but poisoning is reported most frequently in cattle.[19, 20] Severe blistering of the mouth was seen in housed goats fed *Ranunculus acris* and *Ranunculus sceleratus*. One animal died and two others were severely ill.[3] On a pasture consisting mainly of *Ranunculus acris* and *Ranunculus sceleratus* a horse developed paralysis, muscle tremors, colic, and convulsions; there was also loss of hearing and sight. Recovery occurred in a few days but general weakness persisted for two weeks.[21]

Human poisoning

In separate incidents reported in Britain,[3] vomiting occurred almost immediately in two children after chewing the bulbous roots of *Ranunculus bulbosus* mistaken for pignuts (*Conopodium majus*). Skin contact with buttercups can result in severe blistering of the skin.[5]

187

ALKALOID GROUP

This group includes species of *Aconitum* and *Delphinium* that contain polycyclic diterpene alkaloids.

Aconitum napellus Monkshood (Plate 65)

Other common names: Aconite

The common name, aconite, could lead to confusion with another plant in the Ranunculaceae, the winter aconite, a small plant with yellow flowers that is an *Eranthis* species; although no reports have been found of this plant having caused poisoning, it does contain potentially toxic substances.

According to most authorities *Aconitum napellus* is an aggregate of forms varying in morphological detail in different ecological and geographical areas; various subspecies are recognized. Wild aconites are now seldom found in Britain except in a few localized areas of south-west England and Wales, usually beside streams, in the shade. Many cultivated forms of *Aconitum* are grown in gardens throughout the country and in some areas these have become naturalized.

Monkshood is a perennial plant with a dark, tuberous tap root and a usually unbranched stem up to 1 m high. The leaves are light green, soft, and more or less triangular in outline, but deeply and irregularly divided into narrow pointed segments. The flowers form in a terminal spike and are helmet-shaped, and deep blue or bluish mauve (white in some cultivated varieties). The fruits usually form in a compact group of three elongated follicles, up to 2 cm long, and contain seeds with winged edges.

Poisonous principles

The plants contain the polycyclic diterpene alkaloid aconitine; other similar alkaloids including isoaconitine, lycaconitine, and napelline are also present. Because of the highly toxic nature of aconitine, monkshood has the reputation of being the most poisonous British plant. Despite this, or perhaps because its poisonous nature is so well known and it has been removed from places where animals could eat it, there are very few reports of animal or human poisoning by the plant. It is thought that, in the USA, some cases of poisoning attributed to monkshood were due to ingestion of the closely related larkspurs (*Delphinium* species), which are much more common plants. The alkaloid content varies according to the part of the plant examined, the stage of growth, and the growing conditions.

Animal poisoning

The alkaloids in monkshood are toxic either by ingestion or, to a lesser extent, by absorption through the skin. The effect is at first stimulatory, with rapid breathing and excitation of heart muscles, but soon becomes depressive, with numbness progressing to paralysis, slow laboured breathing, and a slow, irregular pulse.[22, 23] Death, which may occur within an hour of eating the plant, results from asphyxia and circulatory failure and is usually sudden. A fatal dose of dried root of the plant has been estimated as 5 g for a dog and 350 g for a horse.[23] Cattle that had eaten considerable quantities (an estimated 5 kg each) of delphiniums and monkshood discarded from a garden[3] showed little evidence of pain, but were unable to rise, and had cold skin, dilated pupils and very feeble breathing and pulse. Despite attempts to save the two animals they died within five hours. Post-mortem examination revealed the plants in the stomach, changes in the heart and lungs consistent with suffocation, but little damage to the digestive system. Cases of poisoning in horses have been described in early literature.[24] In Britain, a dog that ate monkshood vomited and had diarrhoea.[25] An increased heart rate and disturbances in cardiac rhythym were also reported; the dog recovered.

Human poisoning

Burning of the mouth and throat, abdominal pain, vomiting accompanied by intense thirst, headache, coldness, slow pulse, paralysis, convulsions, delirium, and coma have been reported in cases of monkshood poisoning;[24,26] in this context the plant is often referred to as aconite. Reference is made in older literature to poisoning resulting from the roots being eaten in mistake for horse radish.[6] Intentional ingestion of the roots by a 40-year-old man in Britain resulted in his death within a few hours, despite emergency life-support treatment in hospital.[25] He had shown typical symptoms of monkshood poisoning, and was cyanotic, with extremely cold skin and fixed dilated pupils before cardiac arrest. A fatal case was also reported in a 20-month-old child who had picked and eaten the flowers in a garden; vomiting and signs of severe abdominal pain were followed by cardiac and respiratory arrest.[27] Some Chinese herbal medicines stated to contain aconite have given rise to rapid heart rates and have caused death.[28]

Symptoms can even result from handling the plant: a botanist dissecting monkshood experienced palpitations, and tingling in the fingers, but had recovered by the next day;[29] and in a flower seller who had been handling and trimming blooms,[25] nausea, weakness, a rapid heart beat, and headache were reported. She was admitted to hospital, but recovered rapidly when no longer exposed to the plant.

There is no specific antidote for monkshood poisoning. Stomach lavage, warmth, oxygen to assist breathing, and drugs to stimulate the heart may be beneficial.

Delphinium species Delphiniums and Larkspurs

Larkspurs are not native in Britain, but some species have been introduced and become established locally, and many hybrid perennials (delphiniums) are cultivated throughout the country. Although there is considerable variation in the size and form of *Delphinium* species, they resemble monkshood but are generally larger; the flowers are not helmet-shaped, and the elongated spur on the flowers is a distinguishing feature. As in monkshood, the flowers are usually blue, but many shades of the colour are found and some are white or mauvish red.

Poisonous principles

All species of *Delphinium* are poisonous, as they contain polycyclic diterpene alkaloids similar to those in monkshood, but different species vary in toxicity. Of the numerous diterpene alkaloids identified, the most toxic seems to be methyllycaconitine, a potent neuromuscular blocking agent.[30] The concentration of these alkaloids is highest in young plants and in the seeds.[31]

Animal poisoning

Delphinium poisoning causes severe and often fatal illness, with clinical signs similar to those produced by the monkshood alkaloids, but it is unlikely that animals will be poisoned by *Delphinium* in Britain unless they have access to gardens or garden rubbish containing the plants. Cattle in particular will consume the plants readily if they are available, and in North America[32] where larkspur (mainly tall larkspur, *Delphinium barbeyi*) is well established, especially in the Western Ranges, it is considered the most dangerous plant in the area and is responsible for many deaths. Spraying of the plants with weedkillers appears to increase their toxicity[33] and palatability.[34] The injection of calves with methyllycaconitine has caused agitation, difficult breathing, and incoordination;[35] an effective treatment was the intravenous injection of physostigmine (0.08 mg per kg body weight). Intravenous or intraperitoneal administration of physostigmine is effective, but intravenous injections must be given slowly to avoid the adverse effects of the drug; this treatment can be fatal if given to an animal not poisoned by larkspur alkaloids.[36] In New Zealand, poisoning of rams occurred after eating *Delphinium hybridum* that had been thrown to them from a garden.[37] Of 16 rams that ate the plants, eight died within a few hours with clinical signs including incoordination, violent muscular spasms, particularly of the hind limbs, and inability to rise. An earlier outbreak of poisoning of sheep from eating *Delphinium consolidum*[38] occurred in New Zealand. The signs were similar to those described in the rams. Persistent vomiting was reported in a puppy that ate delphinium stalks.[25]

Human poisoning
This is an unlikely occurrence, but a man who ingested an unknown number of leaves and seeds of delphinium developed symptoms five hours later.[25] These included nausea, vomiting, abdominal pain, blurred vision, and dry skin and mouth. Restlessness, agitation, and dilatation of pupils persisted for 12 hours, after which he recovered fully.

Other members of the Ranunculaceae family

The marsh marigold (*Caltha palustris*), meadow rue (*Thalictrum* species), and globe flowers (*Trollius* species) contain protoanemonin. Lesser celandine (*Ranunculus ficaria*) and lesser spearwort (*Ranunculus flammula*) have poisoned grazing animals, and greater spearwort (*Ranunculus lingua*) also contains a similar irritant substance (possibly protoanemonin).

Columbines (*Aquilegia* species) are said to contain alkaloids similar to those in monkshood (*Aconitum napellus*), but no reports of poisoning have been found. Pheasant's eye (*Adonis annua*) may contain both protoanemonin and also glycosides that could affect the heart. Baneberry (*Actaea* species) can cause severe gastrointestinal disturbances and also affect the nervous system (dizziness, confusion, and hallucinations have been reported), but there is lack of agreement on the nature of the toxin(s) involved.

RHAMNACEAE

In this family there are two native British shrubs that cause a similar type of poisoning: alder buckthorn (*Frangula alnus*) and purging buckthorn (*Rhamnus cathartica*).

Frangula alnus Alder Buckthorn

Alder buckthorn (formerly named *Rhamnus frangula*) grows on damp, peaty soils in many parts of Britain, but is absent from Scotland. It is commonly 4–5 m high, has no thorns, and the branches grow upwards at an acute angle to the main stem. Except in very old trees the bark is smooth. The buds have no scales but are covered with brownish hairs. The shiny, green, stalked leaves, which turn yellow or red in autumn, are oval with a pointed tip and not toothed. Small, whitish-green, bisexual flowers develop in groups of two or three throughout the summer. The fruits are berries that change from green to red and then to purplish black as they ripen. Details of poisoning follow the description of *Rhamnus cathartica* (see below).

Rhamnus cathartica Purging Buckthorn (Plate 66)

Other common name: Common Buckthorn

This shrub is native in Britain where it grows in scrub and open woodland on fen peat and calcareous soils. It is a thorny, deciduous shrub, usually 4–6 m tall. The branches are opposite and grow almost at right angles to the main stem. The old bark is fissured and scaly, with an orange blaze. The buds have dark scales and from them develop stalked, dull green leaves that turn yellow or brownish in autumn. They are oval, with prominent veins and small, regular serrations at the edges. The male and female flowers, which appear from early summer, are borne on separate plants. They are small, inconspicuous, and yellowish green. The fruit is a 3–4-seeded berry that changes from green to black as it ripens.

Poisonous principles

Both of these shrubs contain glycosides that, on hydrolysis, yield purgative anthraquinones. Of these, emodin (a trihydroxymethylanthraquinone) is the active principle of some purgative drugs, such as the common laxative, cascara sagrada, which is derived from the dried bark of *Rhamnus purshiana*.

Animal poisoning

Poisoning by the growing plants is rare, but a fatal case was reported in a cow,[1] which ate a large amount of leaves, twigs, and berries of alder buckthorn (*Frangula alnus*). The animal became ill suddenly and developed diarrhoea, vomiting, cramps, slow pulse, and slight fever before death, which occurred within a few hours of eating the plant. Post-mortem examination revealed leaves of the shrub in the stomach, and gastrointestinal inflammation. Access to alder buckthorn clippings on pasture resulted in signs of colic in one of ten horses and diarrhoea in seven;[2] all recovered within a week. In dogs, overdosing with a laxative prepared from *Rhamnus cathartica* has caused illness and death, with severe gastrointestinal haemorrhages.[3]

Human poisoning

In the past, this has sometimes followed the medicinal use by adults of buckthorn as a laxative or abortive, but now most frequently involves only children, who eat the berries or chew the twigs. The symptoms are usually mild and limited to transient abdominal pain with vomiting and diarrhoea, but, depending on the quantity eaten, there may be violent haemorrhagic, gastrointestinal symptoms accompanied by fluid depletion and kidney damage; muscular convulsions, difficult breathing, and collapse may occur.[4, 5] Fatal poisoning was reported in Poland in two young children who had been playing with and eating berries of *Rhamnus cathartica*.[6] The main symptoms were vomiting and diarrhoea, followed by skin haemorrhages, muscular weakness, and coma. Haemorrhages of the adrenal glands and signs of adrenal failure were seen at post-mortem examination.

Treatment, in severe cases, should include stomach lavage, after which fluids and demulcents should be given.[7]

ROSACEAE

This family includes many of the common fruit trees (grown commercially or in gardens) such as apple (*Malus domestica*), cherry (*Prunus cerasus*), plum (*Prunus domestica*), peach (*Prunus persica*), and pear (*Pyrus communis*), as well as blackthorn or sloe (*Prunus spinosa*) that grows wild in Britain, almond (*Amygdalus communis*), various ornamental shrubs, and cherry laurel (*Prunus laurocerasus*). In this country, cherry laurel is the most likely of these to cause poisoning.

Amygdalus communis Almond
Prunus species and *Pyrus* species Fruit Trees

The foliage of these trees and especially the seeds (kernels or pips) in the fruits are poisonous as they contain cyanogenic glycosides. The toxic reactions in animal and human poisoning are similar to those described for the cherry laurel (*Prunus laurocerasus*, see below).

Animal poisoning
Some cherries that are garden trees or have become naturalized in Britain have caused poisoning in other countries. In North America, cyanide poisoning by various cherry trees, particularly the leaves of the wild black cherry (*Prunus serotina*) and the chokecherry (*Prunus virginiana*) cause significant losses of livestock.[1] All parts of these bushes or trees contain the cyanogenic glycoside prunasin, the concentration being highest in dry years. Higher prunasin levels have been demonstrated in buds and flowers than in fruit;[1] leaves may contain many times the amount considered dangerous. Death, preceded by signs typical of cyanide poisoning, has been reported in three horses and a cow,[2] and a young dog[3] that ate chokecherry leaves. Two donkeys died after eating the bark of the chokecherry.[4] These species of *Prunus*, with high cyanogenic glycoside content, do not occur in Britain except as ornamentals.

Stones from the fruit of some members of the Rosaceae have also been known to poison animals. In one outbreak, 18 pigs died after feeding on plum stones left after jam or fruit juice preparation.[5] A dog that ate about ten plum stones became unable to stand, was hyperexcitable and had fits for about 36 hours; it recovered.[6] In Norway when, after a heavy crop, plums were added to feed given to bacon pigs,[7] a very distinct almond taste was noticed in the meat, irrespective of the method of preserving or cooking. Cattle have been poisoned by eating cherry leaves,[8] plum stones[9] or bitter almonds.[10] In Scotland, three cows died after eating the foliage and flowering shoots of bird cherry (*Prunus padus*) that had grown through a netting fence.[11] They also had liver damage as a result of chronic ragwort poisoning. This complication may explain some of the nervous signs they showed (aggressive behaviour, circling, and stupor). Fruits and leaves of crab apple (*Malus sylvestris*) were eaten by two goats.[12] Typical signs of cyanide poisoning developed; one goat died. Vomiting, diarrhoea, muscular twitching, increased body temperature, and collapse occurred in a 10-month-old puppy that ate eight crab apples;[6] it recovered after symptomatic treatment. Sloes were reported to have caused cyanosis, collapse and death in a rabbit, and incoordination, congested mucous membranes and collapse in two dogs that recovered.[6]

Treatment must be initiated quickly as hydrocyanic acid is absorbed readily. Stomach lavage or an emetic (where appropriate) should be given. The most effective treatment is intravenous injection of sodium thiosulphate;[13, 14] this combines with hydrocyanic acid to form non-toxic thiocyanate, which is excreted readily. Intravenous sodium nitrite[13, 14] helps to induce the formation of methaemoglobin, which combines with hydrocyanic acid to give non-toxic cyanmethaemoglobin.

Human poisoning

The most likely sources are the kernels of fruits, or almonds. The so-called 'sweet' almonds have a lower content of cyanogenic glycosides than 'bitter' almonds. In separate outbreaks in Israel,[15] eight children were poisoned after eating a large number of apricot kernels, and 16 children became seriously ill after eating a dessert prepared from the kernels. Such desserts are common local dishes, but prolonged boiling of the kernels is part of the normal preparation, and an acid environment is also maintained, inhibiting the activity of the enzyme that releases hydrocyanic acid. This pre-treatment was omitted in the outbreak reported. In the first incident the symptoms began two hours after the kernels were eaten and included vomiting, distress, faintness, weakness, unsteadiness, rapid breathing, flushing of the face, and headache. One child became comatose and died. In the second incident, symptoms became apparent half an hour after eating the dessert. They were similar but more severe, and three children died. Although apricot kernels are often eaten in some countries, poisoning rarely occurs, possibly because the content of the cyanogenic glycoside, amygdalin, varies considerably (from 9 to over 200 mg per 100 g), the concentration being higher in wild apricots.[15] Apricot kernels have also given rise to cyanide poisoning in Turkey[16] and the USA. Toxic reactions have also followed the use of laetrile (amygdalin) that was claimed to be an anti-cancer drug.[17] In a case reported from the USA, a man died of cyanide poisoning after eating a cupful of apple pips.[18] A two-year-old boy who had eaten five or six fruits from an ornamental cherry in this country developed blisters on the tip of his tongue and had flushed cheeks and a rapid pulse.[6] The common practice of adding a few fruit stone kernels to the fruit in jam making should present no hazard, as the prolonged boiling involved and the acidity of the fruit will inhibit the enzymes responsible for releasing hydrocyanic acid.

In addition to the treatment described under animal poisoning, the administration of dicobalt edetate, oxygen, 4-dimethylaminophenol, amyl nitrate, and hydroxycobalamin can also be used.[19]

Prunus laurocerasus Cherry Laurel (Plate 67)

The name of this plant sometimes causes confusion with the plant commonly called laurel or sweet bay (*Laurus nobilis*), which is a member of the Lauraceae family, and with spurge laurel (*Daphne laureola*), a poisonous plant in the Thymelaeaceae family.

Cherry laurel is not native in Britain, but has become naturalized in many places and grows as an evergreen shrub or small tree, up to 6 m high. It is commonly found in parks or gardens, where it is often used for hedging. The bark is dark and fairly smooth and the leaves elongated (up to 18 cm long), narrowing to a rounded point at the tip. They are leathery, dark green, and glossy above and have stalks 5–10 cm long. The white or creamy-white flowers are borne in erect clusters. The fruits are single-seeded, purplish-black, ovoid berries up to 1 cm long. There are several cultivated forms with different growth habits, leaf sizes, and colours.

Poisonous principles

The leaves and the seeds within the fruits contain cyanogenic glycosides (mainly prunasin and amygdalin). The fleshy part of the ripe fruit contains only very small quantities of the glycosides. When hydrolysed by the appropriate enzymes in crushed plant material or, in some circumstances, in the digestive system, the glycosides yield hydrocyanic acid. During hydrolysis, glucose and benzaldehyde are also produced, the latter being responsible for the almond smell of the stomach contents and tissues of poisoned animals. Hydrocyanic acid inactivates cellular respiratory enzymes (cytochrome oxidases), and it is oxygen starvation of the central nervous system that causes death. The toxic reaction depends not only on the cyanogenic glycoside content of the plants, which may vary (the concentration being higher in young plants and during summer), but also on the amount ingested, the rate of digestion, the degree of maceration of the plant tissue, the size and type of animal, and its ability to detoxify hydrocyanic acid.[20] The cyanogenic properties of cherry laurel have been known for many years and sometimes exploited, e.g. by amateur entomologists, who have killed insects by placing them in a closed vessel containing crushed leaves of the plant.

Animal poisoning

All animals are susceptible to cyanide poisoning. The minimum lethal dose of hydrocyanic acid in most species is 2 mg per kg body weight.[21] It has been stated that, in cattle, 1 kg of cherry laurel leaves would be sufficient to kill a 500-kg animal.[13] Ruminants are more susceptible than monogastric animals (e.g. horses, pigs, dogs) to poisoning with cyanogenic plants, as hydrolysis of the glycosides, resulting in hydrocyanic acid production, can also occur in the rumen, where the pH is favourable for the activity of the hydrolysing enzyme. In non-ruminants, the high acidity of the stomach contents inhibits the plant enzymes, although these may be active during further digestion in the duodenum. The situation is somewhat complicated by the fact that, as well as being more susceptible, ruminants (like other animals) can also detoxify hydrocyanic acid, converting it to non-toxic thiocyanate by the action of the enzyme rhodanese.[20] The severity of poisoning is therefore determined by many factors.

In acute poisoning, animals may die suddenly, but in less severe cases the clinical signs[13, 14] include respiratory difficulties, dilated pupils, muscular tremors, distension of the abdomen with gas (particularly in cattle), falling and sometimes convulsions.

Visible mucous membranes are bright red initially, because oxygen from the blood is not being transferred to the tissues.

In one well-documented case,[22] two ewes were found dead and a number of others became ill after grazing in a public park in Scotland. The pasture was poor, and the sheep had free access to a hedge of cherry laurel. The clinical signs were characteristic of cyanide poisoning and included very rapid breathing, jerky movements, staggering, and, in some cases, falling, and convulsions. The severity of the reaction varied among the animals, but in all cases lasted for no longer than a few minutes at a time, after which the signs abated rapidly. They recurred, however, at irregular intervals throughout the flock for five days, when all the animals were slaughtered. It was suggested that the repeated attacks occurred with successive regurgitation and mastication of rumen contents. Post-mortem examination did not reveal any definite lesions, but portions of cherry laurel leaves, in various stages of maceration, were found in the rumen of some of the ewes. In a follow-up experiment,[23] a sheep given 115 g of minced cherry laurel leaves in water showed rapid breathing, followed by collapse, grinding of teeth, salivation and attempts to vomit, twitching of facial muscles, and galloping movements of the limbs; death occurred one-and-a-half hours later. This sheep was apparently unaffected when fed previously with 100 g of the leaves. Goats that ate cherry laurel leaves showed signs that included staggering, cyanosis, panting, drooling, bloat, and recumbency, but all recovered.[6]

If death occurs shortly after eating the poisonous material, post-mortem examination shows little evidence of poisoning, except that plant fragments will be found in the stomach. In cases where death occurs less rapidly, however, the changes (similar in all species) include bright red blood, purplish-blue coloration of organs and tissues (resulting from lack of oxygen), congestion of the lungs with blood, and an almond smell from the stomach contents and, sometimes, from the cut surfaces of other organs.

Human poisoning

Cherry laurel poisoning can occur if the leaves are used by mistake for those of the 'true' laurel or sweet bay (*Laurus nobilis*) for flavouring food.[13] Serious poisoning by the berries is unlikely to occur unless the seeds are chewed.[6, 24]

Other members of the Rosaceae family

Hawthorn (*Crataegus monogyna*) was thought to be the cause of urine discoloration in cows that had eaten berries in a year when the crop was very heavy.[25] The urine was normal in colour initially, but changed to orange, then brown on the floor of the milking parlour and stained the feet of the animals; a temporary drop in milk yield was recorded. The bark of hawthorn contains the toxic lactone glycoside esculin, but no reports of poisoning from this source have been found.

It is popularly assumed that the berries of *Cotoneaster*, *Pyracantha*, mountain ash or rowan (*Sorbus aucuparia*), and other similar shrubs or trees are poisonous, and enquiries about them are among those received most frequently by poisons centres. Vomiting and diarrhoea have been reported in dogs that ate *Cotoneaster* berries,[6] and children who have eaten them are often referred to hospital. The berries are, however, of only doubtful or low toxicity, and the concentration of cyanogenic glycosides varies greatly with the *Cotoneaster* species and the ripeness of the fruit. *Pyracantha* berries caused vomiting in an 18-month-old boy,[6] and mild gastrointestinal disturbances may follow the consumption of fresh *Sorbus* berries.[26] When cooked, e.g. for use in preserves, their toxicity is almost completely eliminated and can be disregarded. The seeds and leaves of quinces (*Cydonia oblonga*) and ornamental quinces or japonicas (*Chaenomeles* species) also contain small amounts of cyanogenic glycosides, but no reports of poisoning have been found.

RUTACEAE

Ruta graveolens Rue (Plate 68)

Rue does not grow wild in this country, but is frequently planted in gardens as it is an attractive foliage plant as well as a flowering shrub. It has a compact habit and can grow up to 1 m high. Near the base the branches are woody, with a pale greyish-brown bark, but nearer the top they are green. The leaves are a pale greyish green, and deeply lobed. The lobes are variable and irregular in shape, the terminal ones being ovoid, and some others thin and finger-like. Small, four- or five-petalled, yellow flowers develop at the top of the plant in summer. Their individual stalks are of variable length, so that all of the flowers on one stalk are at more or less the same level. When crushed the foliage of the plant has an unpleasant acrid smell.

Poisonous principles
The whole plant contains furanocoumarins, including 5- and 8-methoxypsoralen (bergapten and xanthotoxin, respectively) that make the skin hypersensitive to ultraviolet light. The concentrations of psoralens are said to be highest in the seed pods, but are also present on the leaf surface, where they may play a defensive role. In addition, α-pinene, limonene, and eucalyptol (1,8-cineole) are present. The plant and extracts of it have been used medicinally for centuries to treat a variety of ailments; they have also been used for flavouring food.

Human poisoning
Rue is the commonest cause of photodermatitis arising from garden plants in Britain, and the reactions can be very severe.[1] Most cases occur in summer when the skin is more likely to be exposed, and when the psoralen content of the plants is highest. Exposure to sunlight after contact with the plant leads initially to redness and itching. In the days following contact there is often oedema, and very large, fluid-filled blisters form and coalesce. It is not unusual for a brown pigmentation of the skin to persist for several months; the affected areas of skin may remain hypersensitive to sunlight for even longer. Apart from the more usual incidents involving skin contact while gardening, when the plant is handled[2] or harvested[3], or when children brush against it while playing, typical clinical signs have developed after the skin has been rubbed with rue leaves for their allegedly insect-repellent properties.[4,5]

SCROPHULARIACEAE

Digitalis purpurea Foxglove (Plate 69)

The foxglove is widely distributed throughout Britain, particularly in open places in woods and on heaths and hillsides. It is often the dominant plant species at the stage of regeneration of clearings or burnt areas, before shrubs and trees become re-established.

The plant is an erect biennial (occasionally perennial) with a flowering stem up to 1.5 m in height. Basal leaves develop in the first year and grow up to 30 cm long. They are coarsely veined, generally oval in shape but tapering to a point at the tip and narrowing towards the short stalk, which is often winged. The underside of the leaves and, to a lesser extent, the upper side and the stem are covered with short, soft hairs, giving the plant a greyish-green appearance. The bracts on the flowering stem are similar to, but smaller than, the leaves, the upper ones being the smallest and usually lying close to the stem. The inflorescence matures from mid to late summer as a terminal spike, which may bear more than 50 flowers. These are purplish-pink, pendulous, tubular structures, 4–5 cm long. At the opening of the tube there is a projecting lip which is often paler on the inside and usually spotted with purple or brown, the spots sometimes being ringed with white. The fruit is an oval capsule, pointed at the tip, which opens when dry and light brown to reveal the very numerous, tiny, dark brown seeds. Foxgloves with a variety of flower colours are available for cultivation in gardens.

Poisonous principles

Foxgloves contain cardiac glycosides that have been given various names (digitoxin, digoxin, digitalin, digitonin, digitalosmin, gitoxin, and gitalonin) derived from the botanical name. During digestion they are split by hydrolysis into a sugar and a non-sugar component (aglycone). The aglycones have a direct influence on the muscles of the heart, this action being potentiated by the glycoside sugar.[1, 2] The toxicity of the plant is unaffected by drying, storage, or boiling, and hay containing foxgloves can poison animals. *Digitalis* preparations have been used medicinally for centuries[3] to treat heart disease and secondary conditions, including fluid retention, that were not necessarily known to be associated with the heart disease. The English physician, William Withering, who worked extensively on drugs from foxglove in the late 18th century, wrote *An account of the foxglove and some of its medical uses: with practical remarks on dropsy, and other diseases*, which was published in 1785.[4] Several pharmaceutical drugs in current use are derived from foxgloves, e.g. digoxin and digitoxin, that are prepared mainly from *Digitalis lanata* and *Digitalis purpurea*, respectively, but also from several other *Digitalis* species.[5] These drugs are used principally for controlling heartbeat, and in the treatment of congestive heart failure.

Animal poisoning

Foxglove is not usually eaten and there are few reports of poisoning. When food is scarce, however, animals may eat the plant, and even develop a craving for it after they have been poisoned. A female goat that had become ill after eating foxglove recovered after several days' housing, but when returned to the field, went straight back to the plants and began eating them.[6] A dog that became unsteady on its legs every morning for several days was found to be eating foxglove leaves and flowers on being let out.[7] Most animals appear to be susceptible to *Digitalis* poisoning, which has been reported

197

in cattle,[8] sheep,[9] horses,[6] pigs,[10] goats,[6] deer,[6] dogs,[7] guinea pigs,[11, 12] turkeys,[13] and canaries.[14]

Clinical signs of *Digitalis* poisoning, which are basically the same in all species, include diarrhoea, abdominal pain, irregular pulse, tremors, and convulsions.[1, 2, 15] Several dairy cows in a herd of 34 recently put on good new pasture developed signs including laboured breathing and reluctance to move.[8] Most of the affected animals recovered within three days, but one died and another aborted. Foxgloves, with evidence of grazing, were present in the hedgerows, and digitoxin was detected on chromatographic examination of the rumen contents of the animal that died.

In Scotland, foxgloves were suspected of poisoning four sheep[9] that died after showing signs that included dullness, abdominal pain, frequent urination, and diarrhoea. The sheep had been sheltering from a storm, behind a bank on which young foxgloves were growing. Some of the plants appeared to have been eaten. In another case, also in Scotland, two colts on very bare pasture with numerous foxglove plants died after showing clinical signs resembling tetanus, but with very loud heartbeats. Post-mortem examination revealed foxgloves in the stomach.[6] Five of a group of ten pigs died within 24 hours after they had been given feed containing 50–100 g of foxglove leaves.[10] The most prominent post-mortem findings were gastrointestinal inflammation, small necrotic areas along the border of the spleen, and fatty degeneration of some nerve fibres in the heart. The other pigs were treated successfully with 1% atropine and 1% apomorphine.

A more detailed account[6] has been given of foxglove poisoning in a herd of farmed deer in Scotland in the winter of 1975–1976. One of three hinds and seven of 64 calves died in an enclosure in which foxgloves were growing. Most were found dead, but before death one calf showed a sharp drop in body weight from 36.5 to 30.5 kg over two weeks, and dullness, weakness, haemorrhagic watery diarrhoea, and a slow but strong heartbeat. Sixteen other calves that had lost weight recovered after removal to another pasture. Post-mortem examination of the deer revealed foxglove leaves in the rumen, distension of the heart with clotted blood, and engorged blood vessels in the gastrointestinal tract, liver, kidneys, brain, and lymph nodes. Analysis of body tissues by thin layer chromatography showed the presence of digitoxin. There were similar clinical and post-mortem findings in a 13-month-old deer given 60 g of powdered foxglove leaves containing 0.35 mg per g of a digitoxin-like substance. Muscular twitching, incoordination, and collapse were reported in four guinea pigs that ate foxglove leaves.[11] Other guinea pigs kept for feeding purposes at a zoo in Berlin died after they were inadvertently given foxglove in their green feed.[12] After eating foxglove leaves 68 young turkeys became drowsy, lost their appetite, and had dilated pupils;[13] the ten birds that died had convulsions immediately before death. The others recovered after removal of the crop contents. Canaries poisoned experimentally with a suspension of dried foxglove leaves died in 140–150 minutes. They showed ruffled feathers, depression, trembling, and rigidity before death.[14]

Human poisoning
The symptoms reported are similar to those in animals and include nausea and gastrointestinal disturbances, which may last for at least two days, but which also limit the severity of the toxic reaction on the heart. Headache often occurs and the heartbeat is irregular; there may be convulsions. Poisoning has occurred in children who have eaten the flowers, and is even said to have resulted from drinking water from

vases that had contained foxgloves.[16] A seven-year-old boy was severely poisoned (but later recovered) after eating plant material that was identified as foxglove by the detection of high concentrations of digitoxin in his blood plasma.[17] A man, who drank tea made from the leaves of foxglove, became weak, with increasing nausea, and noticed yellow halos around objects. He also had an abnormally fast heartbeat.[18] After drinking, in a suicide attempt, the liquid in which foxglove and laburnum leaves had been boiled, a man was admitted to hospital with stomach cramps and vomiting.[11] An electrocardiogram showed disturbances in his cardiac rhythym consistent with poisoning by digoxin, very high levels of which were found in his blood; his condition improved gradually, without requiring treatment. Another man, who drank a litre of herbal tea made from foxglove leaves mistaken for those of comfrey,[19] was admitted to hospital with severe vomiting and diarrhoea, confusion, weakness, and a slow irregular pulse. Complete heart block necessitated the insertion of a temporary pacemaker. Despite the well-proven efficacy of the cardioactive drugs derived from foxglove, unwanted effects can also occur. These include toxicity,[20] steroidal action resembling that of oestrogens,[21] visual disturbances,[22] and magnesium deficiency.[23] *Digitalis* poisoning (from medicinal preparations) has been suggested as a possible explanation of the halos and predominance of yellow in Vincent van Gogh's late paintings.[24] On two occasions he painted his physician holding a foxglove plant.

Treatment is symptomatic; stomach lavage may be required. Poisoning by the drugs digoxin and digitoxin can be treated successfully by the administration of digoxin-specific Fab antibody fragments.[25] These remove the drug rapidly from its binding sites in body tissues.[26, 27]

Orobanche species Broomrapes

Several species of *Orobanche* are native in Britain, where they parasitize the roots of other plants. The parasitic nature of broomrapes renders them undesirable in crops, and in former times it was even considered necessary to stop growing certain clover crops because of this parasitism.[28] Broomrape is not now a problem in crops in Britain, but can still be found parasitizing wild plants.

The broomrapes attach themselves to their host plants by underground tubers. From these tubers fleshy, aerial, flowering shoots develop. They are devoid of chlorophyll, and are usually yellowish in colour although often tinged with russet brown, red, or purple. Depending on the species, the shoots may have a few or many scales at the base. The two-lipped flowers form in densely packed terminal clusters and may be lobed. At least part of the flowers is usually purple.

Poisonous principles
These are said to be glycosides, resins, and tannins,[29] but little is known about them.

Animal poisoning
There are references in old literature[28, 30] to the noxious effect of broomrape on domestic animals, in which gastrointestinal disturbances occurred, but there are few reported cases of poisoning, possibly because the plant is unattractive to animals. However, poisoning by lesser broomrape (*Orobanche minor*) has been demonstrated in feeding experiments in goats and dogs given either the plant itself or extracts of it.[29] Reduced appetite and rumination, depression, prostration, and thirst were reported in four goats, two of which died. Dose-related signs of poisoning also occurred in dogs. A

diuretic effect of broomrape was demonstrated by increased urine production in the experimental animals.

Scrophularia aquatica Water Betony

Other common name: Water Figwort

Water betony grows in wet ditches and meadows or beside streams or ponds throughout England and Ireland but is rarely found in Scotland. It is an erect perennial that grows up to 1 m high. The four-angled, winged stems, bear leaves, with winged stalks, in opposite pairs. The leaves have serrated edges, are pointed at the tip and generally oval in shape, although there may be one or two small lobes at the base. The inflorescence is made up of branching stalks which bear, throughout the summer, loose clusters of brownish-purple flowers, with greenish undersides. The flowers are up to 1 cm across, and have a basal, rounded, tubular portion which opens into five small lobes, the upper two being joined together at the base. The fruit is a more or less spherical, but angled, capsule that contains small, rough, oval seeds.

Poisonous principles
Glycosides are thought to be responsible for the toxicity of this plant, but little is known about them.

Animal poisoning
The plant has an unpleasant odour and taste and is not usually eaten. There has, however, been one report of poisoning in young cows.[31] The clinical signs were excitement, accelerated respiration, dilated pupils, congested mucous membranes of the mouth with slight ulceration, infrequent and painful urination, profuse dark foetid diarrhoea, thirst, loss of appetite, and decreased milk production; older cows were unaffected. Treatment with purgatives and stimulants resulted in complete recovery within two days.

Other members of the Scrophulariaceae family

Toadflax (*Linaria* species), cow wheat (*Melampyrum* species), louseworts (*Pedicularis* species), and yellow rattles (*Rhinanthus* species) are wild plants in Britain that also contain poisonous glycosides, which could cause illness and death in the unlikely event of animals eating a sufficient quantity of them.

SOLANACEAE

Most of the poisonous species of this family in Britain can be classified into three groups according to their poisonous principles: tropane alkaloids in *Atropa belladonna*, *Datura stramonium*, and *Hyoscyamus niger*; the alkaloids nicotine and anabasine in *Nicotiana tabacum*; and steroidal glycoalkaloids in *Solanum* species.

Atropa belladonna Deadly Nightshade (Plates 70 and 71)

Other common name: Dwale

Deadly nightshade is native in Britain, in localized areas of woodland and scrub or at the edges of fields, chiefly on calcareous soils in south-east England, but is now rather uncommon. Other members of the Solanaceae family are often wrongly called deadly nightshade or belladonna.

The plant is smooth or slightly hairy with erect, branching stems which grow annually up to 1.5 m high from the perennial, fleshy rootstock. The leaves are borne on short stalks on the stems, sometimes arranged alternately, but more often in pairs of unequal size. They are up to 20 cm long, generally oval in shape but narrowing near the stalk and terminating in a point. The drooping flowers are borne singly on short stalks in the axils of leaves or the fork of branches. They are up to 3 cm long with a basal tubular portion widening into five obtuse lobes. The most common colour for the flowers is a dull brownish purple, but they may be a pale bluish purple, violet, or have tinges of green. The fruit is a shining black berry with its base partially enclosed by the five pointed lobes of the persistent calyx.

Poisonous principles

Atropa belladonna contains various tropane alkaloids: atropine, hyoscyamine, and the hallucinogen hyoscine (also known as scopolamine). The first two are the *dl*- and *l*-tropic acid esters of tropine,[1, 2] respectively. It is difficult to determine accurately the relative amounts of these two stereoisomers present in the living plant, as they are readily converted from one form to another (e.g. by hydrolysis, alkalis, or heat), and may be changed during the extraction process. All parts of the plant are poisonous.[3] Other toxic components isolated have been named apoatropine, noratropine, belladonnine, tropacocaine, and meteloidine.[4] The toxic effects of these alkaloids differ only in their severity and the relative proportions of each present.

Animal poisoning

The plant is seldom eaten but it did cause the death of three calves that strayed into a derelict garden.[5] Parts of the leaves and stems were found in the rumen at post-mortem examination. Poisoning has also been reported in pigs[6] that ate the plant during a drought; they were found lying down and kicking and were unable to stand. They had dilated pupils and inflamed mucous membranes. The animals exhibited nervous excitation and died the next day. A goat, which had been tethered in a lane near a hedge, died about 24 hours after showing clinical signs that included tympany, strongly dilated pupils, a dry mouth, a feeble rapid pulse, laboured breathing, continuous weak crying, cessation of gastric movement, and coma.[7] Post-mortem examination revealed detachment and inflammation of the gastric and intestinal mucous membranes; leaves and stems of *Atropa belladonna* and elder (*Sambucus nigra*) were found in the stomach. The clinical signs were typical of deadly nightshade poisoning, but may have been exaggerated by the simultaneous presence of elder. Rabbits are not necessarily poisoned if they eat deadly nightshade, as some possess an enzyme, atropinesterase, which inactivates the alkaloids.[8] It has been stated, however, that their flesh can cause poisoning if eaten.[5] The presence or absence of atropinesterase is genetically determined; the enzyme is more common and occurs in higher concentrations in females. Atropinesterase activity is not demonstrable until the rabbits are at least 1–2 months old.[8]

Human poisoning

Most cases involve children, who eat the berries, but deliberate or accidental consumption of berries or concoctions of leaves by adults has been reported. Drinking comfrey tea contaminated with belladonna (deadly nightshade) caused poisoning in two elderly persons;[9] others were also affected by the same product.[10] Their symptoms included thirst, confusion, dizziness, and hallucinations. Similar, but more severe effects were experienced by a group of young men in Switzerland,[11] who drank tea prepared from *Atropa belladonna* leaves, which they knew to be hallucinogenic; hospital treatment was required by some. Between 1967 and 1979, 34 incidents of poisoning by the plant were recorded by the London poisons information service.[12] In each case more than five berries had been eaten, and all developed symptoms of varying severity. Between 1980 and 1993 another 12 cases of the ingestion of up to 20 berries were recorded. Symptoms occurred in young children eating two or more berries, and in adults eating 3–4 berries or more. All recovered after treatment. The most serious poisoning usually results from large numbers of berries being eaten raw or cooked, when mistaken for the fruit of other plants, e.g. bilberries (*Vaccinium myrtillus*). Hallucinations, tremors, and extreme agitation developed ten hours after a man ate 'a number' of berries identified later as deadly nightshade; he recovered the following day.[13] A family that ate approximately 150 g each of the stewed berries, developed gastrointestinal symptoms, convulsions and, in one case, coma;[12] all recovered within six days. Another adult ate 10–15 raw berries and, after six hours, developed abdominal pain, vomiting, dry mouth, visual disturbances, disorientation, dilated pupils, and rapid pulse.[14] Similar but more severe symptoms, including aggression, delirium, and coma, occurred in a nine-year-old boy who ate 20–25 berries.[15] He recovered after hospital treatment.

Where possible, and soon after consumption of the plant, stomach lavage should be performed and activated charcoal given to adsorb any residual poisonous material.[3] Sedation may be required. A specific antidote, physostigmine salicylate (3 mg in 1 mg doses) injected intramuscularly at intervals of several hours,[10] or intravenously,[3] has proved effective in neutralizing the most dangerous effects of the alkaloid; this measure, however, should be considered only in very serious cases. Haemodialysis seems to be ineffective.[16] Preparations containing morphine or opiates should be avoided as they have a synergic action with atropine.

Datura stramonium Thorn Apple (Plate 72)

Other common name: Jimsonweed

Thorn apple is not native in Britain, but it now has very localized distribution in southern England, growing mainly on cultivated ground, rubbish tips, and embankments. It is sometimes grown in gardens. The plant is a smooth, wide-branching annual which grows up to 1 m high in Britain. The leaves are stalked and up to 20 cm long with irregular lobes terminating in pointed teeth. The flowers are borne singly on stalks in forks of the stem in early summer. They are funnel-shaped, up to 10 cm long, and either white or purple. They, and the rest of the plant, have an unpleasant odour. The fruit develops rapidly after the flower has fallen. It is a prickly, ovoid or globular capsule, which ripens in autumn and splits open to reveal numerous, wrinkled, black seeds.

Poisonous principles

These are the alkaloids hyoscyamine (an isomer of atropine) that blocks the parasympathetic nervous system, and hyoscine (sometimes called scopolamine) that is hallucinogenic. Traces of atropine may also be present.[17] The proportions of the various alkaloids vary in different parts of the plant and at different stages of growth, but all parts are poisonous. The concentration of alkaloids may also differ in plants grown in different climatic regions. In India, *Datura stramonium* grown at an altitude of 2000 m had no adverse effects when fed to bulls, goats, and sheep (two of each). When grown at a lower altitude the same quantity of the plant caused poisoning when fed to the same animals;[18] factors other than altitude may, of course, have been involved. The alkaloid concentration in seed samples from different parts of the USA varied by as much as 50%: 1.69–2.71 mg per g for atropine and 0.36–0.69 mg per g for hyoscine.[19]

In the past, *Datura* was used in various medicinal preparations, and for the relief of bronchitis and asthma by inhaling smoke from burning leaves; it has also been used as an anaesthetic.[20] Medicinal and culinary use of the plant, however, has often resulted in poisoning. A famous case of human poisoning occurred in 1676 in Jamestown, USA. Soldiers who ate the plant in a salad experienced what was described as 'a very pleasant comedy', and it was from this incident that *Datura* acquired the common name jimsonweed (Jamestown weed). Most of the recent cases of poisoning have resulted from its recreational use as a hallucinogen.

Animal poisoning

This is very rare in Britain. Probably because of its strong odour and unpleasant taste, animals do not eat the growing plant, provided that other vegetation is available. Poisoning can occur, however, if *Datura* is incorporated into hay, or its seeds into grain mixtures or meal fed to livestock. Poisoning or suspected poisoning has been reported in horses,[21–23] cattle,[12, 24, 25] buffaloes,[26] sheep,[18, 27, 28] goats,[18, 28] and pigs.[29, 30] The clinical signs usually include restlessness, incoordination, dilatation of pupils, paralysis, and increased respiration rate; death may result. In the USA, *Datura* was thought to be the cause of poisoning in 15 ponies[21] that developed impaired vision, frequent urination, and intermittent muscular spasms; 11 died after 7–17 days. The ponies had been given feed that contained a large amount of *Datura stramonium* seeds. Similar clinical signs occurred in two horses in New Zealand within a few days of being fed on meal that was found to contain 0.5% by weight of *Datura stramonium* seeds.[22] In Hungary in 1993, nine horses died 24–72 hours after eating feed containing 60–300 g of *Datura stramonium* seeds.[23] The clinical signs developed in 6–24 hours and included restlessness, colic, laboured breathing, rapid heart rate, constipation, dilated pupils, and dryness of the oral and nasal mucous membranes.

When cattle were fed diets containing various levels of the seed (calculated to be 8.8, 881, or 4408 seeds per kg of feed) for 14 days, only those fed the highest level showed signs of toxicity that included anorexia, bloat, a dry muzzle, and straining. It was concluded that such poisoning is self-limiting because of the anorexia and cessation of rumination, and that the toxic dose is 2.49 mg atropine and 0.5 mg hyoscine per kg body weight (about 107 seeds per kg).[31]

In experiments on sheep and goats the leaves and fruits of *Datura stramonium* given by stomach tube resulted in reduced water intake, tremors, rapid breathing, incoordination, and recumbency; some animals died.[28] Post-mortem findings included haemorrhages in the liver, kidneys, and heart and congested blood vessels in the lungs. In Scotland, eight ewes died after eating kale from a crop contaminated with *Datura stramonium.* This case is unusual, as it occurred outside the normal range of the plant.[27]

Pigs were poisoned by being fed *Datura* seeds equivalent to 2.7 mg hyoscyamine per kg of body weight;[29] in a similar experiment pigs tolerated up to 2.2 mg hyoscyamine per kg of body weight in barley and soya meal contaminated with ground *Datura* seeds.[32] When fed meal contaminated with whole seeds the pigs reduced their food consumption (presumably because of the unpalatable taste) and consequently lost weight. They showed no signs of poisoning with a dose of up to 2 mg hyoscyamine per kg of body weight, although this may not be an accurate estimate of hyoscyamine absorption, as undigested seeds were found in faeces. In the USA, *Datura* was suspected of causing congenital arthrogryposis (persistent joint contraction) in 25 piglets in eight litters over a period of five years. The litters had been farrowed in an area surrounded by dense growth of *Datura.* The sows had shown signs of poisoning, such as incoordination, during pregnancy.[30] Reduced growth rate was reported in other pigs given meal contaminated with *Datura* seeds.[33]

In experiments with chickens the incorporation of *Datura* at 3% in meal depressed growth rate;[34,35] 1% was considered to be the upper dietary limit that can be used safely.[34] *Datura* seeds are sometimes harvested with soya beans and incorporated into soya bean meal.[36] From experimental feeding with *Datura* seeds, it was found that laying hens could tolerate up to 2000 seeds a day, but 100 seeds caused three-week-old chicks to lose weight.[37] These amounts are greater than the highest recorded natural contamination of soya bean meal (0.023%).[38]

Human poisoning

The toxic, medicinal, and mind-altering properties of *Datura* species have been known for centuries.[3, 20] The leaves, flowers, and particularly the seeds have caused poisoning after being taken or administered in a variety of ways, either deliberately for criminal, suicidal, medicinal, or hallucinatory purposes, or accidentally when present as a contaminant of food. The fresh plant is rarely eaten, possibly because of its unpleasant odour, but poisoning was reported in three children in Saudi Arabia who ate some of the fruits while on a picnic.[39] Drinking infusions of the flowers[40] and leaves[41–43] has caused poisoning. Of two young men who prepared and drank, for hallucinatory purposes, tea containing the seeds, one died.[43] In France, where three teenagers died after drinking *Datura* tea, the sale of herbal medicines made from the plant has been banned.[44] Most cases of poisoning by ingestion of the seeds have occurred in persons using or experimenting with them for their known psychoactive properties.[45–49] The reported numbers of seeds eaten vary enormously (from two or three to several hundred). In parts of the world where *Datura stramonium* is a common weed, the seeds may be harvested with crops and ground into flour. In Tanzania, for example, people have been poisoned after eating various foods including bread, pancakes, and chapattis prepared with contaminated wheat or maize flour.[50, 51] Smoking cigarettes made from or treated with extracts of *Datura* have given rise to symptoms of poisoning,[45, 46] as did a toothpaste containing *Datura* leaves[52] (applied to the gums to treat gingivitis), and sucking nectar from a flower.[4] The eyes can be affected (dilatation of pupils) after trimming or working with *Datura* species.[53, 54] The symptoms of *Datura* poisoning are similar, irrespective of the plant parts involved or the manner in which they are taken. They include dryness of the mouth and throat, flushing of the skin, increased body temperature, dilatation of pupils, blurred vision, retention of urine, incoordination, hallucinations, muscle twitching, agitation, drowsiness, confusion, and delirium; later there may be deranged behaviour, convulsions, coma, rapid pulse, high blood pressure, and sometimes death.[12, 55] Dilatation of the pupils may persist for several days. The toxicity of honey made from *Datura* and other solanaceous plants has been attributed to the alkaloids hyoscine and/or atropine.[56] Such honey is unlikely to be produced in Britain as these plants are not sufficiently common.

Initially treatment should be symptomatic. In the first 24–48 hours after ingestion, emptying of the gastrointestinal tract should be considered by stomach lavage and purgatives. The administration of activated charcoal appears to be effective; sedatives may be given to control agitation.[49] There are conflicting recommendations on the use of physostigmine, a specific antidote to anticholinergic agents such as atropine. The drug is effective, but potentially toxic, so that its use should be restricted to cases with severe hallucinations or life-threatening conditions.

Hyoscyamus niger Henbane (Plate 73)

Although native in Britain, this rather spectacular plant is now seen only occasionally in sandy, coastal areas, waste places or adjacent to old buildings, where the plants sometimes survive from their former cultivation for medicinal purposes.

Henbane is a sturdy annual or biennial plant, up to 80 cm high. The whole plant has a strong, unpleasant smell and is hairy and somewhat sticky. The stem is woody at the base, where there are stalked leaves, up to 20 cm long; these have undulating edges, usually with a few irregular, large teeth. The stem leaves are arranged alternately; they have no stalks, are unevenly lobed, and the upper ones clasp the stem. The inflorescences are borne in the forks of lower branches or laterally from upper shoots. The bracts are leaf-like and the flowers funnel-shaped, 2–3 cm across and yellowish or white (occasionally mauve). They are conspicuously marked with a network of dark red or purple veins; the anthers of the stamens and the interior, basal part of the flowers are also purple. After flowering, the calyx continues to grow, around the fruit, its five points hardening to form spines. The exposed cap of the fruit is shed, when ripe, revealing numerous seeds.

Poisonous principles
All parts of the plant, but particularly the roots, are poisonous. Henbane contains alkaloids of the same group (tropane) as those in *Datura*. The main alkaloid is hyoscyamine, but the hallucinogen hyoscine (scopolamine), and atropine are also present. Preparations of the plant have been used medicinally for eye disorders, rheumatism, and sedation.[57] In the Middle Ages it was used in sorcery.[57]

Animal poisoning
Hyoscyamus has a long-standing reputation for being poisonous,[58] but there are few actual reports. It is probable that the disagreeable odour and sticky texture of the plant make it unattractive to animals. In one outbreak in Poland,[59] when *Hyoscyamus niger* was present in cut forage, cows developed nervous signs including restlessness, excitation, and convulsions; four of eight animals had to be slaughtered. Post-mortem examination revealed 0.7% of henbane shoots in the rumen contents, degeneration of heart muscle, and bluish coloration (cyanosis) of mucous membranes. Similar nervous signs were reported in other cattle after eating henbane, but, in addition, dilatation of

pupils, laboured breathing, increased heart rate, and bloat were seen in adult cattle; incoordination occurred in calves.[60] No outbreaks appear to have been reported in animals in Britain since early this century.[61] Henbane retains its toxicity after drying (dried leaves are said to contain 0.04% alkaloids)[62] and storage. It is said to impart an unpleasant taint to the milk of cows that eat it.[63]

Human poisoning

As with many other plants used medicinally, there have been incidents of accidental poisoning by henbane reported, mainly in the older literature,[58, 64] but there have also been some recent cases reported in Britain.[12] The symptoms are similar to those in animals. The roots of the plant have caused poisoning when eaten in mistake for those of other plants. When boiled roots were eaten, typical symptoms, including blurred vision, dilated pupils, dry mouth, thirst, purposeless movements (picking at the air), intermittent mental confusion and disorientation, warm flushed skin, and rapid heartbeat, persisted for 12 hours.[12, 65] An inconsistent finding reported is excess salivation; other reports mention dryness of the mouth. It has even been suggested that this salivation is a feature distinguishing henbane poisoning from that caused by *Atropa* and *Datura*. It appears, however, that the allusions to salivation are repeated from one old reference.[58] Poisoning has resulted from eating honey made from solanaceous plants (including henbane), atropine and/or hyoscine being the toxic principles.[56] This is most unlikely to occur in Britain as the plant is not sufficiently common.

Stomach lavage and the administration of activated charcoal are recommended for treatment; physostigmine injections could be considered in very serious cases.

Nicotiana species Tobacco

Tobacco for smoking (the dried leaves of *Nicotiana tabacum*) is not grown commercially in Britain, but this, and several ornamental varieties as well as other *Nicotiana* species, are cultivated in gardens.

Poisonous principles

These are alkaloids, of which the best known is nicotine. Others present in various *Nicotiana* species include anatabine (present in the roots of the plant) and anabasine. Animal and human poisoning has occurred after contact with agricultural pesticides containing nicotine, and adverse effects have followed its internal and external use in veterinary medicine.[66]

Animal poisoning

Most reported cases have involved pigs. In an incident in Britain, death occurred within four hours in two pigs that ate growing tobacco plants after breaking loose and entering a garden. At post-mortem examination, the plants were found in the stomachs, but there was no other indication of the cause of death.[66] Congenital defects (limb deformities) have been recorded in the USA in many newborn pigs[67] after feeding burley tobacco forage (*Nicotiana tabacum*) and the wild tree tobacco (*Nicotiana glauca*) to pregnant sows.[68] *Nicotiana glauca* but not *Nicotiana tabacum* also induced cleft palate in piglets.[68] Limb deformities were also seen in calves[69] and lambs[70] after experimental feeding of *Nicotiana glauca* to their mothers during pregnancy (particularly in the early stages). The piperidine alkaloid anabasine and not nicotine is responsible for the congenital defects.[68] In the USA, six mules died during a 24-hour period after consuming hay contaminated with nicotine in the fluid that dripped from tobacco leaves suspended over the hay to dry.[71] A puppy that ate chewing tobacco vomited twice, had constricted pupils, salivation, incoordination, trembling of the head, an increased heart rate, tremors over most of the body, and some spasmodic arching of the back. It recovered in 24 hours.[72]

Human poisoning

Although highly toxic, poisoning by nicotine is rarely recorded. The alkaloid is absorbed through the mucous membranes, lungs, and skin. Poisoning induces nausea, vomiting, diarrhoea, headaches, and muscular tremors. It is stated that severe poisoning can result in circulatory collapse, convulsions, and loss of consciousness.[3] Babies and toddlers sometimes eat cigarette butts or whole cigarettes. Vomiting generally occurs, without any other symptoms appearing.[73, 74] The danger of chronic poisoning from smoking tobacco has been well publicized; it is a huge topic and outside the scope of this book.

Solanum dulcamara Woody Nightshade (Plates 74 and 75)

Woody nightshade is common throughout Britain except in some northern areas and Scotland. It is sometimes found growing along the ground on waste land or on shingle near the sea, but occurs most frequently as a climbing plant in woods and hedges where it scrambles and trails over bushes and trees.

Most of the plant usually dies back in winter, but the roots and the woody base of the stems are perennial. The plant grows up to 2 m long and the stems bear dark green, pointed leaves up to 8 cm long. These have smooth edges, but 1–4 (usually two) deeply indented lobes near the base. The upper leaves may be oval or heart-shaped, without basal lobes. The flowers appear in summer in loose clusters. They are purple in colour (rarely white), about 1 cm across, and usually have five pointed lobes. The stamens are a prominent feature as they cohere and project from the centre of the flower as a bright yellow cone. The fruits are oval, green berries that become a bright shiny red when ripe.

Poisonous principles

All parts of the plant contain a mixture of steroidal glycoalkaloids often referred to collectively as solanine. The glycoalkaloids have in common the aglycone solanidine. The alkaloids are degraded during maturation of the fleshy fruit. It has been suggested that this loss of chemical defence occurs to make the fruits attractive to animals that will eat them and thus act as dispersal agents.[75] The berries should not, however, be considered safe at any stage, as poisoning has resulted from eating them. It is impossible to determine visually whether degradation of the toxin has taken place.

Animal poisoning

This is uncommon, and no recent cases have been recorded. Early literature quotes conflicting reports, one stating that the fruits have no harmful properties and another that poultry died as a result of pecking the berries.[76] Straying sheep that ate the plant developed rapid respiration, feeble intermittent pulse, elevated temperature, dilated pupils, green diarrhoea, staggering, and falling before death.[77] Post-mortem examination revealed dark, tarry blood, contracted ventricles of the heart, and parts of the stem and seeds of the plant in the stomach. *Solanum dulcamara* poisoning in cattle[78, 79] caused nervous excitement, rapid pulse, incoordination, muscle tremors, and subnormal temperature. One animal salivated profusely and another developed oedema of the front part of the body. Fruits and seeds of woody nightshade were found in material regurgitated by the cattle, and the flesh of a slaughtered animal smelled strongly of the plant.

Human poisoning

This is usually caused by eating the berries, whose bright colour is attractive to children. The poisons information service in London[12] recorded 25 cases of ingestion of the plant in Britain between 1963 and 1979. Of these, 19 did not show symptoms, but varying degrees of abdominal pain, flushing of the skin, and tiredness were seen in the others. A fatal case of woody nightshade poisoning in a nine-year-old girl was reported in 1948 in Britain.[80] She experienced abdominal pain, vomiting, thirst, distressed breathing, restlessness, and exhaustion. Some improvement was achieved after stomach lavage, administration of an enema, and fluid therapy, but this was followed by further deterioration, with shallow respiration, cyanosis, and extreme weakness preceding death. Post-mortem examination revealed acute inflammation and small haemorrhages of the mucous membranes of the stomach and intestines. Small fragments of the skin of woody nightshade berries were seen on microscopic examination of stomach contents. The lungs were congested and oedematous, and the liver was fatty and necrotic. A product, consistent with solanine, was extracted from the liver. Woody nightshade berries were growing (entangled with blackberries) where the child had been playing. Over a four-month period in the USA, a survey was carried out on 235 children (eight months to five years of age) reported to have eaten *Solanum dulcamara* berries.[81] The identity of the berries was not always clear, but only 17 children developed symptoms: drowsiness (9), vomiting (4), diarrhoea (4), and stomach upset (1). Despite the fatal case reported in Britain, this survey and experiments in mice[82] indicate that *Solanum dulcamara* berries, especially when ripe, are generally not very toxic. Treatment is symptomatic; stomach lavage and rehydration are recommended.

Solanum nigrum Black Nightshade (Plates 76 and 77)

Other common name: Garden Nightshade

Black nightshade, which has almost world-wide distribution, occurs throughout England but is found only very locally in Scotland. It is a highly successful and very troublesome weed of cultivated land. Both morphological and physiological variations occur in different locations and among different populations, some of which are developing resistance to herbicides.[83] It is probably more accurate to consider *Solanum nigrum* as a complex group of subspecies and forms, with varying degrees of similarity, rather than as a clearly definable species.

Solanum nigrum is an erect, much branched annual (occasionally biennial) plant varying in height, according to its habitat, from 10 to 60 cm. The stems are smooth or very slightly hairy and bear stalked oval or diamond-shaped, dull green leaves, which may or may not have coarsely toothed margins. White, or occasionally pale mauve flowers about 0.5 cm across, with pointed petals and yellow stamens, appear in clusters on the stem from mid to late summer. The fruit is a shiny globular berry, green at first, usually ripening to black, although some forms are red or persistently green. Each berry contains numerous seeds, which have a high germination rate and may retain their viability for many years.[84]

Black nightshade can cause serious problems at harvesting, as it may be collected with other crops, such as kale, or its berries with peas, beans, or maize from which they are difficult to separate; the berries may also contaminate crops with the thick juice released from them when squashed. Dissemination of the plant can occur if its seeds are collected with crop seeds such as sugar beet, for subsequent sowing.

Poisonous principles
All parts of the plant, but particularly the green unripe berries, contain a steroidal glycoalkaloid, solanine, with solasodine being the aglycone component.[85] Solasodine has been found experimentally to cause foetal malformations in hamsters.[86] Nitrates and nitrites also occur in variable amounts in black nightshade,[87] and can contribute to its toxic effects. The amounts of the poisonous principles present vary greatly with climate, season, and soil type. The glycoalkaloid concentration of the plant is reduced in silage,[84] and is also reduced when the plant is boiled and the water discarded. The toxic potential of the plant has been utilized experimentally in the production of an anthelmintic, a 0.1% extract of crushed dry leaves having killed the miracidia of *Fasciola gigantica* in five minutes.[88] Variability in the toxic alkaloid and nitrate concentrations of the plants in different situations accounts for the conflicting reports of their being harmless in some cases (for example, when a horse consumed 3 kg of the green plant without ill effects,[89] or in Mauritius and Réunion where people eat the cooked plant like spinach[90]), and harmful in other cases (when deaths occurred in pigs on land where the plant was growing[91] and among children after eating the berries[92]).

Animal poisoning
Black nightshade should be considered potentially toxic to all animals. Cattle, sheep, goats, pigs, dogs, and poultry can be severely poisoned.[93] In an outbreak of black nightshade poisoning in pigs,[91] rapid pulse and respiration, pale mucous membranes, widely dilated pupils, low body temperature, incoordination, and tremors were reported. In a valuable herd of British Saanen goats, severe abdominal pain, vomiting, depression, and staggering movements occurred.[94] In the latter outbreak, leaves of the plant were seen in ingested material. In India, calcium deposits in blood vessels of Corriedale sheep[95] were thought to have been caused by ingestion of *Solanum nigrum*, which grew in the area where the animals were kept. The effects were similar to those of enteque seco, a form of calcinosis found among sheep in Argentina, associated with ingestion of *Solanum malacoxylon* (a species that does not occur in Britain). In addition to clinical signs similar to those described for pigs and goats, cattle may develop areas of oedema[96] around the lower jaw, neck, and front of the body, including the top of the forelegs. Laboured respiration, dark-coloured diarrhoea following constipation, lack of rumination, dry muzzle, and cold extremities have also been reported in cattle.[84] Some of the clinical signs are typical of poisoning by nitrates/nitrites, which this plant contains, in addition to alkaloids. Silage made from maize contaminated with up to 25% black nightshade has been considered safe to feed to cattle and sheep.[97]

Human poisoning

Symptoms associated with *Solanum nigrum* poisoning are headache, vomiting, diarrhoea, elevated temperature, dizziness, speech impairment, and unconsciousness.[93] Death may occur from cardiac or respiratory failure. Although, when ripe, the berries are the least toxic part of the plant and are sometimes eaten without ill effects,[98] consumption of berries may produce mild abdominal pain, vomiting, and diarrhoea, or even cause acute illness and death. The toxicity of berries appears to be variable; unripe (green) fruits should always be considered poisonous.

Solanum tuberosum Potato (Plate 78)

Potato plants produce underground stem tubers (potatoes) that are a major food and are very widely grown commercially and in gardens in many countries, including Britain. The foliage, flower and tuber characteristics vary among the many varieties, some of which also produce fruits after flowering. All of the above-ground parts of the plants are poisonous and, under certain conditions, the tubers can cause animal and human poisoning.[99]

Poisonous principles

These are alkaloids that were given the name solanine when first isolated in the 1820s. This substance is, however, a mixture of glycoalkaloids. The chief toxic glycoalkaloids in potato tubers are α-solanine and α-chaconine, which have a common aglycone, solanidine. These and other spirosolane alkaloids of the solasodine type that may be present in potatoes have caused foetal resorption or malformations in laboratory animals. Phenolic compounds (chlorogenic and caffeic acids) and coumarins (scopolin, umbelliferone, coumarin) are also present.[100] Inhibitors to enzymes (trypsin and chymotrypsin) that break down proteins during digestion are present in some potato tubers.[101] There is considerable variation in their content in different varieties. The inhibitors are present in both the peel and the flesh of the tubers and are destroyed by heating. It is inadvisable to feed such products as potato peelings (from commercial chip production) to animals without prior heat inactivation (e.g. steaming).

The stems, leaves, flowers, and fruits (haulm) of the potato plant contain toxic glycoalkaloids, but most cases of poisoning involve ingestion of potato tubers. The tubers naturally contain steroidal glycoalkaloids, the concentration of which varies considerably (a range of 10–650 mg per kg has been reported) and is influenced by many factors. These include the potato variety, geographical location of the crop, climatic conditions, tuber size, and maturity, but mostly relate to the post-harvesting treatment of the tubers. The glycoalkaloid content increases with mechanical injury of the tubers, exposure to light, and sprouting. The green colour that develops in tubers exposed to light is chlorophyll, and in itself is not poisonous, but is usually associated with a high glycoalkaloid content. However, potatoes that have not become green may also be toxic, as the processes of greening and the increase in glycoalkaloid content that occurs with light exposure proceed independently. There is evidence that glycoalkaloid levels of 200 mg per kg and above in potatoes may lead to acute poisoning,[102] but levels below this should not be assumed safe, and the levels that give long-term (chronic) toxic effects are not known. The glycoalkaloids are eliminated very slowly from the body and have been found to accumulate in some organs, such as the liver.[102] The toxins are present at their highest concentration in the skin, eyes, and sprouts of the tubers, so that peeled potatoes are less toxic. Boiling in water also reduces, but does not eliminate, the alkaloids or render safe potatoes that have become green. Infection of tubers with the potato blight fungus (*Phytophthora infestans*) also increases the concentration of toxins in the tubers. However, potato varieties with a high glycoalkaloid content are more resistant to potato blight. In some countries plant breeders are required to work to an upper limit of 60–70 mg per kg of glycoalkaloids in cultivars for human consumption. Work on the genetics of the toxins and the enzymes involved in their biosynthesis is in progress.[102]

Another possible source of poisoning is from the berries of potato plants. Those on potato plants that grow from tubers left from the previous year (volunteers) may be harvested with subsequent crops of a different type.[103] Whole or parts of these potato fruits could then be incorporated inadvertently in frozen produce such as peas or beans. The concentration of alkaloids in these berries may be 10–20 times that in tubers. Many of the newer varieties of potatoes used in Britain produce fruits more freely than older varieties.

Animal poisoning

Potato tubers can provide a useful addition to animal feed, and the vines (haulms), harvested before senescence and used for silage, can be a nutritious feed for ruminants. In Canada, silage made with 75% potato haulms was readily acceptable to sheep.[104] There are, however, many reported incidents of poisoning in animals as a result of being fed with parts of the plant. Whole potatoes, their sprouts or peelings have poisoned pigs in several countries, including Britain.[105] In Poland, 28 outbreaks of solanine poisoning involving 180 pigs were diagnosed between 1949 and 1961, and there was a 64% mortality.[106] Some animals die suddenly, while in others there are nervous signs including restlessness, incoordination, and convulsions, the animals often appearing dazed or semi-comatose. Loss of appetite, excessive salivation, vomiting, and diarrhoea or constipation are also seen, and dilatation of pupils and circulatory failure may occur. In addition, a generalized, dry eczema appeared in pigs whose feed had been mixed with water in which potato peelings had been cooked.[107] Necrosis of the feet, necessitating amputation, developed in some cases.

Outbreaks of poisoning in cattle have followed feeding with green, decayed, or sprouting potatoes[108] or with excessive quantities of potato pulp[109] (up to 60 litres per animal daily). The clinical signs were similar to those described for pigs. Feeding large quantities of stored potatoes to young cattle over long periods is a well-recognized cause of severe chronic anaemia in many European countries.[110] Skin lesions, with some swelling, developed mainly on the legs and udders of buffaloes fed with potato plants in India.[111] Pain in the teats during milking, and lameness were noted.

Sheep may also be affected, although they are less likely to be fed potatoes than pigs or cattle. In the USA, 14 of 39 sheep became weak and uncoordinated and died shortly after eating green cull potatoes that had been spread on their pasture.[112]

A horse developed gastrointestinal disturbances and a weak pulse, and died after being fed greened potato sprouts.[113] In Britain a pony died after eating rotting potatoes that had been disposed of by spreading on pasture.[114] The animal developed profuse, watery diarrhoea; it became recumbent, had laboured breathing, and produced frothy fluid from the mouth and nostrils before death. No abnormalities were seen at post-mortem examination; chewed potato was present in the stomach. The rotted potatoes contained 30% more toxic glycoalkaloids (7.3 mg per kg) than the greened tubers that had been used, without ill effects, to supplement the feed of milking cows. Deer that ate the rotted potatoes on the same pasture where the pony died were also unaffected.[114]

Potato poisoning was reported in a dog that became unusually quiet, then comatose, with dilated pupils, irregular weak pulse, and slow breathing. Unconsciousness persisted for a period of four days, after which the animal was killed. Post-mortem examination revealed ten small, green potatoes in the stomach, which was acutely inflamed. There was blood-stained urine in the bladder.[115] Experimental feeding of rabbits with potato plants resulted in diarrhoea after six days.[111] This was followed by extension of the back and legs, with coma and death occurring in 7–17 days. Other rabbits fed greened potatoes lost weight and condition;[116] changes were noted particularly in the heart and liver, which were enlarged, and in the concentrations of various constituents of the blood. Poultry, however, seem more resistant to potato glycoalkaloids, as, in feeding trials, laying pullets tolerated green haulm, cooked and raw green potato sprouts, and ground tubers as 10% of their diet.[117]

Although not recorded in domestic animals, deaths and rib abnormalities have occurred in the foetuses of rats given potato sprouts or solanine,[100, 118] and the young of many litters died before weaning. When pregnant hamsters were given orally equal quantities of α-solanine, α-chaconine, and solasodine extracted from potato sprouts, only α-solanine and α-chaconine produced clinical signs of poisoning, but all three resulted in malformations in 18–20% of the foetuses.[119] It has been suggested that solanine may interfere with milk production. No evidence of transfer of solanidine to milk was found in an experiment in milking cows given potato meal.[120]

The post-mortem findings are similar in all animals, and are those of non-specific gastroenteritis with occasional haemorrhages of the intestinal mucous membranes and degeneration of heart muscle and liver. In rabbits the brain was also found to be affected.[111]

Human poisoning

Poisoning can result from eating potato foliage (haulm) as a vegetable,[121] but this is unlikely to occur except under conditions of food shortage. Children have been poisoned by eating potato fruits, and abdominal pain and vomiting have been reported.[12] Most cases of human poisoning involve badly stored or very old tubers. The family of a hotel proprietor were poisoned by eating potatoes baked in their skins, while guests in the hotel, who ate potatoes from the same source, but without skins, were unaffected.[122] The potatoes were of excellent flavour and appearance. Reference is made frequently in the literature to an outbreak involving 78 schoolboys who were poisoned after eating potatoes from a sack that had been stored for several weeks.[123] Symptoms began 8–10 hours after eating the potatoes, when there was generalized abdominal pain, followed by vomiting and diarrhoea. The severity of the reaction varied among individuals, three boys becoming dangerously ill and 17 requiring admission to hospital. Varying degrees of restlessness, delirium, visual disturbances, drowsiness, or coma were experienced, but the boys made a complete recovery, most within a few days and all within 4–5 weeks. Analysis revealed the presence of α-solanine and α-chaconine at concentrations of up to 0.012%, as determined by chromatographic methods. It was suggested in the 1970s that potatoes (particularly tubers infected with the potato blight fungus) eaten during pregnancy, may be a cause of human birth defects.[124] Work in laboratory animals has demonstrated the presence of some potentially teratogenic substances in potatoes,[119, 125] but there is insufficient evidence to extrapolate these results to imply a human risk.

Treatment is symptomatic, but should include fluid replacement. Tranquillizers or anticonvulsants may be required.

Other members of the Solanaceae family

Two other members of the family that have caused a few cases of poisoning in Britain are tomato plants and the Chinese (or Japanese) lantern; some others have caused poisoning abroad.

Tomato plants (*Lycopersicon lycopersicum*) contain the steroidal glycoalkaloid α-tomatine, with tomatidine as its aglycone component, but they rarely cause poisoning, as the only part of the plant eaten regularly is the fruit, in which the concentration is too low to cause any harm. In a trial in Israel, cattle were given dried tomato vines (haulm) at about 3 kg per animal daily for 42 days;[126] there were no signs of illness. Dried tomato vines, however, have caused poisoning of cattle in Israel, with mortality and abortions, possibly because of a high nitrate content. In Britain, feeding pigs with green sideshoots picked from tomato plants by growers has caused acute illness and death.[110] Mild skin reactions to tomato foliage are fairly common in gardeners, and allergy to tomato skins has been reported in people handling them during food preparation.[127]

The Chinese lantern (*Physalis alkekengi*) is a perennial garden plant with characteristic, orange lantern-like structures (formed from the calyx), each surrounding a single, orange-red, fleshy fruit. An 11-month-old Burmese cat showed depression, loss of appetite, and diarrhoea after eating parts of the plant; it recovered in 24 hours.[12] The unripe berries have caused digestive disturbances in children, but are harmless when ripe.

Some other members of the family that are grown in this country as garden or house plants are also poisonous. Tree daturas including angel's trumpets (*Brugmansia* species) have hallucinatory properties and contain toxins similar to those of thorn apples (*Datura* species). The nature of the toxic constituents of others is said to be similar to that of the nightshades, but there is lack of agreement on the toxins and toxicity of the individual plants, including jessamines (*Cestrum* species), the Duke of Argyll's tea plant (*Lycium chinense*), and chalice vines (*Solandra* species). The toxicity of the apple of Peru (*Nicandra physalodes*) seems to be slight, and resembles that of the Chinese lantern (*Physalis alkekengi*). Poisons centres receive many calls about Christmas cherries (*Solanum capsicastrum* and *Solanum pseudocapsicum*), but although the berries are sometimes eaten by children, there are often no symptoms or only mild digestive system disturbances.

TAXACEAE

Taxus baccata Yew (Plate 79)

Other common names: English Yew; Common Yew

Yew is native in Britain, where it grows wild in southern England as an evergreen tree or bush, usually on chalk. It has, however, been planted throughout the country for hundreds of years and is suitable for hedges and topiary. In the past, yew was sometimes associated with religious rituals and the trees were planted in churchyards, which were enclosed, and therefore inaccessible to livestock. The Irish yew (*Taxus baccata* var. *fastigiata*), sometimes called the churchyard yew, is often grown in Britain, and the Japanese yew (*Taxus cuspidata*) is sometimes planted in parks and gardens.

Yew trees grow up to 20 m high and may attain a great age. The trunks of old trees are massive and gnarled. The bark of yew is reddish brown, scaly, and somewhat fibrous. The branches of the common yew spread more or less horizontally from the trunk and a typical specimen tree has a roughly triangular outline. The branches of the Irish yew are more erect and the trees are consequently more rounded and compact in habit. The leaves are attached close together all around the stems, but, in the English yew, they usually spread in one plane in two opposite ranks, giving a flat appearance to the twigs. The young leaves are bright green, and the mature ones dark green, but paler on the underside. They are uniformly narrow, 1–3 cm long, shiny, and slightly convex on the upper side. The male and female flowers are almost always borne on separate trees. They are small, pale greenish yellow, and inconspicuous; they are found in the leaf axils in spring. The seeds develop singly from the flowers and are partially surrounded by the fruit (aril), which is a bright, pinkish-red, fleshy, translucent cup.

Poisonous principles

A great deal of work has been done on the constituents of yew, and many substances have been isolated; several of these have very similar names, mostly derived from the botanical names of the tree. One of the many taxane derivatives, taxine, is present in all parts of the tree; it is a complex mixture of at least 11 alkaloids. Of these only two, taxines A and B, have been characterized structurally; taxine A is the major constituent of the alkaloid mixture. Taxine is absorbed rapidly from the digestive tract and interferes with the action of the heart. A volatile oil and traces of a cyanogenic glycoside, taxiphyllin, are also said to be present. The volatile oil may be the cause of the intense irritation sometimes seen in the stomach. The toxicity of yew is not decreased by wilting or drying, so that clippings and fallen leaves are as toxic as the fresh plant. Substances that disrupt the normal process of cell division (anti-mitotic compounds) have been isolated from *Taxus* species. Two of these substances, paclitaxel (Taxol) and docetaxel (Taxotere) have been produced semi-synthetically, licensed, and used with considerable success as anti-cancer drugs in human medicine.

Animal poisoning

There are conflicting reports on the toxicity of yew for animals.[1] In general, the trees should be considered highly toxic, but if eaten often, in small quantities, there may be no adverse effects, e.g. on the North Downs in Surrey deer graze them regularly,[2] and yew has even been fed intentionally. Poisoning was said to occur only when considerable amounts of yew were eaten, often in the absence of adequate supplies of other feed. Such information is misleading, and yew should never be fed to animals as the risk of rapidly fatal taxine poisoning is too great; yew is even considered by some to be the most toxic plant in Britain. Similar toxic reactions occur with all species of yew. Because of its long-standing and well-known reputation for being poisonous, farmers do not allow animals near yew. Most recent cases of poisoning have resulted from accidents (when fallen branches of yew have been browsed by animals, or when fences have been broken, giving animals access to the trees), or through ignorance of the toxicity of the trees (such as when garden refuse, including yew hedge clippings, is thrown on to grazing land). An unusual outbreak in Ohio, USA, resulting in the death of several fairground bulls,[3] occurred when their attendants, not realizing the dangers, enlarged the enclosure of the animals, using a hedge of Japanese yew (*Taxus cuspidata*) as a boundary.

Yew is most toxic in winter,[4] a time when animals are more likely to eat it, as other food is scarce. In experimental work, yew twigs offered to adequately fed cattle, horses, sheep, and goats were not eaten,[3] but, irrespective of their nutritional status, animals have been poisoned by yew throughout the year. Most outbreaks involve horses[5-9] or cattle,[10-16] but yew poisoning has also been recorded in sheep,[17-21] goats,[12, 19, 22, 23] deer,[24-26] kangaroos,[24] a dog,[27] emus,[28] pheasants,[29,30] and canaries.[31] No reports of poisoning in pigs have been found, but a fatal dose of 3 g per kg is widely quoted from an old source.[32] The lethal dose has been estimated as 1–10 g per kg body weight for ruminants and 0.5–2 g per kg for horses;[33] other estimates are lower than this. The clinical signs reported in all animals are similar. They include muscular trembling, uncoordinated movements, coldness, rapid then weak pulse, and sometimes excitability preceding stupor and collapse during which breathing may be accompanied by groaning; in others sudden collapse is the only sign. In many cases, signs are never seen, as the animals may die only a few hours after eating yew; death usually follows collapse, with or without convulsions. A recent outbreak in Britain is of interest, however, as it emphasizes that yew poisoning is not necessarily fatal.[34] Of 24 cattle that broke into a copse that contained an Irish yew tree, two died and yew leaves were found in their rumens. The others appeared unaffected, but some hours later two other animals started staggering and developed pronounced stiffness of the hind legs. Almost immediately they collapsed and lay apparently dying, but within five minutes they had risen and made a spontaneous recovery. In some cases there may, in addition, be dilatation of pupils and abdominal pain.[35] Yew poisoning, with typical signs after one hour and death 15 minutes later, occurred in a pony given, by stomach tube, a strained aqueous extract of ground yew (*Taxus cuspidata*) twigs and berries.[6]

At post-mortem examination it is not unusual for there to be no evidence of poisoning, other than the presence of yew in the mouth and stomach. There may, however, be inflammation of the stomach and intestines, and distension of the stomach with gas, particularly if death did not occur for two or three days. It has been found that one side of the heart is usually flaccid, dark, and filled with blood having a tarry appearance, while the other side is contracted and empty.[35, 36] The liver, spleen, and lungs may also be engorged with dark blood.[36]

It is important to remove the stomach contents as soon as possible (by induction of vomiting, where appropriate, or by surgery in ruminants).

Human poisoning
The possibility of fatal poisoning by yew has been known at least since Roman times.[1] As with other plants whose toxicity has been known from antiquity, yew has been used

medicinally; it was given to 'steady the heart' and was said to be an antidote for adder bites and rabies.[1] There are reports of adults who have died after taking medicinal decoctions prepared from yew leaves.[35]

The toxicity of yew fruits has been the subject of controversy for many years. It is now accepted that the red, fleshy aril is not poisonous, or is of very low toxicity, but that the seeds are poisonous. The fruits are attractive to children and are most often eaten by them. When the berries are eaten, the seeds are not necessarily chewed, and they pass through the digestive system without the toxins they contain being released. In such cases there may be no symptoms[37] or only very mild digestive disturbances,[38] even if as many as 40 berries are eaten. Of 41 cases in children aged 12 months to 14 years that were studied in a poisons centre in the USA,[39] 34 had no symptoms; all had eaten berries. Most of the severe or fatal cases reported involve the leaves,[40–46] infusions of them,[47, 48] and occasionally the bark.[44, 46]

The initial symptoms, which are noticed within an hour of ingestion, include headache, lethargy, dizziness, dilatation of pupils, nausea, vomiting, and abdominal pain. Depending on the amount of plant material eaten, these may be followed by muscular stiffness, rapid then slow heart beat, and disturbances to cardiac rhythm that may be very severe and result in heart failure and death.

Diagnosis of yew poisoning was formerly limited to finding plant fragments in stomach contents, but there are now more sophisticated methods,[49, 50] such as various chromatographic techniques, mass spectrometry, and nuclear magnetic resonance, by which the toxins of yew can be detected specifically. For treatment, there should be rapid removal of stomach contents by lavage. Lidocaine, given intravenously, has been used successfully to control accelerated heart beat;[47] in some cases it is necessary to fit a pacemaker. Otherwise, basic symptomatic and supportive measures are all that can be taken.

THYMELAEACEAE

In this family a wild shrub, spurge laurel (*Daphne laureola*), and one that is frequently grown in gardens, mezereon (*Daphne mezereum*), can cause a similar type of poisoning.

Daphne laureola Spurge Laurel (Plate 80)

Other common names: Wood Laurel; Copse Laurel

The name of this plant can cause confusion with other shrubs whose common name is also laurel. They are, however, unrelated botanically, the other laurels being species of *Prunus* and belonging to a different family (Rosaceae). *Daphne laureola* has a widespread distribution throughout England and Wales, mainly on calcareous soils, but is seldom abundant.

Spurge laurel is an erect, sparingly branched shrub, growing up to 1 m in height. It is evergreen, the leaves that remain at maturity being clustered together near the top of the plant. The leaves are tough, smooth, glossy green, and up to 12 cm long. They are narrow where attached to the stem then widen gradually up to 4 cm before terminating in a blunt point. The midrib is a prominent feature, the longitudinal axis of the leaf being slightly grooved. The flowers develop throughout the spring in short 5–10-flowered clusters in the axils of the leaves and are green, with yellow stamens appearing where the tubular base of the flower opens into four lobes, each 8–10 mm across. The fruit is an oval berry up to 12 mm across. It is green at first, then bluish, and finally black when fully ripe. Details of poisoning follow the description of *Daphne mezereum* (see below).

Daphne mezereum Mezereon (Plate 81)

Other common names: Spurge Olive; Spurge Flax; Dwarf Bay; Wild Pepper

Mezereon grows in woodlands on calcareous soils. It is local in distribution and now very rare in Britain, many specimens having been removed to gardens where both wild and cultivated varieties are grown; it is now a protected species.

It is a compact, erect, deciduous shrub up to 1 m tall. The smooth, light green leaves are usually 3–10 cm long, rarely more than 1 cm wide, and taper to a point at both ends. The fragrant pink (occasionally white or purple) flowers appear in small clusters in early spring, before the leaves. The basal tubular portion of the flower expands into four lobes 8–12 mm across, on which there are often dark pink lines. The fruit is an oval, scarlet berry, up to 12 mm across, that often persists into the winter.

Poisonous principles

Those of spurge laurel, mezereon, and other *Daphne* species not found in Britain are similar, and are contained in the acrid irritant sap of all parts of the plants, but particularly the bark and the seeds in the berries. Tricyclic diterpenes with a daphnane carbon skeleton, principally daphnetoxin and its ester mezerein, are thought to be mainly responsible for the irritant toxic effects of these plants.[1] Possible anti-tumour activity of some daphnane derivatives (including mezerein) has been reported.[1,2]

Animal poisoning

Daphne is usually avoided, probably because of its unpalatability, but can cause poisoning if eaten. The practice (now largely discontinued) of giving crushed dried leaves of *Daphne* to horses as a treatment for intestinal worms resulted in some cases of abdominal pain and poisoning. A cart-horse that ate *Daphne laureola*, while waiting to be unloaded, refused further food and developed severe abdominal pain, a staggering gait, and laboured breathing. The following day the animal died after excessive purgation and an elevated body temperature. Post-mortem examination revealed inflammation, swelling, and blood-stained contents of the gastrointestinal tract.[3] Experimental feeding of *Daphne* to another horse produced similar clinical signs, but was not fatal.[4] In three days the animal ate only 100–150 g of the plant. Cattle were poisoned in Austria in 1992.[5] Following a dry summer 20 heifers were moved in September to poor grazing with access to partially cleared woodland; within 24 hours seven had died after showing signs of colic, salivation, dilatation of pupils, incoordination, blindness, laboured breathing, recumbency, convulsions, and paralysis. *Daphne mezereum* was present in the woodland and in the rumen of the dead animals. Terpenes were detected in the ruminal contents by thin layer chromatography with the findings being similar to those obtained with a *Daphne mezereum* extract. Mezereon berries thrown to a litter of 10-week-old pigs resulted in the sudden death of all but the smallest one, which had not gained access to the trough.[6] All the pigs vomited before death, and post-mortem examination revealed white, burned patches in the mouth and stomach, which was intensely inflamed.

Human poisoning

This usually involves children who mistake the ripe berries for currants, and has been reported from the time of Dioscorides (first century AD) to the present.[7-10] Because of their acrid taste, usually only a very few berries are eaten, and the symptoms, which include a burning sensation in the mouth, nausea, abdominal pain, vomiting, and diarrhoea, are relatively mild and transient. Even limited oral contact with other parts of the shrub can also produce similar symptoms, which were reported in Norway in a young man who used his teeth to sever a flowering shoot of *Daphne mezereum* that he was trying to pick; he recovered the following day.[11] If a sufficient quantity of the plant or its berries is eaten, there may be prostration, shivering, pallor, dilated pupils, violent vomiting, and diarrhoea with blistering and shedding of the lining of the oral and intestinal mucous membranes. Convulsions may occur and muscular twitching and somnolence may persist for several days.

UMBELLIFERAE

In this large family, which has species of over 40 genera native in Britain, most plants are harmless. Parts of some are edible, e.g. the roots of carrot and parsnip, the stem of angelica, the leaf stalk of celery, the leaves of parsley and fennel, and the seeds of caraway. A few are poisonous by ingestion and others can give rise to skin reactions (photosensitization) after contact; the plants considered here are divided into these two groups.

Accurate identification of plants in this family presents difficulties due to the superficial similarity of many of them, and mistaken identity has resulted in cases of human poisoning. Fool's parsley (*Aethusa cynapium*) and hemlock (*Conium maculatum*) have been mistaken for true parsley (*Petroselinum crispum*), and curly leaved varieties of the culinary herb are now grown commercially, partly to avoid such mistakes. The roots of fool's parsley have been mistaken for young turnips or radishes, those of cowbane (*Cicuta virosa*) for parsnip, and those of hemlock water dropwort (*Oenanthe crocata*) for carrot or parsnip. The many alternative common names used for British members of the family are an additional source of confusion as a name applied to one plant, e.g. hemlock, may be part of the name of other plants such as hemlock water dropwort or water hemlock, the latter being another name for cowbane. Without positive identification, none of the wild Umbelliferae should be eaten, and they should be considered as potentially toxic to animals.

POISONING BY INGESTION

There are three plants in the Umbelliferae family in Britain that can cause severe poisoning; these are hemlock, hemlock water dropwort, and cowbane. They were involved in nearly 10% of all cases of plant poisoning in animals reported to the Veterinary Investigation Centres in 1975–1977.[1] Another plant in this group is fool's parsley, which is of relatively low toxicity, but has caused poisoning here.

Aethusa cynapium Fool's Parsley

This annual plant is common on pastures, cultivated ground, and waste land throughout Britain, but is found infrequently in the north. Fool's parsley grows up to 120 cm high and has hollow, finely lined, somewhat bluish-green stems. The compound leaves are finely divided into narrow segments and the flat-topped inflorescence (umbel) is 2–6 cm across. The fruits are oval, ridged longitudinally, and 3–4 mm in diameter. The three or four narrow, pointed bracteoles, up to 1 cm long, which are present on the outer side of the stalks of individual rays, are characteristic of the plant.

Poisonous principles
The plant is unpalatable in the fresh state and emits a repulsive odour, which becomes greater when crushed or bruised. The poisonous principles have not been determined precisely, although the plant is said to contain the alkaloid cynapine and also a coniine-like alkaloid.[2] It seems that a large quantity of the plant has to be eaten to produce poisoning, and there may be variations in its toxic properties with stage of development and climate. Hay containing the plant is harmless to livestock.

Animal poisoning
Incoordination, particularly affecting the hindquarters, and death have been reported in a sow and her piglets, which consumed a large quantity of fool's parsley after being deprived of green feed.[3] Indigestion, panting, and incoordination have been seen in goats,[4] and poisoning has been reported in cattle and horses.[5] No signs of poisoning occurred when the plant was fed to guinea pigs, or when extracts of it were given orally or by intraperitoneal injection to mice.[6]

Human poisoning
This has occurred from mistaking the leaves for parsley and the roots for radishes; symptoms have included nausea, vomiting, diarrhoea, salivation, headache, muscular tremors, and stiffness of the limbs.[7]

Cicuta virosa Cowbane

Other common name: Water Hemlock

This plant is very localized in its distribution in Britain, being confined to shallow water, ditches, and marshes in East Anglia, small parts of the Midlands, areas in southern Scotland, and central and northern Ireland.

Cowbane is a stout, erect perennial, 30–130 cm high with a somewhat ridged, hollow stem. The compound leaves are up to 30 cm long, have hollow stalks and narrow, elongated, unequally toothed segments up to 10 cm long. The inflorescence (umbel) develops in midsummer, is 7–13 cm in diameter and bears numerous, small, white flowers. The ripe fruits are up to 2 mm across, rounded at the base, and tapering slightly towards the apex. Characteristic features of the plant are the elongated leaflets and the underground parts, the roots growing from a thick, white, fleshy portion, which is divided internally by cross partitions into a series of hollow compartments.

219

Poisonous principle

The active principle is a highly unsaturated aliphatic alcohol, cicutoxin. It is found in the yellow juice of the roots and in smaller quantities in the stems, and is present in greatest concentration between late autumn and early winter. Its action on the body is that of a convulsant poison, and part of a root has been enough to kill horses, cattle, and children. Cowbane roots may be dug up and left lying on the surface after cleaning out ditches. As the poison persists in the dried plant, it may cause the death of an animal long after it has been unearthed. The leaves and stem are poisonous, but to a lesser extent; they are sometimes eaten when the grass is short.

Animal poisoning

Signs of cowbane poisoning are nausea, salivation, widely dilated pupils (constricted pupils have occasionally been noted), vomiting, abdominal pain, muscular spasms, violent convulsions, and death from asphyxia; there is no diarrhoea. Clinical signs appear within an hour of ingestion, and death can occur in a few hours; animals that survive 5–6 hours generally recover completely in 4–5 days. Cases have been described in horses,[8-10] and cattle;[9, 11-13] pigs appear to be less susceptible.[9] In an outbreak in Germany,[14] nine of 62 beef cattle were found dead during a drought when there was little green growth except for cowbane near a lake; roots of the cowbane had been exposed by a drop in the water level and showed signs of having been eaten. Clinical signs in another eight affected animals were hyperactivity, dilatation of pupils, salivation, slight bloat, colic, staggering, muscular spasms, and convulsions. One of the eight died with signs of respiratory paralysis, the other seven had recovered in three days after removal from the area.

At post-mortem examination, there may be no diagnostic lesions, although congestion of blood vessels and haemorrhages have been reported in the gastrointestinal tract.

Human poisoning

The symptoms[15-18] are similar to those described in animals. In Sweden, half an hour after eating a whole root of cowbane in mistake for that of angelica,[18] a man became dizzy and nauseous; he vomited, had convulsions, and became unconscious. A reddish cyanosis of the skin, an increased heart rate, and widely dilated pupils were also reported. He recovered after treatment that included stomach lavage, administration of activated charcoal and a muscle relaxant, artificial respiration, haemodialysis, and haemoperfusion.

Human poisoning by this plant is life-threatening and immediate hospitalization is required. Stomach lavage and activated charcoal should be used to reduce the absorption of toxin, and diazepam given to control convulsions. Supportive measures should include the maintenance of respiration, and the correction of a metabolic acidosis. As the cicutoxin molecule (molecular length 248.2 nm) is dialysable, haemodialysis and haemoperfusion are considered to be of value.[18]

Conium maculatum Hemlock (Plate 82)

Hemlock grows in damp places, open woods, and waste ground throughout Britain, although it is less frequent in the north. In recent years the plant has become common along main road verges in many parts of the country.

The plant is an erect, branched biennial (sometimes annual or perennial), which may exceed 2 m in height. The leaves are up to 30 cm long, with finely divided leaflets that have deeply serrated edges, giving the plant a rather delicate appearance. The inflorescence (umbel) produced in early summer is 2–5 cm across and bears numerous white flowers 2 mm in diameter. The root is a white, fleshy, usually unbranched, tap root. Characteristic features of the plant are the irregular purple blotches on the smooth, slightly ridged, hollow stem, the laterally compressed fruits that have five prominent wavy longitudinal ridges and are about 3 mm long when ripe, and the odour of mice emitted by all parts of the plant when bruised or crushed.

The poisonous nature of hemlock has been known from very early times, and it is generally accepted that an extract of the plant was used by the Greeks for the execution of Socrates in 399 BC. In 1578, in a translation of a herbal from French, Henry Lyte called it a 'naughtie and dangerous herbe'. It was used in medicine, but this practice ceased in the 19th century owing to the uncertain actions of the preparations.

Poisonous principles

The toxicity of hemlock is due to the presence of a group of highly poisonous alkaloids: coniine, N-methylconiine, γ-coniceine, conhydrine, and pseudoconhydrine. All these alkaloids act in a similar way, inducing paralysis, convulsions, and death from respiratory paralysis. All parts of the plant contain the alkaloids, the roots at all times containing the least. Before flowering the leaves contain the most alkaloids, but the greatest concentrations are found in the flowers and fruits. The alkaloid content, however, does vary with the climatic conditions; in sunny summers the average weight of the fruits and thus the quantity of alkaloids can be twice those under wet, cloudy conditions. When dried, the plant loses a large part of its toxicity.[19]

Animal poisoning

The unpleasant mousy odour of hemlock probably makes it unattractive to animals. Poisoning of livestock occurs mostly in spring, when pastures are short and the young leaves are growing among the more luxuriant grasses of sheltered hedge banks and the sides of ditches, although at this period of the year the plants are at their least poisonous stage.

The hemlock alkaloids cause paralysis of the motor nerve endings and stimulation followed by depression of the central nervous system. They induce vomiting, or vomiting attempts, at an early stage of their action. Large doses can slow the heart rate. Respiration is generally accelerated and deepened at first, but eventually becomes slow and laboured and finally ceases, while the heart is still strong and consciousness has just disappeared.

Animal species differ in susceptibility: cattle developed severe signs of toxicity when given as little as 3.3 mg coniine per kg body weight, horses when given 15.5 mg per kg, whereas sheep were quite resistant, showing only moderate signs when given 44 mg per kg.[20] Clinical signs appear within a few hours of ingestion of the plant, and in cattle,[21] sheep,[22] and goats[23] include apathy, rapid respiration, difficulty in movement, salivation, frequent regurgitation, muscular tremors, ruminal atony, groaning, grinding of teeth, diarrhoea, and a drop in milk yield. Convulsive attacks have occasionally been described. Poisoning has also been reported in horses,[24] pigs,[25–28] rabbits,[29,30] chickens,[29] and turkeys.[31] Quails appear to be more susceptible than chickens, and chickens more so than turkeys.[32] In 1971 in the USA, *Conium maculatum* poisoning was observed in pregnant sows, which gave birth two months later to malformed piglets and also piglets with the central nervous signs of hemlock poisoning.[33] In Britain, limb deformities, cleft palate, and muscular tremors have been reported in piglets born to sows with access to hemlock; signs of hemlock poisoning were not observed in the sows in one outbreak,[34] but in others the sows had shown clinical signs that included trembling, incoordination, and collapse.[27, 28] Limb deformities have been produced experimentally in the calves of cows given coniine[35] or the fresh green plant.[36] Cleft palate was produced experimentally in piglets born to gilts given *Conium maculatum* seed or young plants from the 30th to 45th day of pregnancy.[37] When the seeds and autumn growth of the plant were fed to gilts between 43 to 53 or 51 to 63 days of pregnancy their piglets had limb deformities at birth.[38] These effects were attributed to the γ-coniceine content of the plant material.[39] Similar effects were induced in ewes and their lambs, but at higher dosages than those for cattle and pigs.[40,41] Laboratory rats and rabbits are less susceptible to these toxic effects on their young.[42] It is reported that animals that survive for eight hours after the onset of clinical signs recover comparatively quickly. There are no specific post-mortem findings.

Human poisoning

Fatal poisoning has occurred as a result of mistaking the plant for wild carrot or parsley. The symptoms are similar to those in animals, with vomiting, dilatation of the pupils, incoordination, coldness of the extremities, coma, convulsions, and eventually death from respiratory paralysis. In the USA, a four-year-old boy who ate hemlock foliage in mistake for carrot tops became sleepy within 30 minutes, and could not be woken two hours later.[43] He had vomited green plant material, and was admitted to hospital, where he was given stomach lavage and activated charcoal; he was awake four hours later. Leaves from a plant identical to that eaten contained 850 µg of γ-coniceine per g of fresh material. Acute renal failure and muscle damage have also been described in addition to the neurological effects.[44] In Italy, acute renal failure occurred after ingestion of small wild birds (skylarks, chaffinches, robins) that had eaten *Conium maculatum* buds on returning in the spring from North Africa. The birds were not affected but their meat was toxic.[45]

Treatment is symptomatic; charcoal may be given to adsorb the alkaloids, respiration assisted, and convulsions controlled, e.g. with diazepam. Stomach lavage is recommended.

Oenanthe crocata Hemlock Water Dropwort (Plate 83)

Other common name: Dead Men's Fingers

This plant has a scattered distribution throughout Britain in damp places, particularly on calcareous soils. Hemlock water dropwort is an erect perennial, 50–150 cm high, with branched stems that are grooved and hollow. The compound leaves are triangular in outline, 30 or more cm long, and have leaflets with bluntly toothed edges. The inflorescence (umbel) is 5–10 cm across and is formed in early spring, from dome-shaped clusters of white flowers; cylindrical fruits, 4–6 mm long when ripe, develop in autumn. Characteristic features of the plant are the leaf stalks, which entirely sheath the stem, the flower styles, which are erect and protrude above the petals, and the rootstock, which is composed of five or more fleshy, pale yellow or white, finger-like tubers (hence the alternative common name, dead men's fingers). When damaged, these exude juice that becomes yellowish on exposure to the air.

Poisonous principle

The active principle, oenanthetoxin, is a polyunsaturated higher alcohol, chemically very similar to cicutoxin found in cowbane (*Cicuta virosa*). It is a convulsant poison that is not affected by drying and storage. The roots are the most toxic part of the plant and very small amounts are sufficient to cause death. There appears to be some seasonal variation in the amount of toxin in the roots, with the greatest concentration in winter.

Animal poisoning

Poisoning of farm stock usually occurs from eating roots that have been brought to the surface during ditching or drainage operations. Death is rapid and few clinical signs may be seen before it occurs. Horses[46] and cattle[47, 48] show salivation, dilated pupils, respiratory distress, and spasmodic convulsions; they usually die in a convulsion. Sheep are less susceptible to its effects than other animals, and at least half of a poisoned flock may recover from acute poisoning. After the acute clinical signs have subsided, the animals may develop diarrhoea for about two days, and then slowly return to normal. Pigs that have eaten the roots of hemlock water dropwort may vomit for a short time, but death is usually sudden, without the appearance of any clinical signs. There are no specific diagnostic lesions at post-mortem examination.

Human poisoning

Fatal cases have occurred when the leaves of hemlock water dropwort have been mistaken for those of celery, and the tuberous roots for parsnips.[49-52] In two incidents reported in 1987, in which parts of the plant were boiled to make soup, three of the six cases showed severe symptoms (one requiring mechanical assistance with breathing), but all recovered.[53, 54] In a recent case in Britain,[51] a woman who ate the root of hemlock water dropwort, had symptoms that included vomiting, diarrhoea, and mental confusion for five hours before admission to hospital for observation. She made a gradual recovery over the following two days.

First-aid treatment consists of keeping the patient warm and avoiding any excitement. Stomach lavage should be performed and attempts made to control the convulsions by intravenous injection of barbiturates or other anti-convulsants.

Other members of the Umbelliferae family poisonous by ingestion

In addition to *Oenanthe crocata*, six other *Oenanthe* species occur in Britain; all of these are considered poisonous, but to a lesser degree than hemlock water dropwort. *Oenanthe pimpinelloides* was suspected of poisoning cattle in Britain,[55] while *Oenanthe aquatica* poisoning has been reported in cattle in Poland[56] and Sweden.[57] A family in Greece was poisoned by *Oenanthe silaifolia*,[58] when the boiled plant was included in a salad; the intravenous injection of extracts of this plant caused death in rabbits and clinical signs of poisoning in dogs and a sheep. The effects that these other *Oenanthe* species produce are not so acute, and are of the depressive type, generally not progressing to convulsions.

Some toxicity has been attributed to cow parsley (*Anthriscus sylvestris*), lesser water parsnip (*Berula erecta*), rough chervil (*Chaerophyllum temulum*), and greater water parsnip (*Sium latifolium*), but no recent reports of poisoning by these plants have been traced.

PHOTOSENSITIZATION BY SKIN CONTACT

Heracleum mantegazzianum Giant Hogweed (Plate 84)

This plant is not native in Britain but was introduced from the Caucasus and found a place among the more exotic garden plants. In the early 1900s it was found growing wild, and since then has become naturalized in various localities, often near water but also on waste ground.

When fully grown, giant hogweed can be distinguished from other members of the Umbelliferae by its large size, the hollow, ridged stem being up to 3.5 m high and the compound leaves 1 m long. The inflorescence (umbel), which develops in early summer, can be 50 cm in diameter and has numerous rays up to 20 cm long. The fruit may measure 13 mm across and is oval or elliptical in shape. Apart from its huge size, characteristic features of the plant are the reddish spots on the stem and the strong, resinous, aromatic smell that is readily noticeable when the plant is cut or crushed.

Poisonous principles

Giant hogweed contains psoralens (linear furanocoumarins) that make the skin hypersensitive to sunlight.

Animal poisoning

There are few reports of giant hogweed affecting animals, but skin damage can occur. A short-haired dachshund, which had been playing with children who developed blisters after playing with the plant, also had lesions on the hairless part of the underside of its body.[59] The plant is thought to have caused lesions in a five-year-old pygmy goat in a municipal park.[60] The animal became subdued, refused to eat and drink, and developed diffuse salivation with severe mouth ulceration; it took about six weeks to recover. When one-week-old ducklings were in a paddock containing young giant hogweed plants, large blisters appeared on their feet and the upper part of the beak; three weeks later the feet had heavy scab deposits and dark pigmentation.[61] The two birds with beak lesions had to be killed because deformity of the beak prevented feeding.

Human poisoning

After contact of the bare skin with the plant and exposure to the sun, affected areas of the skin develop burn-like lesions, with reddening within 24 hours and blister formation[62] within another 24 hours. The associated lymph nodes may be tender. The fluid-filled blisters can be large and very irritating, but they subside in a few days; the brown pigmentation that develops on the affected parts can persist for several months.[51, 63–65]

Success has been claimed for treatment of the skin lesions as partial skin thickness burns;[62] thorough removal of dead tissue and daily application of silver sulphadiazine led to more rapid healing than is usual after contact with this plant.

Other members of the Umbelliferae family that can cause skin damage

Furanocoumarins are also found in several other members of the family and, like giant hogweed, these plants can also sensitize the skin to sunlight and lead to blistering or dermatitis. This type of skin damage has not been reported in animals in Britain, but on pasture where wild parsnip (*Pastinaca sativa*) was growing in Argentina, lesions occurred on the white areas of the skin of two horses.[66] In New Zealand, blisters resembling those of foot and mouth disease appeared on the snout and feet of white-skinned pigs that were in contact with vegetable material containing parsnips and celery (*Apium graveolens*); the lesions were reproduced experimentally with both of these plants.[67, 68] When ostriches were fed dried, ground parsley (*Petroselinum crispum*), they developed typical skin lesions, which were reproduced in ducklings.[69] Skin damage similar to that following contact with giant hogweed (*Heracleum mantegazzianum*) was reported in an 18-year-old man who had been harvesting parsley for two days in sunny conditions.[62]

Human contact with these photosensitizing plants can lead to skin changes ranging in severity from reddening to oedema and severe blistering. A case has been reported of a child who had extensive skin lesions on the exposed parts of her body after playing on waste ground where wild parsnip plants were flowering.[70] Contact with cow parsley (*Anthriscus sylvestris*) and hogweed (*Heracleum sphondylium*) that are common wild plants in Britain can produce similar effects, and are responsible for a condition known as 'strimmer rash'.[65] This type of reaction can also develop in adults coming into contact with the wild plants, or handling the cultivated plants in the course of their work.[71] There is a well-recognized condition known as 'celery rash' that develops on the hands of celery growers.[65] It is associated with the high furanocoumarin content induced in celery infected with the fungus *Sclerotinia sclerotiorum*, and present naturally in celery cultivars that have been bred for resistance to this infection. Photosensitization can also follow the ingestion of plants of this family. The furanocoumarins are not inactivated by cooking, and severe reactions have been reported after eating vegetables containing furanocoumarins in patients receiving PUVA therapy (oral psoralens with ultraviolet light) for eczema.[72]

URTICACEAE

Urtica dioica Stinging Nettle

Other common name: Common Nettle

Stinging nettles are abundant in Britain, and grow in a wide range of habitats including woodland, cultivated ground, and waste places. These perennial plants have well-developed, branched, yellow roots, and underground stems from the nodes of which strong, rapidly growing shoots emerge in spring. They are variable in height, according to the habitat, but frequently exceed 1 m. The leaves arise in opposite pairs on the stem, and are stalked, pointed at the tip, and toothed at the edges. The leaves and stems of almost all forms of this very variable plant have abundant stinging hairs, the tips of which are readily broken off on contact, leaving a sharp point. The nature of these hairs, their stinging mechanism, and the irritants they contain have been investigated for over 300 years,[1] and are still not fully understood. The flowers are small and green, and develop in tassle-like inflorescences from the leaf axils. In some plants the stems and flowers appear to have a purple or brownish tinge.

Poisonous principles

The active irritant substances that are released into the skin from the stinging hairs are 5-hydroxytryptamine, acetylcholine, and histamine.[2] These are thought to cause the initial pain, while other substances that have a direct effect on nerves, or mediate the release of such substances (possibly histamine) may be involved in the more persistent inflammatory reaction that follows.[3,4] In the past, formic acid was said to be responsible for the stinging reaction, but is now not thought to be involved.

Animal poisoning

Adverse effects after contact with *Urtica* rarely occur in animals, but there have been cases in hunting dogs in the USA.[5] After massive exposure to the plants, clinical signs including trembling, vomiting, difficult breathing, and weakness were reported; several animals died. Reactions to stinging nettles are included among the many possible causes of the raised, itching, evanescent weals (urticaria) that develop on the skin of horses, cattle, and pigs.[6] Horses appear also to experience a neurological reaction.[7] In separate incidents, three horses showed signs of distress, incoordination, and muscle weakness after being in contact with stinging nettles. An urticarial rash was seen on two of the animals; all three horses recovered in 3–4 hours. Little experimental work has been done on feeding nettles to animals, but enlargement of the kidneys was recorded in guinea pigs and mice fed exclusively on the plants.[8]

Human poisoning

This plant does not appear to be poisonous when taken internally. It has been recommended as a food plant,[9] is sometimes made into a tea, and forms the basis of a traditional dish in Scotland. Experimental nutritional work on the stinging nettle revealed that it is a good source of proteins, vitamins, and fibre.[8]

It is the stinging sensation experienced on contact with the plant, and the resultant skin reaction, for which nettles are well known; the term 'urticaria' is derived from the botanical name of these plants. Nettles are thought to be the most common non-allergic cause of urticaria in Britain.[3] The irritant substances released into the skin give rise to a localized contact reaction and do not usually involve hypersensitivity. Initially there is pricking and tingling, and the skin becomes red. Within a few minutes white weals develop, and may coalesce; itching of the affected areas is common. The reaction may be transitory, but more often the tingling and itching persist for at least 12 hours. Similar symptoms were recorded in six volunteers after skin application of nettle stems in a study of the cellular and molecular mechanisms in affected skin.[3] The popular idea that the application of dock leaves will cure nettle rash is unproven, although the coolness of the large leaves may be soothing. Cold compresses, vigorous massaging,[4] or bathing in tepid water[10] may be beneficial.

Other members of the Urticaceae family

The stinging hairs of the small nettle (*Urtica urens*), an annual plant that is found on waste and cultivated ground in Britain, have the same effect as those of *Urtica dioica*.

VERBENACEAE

Lantana camara Lantana (Plate 85)

Other common names: Yellow Sage; Red Sage

Lantana species do not grow wild in Britain, but some are cultivated here. Most of these are *Lantana camara*, which is best considered as a group rather than as a single species since there are so many variations among the plants. They can grow as shrubs up to 2 m in height and width, but are more common here as indoor plants or annuals for summer bedding.

The stems, which are square in section and sometimes prickly, bear pairs of rather coarse, prominently veined leaves that are oval, pointed at the tip, and may have scalloped or toothed margins. The flowers, which are produced throughout most of the year, develop in dense clusters. As they mature, many undergo a characteristic colour change, usually from yellow to shades of pink or red, but varieties with other colours are also cultivated. The small, round fruits, which develop in a tightly packed group on the thickened flower head, ripen from green to purplish black.

Poisonous principles

There is lack of agreement on the toxic constituents of *Lantana* species.[1] The plants contain both toxic and non-toxic triterpenes. Those commonly reported to be involved in poisoning are the pentacyclic triterpenes lantadene A and lantadene B; lantadene A is sometimes referred to as the more, or even the only, toxic component. However, in pure crystalline form, lantadene A was found not to be toxic to guinea pigs, whereas a partially purified fraction was toxic. The photosensitizing agent present is said by some to be lantadene A, and by others not to be lantadene A. There is general agreement that the leaves and unripe (green) fruits are poisonous, but opinions differ on the toxicity of the ripe fruits. Some forms of the plant appear to be non-toxic.

Animal poisoning

This has not been reported in Britain, but poisoning of grazing animals (mainly cattle and sheep, but also horses and goats) is a serious problem in several other countries, where the plants grow wild.[2, 3] Initially there is loss of appetite, and (in cattle) rumination becomes slow or ceases altogether. After a short period of diarrhoea, there is constipation. There may be liver damage, associated with jaundice, from the accumulation of bilirubin, and also photosensitization reactions on exposed or non-pigmented skin. The photosensitization is accompanied by the accumulation of phylloerythrin (a breakdown product of chlorophyll) in the blood, and can lead to severe cracking and necrosis of the skin. Affected animals may have ulceration and itching of the mouth, nostrils, and eyes, haemorrhages of the intestines, and kidney damage; some become weak, and stagger as they move. Severe photosensitization reactions may be accompanied by blindness, possibly resulting from injuries caused by rubbing to relieve itching. In acute poisoning death can occur in only a few days, with haemorrhagic gastroenteritis and jaundice being the only findings, but it is more usual for clinical signs to develop more slowly, with death in 1–4 weeks.[4] Dogs can also be affected; they may vomit (sometimes with blood) and develop anaemia and liver damage.[3,5] Considerable success has been achieved in treating poisoned cattle and sheep by giving them a suspension of activated charcoal in an electrolyte solution.[6]

Human poisoning

This is most likely to result from children eating the unripe green berries. The symptoms described in four of 17 such cases in Florida in the 1960s[7] are typical of *Lantana* poisoning. They included vomiting and diarrhoea, weakness, dilated pupils and photophobia, cyanosis, and slow laboured breathing. There was one fatality, and three others had severe symptoms. The child that died became unconscious before death; it was noted that all of the other 16 children (including 11 with no symptoms) had had stomach lavage. Skin contact may cause dermatitis.[8]

Other members of the Verbenaceae family

The pigeon berry (*Duranta repens*) is sometimes grown as a garden shrub or used for hedging in Britain. Poisoning by this plant appears to be a rare occurrence, but ingestion of the berries is said to cause digestive system disturbances, sleepiness, an increase in body temperature, convulsions, and death.

VISCACEAE

Viscum album Mistletoe (Plate 86)

This plant was formerly classified as a member of the Loranthaceae family, which still includes other mistletoes. *Viscum album* grows as a partial parasite, almost exclusively on deciduous trees, and is common in southern England and parts of the Midlands, but infrequent elsewhere and absent from Scotland. The plant is much branched and woody and readily recognized by its dense, twiggy, compact appearance on host trees. The stems, which may grow up to 1 m in length, bear thick, tough, evergreen leaves, 5–8 cm long, and up to 2 cm across. They have clearly parallel veins, are rounded or bluntly pointed at the tip, and narrow into a short stalk at the base. In spring, small compact clusters of yellowish-green flowers, which are usually unisexual, grow on very short stalks at the tips of branches or in the axils of the leaves. The fruits remain until the winter and are white, slightly translucent berries containing viscous juice and a single seed.

Poisonous principles

The nature and effects of these, particularly in human medicine, have been studied for at least 2000 years, but the information reported is rather confusing and sometimes contradictory. There are conflicting reports on the toxicity of mistletoe berries; most state that they are not or only mildly toxic. There is now general agreement that the two main classes of toxin present in mistletoe are viscotoxins and mistletoe lectins.

The foliage of the plant contains toxic basic proteins, the viscotoxins, which are a mixture of several closely related polypeptides.[1] The amino acid composition of some of these, viscotoxins A and B, has been studied in detail.[2] Viscotoxins A_2, A_3, and B have been identified. Recent work has focused on the toxic lectins also found in mistletoe foliage. They have been named mistletoe lectins (ML) I, II, and III.[3] MLI, also known as viscumin,[4,5] is the most toxic; MLII and MLIII have slight structural differences.[6] These lectins inhibit protein synthesis[7] and consequently cell growth, and are of interest as possible anti-cancer agents.[3,8] A fermented mistletoe and oak extract

(Iscador) is available in some countries and has been used for treating cancer. Analysis of this product indicated that it contains only MLII and MLIII.[9] The viscotoxins also inhibit cell growth, but only at a much higher concentration than the lectins.[8] Mistletoe extracts and powdered mistletoe have been found to reduce blood pressure when administered to experimental animals and some human patients. Variations in the effects of preparations of mistletoe from different host trees have been studied in experimental animals and in cell cultures, but no overall conclusions can be drawn because of the different preparation and administration methods used.[10, 11]

Animal poisoning

Poisoning by *Viscum album* has been reported in dogs, a cat, and a horse. A small dog (griffon) that ate part of a spray of mistletoe with berries[12] developed nervous signs, including constant nodding of the head and incoordination of the hindquarters. Later the animal was unable to stand, and handling produced muscular twitching. There was slight salivation, frequent production of dark urine, a progressive decrease in body temperature and strength of pulse, and the animal died 50 hours after eating the mistletoe. Another dog that ate mistletoe experienced prolonged periods of excitation, was sensitive to its abdomen being touched, had dilated pupils and a slow respiratory rate, but recovered after 24 hours.[13] After eating about ten berries, two dogs vomited and became weak; both recovered.[14] Post-mortem examination of the griffon that died revealed slightly increased amounts of blood (hyperaemia) in the intestines, liver, and brain, and oedema of lymph nodes, lungs, and around the brain and kidneys, which were pale in colour. Microscopic examination revealed some fatty changes in the liver.[12] A cat collapsed 45 minutes after eating an unknown number of berries; it showed rapid breathing and head-shaking.[14] Clinical signs described in the horse included incoordination, abdominal pain, and difficult breathing.[15]

Human poisoning

Suspected mistletoe poisoning is most likely to be encountered around Christmas time when the plant, normally inaccessible in trees, is brought indoors. Most human cases involve children, who have eaten the berries. An early report of poisoning in a child[16] gives symptoms including pale lips, inflammation of the eyes, dilated pupils, slow pulse, laboured breathing, hallucinations, and coma. Induced vomiting revealed mistletoe berries. The severity of the symptoms varies with the number of berries eaten and the age of the child. As few as 3–4 berries may produce mild symptoms, and gastroenteritis may result if large numbers are consumed.[17] In most cases, however, there are usually no or only very mild gastrointestinal disturbances, indicative of the effects of an irritant substance.

Mistletoe is a possible toxic agent in some herbal remedies and has been suspected of causing hepatitis in individuals who have taken them.[18,19] Allergic rhinitis was reported in a person who packed tea made from mistletoe;[20] the specific allergen was not identified.

Other members of the Viscaceae family

Some other mistletoes, including *Phoradendron* species, as well as *Loranthus* species (Loranthaceae), which are not native in Britain, are highly toxic.

Poisonous Fungi

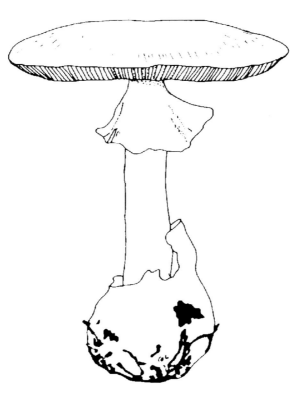

Amanita phalloides
Death cap

This general account of the poisonous fungi found in Britain is not intended to give comprehensive coverage of all aspects of the subject; more information can be found in specialist books, some of which are listed in the Bibliography (pp. 293–294). The account includes: the larger fungi (mushrooms and toadstools) for their direct toxic effects; ergot, which can be ingested with the grain on which it grows; and some mould fungi, which, under certain conditions, produce potent toxins (mycotoxins) in growing plants or plant products stored for use as human and animal food or for animal bedding.

LARGER FUNGI

There are not many reports of animals being poisoned by fungi; most cases are of human poisoning, and for this reason human poisoning is dealt with first. Few of the fungi found in Britain are dangerously poisonous, but quite a number can cause illness or discomfort if eaten. It cannot be emphasized too strongly that a fungus whose identity is not properly known should never be eaten. For identification of the larger fungi, reference should be made to the many books that are available, giving written descriptions and some excellent illustrations. In addition, spore characteristics (mainly colour) can be useful in distinguishing between similar fungi; spores for examination are obtained by preparing a 'spore print'. This is made by placing the cap of a gill fungus (stalk removed) or the fruiting body of a pore fungus on to a piece of clean white paper and leaving for several hours, during which time spores released from the fungus will be deposited on the paper. Placing other fruiting bodies on black (or dark) paper will enable white or pale-coloured spores to be seen.

Contrary to popular belief, there are no characteristics that separate edible from poisonous species, and even recognized edible species may cause poisoning if eaten when old and damp. The names 'mushroom' and 'toadstool' should not be taken to imply any distinction in edibility. Both are common names for the fruiting bodies of some of the larger fungi, the vegetative part of which consists of fine threads (hyphae), which grow in the soil or on rotting plant material. It is inadvisable to eat any fungi raw or undercooked as many are potentially poisonous in that state although rendered harmless by adequate cooking. In Britain the only fungus collected and eaten in any quantity is the field mushroom (*Agaricus campestris*). There is, however, continuing interest in gathering edible fungi in the wild, a practice that is much more common in some Continental countries than in Britain. Errors have been made in the identification of some 'wild' fungi collected in this way, or for commercial distribution and sale. Inexperienced collectors or those paid by the quantity picked may include toxic look-alike fungi among edible ones. There is great variation among individuals in their response to the potentially toxic effects of fungi, and also variation in the toxicity of the fungi themselves, depending on several factors, including their growing conditions and state of maturity. Another possible cause of poisoning from eating fungi is the intake of such substances as mercury,[1] arsenic, and cadmium[2] that can accumulate to toxic levels within them; this is unlikely in Britain, but has been reported in areas where there has been pollution in Eastern Europe.

In this account the poisonous larger fungi have been grouped according to the type of toxic reaction they produce or the toxins they contain, rather than taxonomically. The groups generally recognized are those giving rise to: cytolytic poisoning (cellular degeneration of body tissues); psychotropic poisoning (involving the central nervous system); muscarine poisoning; poisoning in the presence of alcohol; gastrointestinal poisoning; haemolytic reactions; and allergic reactions. By this classification, some fungi within the same genus may be dealt with in different groups, e.g. *Amanita phalloides* under cytolytic poisoning, and *Amanita muscaria* under psychotropic poisoning.

CYTOLYTIC POISONING

Amanita species

The fungi in this genus are characterized by being completely covered, when they first emerge, by a skin-like structure (the universal veil), parts of which may remain on top of the cap and at the base of the stem. Unless positively identified, all members of the genus *Amanita* should be considered potentially poisonous. A few can cause fatal poisoning; all are poisonous when raw, although some are edible when cooked. Not all *Amanita* species cause cytolytic poisoning; for details of some others that cause psychotropic poisoning, see pp.240–242.

Amanita phalloides Death Cap (Plate 87)

The death cap is responsible for more cases of severe and fatal poisoning than any other fungus. The fruit bodies appear in late summer and autumn and are most common in or at the edges of beech and oak woods.

As with other *Amanita* species, the fruit body of this fungus is enclosed at first in a white skin, the veil, which is ruptured during growth, occasionally leaving evanescent patches on the cap, and often a residual cup, the volva, sheathing the wide base of the stalk. The fully expanded cap is convex or flat, easily peeled, and up to 12 cm across. It is variable in colour, usually yellowish to olive green and faintly streaked radially with darker fibrils, particularly near the centre. The flesh of the cap is white, except just beneath the skin, where it is tinged yellow or green. The stem is smooth and white, up to 12 cm high and 2 cm thick, solid when young but hollow when old. Near the top it has an irregularly torn white ring, the remains of a membrane that joined the edge of the cap to the stem when young. The gills are crowded together, white at first, then cream (never pink or brown as in the edible field mushroom) and the spores are white. The whole fungus has a rather sweet, foetid smell when mature.

A closely related species, sometimes confused with the edible field mushroom (*Agaricus campestris*), is the destroying angel (*Amanita virosa*). It is far less common in Britain than *Amanita phalloides*. The fungus has a more slender, shaggy stem, a rather conical cap and is uniformly white. Another white species, the fool's mushroom or deadly agaric (*Amanita verna*), does not occur in Britain. Both fungi are highly poisonous. The specific name of *Amanita verna* is misleading as it is also an autumnal fungus. Many excellent descriptions of the toxic effects of these fungi can be found in medical and mycological literature.[3-5]

Poisonous principles
The first poisonous component isolated from *Amanita phalloides* was originally called phallin, but later renamed phallolysin. It is now known to be a protein, although still

frequently referred to as a glycoside. Phallolysin can cause severe damage to red blood cells (haemolysis); it is destroyed rapidly by heating. It was thought for many years that haemolysis could result from eating the uncooked fungus, but it has now been demonstrated in laboratory animals that phallolysin is active only when given by injection, and not orally,[6] so that it is not involved in the toxic reaction that follows after eating this fungus.

The main toxic components of these fungi are two closely related groups of compounds, the amatoxins (cyclic octapeptides of which there are at least seven, including the main toxin α-amanitin) and the phallotoxins (cyclic heptapeptides of which there are at least five, including phalloidin). The phallotoxins were thought to be responsible for the early, acute, gastrointestinal symptoms and the more potent amatoxins for the later liver and kidney damage. However, this was not confirmed by experimental work in dogs in which amatoxin, but not phallotoxin, caused gastrointestinal signs.[7] It has now been established[6] that the phallotoxins are inactive when taken orally and therefore are not normally involved in human poisoning (although they are potent toxins when given by other routes). Thus, the amatoxins appear to be the only components involved in poisoning by this highly toxic group of fungi. Amatoxins interfere with the activity of the nucleic acid enzyme, RNA polymerase II, thereby inhibiting protein synthesis; this leads to cell death.[6] The toxic reaction is accompanied by destruction of cells, particularly in the liver. Amatoxins are excreted mainly by the kidneys, in which they cause damage to the proximal tubules.[8] The amatoxin concentration varies in different parts of the fungus; it is reported to be highest in the ring, gills, and cap.[9] Immunoassays can be used to detect amatoxins in blood and urine. An antitoxin has also been isolated from some of these fungi and was named antamanide as it was thought to act against amatoxin. In fact it acts only against the phallotoxins and, like them, is not active orally.[6] Poisoning by *Amanita phalloides*, and other fungi, is less common in Britain than in some other European countries where it is more usual to gather and eat wild mushrooms. Cases do occur in this country, however, 11 incidents having been reported (including one fatality) to one poisons centre between 1973 and 1981.[10]

Human poisoning

Half a fruit body or less of *Amanita phalloides* can be sufficient to kill an adult. Three stages can be recognized in the course of amatoxin poisoning. The first symptoms, which develop 6–24 hours after eating the fungi, include dry mouth, nausea, vomiting, abdominal pain, and diarrhoea (often with blood). These symptoms, which usually last about 24 hours and may be very violent, are followed by a latent period of apparent recovery that may last for up to three days, although major disturbances to enzymes, particularly in the liver, take place at this stage. This is followed by the most serious phase of intoxication, during which severe kidney and liver damage caused by the toxins may result directly in death from failure of one or both of these organs, or indirectly by heart failure. In this final stage, when there may or may not be a recurrence of the gastrointestinal symptoms, the pulse is weak and rapid, the skin cold and clammy, the visible mucous membranes bluish purple (cyanosis), and jaundice develops. There are also nervous symptoms, including muscle twitching, restlessness, delirium, hallucinations, and convulsions. Coma usually precedes death, which occurs in 50–90% of untreated cases, depending on the susceptibility of the individual, the toxicity of the fungi, and the quantity eaten. Despite the well-known toxicity of

Amanita phalloides there are still many cases of poisoning throughout Europe.[11-21] *Amanita virosa*, which also contains amatoxins, has been reported to cause poisoning, although less frequently than *Amanita phalloides*.[11, 22-25]

It is strongly advised that, in cases of mushroom poisoning, the fungus eaten should be identified whenever possible, but particularly if amatoxin poisoning is suspected, as the success of any treatment depends on its being started as soon as possible. Many far less toxic fungi also cause gastrointestinal disturbances, followed by recovery, and this may be confused with the initial and second stages of amatoxin poisoning. Treatment started in the final stage will be ineffective, as damage to the liver and kidney is, by then, almost always irreversible.

There is no specific antidote for amatoxin poisoning. All suspected cases should receive rapid medical attention and admission to hospital. The treatment given is determined largely by the preferences of individual hospitals and, because of the life-threatening nature of the poisoning, most use a combination of methods.[11, 18, 21, 26, 27] Emetics are sometimes given (if vomiting has not already occurred), although their use is not recommended by the poisons centres in Britain. Stomach lavage should be performed in cases admitted to hospital within 36 hours of ingestion. In addition, activated charcoal can be given orally, to adsorb residual toxins in the stomach. Aspiration of duodenal contents should be carried out to prevent further absorption of the toxin. Considerable success has been claimed for forced diuresis,[28] plasmapheresis,[17] haemodialysis,[13] charcoal haemoperfusion,[29] and hyperbaric oxygenation.[30] Injections of prednisolone,[31] thioctic acid,[32-34] cytochrome C,[35] benzylpenicillin (penicillin G)[19, 30, 36] or other antibiotics (in large doses),[30] or silymarin[6, 19, 36] (a mixture of flavones from the milk-thistle *Silybum marianum*) are used separately or in combination.[36-39] Silymarin (and its main component, silibinin) is active against phalloidin, but appears to protect against amanitin as well.[37] (The anti-phalloidin serum used by some hospitals in Europe is unlikely to be of any use, since phalloidin taken orally does not produce poisoning.) The relative efficacy of the individual treatments is hard to assess, and care should be taken in the choice of methods used. Elimination of material from the gastrointestinal tract, as described above, followed by fluid and electrolyte therapy, are obviously of prime importance initially. Of the secondary detoxification methods, the administration of benzylpenicillin and silibinin has been shown clinically and experimentally to be effective.[19,30,38] It has been suggested that some of the other methods used in addition may even reduce the chances of survival.[4, 30] It seems most probable that the amount of the fungus eaten, rather than any of the treatment methods, determines the outcome. In some cases of severe liver damage, patients have recovered after liver transplantation;[15, 24] it has even been suggested that all cases requiring hospitalization should be sent to a centre where liver transplantation can be performed if required.[40] Immunotherapy should not be used as amanitin becomes more toxic when bound to immunoglobulin.[41] Patients that survive may remain ill for at least 30 days, and exertion during recovery may result in a serious relapse.[42] Kidney function takes longer to recover than liver function.[8]

A much simpler method of treatment,[43] which attracted attention in the 1970s, involved oral administration of common antidiarrhoeal agents (nifuroxide and dihydrostreptomycin), followed by intravenous injections of vitamin C and a diet consisting solely of cooked, mashed carrots. There has been considerable scepticism of this regimen, as it has no known theoretical basis. However, it was successful on more than one occasion when the originator of the method deliberately ingested more than the recognized lethal quantity of *Amanita phalloides*.[44] The method has also been used successfully in at least one French hospital.[45] To be effective, the treatment must be started as soon as gastrointestinal symptoms appear.

Animal poisoning

Amanita phalloides is also toxic for some animals. Mice, rats, and, more recently, dogs[46] have been used as experimental models, but poisoning of animals by these fungi under natural conditions seems rare. Poisoning by *Amanita phalloides* was recorded in two Saanen goats,[47] one of which died after four days, with remnants of the fungi in its stomach. The clinical signs included restlessness, frequent urination, irritation and blistering around the anus, thirst, abdominal pain, jaundice, and somnolence. Post-mortem examination revealed degeneration of the liver, intestinal haemorrhages, and red-coloured urine in the bladder. The second goat recovered in three weeks, having been given only symptomatic treatment. In two separate incidents dogs were poisoned fatally by *Amanita phalloides*. One dog vomited repeatedly, had blood-stained diarrhoea and urine, became unconscious, and, despite treatment, died three days later.[48] The other, a puppy that ate part of the cap of a young specimen of the fungus, vomited, became lethargic, collapsed, and died about two days later.[49] Chickens fed experimentally with 0.39 g of dried *Amanita phalloides* showed no obvious signs of liver damage when killed 2–10 days later.[50] Losses in a herd of cattle in the USA in the 1940s[51] were thought to have been due to ingestion of *Amanita verna*, of which an unusually large number were present in the woods that formed part of their grazing area. The chief symptom was painful defaecation, the faeces being highly irritant and causing ulceration of the rectum, anus, and surrounding areas. In fatal cases the animals died in convulsions, and post-mortem examination revealed severe gastrointestinal inflammation, enlargement and haemorrhage of the liver, pale kidneys, distension of the bladder with urine, and haemorrhages of the heart. Also in the USA, *Amanita verna* was reported to be responsible for the death of two dogs.[52]

Some fungi of other genera also contain toxic cyclopeptides, especially amatoxins. These include species of *Lepiota* (see p.240), *Conocybe*,[53] and *Galerina*.[54,55] As some other species of these genera are edible, and some could be mistaken for hallucinogenic fungi, correct identification is highly important.

Cortinarius species (Plate 88)

This genus includes a large number of species, with many variations in shape, size, and colour, which form the basis of subdivisions into smaller groups. Features common to most species are brown spores which, at maturity, give a rusty-brown colour to the gills, and a cobweb-like partial veil (cortina), which extends from the edge of the cap to the stem, covering the gills when young, but tearing during growth and sometimes leaving a girdle that adheres closely to the stem. The universal veil, when present, is distinct from the cortina. It adheres to the surface of the cap forming silky, cobweb-like fibrils or a slimy, glutinous layer, especially when wet, and in some species it forms a distinct ring or series of partial rings on the lower part of the stem. Several *Cortinarius* species are edible, but others, seen comparatively rarely in Britain, are highly toxic. These include two orange-coloured fungi, *Cortinarius speciosissimus*, found occasionally in coniferous woods in Scotland, and *Cortinarius orellanus*, found in deciduous woods further south. A full description of *Cortinarius speciosissimus* and details of its distribution in Scotland have been given;[56] reports indicate that it may be more widely distributed than was previously thought. Cases of poisoning by these fungi have been the result of mistaken identification, sometimes for hallucinogenic fungi.[57]

Poisonous principles

A toxin, whose action was demonstrated experimentally on dogs and cats, was isolated in the 1960s from *Cortinarius orellanus* and named orellanine.[58] This has been described variously as a homogeneous substance or a mixture of toxic and non-toxic fractions.[59] There is general agreement, however, that the toxins are cyclopeptides with a bipyridyl structure. The isolation from *Cortinarius* species of a fluorescent compound, another cyclopeptide, was reported in the early 1980s.[60] This and related compounds, called cortinarins, have been described,[61] but their presence in these fungi has been questioned and debated.[62-64]

Human poisoning

Poisoning by *Cortinarius* was reported first in Poland in the late 1950s,[65] under the generic name *Dermocybe*. Since then there have been reports of *Cortinarius orellanus* poisoning from other European countries including Switzerland,[66] Italy,[67] France,[68-70] and the Czech Republic.[71] The first case of human poisoning by *Cortinarius speciosissimus* was reported in Finland,[72] then later this species was recognized in Britain[56, 73] when three adults ate the fungus, collected in northern Scotland. More recently, cases have been reported in Sweden.[74]

A latent period of 2–17 days, during which there are no symptoms, or only fairly mild digestive system disorders, is characteristic of *Cortinarius* poisoning. The severity of symptoms can vary greatly among individuals, as in the outbreak of poisoning that occurred in 26 young soldiers on a survival exercise who each ate the same quantity of 'mushroom' soup prepared from *Cortinarius orellanus*.[68] Kidney failure occurred in only 12 of the men; in four it persisted for several months, and one required a kidney transplant. Nausea and vomiting are usually the first symptoms and are followed by sweating, shivering, and stiffness, headache, pain in the limbs and abdomen, constipation (or occasionally diarrhoea), severe thirst, urine excretion being reduced initially, then increased in volume and frequency, as kidney function deteriorates.[67, 73, 75] There may be disturbance of liver function, and nervous system involvement with sleepiness and convulsions,[75] but the kidneys are the main organs affected.

If it is known that *Cortinarius* species have been eaten, treatment should be started immediately, even in the absence of symptoms, as these may not appear until much later. All possible efforts should be made to remove the toxins from the body. Emesis and stomach lavage may be effective in the very early stages of poisoning, followed by haemoperfusion and haemodialysis. As this type of poisoning can be fatal, several methods of treatment are usually tried;[76] their individual efficacy has not been demonstrated. Despite treatment, renal failure has sometimes necessitated kidney transplantation (as in two of the cases in Scotland).[56, 73]

Animal poisoning

Cortinarius speciosissimus caused severe kidney damage in four sheep that died after eating the fungus while grazing in Norway.[77] When three lambs were fed the fungus experimentally, two had disturbed kidney function after a single administration of fresh fungi and the third, given the dried fungus daily for 13 days, developed severe kidney damage and died.[77] Also in Norway, *Cortinarius speciosissimus* was suspected of causing kidney damage and death in cattle.[78] The effect of *Cortinarius* on other animals is not known, but it would be prudent to consider the fungus toxic and not allow access to it.

Gyromitra esculenta False Morel (Plate 89)

Other common name: Turban Fungus

This fungus grows on sandy soils in coniferous woods in spring, and is more common in northern areas of the country. It has an irregular, convoluted, dark chestnut-brown cap (up to 10 cm high and 15 cm wide) with brain-like grooves and ridges. The thick stem is up to 6 cm high, pale flesh-coloured or grey, somewhat grooved, and hollow. False morels are sometimes confused with the edible morel (*Morchella esculenta*) and may be present among morels offered for sale.[79]

Poisonous principles

A compound named helvellic acid (from the old generic name *Helvella*) was isolated from this fungus in the 1880s and said to be the active toxin. It was stated later that this substance could damage red blood cells (haemolysis) if the fungi were eaten raw, but that as it was destroyed by heat and soluble in water, the fungi were harmless when cooked. Helvellic acid is now known to be a mixture of harmless fatty acids and not responsible for any of the poisonous properties of *Gyromitra*.

The toxic principles are *N*-methyl-*N*-formylhydrazones of low molecular weight aldehydes. The first to be isolated was named gyromitrin, the hydrazone of acetaldehyde. Another substance, also called helvellic acid, isolated in the 1930s, was probably a crude product containing gyromitrin. Hydrolysis products of gyromitrin, including monomethylhydrazine (usually stated to be the *Gyromitra* toxin) and *N*-methyl-*N*-formylhydrazine are thought to be the main agents responsible for the cases of human poisoning.[80] Other homologous hydrazones have been detected in smaller amounts. The toxicology of monomethylhydrazine (and related compounds) has been studied extensively because of their use as rocket propellants and fuel for spacecraft.

Human poisoning

False morel is said to be safe to eat if dried or boiled in water for at least ten minutes (and the water discarded), but is best avoided altogether. Formerly it was grown commercially (350,000 kg in Poland in 1930), but sale of the fungus is now prohibited in some European countries, because of the danger of poisoning if inadequately cooked, and because cooks and workers in the canning industry have been poisoned by exposure to the volatile toxins released during preparation of the fungi.[81] Irritation of the skin and eyes can result from handling (usually large quantities) of the fungi. The apparent differences in the susceptibility of individuals, and of the same individual at different times, may be explained by the very narrow margin between the amount of toxin that has no effect, and a lethal dose.[82]

There have been several reports of poisoning after eating the false morel.[82–84] A survey of cases of *Gyromitra* poisoning in Europe (mainly from Germany and Poland) from 1782 to 1965[85] revealed a mortality rate of 14.5%. Symptoms usually appear 6–8 hours after ingestion, but have been reported after 2–12 hours. Nausea, persistent vomiting, abdominal pain, muscular cramps, and watery diarrhoea (sometimes with blood) occur initially, followed by lassitude, incoordination, dizziness, and jaundice. In severe cases, laboured breathing, rapid feeble pulse, convulsions, and coma occur, and death may follow in 2–5 days. In the later stages of poisoning there may be damage to red blood cells (haemolysis). Post-mortem examination reveals inflammation of the kidneys, enlargement of the spleen, and fatty degeneration of the enlarged liver.

Treatment is symptomatic, but all suspected cases should be referred to hospital as stomach lavage, correction of fluid and electrolyte imbalance and other measures may be required.

Animal poisoning

Many experiments have been done on gyromitrin poisoning in laboratory animals[86–90] in which liver and kidney damage often occurs. There have been reports of death of foetuses, birth defects, and carcinogenic effects in rodents,[91] but none of these has been suspected in human poisoning. A puppy that had been chewing *Gyromitra esculenta* in a field vomited 2–3 hours later; it became lethargic, then comatose, and died within nine hours.[92] Post-mortem findings included haemorrhages in the kidneys and haemoglobin in the urine.

Lepiota species

Common features of fungi of this genus are the mealy or scaly surface of the cap, which is convex when young, the dissimilar flesh of the stalk and cap that separate readily, and the white or pale gills that do not join the stalk. Many species have a well-defined ring or ring zone on the stalk. The spores are usually white.

The edibility of some members of the genus *Lepiota* (with caps up to 5 cm across) is suspect. Some species (particularly those that are pink, red, orange, or rust brown) contain toxic cyclopeptides (mainly amatoxins) similar to those found in some species of *Amanita*. Some amatoxin-containing *Lepiota* species that grow in Britain have been involved in the increasing number of cases of poisoning reported abroad.[93–99] *Lepiota cristata*, which has a white cap with tiny, nut-brown scales, emits an odour of radish when bruised, is unpleasant to taste, and is considered by some to be poisonous.

The related genus *Macrolepiota* contains several edible species, including the excellent parasol mushroom (*Macrolepiota procera*), although even this can have adverse effects in some individuals; palpitations, flushing of the skin, and shivering were recorded after eating one specimen.[10] Recovery occurred within a few hours.

PSYCHOTROPIC POISONING

Within this group are two distinct types of poisoning: that due to ibotenic acid, as in *Amanita muscaria*, and that due to psilocybin, a hallucinogen present in *Psilocybe* and some other genera.

IBOTENIC ACID

This is found in toxicologically significant quantities in some British species of *Amanita*, notably *Amanita muscaria* and *Amanita pantherina*. The severity of the symptoms varies in different individuals, but complete recovery can be expected, and death is rare.[100]

Amanita muscaria Fly Agaric (Plate 90)

This attractive fungus, often illustrated in children's books, is common in Britain. It is found from summer to late autumn on poor soils, usually under birch trees but occasionally with pine. It is characterized by a bright red or reddish-orange, convex or saucer-shaped cap, up to 15 cm across, dotted with white wart-like portions of the skin (universal veil) with which the young fruiting body is covered. The flesh is white except just beneath the skin, where it is yellowish. The stem is firm and white, hollow when old, and up to 20 cm high. It tapers towards the top, where a torn white ring hangs as the remains of the membrane which, in young specimens, attaches the edge of the incurved cap to the stem. The base of the stem is bulbous and a few scaly fragments of the volva remain on it as irregular rings. The gills are white or cream and crowded together. They reach the stem but are not attached to it. The spores are white. Details of poisoning follow the description of *Amanita pantherina* (see below).

Amanita pantherina Panther Cap

Other common name: False Blusher

This fungus is smaller than, but resembles the fly agaric (*Amanita muscaria*) except in the colour of the cap, which is dull brown and dotted with crowded white warts. It may be mistaken for the true blusher, *Amanita rubescens*, which can cause haemolysis if eaten raw or undercooked (see p.255). The two fungi can be distinguished by bruising the flesh, when that of the true blusher will become tinged pinkish red, while that of the panther cap will remain white.

Poisonous principles

The early isolation, in 1879, of a poisonous compound, muscarine, from *Amanita muscaria* has resulted in confusion over the active toxic constituents of this fungus and of *Amanita pantherina*, which induces the same type of poisoning reaction. Muscarine is highly toxic, but is not present in these species in sufficient quantities for it to cause poisoning. It is, however, present in higher concentrations and is actively toxic in several species of *Clitocybe* and *Inocybe* (see pp. 246–247). This confusion can have serious consequences if atropine, a specific antidote for muscarine, is given in cases of poisoning by *Amanita muscaria* or *Amanita pantherina*, the activity of whose chief toxic constituent, ibotenic acid, is potentiated by atropine.

Ibotenic acid and related compounds, such as muscazine and muscimol, are isoxazole derivatives, and are associated primarily with the toxicity of *Amanita muscaria* and *Amanita pantherina*, but they have also been reported in other species of *Amanita* and other fungi, including *Panaeolus campanulatus*.[101] The presence of muscimol (a more potent toxin than ibotenic acid) as a natural constituent of these fungi is difficult to establish,[102] as ibotenic acid readily undergoes decarboxylation to muscimol. There is considerable variation in the ibotenic acid content of different specimens of the fungi. The toxins have psychotropic effects for which the fungi are sometimes eaten deliberately. This practice cannot be recommended, because severe reactions, including coma, occur in some individuals, although full recovery can be expected and it seems inappropriate to classify these fungi as deadly. Although the reaction induced by eating these fungi is generally attributed to ibotenic acid (and its derivatives) and described as hallucinogenic, this concept has not received universal acceptance. It is considered by some that the only orally active principles in fungi capable of producing true hallucinations are psilocybin and psilocin. These compounds occur in species of *Psilocybe, Panaeolus,* and others (see pp. 242–246), but no reports of their presence in fly agaric or panther cap have been found.

Human poisoning

The first symptoms of poisoning by these fungi are drowsiness, dizziness, and mental confusion that may or may not be associated with digestive disturbances. Depending on the individual and the amount of fungus eaten there may be excitability, feelings of well-being and inebriation, delirium, and illusions of colour and false visual images (rather than true hallucinations).[103] Incoordination and muscular twitching are frequent symptoms and drowsiness leading to deep sleep or even coma is characteristic. Headache and respiratory difficulty may also occur.[10] It is usual for symptoms of ibotenic acid poisoning to develop within one-and-a-half hours of ingestion and to last for 4–8 hours (sometimes longer).[104] A recent case of poisoning by *Amanita muscaria* and eight cases by *Amanita pantherina* have been described in children (aged 1–6 years) in the USA;[105] all recovered.

Treatment should include stomach lavage as long as the patient is not 'hallucinating'. Sedation using diazepam or chlorpromazine and other symptomatic measures may be required.

Animal poisoning

Poisoning of dogs by *Amanita muscaria*,[106] and of dogs[107] and cats[108] by *Amanita pantherina* has been reported. The clinical signs were similar to those described for human poisoning, but, in addition, paralysis of the limbs occurred in the dogs. The convulsions experienced by some of the animals and the severity of the reaction, which was fatal in some cases, may have resulted from their being treated misguidedly with atropine sulphate, which enhances the effects of ibotenic acid.

PSILOCYBIN

Hallucinogenic fungi occur in several genera and have many common names including magic mushrooms, happy mushrooms, laughing mushrooms, and blue legs. These names are not specific and are often applied to different fungi within the group, related only by their containing hallucinogenic substances (usually psilocybin, a tryptamine derivative). In general the fungi have small caps and slender stems. Taxonomic studies have resulted in the reclassification of some members of this group; thus they may be referred to by their old or current names in different texts. Authorities also differ on which of the genera and species contain psilocybin; this may be due to variations among those from different geographic regions or in the fungi themselves. All agree, however, that psilocybin is present in several *Psilocybe* and

Panaeolus species. Other genera in which it is said to occur are *Conocybe*,[109] *Gymnopilus*,[109] *Inocybe*,[110] and *Pluteus*.[109] Some *Stropharia* species that grow in other countries contain psilocybin, but those that grow in Britain are said not to contain it.[111, 112]

Gymnopilus species

Species of *Gymnopilus* grow at the base of tree trunks, on stumps or fallen branches and twigs and are very common in autumn. They all have golden yellow or tan-coloured caps from 3 to 12 cm across, according to the species. The caps are covered with thin radiating fibrils, are sometimes slightly scaly, and may have a central boss. The gills and stems are of a similar colour to, or paler than, the caps and may be thick and somewhat fibrous and bear a membranous ring (as in *Gymnopilus junonius*), or may be more slender and without a ring. The spores are rusty brown. *Gymnopilus junonius* may be confused with the honey fungus (*Armillaria mellea*, see p.250). Details of poisoning follow the description of *Psilocybe semilanceata* (see below).

Panaeolina foenisecii Brown Hay Cap

Other common name: Mower's Mushroom

This small fungus, sometimes referred to as *Panaeolus foenisecii*, is widespread in Britain and is common in short grass. It has a moist, bell-shaped or convex cap, 1–2 cm across, which is dull brown, with a slightly reddish tinge, and dries to clay-coloured from the apex outwards, often leaving the margin darker and water-soaked. The gills are pale brown at first and finally mottled dark brown. The brownish stalk is slender and fragile and up to 8 cm high. The spores are dull brown and ornamented. Details of poisoning follow the description of *Psilocybe semilanceata* (see below).

Panaeolus subbalteatus (Plate 91)

This fungus often grows on freshly manured soil in gardens in tufts of 2–4 fruiting bodies. The caps are 2–4 cm in diameter and convex at first, but the edges often become slightly upturned at maturity. They are dark brown when moist, but paler when dry. The crowded gills are mottled dark brown, and join but do not grow down the stem, which is slender, paler than the cap, and up to 8 cm high. The spores are dark greenish black. Other species of this genus, including the grey mottle gill (*Panaeolus sphinctrinus*), may also be hallucinogenic. Details of poisoning follow the description of *Psilocybe semilanceata* (see below).

Psilocybe species

In general, species of *Psilocybe* have small caps and slender stems, and grow on soil, dung or plant remains.

Psilocybe semilanceata Liberty Cap (Plate 92)

Other common names: Blue Legs; Magic Mushroom

This fungus is widely distributed and common on grassland and heaths throughout Britain. It grows in groups but is not tufted. The buff to clay-coloured caps are up to 15 mm wide (but usually less), conical, typically with a sharp apical point, an incurved margin, and a moist, separable covering. The gills are purplish or black with a white edge. The stems are slender, up to 8 cm high, paler than the cap, and often rather wavy. The spores are dark or purplish brown.

Poisonous principles

The active principle of most of these fungi is the hallucinogen, psilocybin, an indole, sometimes referred to as an alkaloid, and usually designated as 4-phosphoryloxy-*N*, *N*-dimethyl tryptamine. Psilocin, an even more potent hallucinogenic agent, may occur in varying amounts in the fungi, but is also produced by hydrolysis of psilocybin after ingestion. Both psilocybin and psilocin have an effect similar to that of the drug lysergic acid diethylamide (LSD), and were listed as controlled drugs in the Misuse of Drugs Act, 1971. However, at present there is no legislation against possessing the fungi, and 'harvesting kits' or 'growth kits' and several booklets for potential users can be bought.[112, 113]

Fresh specimens of fungi that contain psilocybin (or its hydrolysis product, the closely related substance psilocin) tend to stain blue or blue-green if bruised,[114] particularly at the base of the stalk (hence the common name 'blue legs'). The blue colour, which may take 2–3 hours to develop, results from enzyme action in the presence of tryptamine derivatives, but its intensity is not necessarily related to the concentration of hallucinogens present. (The blueing of some species of *Boletus* involves an entirely different chemical process.)

Human poisoning

In recent years there has been a dramatic increase in several countries in the use of these fungi as hallucinogens, although this property has been known and exploited for many centuries, particularly by Mexican Indians who eat them to induce trances in religious and magic rituals. The earliest recorded poisoning by hallucinogenic fungi in this country was described in 1803; a poor London family was indiscreet enough to eat a quantity found in St James's Green.[115] The fungi involved were named as '*Agaricus semiglobatus*' and '*Agaricus glutinosus*'. From careful study of the written descriptions and illustrations of these fungi it is reasonable to assume that they were *Stropharia semiglobata* and *Psilocybe semilanceata*, respectively;[115] it was almost certainly *Psilocybe semilanceata* that caused the poisoning. The fungi were mistaken for edible mushrooms and eaten by a man and his four children, all of whom had physical and mental reactions.

The deliberate use of 'magic mushrooms' to stimulate psychic perception is now fairly widespread, particularly among young people.[116,117] The desired effects (euphoria, visual and auditory hallucinations) are often accompanied by undesirable ones,[118] as in the case of two young men who consumed 30–60 liberty caps (*Psilocybe semilanceata*). They experienced confusion, agitation, tremors, paranoia, palpitations, visual disturbances, and respiratory difficulties.[119] Poisoning by these fungi is rarely serious, spontaneous recovery usually occurring within 6–18 hours. They are not thought to be addictive and their recreational use appears to be relatively harmless in the short term. The possibility of problems from long-term use has not been evaluated, although the risk of premature mental and physical ageing after prolonged periods of regular use is recognized in Mexico. The increased risk of accident to hallucinating individuals and the cost of treating the growing number of cases admitted to hospitals is causing concern.[113, 120] Mistaken identification can also be a problem,[120] either when highly toxic fungi are eaten instead of magic mushrooms, or when magic mushrooms are eaten instead of edible species, as occurred in an accidental case of poisoning of two individuals who ate *Gymnopilus validipes* (a non-British species), which they assumed to be the honey fungus (*Armillaria mellea*).[121]

No indolyl compounds related to psilocybin have been found in *Gymnopilus*, whose hallucinogenic principle has not been identified with certainty. A yellow constituent, bisnorgangonin, has been isolated and may be involved in the toxic reaction.

Hallucinations can result from eating the fungi raw or cooked, or from drinking the liquor in which they have been stewed. Within less than an hour of ingestion, psilocybin (chiefly converted to psilocin) is distributed throughout the body. The psychic effects are correlated with the concentration of the toxins in the brain, but their mode of action has not been elucidated fully. Adverse physical reactions do not always occur, but may include rapid pulse, dilated pupils, restlessness, nausea, laboured breathing, and headache. Varying degrees of delirium, sometimes with uncontrollable laughter, are experienced, as well as visual aberrations of speed, light, and colour.[119, 122] Typical signs, including hallucinations, accompanied by a feeling of well-being, then visual aberrations were reported in three young men, each of whom had eaten 20–30 specimens of *Panaeolina foenisecii*.[123] Stiffness and a sensation of swelling of the limbs have also been reported.[120] Occasionally there can be acute panic and frightening mental disorientation. As few as four specimens of fungi have produced hallucinations,[119] but it is not uncommon for up to 100 to be eaten at a time.[122]

A rather different type of poisoning, with a more prolonged reaction, was experienced in Scotland by two adults who ate 5–9 cooked specimens of *Panaeolus subbalteatus* with their breakfast.[124] Within ten minutes one became cold and unsteady, and both suffered nausea and difficulty in coordinating physical and mental activities for several days. After nine days, sharpening of the senses was reported in one case.

Apart from observation to prevent abnormal or dangerous behaviour during hallucinations, treatment is not usually necessary, as the toxins are largely eliminated from the body (in urine) within about four hours, and symptoms rarely persist for more than 12 hours. Stomach lavage should not be performed during hallucinations, as this could be very distressing. Treatment should consist of rest, continuous observation, and reassurance. Sedation, using chlorpromazine, may be given but is not usually necessary.

Animal poisoning

Suspected cases of poisoning by 'magic mushrooms' growing in pasture have been reported in horses in two separate incidents. One horse appeared to be in pain, but exhibited aggressive behaviour when examined and excitability if disturbed; it recovered after two days in a darkened stable.[125] The other, a colt, also showed signs of colic and had periods of hyperexcitability, then recumbency and semi-consciousness; the animal died in two days.[126] Psilocybin was found in the blood of a dog[127] with similar clinical signs to those of the horses; the animal recovered. In addition, the body temperature control system of the dog seemed to be affected.

MUSCARINE POISONING

The fungi mainly associated with muscarine poisoning are species of *Clitocybe* and *Inocybe*, but some *Omphalotus* species also contain muscarine-like toxins.

Clitocybe species (Plate 93)

This genus contains many large, medium-sized, and small fungi that have fleshy caps, often with a somewhat wavy outline. The poisonous species are mainly top-shaped or funnel-shaped and have smooth, whitish, pallid or greyish-brown caps. The gills of all species run down the stem to some extent and are whitish or greyish in colour. The spores are white.

Many *Clitocybe* species are poisonous or suspect, and all are best avoided. The most poisonous are *Clitocybe rivulosa* and *Clitocybe dealbata*. These two species grow in short grass or pasture and are similar in appearance; both have a pale greyish-yellow cap, covered, at first, with a white silky bloom and sometimes becoming tinged pink at maturity. *Clitocybe dealbata* often grows in complete or partial rings and may be confused with the true fairy ring fungus (*Marasmius oreades*), which is edible. The latter is buff, pale tan, or ochre in colour. Details of poisoning follow the description of *Omphalotus olearius* (see below).

Inocybe species (Plate 94)

This group of small or medium-sized fungi is characterized by the cap which is convex, sometimes with a central boss. Its upper surface is covered with radiating fibrils or scales; the gills are clay-coloured. The spores are yellowish or light brown. In young specimens, a delicate cobweb-like veil connects the edge of the cap to the stem, covering the gills.

All *Inocybe* species are best avoided because many are similar in appearance and some are poisonous. *Inocybe rimosa* (formerly known as *Inocybe fastigiata*), which has a brownish-yellow cap that often splits at the edge, and yellow gills, is dangerously poisonous, as is *Inocybe patouillardii*, a somewhat atypical species found on calcareous soils. The latter appears early, either in late summer or early autumn, is white when young, but tinged yellowish brown as it matures and may eventually become bright red. It develops a characteristic pinkish-red coloration when bruised or cracked.

Inocybe geophylla is one of the most common *Inocybe* species in Britain. It is found on damp soil, often growing in woods, and is poisonous. The fungus has a white stalk and cap which, when expanded, has a prominent central boss. There is a lilac form (var. *lilacina*). Details of poisoning follow the description of *Omphalotus olearius* (see below).

Omphalotus olearius Copper Trumpet

Other common name: Jack O'Lantern

This is a very rare fungus in Britain; it is sometimes known as *Pleurotus olearius* and was classified previously as *Clitocybe olearia*. It grows in clumps at the base of oak trees. The funnel-shaped cap is up to 15 cm across and the gills run down the stem. The whole fungus is coppery orange, but the spores are whitish.

Poisonous principles

The main toxicologically active constituent of several species of *Clitocybe* and *Inocybe* is muscarine, a quarternary ammonium compound. This was first isolated and named in 1869, from *Amanita muscaria* in which, however, it is present only in insignificant amounts. Muscarine-like toxins are also said to be present in *Omphalotus olearius*. Confusion over the toxic constituents of these fungi continues to the present day, sometimes with serious results, when atropine, a specific antidote for muscarine, is given in cases of poisoning by *Amanita muscaria*, the activity of whose chief toxic constituent, ibotenic acid, is potentiated by atropine.

Human poisoning

Muscarine acts by inhibiting the conduction of impulses between nerve cells. The symptoms of muscarine poisoning develop within 15 minutes to two hours of ingestion. The combination of perspiration, salivation, and lacrimation is diagnostic for poisoning by muscarine-containing fungi[128] and is sometimes referred to as the PSL syndrome. Other symptoms include abdominal pain (sometimes with vomiting), watery diarrhoea, painful need for urination, asthmatic wheezing, nasal discharge, constriction of the pupils, blurred vision, and reduced blood pressure and heart rate.[10, 128] A mortality rate of approximately 5% has been estimated.[129] One report cites 25 cases of poisoning by *Omphalotus olearius* that were treated in former Yugoslavia in September 1969.[130] In addition to the symptoms described for muscarine poisoning, several patients noticed unpleasant, sometimes metallic tastes, and tingling of the fingertips. The importance of correct identification cannot be over-emphasized, as many cases of poisoning in Europe result from eating the copper trumpet (or related *Omphalotus* species in the USA and Japan)[131] instead of the edible chanterelle (*Cantharellus cibarius*).[130, 132]

Of the fungal poisons, only muscarine has a specific antidote, atropine, which should be given as soon as the cause of poisoning has been established with certainty, and thereafter as required.

Animal poisoning

Cases of poisoning have been reported in dogs after eating *Clitocybe dealbata*,[133] *Clitocybe dicolor* and *Clitocybe rivulosa*,[134] and *Inocybe phaeocomis*.[135] The most prominent clinical signs in all cases were salivation, vomiting, and soft faeces or watery diarrhoea. One dog also showed signs of severe colic.[133] All recovered in two days after treatment (fluid therapy and/or atropine).

POISONING IN THE PRESENCE OF ALCOHOL

The fungus most frequently reported to give adverse effects in association with alcohol is the common ink cap (*Coprinus atramentarius*), but the club foot mushroom (*Clitocybe clavipes*) and also *Boletus luridus*, *Pholiota squarrosa*, and *Tricholoma auratum* may induce similar reactions, although they are not definitely known to contain coprine.[136, 137]

Clitocybe clavipes Club Foot Mushroom

This fungus grows in woodland under both deciduous and coniferous trees. It can be recognized by its grey-brown, top-shaped cap, cream-coloured gills, and the bulbous, club-shaped base of the stem.

A toxic reaction, similar to that associated with the ingestion of the common ink cap (*Coprinus atramentarius*) and alcohol, can be experienced after eating this fungus with alcohol. It has been stated that the effects of eating *Clitocybe clavipes* with alcohol are only nausea and vomiting[138] and are therefore different from coprine poisoning, but typical Antabuse symptoms (associated with the drug disulfiram that is used in the treatment of alcoholism) have also been experienced. There were three incidents of this type of poisoning in three different years in Britain.[139] In one case the reaction occurred when alcohol was taken seven hours after eating 4–6 fruiting bodies of the fungus. Specimens of the same fungus, collected from the same location in previous years, had not produced symptoms under the same conditions. The reasons for this variation are not known.

Coprinus atramentarius Common Ink Cap (Plate 95)

The fruit bodies of this fungus grow in clusters adjacent to rotting tree stumps from late spring to late autumn. The pale greyish, bell-shaped cap of the fungus is up to 5 cm high, striated radially, and indistinctly scaly, especially near the centre, where it is often tinged light brown. As it matures, the edge of the cap becomes ragged and moist as the black gills (whitish when young) degenerate into an inky fluid containing the black spores. The stalk grows up to 20 cm high and is 1–2 cm thick, tapering upwards from the slightly bulbous base.

Poisonous principles

An amino acid derivative (N^5-(1-hydroxycyclopropyl)-L-glutamine), named coprine, has been isolated from *Coprinus atramentarius*.[140] The toxic effect of coprine is exhibited only in the presence of alcohol (ethanol) and is similar to that induced by the drug disulfiram (Antabuse) used to treat alcoholism. In the past it was suggested that the fungus actually contained disulfiram, but biochemical studies and experimental work with mice have shown that this is not the case.[136, 140] Coprine acts by preventing the breakdown of acetaldehyde formed during the metabolism of alcohol. It is the accumulation of acetaldehyde in the blood that is responsible for the symptoms experienced.[141] Coprine has been studied extensively for its possible application in the treatment of alcoholism. It has not been used, however, because of the damaging effects it was found to have on the testes of laboratory rats.[142] Without alcohol, the common ink cap is good to eat.

In coprine poisoning, the reported intervals between eating the fungus and taking alcohol are very variable, ranging from an hour or two before, to several days after. It appears that the time of occurrence and the severity of the reaction are related to the blood alcohol level at the time the coprine reaches the liver. In common with many other potentially poisonous fungi, there is considerable variation in the reaction of different individuals, some being unaffected by the coprine/alcohol combination,[143] while others who have eaten the fungi are affected after taking alcoholic drinks[144] or simply by the alcohol in such preparations as salad dressings, medicines, or skin lotions.[145]

Human poisoning
The first effect is flushing of the face and neck (sometimes extending to the chest and arms). This is accompanied by a rapid, throbbing pulse, perspiration, dizziness, and coldness, sometimes with puffiness and tingling of the extremities, particularly the fingertips. There may also be nausea, vomiting, severe headache, and mental confusion. It is usual for the reaction to develop within 30 minutes of taking alcohol and to last for one or two hours. Recurrences of the reaction may be experienced if alcohol is taken again within the next few days. It is often stated that only cooked *Coprinus atramentarius* will elicit this reaction, but, contrary to some reports, coprine does not require heat for its activation and the consumption of raw fungi can also produce the characteristic effects.

As spontaneous recovery is usually fairly rapid, simple symptomatic treatment is usually all that is required. Propanolol may be useful in controlling palpitations.

GASTROINTESTINAL POISONING

Fungi of several genera may cause gastrointestinal disturbances. The severity of the reaction depends on the state of the fungus (raw or cooked, fresh or old) and the sensitivity of the individual.

Agaricus xanthodermus Yellow-staining Mushroom (Plate 96)

This fungus grows in clusters in autumn in pastures, woods and gardens, often on leaf mould. The fully expanded white cap (sometimes slightly grey at the centre) may be up to 15 cm across (usually 5–8 cm) and is broadly domed or convex. The gills change from whitish to greyish pink and finally greyish brown as the purple-brown spores mature. The stem is 6–15 cm high and bears a prominent membranous ring. This fungus is similar to the field mushroom (*Agaricus campestris*) and the horse mushroom (*Agaricus arvensis*) but differs from them in the bright, deep yellow coloration that develops in the stem base when the flesh is broken.

Poisonous principles
The characteristic smell and toxicity of this fungus are thought to be due to the phenol it contains.[146] Other compounds have been isolated, but their possible role in poisoning is not clear.

Human poisoning

Agaricus xanthodermus is best avoided because, although eaten without ill effects by some individuals, in others there is abdominal pain and vomiting.[10] Dizziness, faintness, and a severe headache (with pain behind the eyes) that persisted for several hours, developed in two people who ate, as an experiment, one-eighth of a cooked cap each.[147]

Agaricus praeclaresquamosus (better known as *Agaricus placomyces*), which also shows a bright yellow colour change on bruising, has a cap that is white, but densely covered with minute greyish-brown or sooty-brown scales. The wood mushroom (*Agaricus silvicola*) has a cream cap, bruising yellow, and smells of aniseed. While some individuals are unharmed, ingestion of these two fungi may cause indigestion and diarrhoea.[148] Another similar mushroom (*Agaricus nivescens*), which is good to eat, stains lemon yellow when bruised and has flesh smelling of almonds.

Correct identification should be made and caution exercised when contemplating eating yellow-staining species of *Agaricus*. Stomach lavage should be performed if *Agaricus xanthodermus* has been eaten. Fluid replacement, together with other symptomatic measures, may be required.

Armillaria mellea Honey Fungus

This fungus grows in tufts, at the base of tree trunks, and is tan coloured or pale brown. It can be confused with the hallucinogenic fungus *Gymnopilus junonius* (see p.243), but can be distinguished from it by the gills, which are whitish and tend to run down the stem, and by the thick, whitish or yellow ring. A characteristic feature of honey fungus is the bootlace-like appearance of the underground mycelial strands. It is well-known for causing the death of trees and shrubs.

It is described variously as edible, indigestible, or mildly poisonous when cooked, but causes gastrointestinal upsets if eaten raw.

Boletus species

These fleshy fungi usually have a thick stalk, bearing the cap which has, on its underside, instead of radiating gills, closely crowded vertical tubes, opening by pores, so appearing sponge-like. The spores are released from these pores.

Many *Boletus* species are edible. Some, although not poisonous, are not edible because of their bitter taste, and at least one (*Boletus satanas*) is poisonous.

Boletus satanas The Devil's Boletus

This is not common in Britain but may be found in beech woods on calcareous soils, particularly in the south. The fungus has a whitish to pale grey cap, which may extend up to 20 cm across. The stalk is strikingly bulbous and covered with a red network. At maturity the pores are bright red. The spores are golden brown.

Boletus satanas (and some other *Boletus* species) contain amatoxins and muscarine, but at too low concentrations to cause poisoning. The fungus does, however, contain gastrointestinal irritants. A toxic constituent that is of interest because it is a protein toxin (unusual in fungi), is bolesatine.[149] It has caused death in laboratory mice and had toxic effects on cell cultures.

All red-pored *Boletus* species are best avoided because of their possible toxicity. The blue coloration that develops in some when bruised is of no toxicological significance.[150]

Entoloma species

Fungi of this genus are widely reported in the literature under the (unacceptable) generic name *Rhodophyllus*. There is considerable variation in size among these fungi, some of which are small and delicate and others robust. They often have a mealy smell. The gills are pink at maturity and, depending on the species, may terminate at the stem or extend down it. The spores are pink and angular.

Some, such as *Entoloma sinuatum, Entoloma clypeatum,* and *Entoloma sericeum* are definitely considered poisonous, but all *Entoloma* species are best avoided.

Entoloma sinuatum Livid Entoloma

This fungus is sometimes referred to as *Entoloma lividum.* Although widespread in Britain, it is not common, but may be found in deciduous woodland, especially under oak or beech. It has a thick stalk and a yellowish or greyish-ochre cap up to 15 cm across, with a central boss. The cap has a smooth, moist surface and may have an undulating edge. The gills are whitish yellow at first but become flesh-coloured at maturity.

The taste of the fungus is pleasant, initially, but it can cause severe vomiting, abdominal pain, and diarrhoea. There may also be laboured breathing, slow pulse, and coma.[151] In some parts of Europe the fungus is considered a fairly common cause of poisoning.[152]

Hebeloma species

These vary considerably in size, but most are fleshy, with pale brown caps that are darker towards the centre, and have a somewhat sticky surface.

Members of this genus are not generally considered edible, and some are poisonous, although, as with some other fungi, they are not necessarily poisonous to all individuals.

Hebeloma crustuliniforme Fairy Cake Hebeloma (Plate 97)

Other common name: Poison Pie

This fungus occurs most frequently in woodland, where it may grow in rings, but it is also found in gardens. The cap is usually 3–7 cm across, convex with inrolled edges when expanded, pallid or tinged light brown at the centre and slimy when moist. The stem is approximately 0.5 cm thick, white, often thicker near the base, and bears powdery granules particularly near the top. The gills change with age from a pale clay colour to dull brown and often bear droplets of moisture on the edge in damp weather. The spores are brown and warted.

Hebeloma crustuliniforme has an acrid taste and can cause poisoning, characterized by stomach cramps and diarrhoea.

Hypholoma fasciculare Sulphur Tuft (Plate 98)

Sulphur tuft is common in Britain and grows in dense clusters all through the year on or near stumps of broad-leaved trees. The caps are up to 7 cm across, sulphur-yellow and often have a dark tan centre. The gills are yellow at first, but become greenish. The spores are brownish purple.

Sulphur tuft has a bitter taste and is often considered poisonous. In a case of human poisoning, death was reported after eating sulphur tuft, but doubt has been cast on whether this was the fungus responsible.[152] Two dogs that ate the fungus suffered severe vomiting.[10]

Lactarius species Milk Caps

Members of this genus are mostly reddish brown or grey in colour and have white or yellowish spores. These fleshy fungi are characterized by exuding a milky white (sometimes coloured or colourless) juice, especially from the gills, where broken.

This milk varies in taste from mild to acrid or peppery, but these differences are not necessarily related to toxicity, as the mild-tasting *Lactarius helvus* is toxic,[153] and others with a peppery taste, such as *Lactarius piperatus*, *Lactarius pyrogalus*, and the ugly one (*Lactarius turpis*), are inedible or indigestible and may cause vomiting and diarrhoea, especially if eaten raw. Some species are edible only after parboiling. The woolly milk cap (*Lactarius torminosus*) is considered a poisonous species.

Morchella esculenta Morel

Morels grow in spring on damp, rich soil. Although not particularly common, they are widespread in vegetation under trees and hedges. The oval, yellowish-brown cap of this fairly large fungus (up to 15 cm high) is deeply and irregularly pitted and the stem is thick and usually yellowish. The species occurs only in spring.

It is usually considered good to eat, and is often collected for that purpose, although a report concerning poisoning of dogs given the cooked fungus or the liquid in which it was cooked may have involved this species.[154] The clinical signs included vomiting and blood-stained diarrhoea and urine.

Paxillus involutus Brown Roll Rim (Plate 99)

This fungus is particularly common under birch trees. The cap is convex at first with the edge rolled under, but flattens and expands up to 12 cm across, often with a central depression. Initially the rust-coloured or olive-brown cap is downy, but it becomes smooth, except sometimes at the edges, which are often grooved. The stalk is short, slightly paler than the cap, and may be eccentric. The yellow gills, which become brown when bruised, run from the cap down the top part of the stalk. The spores are brown.

Paxillus involutus is well known to be poisonous when raw, or inadequately cooked, but even cooked specimens are considered by some to be harmful. An allergy can develop to this fungus (see p.256).

Pholiota squarrosa

This fungus grows in autumn in clusters from the base of the trunk of old broad-leaved trees. The cap, which is up to 10 cm across, is convex at first but flattens during growth except at the margin which remains rolled under. Both the cap and stalk are dark yellow and are covered with darker, brownish shaggy scales. The gills are yellow at first, but become rust-coloured or olive-tinged later. The spores are brown.

Pholiota squarrosa does not cause serious poisoning, but it is indigestible and can cause gastrointestinal irritation.

Ramaria species Fairy Clubs

These erect, densely branching, coral-like fungi may grow up to 25 cm high from the basal stalk, which is stout and paler in colour. The spores are yellow-brown and ornamented.

A few of these fairy club fungi are edible, but at least one, *Ramaria formosa*, sometimes known as the handsome clavaria, which is rare in Britain, has a particularly bitter taste when cooked and is poisonous, causing diarrhoea. Other *Ramaria* species have caused poisoning in cattle and sheep in South America.[155] Most of these cases have involved *Ramaria flavo-brunnescens*, which is abundant in eucalyptus woods in Brazil; this type of poisoning in cattle has been called 'eucalyptus disease'.[156]

Russula species Brittle Gills (Plate 100)

Many of the fungi in this large genus have brightly coloured caps, and the gills, usually all of the same length and running the entire distance between the cap margin and the stem, are remarkably brittle. The spores are white to dark yellow. These fungi resemble *Lactarius* species, but no milk is exuded when the flesh or gills are broken.

Several species are good to eat but others, like the sickener (*Russula emetica*), *Russula fellea*, and *Russula nauseosa* that have a hot or acrid taste when raw, are best avoided as they are gastrointestinal irritants and cause vomiting. Many *Russula* species are said to be safe to eat after cooking and discarding the cooking liquid.

Scleroderma species Earthballs

Fungi in this genus are more or less spherical or pear-shaped structures with coarse, root-like threads at the base. Earthballs are fleshy when young, but develop a thick, tough, yellowish, leathery skin, with a scaly or grained surface. At maturity the interior of the fungus varies in colour with different species, from purplish black to dark grey, and consists of a mass of spores traversed by white threads. When mature the leathery coat splits open irregularly to release the dry, powdery spores.

Earthballs have an acrid smell and taste and are considered poisonous. In the USA, a young man who ate a small piece of raw *Scleroderma cepa* developed symptoms that included abdominal pain and nausea, and tingling progressing to rigidity affected the whole body. Rapid recovery occurred after vomiting.[157] Also in the USA a pet miniature Chinese pot-bellied pig died five hours after eating a common earthball (*Scleroderma cepa*). Before death it had vomited, become depressed and weak, and shown signs of extreme abdominal pain.[158] *Scleroderma citrinum* can also cause human poisoning, but few cases have been recorded.[159] Several of the superficially similar puffballs (*Lycoperdon* species) are edible, at least when young, and earthballs may be confused with them.

Stropharia aeruginosa Verdigris Agaric

This attractive fungus grows in grass on heaths, and in pastures, woods, and gardens. When young the cap of this fungus is covered with a bluish-green slime and often has small whitish scales, especially round the edge. The cap is rounded at first, then flattens and expands to about 6 cm across and has a central boss. As it ages the colour changes to a dull yellowish green. The stalk is tinged bluish green and has a distinct ring. The gills are dark brown, sometimes edged with white. The spores are dark brown.

Although apparently eaten in some Continental countries, this fungus is generally considered poisonous.

Stropharia coronilla

This fungus grows on pastures and mown grassland in similar situations to the field mushroom (*Agaricus campestris*) with which it is sometimes confused. It can be distinguished from the field mushroom by its yellowish cap and stem, and by the gills, which tend to run a short distance down the stem or are joined to it by a tooth, while those of the edible mushroom are free from the stem. The spores are dark brown.

Stropharia coronilla is probably poisonous.

Tricholoma species

In this large genus, most of the fungi are fleshy and have well-spaced gills, which have a distinct notch just before their point of attachment to the stalk.

Some tricholomas are edible, but others, including *Tricholoma album* and *Tricholoma sulphureum*, are gastrointestinal irritants.[160] Symptoms, including dizziness, a sensation of warmth, muscular stiffness, numbness and tingling of extremities, weakness, headache and incoordination when walking, developed when dried *Tricholoma sulphureum* was cooked and eaten.[161] Stomach pains were experienced later. Deep sleep preceded recovery.

HAEMOLYTIC REACTIONS

There are a few fungi that can cause damage to red blood cells (haemolysis), especially if eaten raw or undercooked.

Amanita rubescens Blusher (Plate 101)

This fungus can be found in late summer and autumn in both coniferous and deciduous woods. The cap of the blusher expands from bell-shaped to saucer-shaped as it matures. The surface is usually pinkish brown and often has a few warty scales remaining from the volva. The gills are whitish, but become spotted red with age. The stem has a prominent ring near the top, and the base has a reddish tinge. A characteristic of the fungus is the red coloration that develops where the flesh is damaged. Details of poisoning follow the description of *Amanita vaginata* (see below).

Amanita vaginata Grisette

The grisette is usually found in deciduous woods, but sometimes on heathland. The stem, which emerges from a basal volva, has no ring and is tall, relative to the cap, which rarely exceeds 9 cm in diameter. In this species the cap is greyish, but in the closely related tawny grisette (*Amanita fulva*) it is tan coloured. A characteristic of both species is the margin of the cap, which is striated or minutely grooved.

Little is known about the toxins in these fungi, but there is some evidence that haemolysins are present; the fungi should be cooked very thoroughly before eating, to ensure that the haemolytic agents are destroyed. Haemolysis can also be a late reaction in poisoning by the false morel (*Gyromitra esculenta*, see pp.239–240).

ALLERGIC REACTIONS

Allergic (hypersensitive) reactions can occur in some individuals after eating a fungus or inhaling its spores. The most severe reaction of this type is to the brown roll rim (*Paxillus involutus*). A less severe reaction, but possibly of the same type, can occur after eating the cloudy cap (*Lepista nebularis*).

ALLERGIES FROM INGESTION

Lepista nebularis Cloudy Cap (Plate 102)

This fungus (formerly known as *Clitocybe nebularis*) is common in woods in Britain, particularly under coniferous trees. Several specimens are often found together. The cap can be up to 20 cm in diameter and is thick and fleshy and a creamy-grey colour; there is often a depression in the centre. The gills are whitish, crowded, and run a short distance down the stem, which is stout and tends to be wider at the base.

It is considered by many to be good to eat, but there is evidence that repeated ingestion can lead to hypersensitivity in some individuals in whom it causes severe diarrhoea;[162] vertigo has also been experienced.[163] Other fungi that can have adverse effects in some, while eaten with impunity by others, include some of the blewits (other *Lepista* species) that grow in Britain. These have caused gastrointestinal disturbances.

Paxillus involutus Brown Roll Rim (Plate 99)

For a description of this fungus, see p.253.

In addition to the gastrointestinal symptoms that can follow consumption of raw or insufficiently cooked roll rims (see p.253), this species can give rise to an allergic reaction characterized by a haemolytic anaemia in individuals who have become sensitized by eating *Paxillus involutus* on previous occasions. Antibodies, which have developed to an antigen in this fungus, form an antigen–antibody complex that attaches to red blood cells; these cells then become agglutinated and disintegrate. The symptoms of this severe type of poisoning (the *Paxillus* syndrome) usually appear within two hours and include general weakness, abdominal pain, vomiting, diarrhoea, pain in the area of the kidneys, and dark red coloration of the urine. There may be cardiovascular collapse and kidney failure with little or no excretion of urine;[164, 165] deaths have been reported.[166]

Reactions similar to the *Paxillus* syndrome have been caused by another fungus, slippery jack (*Suillus luteus*).[164] This fungus is often stated to be edible, particularly after removal of the slimy cap surface; diarrhoea has occurred when this procedure has been omitted.[167] The treatment methods that have been recommended include removal of the fungus from the digestive tract (by lavage), fluid replacement, and haemodialysis. Plasma exchange has been used successfully to remove the immune complex.[168]

RESPIRATORY ALLERGIES

Inhalation of the spores of some fungi, notably the oyster mushroom (*Pleurotus ostreatus*)[169] by some individuals can lead to respiratory problems.

Pleurotus ostreatus Oyster Mushroom

This attractive fungus grows on living or fallen deciduous trees. Each mushroom has a very short, eccentric stalk, so that superficially it resembles a bracket fungus. Several specimens are often found growing together in compact, overlapping tiers. The caps are variable in colour (dark grey, brownish, or blue-black) and tend to become paler with age. They have a satin-like surface, an incurved margin, and radiating gills that run down almost to the base of the stalk. Oyster mushrooms are gaining in popularity for culinary use, and are now often seen on sale.

Asthma-type reactions, with rhinitis and coughing are reported.[170] This reaction is similar to that called 'farmer's lung', which occurs after the inhalation of the spores of some moulds that are found in the bedding or stored feed of animals (see p.264). In addition, there may be muscular pain, headache, chills, elevated temperature, and nausea.[170] The severity of the symptoms may necessitate hospitalization. Such reactions have been reported from many parts of the world, most often in those involved in the commercial production of fungi in the food industry, when the condition is sometimes referred to as 'mushroom worker's lung'. Inhaled allergens from the compost in which the mushrooms are grown may also be involved.[170]

ERGOT AND MYCOTOXINS

ERGOT

Claviceps species Ergot (Plate 103)

Claviceps is a parasitic fungus that infects, with varying severity, many grasses and cereal crops in whose flowers hard, elongated, blackish-purple spurs of fungal material develop, replacing the ovary and sometimes protruding from the seedhead. These hard masses, the 'ergots', are sclerotia, the resting stage of the fungus, from which, after overwintering in the soil, spores develop and infect new plants. The species most commonly found in Britain is *Claviceps purpurea*.

Symptoms typical of human poisoning by ergot have been recorded for centuries,[1,2] even before a definite connection between the disease and consumption of grain parasitized by the fungus was recognized. In the past the disease was usually associated with rye, a decline in its incidence coinciding with an increase in the use of wheat flour,[2] but wheat and other cereal crops may also be parasitized by *Claviceps* species.[3]

Because of its well-known and long-standing reputation for poisoning, reports of ergot in crops usually receive considerable publicity and cause alarm, even when the incidence of the fungus is low. It is, therefore, difficult to make an accurate assessment of the prevalence of ergot in the country. *Claviceps* in wild grasses that could be a reservoir of infection for cereal crops, and the reluctance of farmers to send infected grain to millers (some of whom reject grain containing even a trace of ergot) are further complications. Grain with a small percentage of ergot is sometimes used in animal feed mixes, since the quantity of infected material eaten would be too low to produce clinical signs of poisoning. The danger to livestock is, however, intensified by some grain dressing operations in which, during grading and cleaning, ergots may be concentrated in the residual material that may be fed to animals.[4]

In Britain, *Claviceps purpurea* has not been common or extensive in home-grown cereal crops for many years, although sporadic outbreaks have been reported. However, from the late 1970s onwards there have been increasing numbers of reports of ergot infection,[4] mainly in winter wheat, but also in wild grasses. The disease in this crop was prevalent initially only in Scotland and northern England but it has now spread south. In 1982 *Claviceps* infection was more widespread in Britain than for many previous years. Crops in many parts of the country, including Wales and south-west England, were affected as well as some in the north.[5, 6] Recommended precautionary measures for farmers and grain merchants were distributed.[7] The only effective treatment of land when *Claviceps* is present is deep ploughing (25 cm) after harvesting, as ergots buried deeply in soil will not germinate. There is considerable variation in the susceptibility to ergot of different varieties of cereals. Open-flowered varieties acquire the infection more readily. Work is in progress on producing resistant plant strains.

Poisonous principles

Claviceps contains alkaloids of which over 40 have been isolated, although not all are toxic. Many of these have been given names derived from the common name of the fungus (ergo-) and some are indicative of their structure or behaviour, e.g. ergotamine, ergocristine, ergonovine (ergometrine). There are several synonyms in current use. The ergot alkaloids can be divided, according to their structure, into two groups: acid amide derivatives of lysergic acid, and clavines, in which the carboxyl group of the lysergic acid has been reduced to the hydroxymethyl or methyl group.[8, 9] It is of interest that a derivative of lysergic acid is the powerful hallucinogenic agent lysergic acid diethylamide (LSD), a drug whose use and misuse has been publicized widely. The total alkaloid content and the type of alkaloids present vary considerably in ergots of different strains and species of *Claviceps*, on different plant hosts, and according to the environmental conditions. Thus it is not surprising that there are no precise figures available on the quantity of ergot considered safe for various classes of livestock or for human consumption. In some instances concentrations in grain of less than 1% ergot (by weight) have caused poisoning.

Some ergot alkaloids stimulate the action of smooth muscles, with consequent local restriction of arterial blood flow. This property is responsible for some of the adverse effects of ergot, but is also of pharmacological value, ergot derivatives being used to stimulate muscle contractions and control bleeding, particularly in obstetrics and in the treatment of conditions involving dilatation of blood vessels (e.g. migraine). Ergotamine tartrate and ergometrine maleate are examples of preparations in general use. Most of the alkaloids available commercially are now obtained from *Claviceps* grown in laboratory culture rather than as a parasite on grass or cereal seed heads. Prolonged or excessive use of the drugs can induce symptoms of poisoning. So far, only the lysergic acid derivatives, and not the clavine alkaloids, have been used therapeutically.[9]

Another fungus, *Acremonium coenophialum*, that is an endophyte of tall fescue (*Festuca arundinacea*), also produces an ergot alkaloid (ergovaline), which is responsible for fescue foot and the 'summer syndrome' in cattle in the USA (see p.115).

Animal poisoning

The effects of ergot poisoning vary according to the concentration and type of alkaloids present and the duration of exposure to infected pasture or grain and grain products. Ergot appears to be unpalatable, as feed intake is usually reduced if it is present. Animals may lose weight and condition,[10, 11] but more specific signs usually occur. Two disease syndromes have been recognized, both called 'ergotism': a nervous (convulsive) form and a gangrenous form. Although there may be some general signs in common, it is unusual for the characteristic features of the two types of ergotism to occur in one outbreak. The nervous form is mainly associated with *Claviceps paspali* infection of *Paspalum* species that are pasture grasses in warmer parts of the world, whereas the gangrenous form occurs with *Claviceps purpurea* infection of cereals and grasses in Britain. It has been suggested that *Claviceps purpurea* does not cause a nervous form of ergotism in animals and that the few previous reports of this were misdiagnoses.[12] When a large amount of ergot is eaten in a short time, irritation of the digestive tract occurs, accompanied by abdominal pain and vomiting.[3, 13] The diminished blood supply that results from eating smaller amounts of ergot over a longer period causes progressive degeneration of tissues, especially in the body extremities, where circulation is weakest. Initial pain and inflammation are followed by coldness, numbness, and the development of dry, gangrenous lesions. It is not uncommon for portions of ears, tails, and feet to be sloughed off. It is sometimes necessary to slaughter severely lame animals.

In cattle the distinctive feature of ergotism in Britain is lameness, with swelling, coldness, and loss of sensitivity in the lower legs, followed by the development of gangrene. The initial signs can appear within a week of starting to consume ergots. Other clinical signs seen in Britain are loss of weight and condition, decreased milk yield, and greatly increased sensitivity of the udder to touch, with a consequent tendency to kick during milking.[14] In January 1990, signs of hindlimb lameness appeared in 15 pregnant heifers tied in stalls and given ergot-containing grass silage;[15] six developed gangrene of the foot and lower leg and had to be slaughtered, but no animals aborted. As cases generally occur in autumn and winter it has been suggested that cold weather aggravates the constriction of peripheral blood vessels that is caused by the ergot alkaloids. With the high environmental temperatures in Australia, gangrene has not been a feature, but there have been increases in body temperature and respiratory rate, and excessive salivation (a hyperthermia syndrome).[16] In addition to the question of whether *Claviceps purpurea* can give rise to nervous signs, there is also controversy about its ability to induce abortion. This is certainly not a common feature of ergotism, but in an outbreak in Scotland, 11 of 36 cows that were close to calving aborted 7–10 days after starting to graze a ryegrass pasture heavily infested with ergot.[17] Placental retention and almost complete absence of milk secretion followed the abortions, but there were no other signs of ill health.

Selective grazing by sheep, which tend to avoid coarse-headed grasses, is an indirect protection against ergot poisoning, although it can occur to a limited extent in these animals.[18] Some deaths occurred in Finland in sheep pastured on grasses with a high (0.2%) alkaloid content.[19] In experimental work in England, ergot sclerotia were well tolerated by housed sheep, but severe lameness developed in an animal pastured in cold, wet conditions while being given ergot (0.5 mg ergotamine per kg body weight daily). It was suggested that the low environmental temperature also reduced peripheral circulation so that the effect of the alkaloid was more pronounced.[20] In experimental work in Norway, four lambs were given suspensions of milled ergot by stomach tube daily in December and January.[21] The three lambs on pasture in cold and wet weather all developed increasing dullness and inappetence within a week, then a high pulse rate, laboured breathing, diarrhoea, and oedema in the distal parts of the legs and tail. When killed 7–16 days after the start of the experiment, they had severe lesions in the digestive tract. The one housed lamb that was dosed daily for 27 days had no clinical signs or lesions.

In general, pigs do not develop the gangrenous syndrome or lameness, but there may be reduced feed intake and consequent weight loss (or reduced rate of weight gain),[11, 22, 23] and interference with nitrogen metabolism.[22, 23] When rye ergot sclerotia were fed (up to 4% of the diet) to sows in early pregnancy, the embryos were unaffected, but when given later in pregnancy the sows lost condition and the number of piglets per litter was low. Some piglets were born dead or were premature, and there was almost total failure of mammary gland development, teat enlargement, and milk production.[24, 25] In separate incidents, piglets being suckled by sows that had eaten ergot developed necrosis of the tips of the tails and ears[26] or lacked vitality, were anaemic, and had watery diarrhoea.[25] In other outbreaks, sows gave birth to normal piglets but did not produce any milk.[27] When ergot was included in the diet of sows at 2 mg per kg of feed,[28] there were no effects on pregnancy and lactation or on piglet birth weight and growth, but when included in the diet of four-week-old piglets at 0.45–1.8 g per kg of feed for 50 days there were histological changes in various organs (liver, kidneys, spleen); the changes became more severe as the ergot levels were increased.

Reports of ergot toxicity in horses are mainly in the older literature. Acute poisoning after eating hay containing ergot sclerotia has been recorded.[29] The hooves, tail, and mane were affected. A chronic form has also been described, with embryonic death, lack of udder development, absence of milk production, difficult birth, placental retention, birth of weak foals, and disturbance of the reproductive cycle (failure to show signs of heat).[30]

Gangrenous ergotism has been suspected in red deer,[31] a cat,[32] and a guinea pig.[33] Feeding chicks with a diet containing more than 0.3% of ergot depressed growth rate and increased mortality.[34] Blackening of the nails, toes, shanks, beaks, and combs was reported. In laying hens, feed consumption, body weight, and egg production decreased, but there was no mortality, even with feed containing 9% of ergot. The addition of ergotamine tartrate to the feed of chicks for 7–51 days[35] resulted in toe and skin necrosis with 243 and 729 mg per kg for ten days, whereas reductions in growth and feed consumption occurred with 100 and 250 mg per kg for 51 days. There were mortality rates of 8–10% with levels at or above 250 mg per kg.

Human poisoning

Ergot poisoning has been known as a human disease for many centuries[1, 36] and was called St Anthony's Fire, after the saint of the 4th century who is said to have suffered from it.[37] This name refers to the burning sensations that may be experienced in the mouth, digestive tract, and extremities after eating food containing ergot. In the 11th century relics of St Anthony were taken from Byzantium to a church in France that became a centre of pilgrimage for sufferers from the disease. It has been suggested that they recovered as, while away on the pilgrimage, they were no longer eating bread made from ergot-contaminated flour that had given rise to their condition. Although human ergotism still occurs in some parts of the world, no outbreak of epidemic proportion has been recorded in Britain since the late 1920s, when Jewish immigrants in Manchester were affected after eating bread made from ergot-infected rye grown in

Yorkshire.[38] Millers in Britain are aware of the danger of ergot and it is unlikely that contaminated grain would be ground into flour for human consumption. However, a return to simpler living in rural areas by people, who grow and grind their own grain on a small scale, could result in a recurrence of human ergotism in this country. Although it is clear that both the gangrenous and nervous forms of ergotism can occur, the reported symptoms vary greatly from a mild tingling in the extremities, and a burning sensation in the mouth, to severe convulsions, and extreme mental confusion. In Britain such symptoms are much more likely to follow the excessive use of medicinal ergot preparations than to result from ergot ingested with food.

Treatment should include symptomatic and supportive measures, and, where necessary, vasodilators such as sodium nitroprusside.

MYCOTOXINS

There is a type of poisoning that results from the consumption of toxic secondary metabolites of the microscopic, filamentous fungi (referred to colloquially as moulds) that may be present in animal feeds or human foods. The fungi most frequently involved are species of *Aspergillus*, *Fusarium*, and *Penicillium* and the toxins are called mycotoxins. Although, by derivation, all fungal toxins (including antibiotics) are mycotoxins, the term is applied almost exclusively to those produced by these moulds, the diseases they cause being called mycotoxicoses. Today there is a vast amount of literature on mycotoxins and mycotoxicoses, too great to be dealt with in detail here. For more information there are reviews that can be consulted.[1-6] This brief description has been included, however, since it is by the ingestion of plants or plant products that poisoning by mycotoxins arises. In the past, the plants themselves were assumed to be responsible for some diseases now known to be mycotoxicoses, e.g. lupinosis (see p.138). A mycotoxin is the cause of facial eczema in sheep (see p.113), and mycotoxins have been suspected, although not proved, to be involved in poisoning by *Narthecium* species (see p.157) and acorns (see pp.108–110). Some fungi (endophytes) that grow within pasture grasses and are disseminated with their seeds also produce mycotoxins (see p.114) that can have adverse effects on grazing animals.[7]

It must be emphasized that feed and food products may contain mycotoxins even though not visibly mouldy, and conversely, that the presence of moulds in growing plants and stored or processed foods does not necessarily indicate the presence of mycotoxins. Relatively complicated laboratory analysis of samples is the only means of determining the type and extent of mycotoxin contamination. Mycotoxins are produced by only a limited number of the mould fungi, and not all strains of these fungi produce them; many environmental factors can also influence their production.

The potential for mouldy food to cause human disease was recognized last century (mainly in Russia), but it was not until much later that toxins produced by the mould fungi were found to be responsible.[8] Several outbreaks of disease associated with mouldy feed given to animals had been reported and studied, but investigation of an unknown disease from which many thousands of poultry died in Britain in 1960 led to intensive research and the development of a new branch of microbiology in which mycotoxins and mycotoxicoses are studied. The poultry disease (originally called 'turkey X disease') was subsequently shown to involve a mycotoxin, named aflatoxin after *Aspergillus flavus*, the mould fungus that produces the toxin. This mould (albeit apparently dead at the time of examination) was found in the groundnut (peanut) meal that had been imported from Brazil and incorporated into the feed of the birds.[8] Later experimental work indicated that aflatoxin also induced tumours of the liver, and research on mycotoxins, in particular those of the aflatoxin group, gathered momentum. It has been found that, as feedstuffs can be contaminated simultaneously with different types of moulds, several mycotoxins can occur together. There is evidence that the disease outbreak in poultry in 1960 was due to the combined effects of aflatoxins and cyclopiazonic acid, another mycotoxin produced by *Aspergillus* and *Penicillium* species.

In Britain it is mainly the climatic conditions that determine the extent of mould development on standing cereal crops, although contamination can occur later if the harvested crop is improperly dried or stored.[9] The main fungi involved are *Fusarium* species; these fungi do not necessarily produce mycotoxins, and when they do, only low levels are found.[10] The levels of most mycotoxins in animal feeds and human food imported into the country also appear to be low.[11]

Mycotoxins have been found in a wide variety of animal feeds and foods for human consumption. In Britain there has been official surveillance of a number of these commodities, initially only for animal feeds, but now also including several human foodstuffs.[11, 12] The levels of some mycotoxins are measured in cereal grains, nuts, figs, milk and milk products, apple juice, herbs, and spices. There is concern that some mycotoxins may enter the food chain and constitute a risk of human disease, especially some forms of cancer. This aspect is being investigated.[13-16]

AFLATOXINS

The aflatoxins, of which 18 have been identified so far, are a group of difuranocoumarins. The fungi that produce them are mainly strains of *Aspergillus flavus* or *Aspergillus parasiticus*. Aflatoxin B_1 is the most prevalent and most toxic of the aflatoxins;[17] it can induce acute toxic effects, and has teratogenic, mutagenic, and carcinogenic potential. The animal species most sensitive to aflatoxin B_1 are ducks, rabbits, and cats; also highly sensitive are trout, pigs, and dogs,[18] whereas sheep and cattle are relatively resistant. One of the reasons for the great toxicity of aflatoxins for birds is that these toxins are absorbed rapidly from their gastrointestinal tract.[19]

The clinical signs of aflatoxicosis vary among animal species, but reduced growth rate is common to most. The duration of exposure to aflatoxin in feed before the appearance of clinical signs is extremely variable and depends on the species of animal and the level of contamination of the feed. In Britain the disease is more likely to be chronic than acute, as the levels of aflatoxin in animal feeds are generally low. Aflatoxins have been shown to cause liver tumours in a variety of laboratory animals and there is some circumstantial evidence from other countries linking aflatoxins with such tumours in the human population. When aflatoxin B_1 is metabolized by animals, it is excreted as aflatoxin M_1 in the faeces, urine, and milk.

Awareness of the risk of aflatoxicosis in Britain led to the general acceptance, in the early 1960s, of a voluntary code of practice that limited the use of groundnuts, thus preventing excessive aflatoxin contamination of animal feeds. These voluntary measures were replaced in 1976 by government regulations[20] stipulating maximum concentrations of aflatoxin B_1 (estimated by a standard analytical method) in feedstuffs for sale. Separate tolerances were given for several domestic animals and poultry, based on their susceptibility to aflatoxin. In 1981, an amendment to these regulations prohibited the importation of groundnuts and cotton seed and their derivatives. These stricter regulations followed a report which showed that liquid and dried milk were still frequently contaminated with aflatoxin M_1, even though at very low levels. In 1982, a further amendment allowed the importation of groundnuts (and their derivatives) in which the level of aflatoxin B_1 did not exceed 0.05 mg per kg.[21] In Britain, different maximum permitted levels of aflatoxin B_1 apply to various animal feeds; in 1988, the range was 0.01–0.05 mg per kg (12% moisture content).[22]

From 1982, a voluntary limit of 30 μg per kg was applied to unprocessed nuts for human consumption.[12] Nuts and dried figs were subject to a 10 μg per kg limit from 1988. In 1992, new regulations came into force to cover the aflatoxin content of some food products, and the sale and import of nuts and dried figs for direct human consumption that contained more than 4 μg per kg was prohibited. Discussions are currently being held with European Community member states about the possibility of harmonizing food legislation to limit levels of mycotoxins.

Various detoxification processes of mouldy feedstuffs have been used in attempts to reduce their aflatoxin content, but only treatment with ammonia gas (usually of grain) has had sufficient effect to warrant its use commercially. Fermentation processes have been developed for animal feeds, but at present no procedure has official acceptance. Aflatoxin binding by aluminosilicates is being investigated in the USA.[23]

OTHER MYCOTOXINS

Of the many (over 400) mycotoxins that have been identified from moulds, some, such as ochratoxins,[24] trichothecenes,[25] zearalenone,[25] moniliformin,[11] and fumonisins[26, 27] have been isolated from animal feeds. Because of their potential for causing animal and human diseases, the levels of some of these mycotoxins in animal feeds and food for human consumption are monitored. Apart from the aflatoxins, official surveillance has been carried out in Britain for the levels of ochratoxin A in cereals, coffee, and pig products (kidneys and black pudding), of fumonisins in maize and maize products, and of patulin in apple juice.

The evidence connecting the presence of mycotoxins and the occurrence of specific animal or human diseases in Britain is largely circumstantial. Such a connection was suspected with a nervous system disease in cattle and sheep in Scotland.[28] Their diet had been supplemented with a distillery by-product (malt culms) that was found to be infected with *Aspergillus clavatus*. A toxin (or toxins) produced by the fungus was thought to be the cause of this disease, which has also been reported abroad. The animals showed frothing at the mouth, incoordination, stiffness of the limbs, knuckling over of the fetlock joints, and recumbency; some animals died. In the winter of 1980–1981, reduced growth rate, poor feathering, and abnormal behaviour in broiler fowls in Scotland were associated with feed contaminated with *Fusarium* species, which produced the mycotoxins zearalenone, deoxynivalenol, and diacetoxyscirpenol.[29]

Some of these other mycotoxins that occur in animal feeds in Britain have been implicated in diseases in other countries. Ochratoxins, originally named after *Aspergillus ochraceus*, are also produced by other *Aspergillus* and some *Penicillium* species. Ochratoxin A has caused kidney fibrosis in pigs, and has also been detected in the meat and offal of animals that have eaten contaminated feed.[30] Ochratoxin A has also been suggested as a cause of a progressive human kidney disease (Balkan endemic nephropathy).[8] The role of mycotoxins in this human disease, however, has been questioned.[24] Zearalenone (F-2 toxin), which is produced in grain infected with *Fusarium graminearum*, is oestrogenic and may cause reproductive disorders (particularly in pigs).[31] Fumonisin, a mycotoxin produced by *Fusarium moniliforme* in corn (particularly in damaged grains) can cause a fatal disease (leukoencephalomalacia) in horses,[32] with clinical signs including incoordination and blindness; this condition has not been reported in Britain. Some *Fusarium* species that infect grain produce trichothecenes, including deoxynivalenol (vomitoxin) and T-2 toxin, which reduce feed efficiency and may induce vomiting (especially in pigs).[31, 33] Various mycotoxins have been found in rotted potato tubers; some are known trichothecenes, but others are still being characterized, such as the new mycotoxin, named sambutoxin, produced in stored potatoes infected with *Fusarium sambucinum*.[34] Another mycotoxin, sporidesmin, is the cause of the photosensitizing disease known as facial eczema that affects sheep, particularly in New Zealand. The toxin is produced by the saprophytic fungus *Pithomyces chartarum*, which grows on dead plant material at the base of pasture plants. The disease is acquired when the animals ingest the toxic spores as they graze.

Apart from the possibility of mycotoxins being present, there are other potential dangers in using mouldy feed and bedding materials. If inhaled, the spores of *Faenia rectivirgula* can produce the human disease called farmer's lung, an allergic respiratory condition that also affects cattle. Inhalation of *Aspergillus fumigatus* spores can cause respiratory disorders in mammals and birds and lead to systemic infection and abortion in cattle.

Poisonous Algae

Microcystin

BLUE-GREEN ALGAE

A.A. Forsyth, in his preface to the 1968 edition of *British Poisonous Plants*,[1] wrote, 'And who can say whether "blooms" of toxic algae, types of which are known to occur in Britain, may . . . prove to be a future potential hazard?' The existence of water blooms has been recorded for centuries, and their toxicity recognized for many years in other countries, but it is only in the last decade that blooms of blue-green algae have emerged as an actual environmental hazard here. The situation was assessed after suspected outbreaks in 1989, and an excellent report was produced by the National Rivers Authority in 1990.[2] Since then algal blooms have been reported in increasing numbers of areas, with many rivers in Britain being affected for the first time in 1995, and record levels being reached in 1996.[3]

The risk of animal poisoning is particularly high if light winds blow the algae along the surface of the water so that they accumulate at the edge, where animals enter or drink the water. Human poisoning can result from contamination of drinking water, or accidental swallowing during participation in water sports.

There has been debate over the taxonomic position of the organisms responsible for these blooms. Botanists have generally referred to them as plants, while microbiologists consider them to be bacteria; in many texts the terms 'blue-green algae' and 'cyanobacteria' are used interchangeably. *Microcystis aeruginosa* is the organism most frequently incriminated, and most work has been done on this, but other blue-green algae that are known to be toxic have also been found in freshwaters in Britain; they include species of *Anabaena, Aphanizomenon,* and *Oscillatoria.*

Microcystis aeruginosa

This organism is widespread in inland waters in Britain. It is a unicellular blue-green alga that is spherical or oval and 3–8 μm in diameter. Aggregates or clusters of the cells are held together by the amorphous material of their capsules. *Microcystis* can be distinguished from other similar organisms by the presence of gas-filled vacuoles in the cells by which their buoyancy can be regulated. They are usually found beneath the surface of the water, but, under certain conditions, they may rise to the surface and appear as a bloom or even a thick scum. The blooms develop on stagnant or slow-flowing water and are associated, in this country, with dry summers, although there are several factors that influence their development.

Poisonous principles

Tests have shown that about 70% of the blue-green algae in water blooms contain toxins, although there are wide variations within and among sampling sites.[2] The toxicity of the blooms in Britain is said to be as high or higher than that in other parts of the world.[3] *Microcystis aeruginosa* contains toxins called microcystins, which are a group of related cyclic heptapeptides. They are potent hepatotoxins that are chemically stable and not inactivated by the usual treatments used for drinking water.[4] The presence of algal toxins in drinking water[5] is recognized as a cause for concern in many countries, and numerous filtration techniques and chemical treatments are being tested to eliminate the algae and their toxins from the water supply.[6] The microcystins are taken up by cells in the liver, where they accumulate and cause extensive damage, although the precise mechanisms involved are not fully known; the possibility that microcystins are carcinogenic is being investigated.[4] Microcystins are released from the algal cells into the water so that, although their persistence as free toxins is not known, water in which the algae have died off or been killed by algicides should not be considered safe.[2] Algal blooms have also been found to contain alkaloidal neurotoxins (anatoxins) and toxic lipopolysaccharides.[2]

Animal poisoning

The presence of algal blooms, including *Microcystis aeruginosa*, was reported on several Scottish lochs in 1983,[7] when it was suspected that they could cause animal poisoning, although no cases were recorded until some years later. In 1989, several dogs, in separate incidents, were referred for treatment after having visited Rutland Water, a reservoir in Lincolnshire that was covered with algal bloom.[8, 9] Typical clinical signs included persistent bleeding from any small wounds, and vomiting and diarrhoea with blood. During that summer 15 dogs died, most of them suddenly, in convulsions. There was strong circumstantial evidence that the dogs became poisoned by drinking the water or licking the algal deposit from their coats after swimming. Post-mortem findings included widespread haemorrhages particularly in the abdominal cavity, and a dark, congested liver. Damage to the liver was also indicated by high blood levels of liver enzymes. Also in 1989, sheep were affected in the same area, and about 20 died.[8, 9] No clinical signs were seen, the animals dying suddenly. Post-mortem findings were similar to those in the dogs, but there were also mild degenerative changes in the kidney tubules.[10] Samples of water from the reservoir produced liver damage in laboratory mice.[2] Later in Britain, five microcystins were identified in the rumen contents of a lamb suspected of being poisoned by algal toxins.[11] The toxic reaction is usually acute, developing shortly after exposure to the algae, but chronic poisoning of sheep,[12] with delayed mortality or recovery during the six months after exposure, was reported from Australia.[13] High levels of bile acids, liver enzymes, and bilirubin, indicative of liver damage, were found. It was noticed that the sheep showed no preference for water free from algal bloom.[12] This type of poisoning by algal hepatotoxins has also occurred in cattle,[14, 15] birds,[3, 15] and fish;[3, 15, 16] horses[15] and pigs[15, 17] also appear to be susceptible. Sudden death, associated with haemorrhagic liver necrosis, was reported during hot, dry weather in Switzerland in 1996. The animals had been drinking water from alpine streams and ponds in which blue-green algae were present.[18] Cattle that survive poisoning by the hepatotoxins may develop photosensitization.[4]

Animals should not be allowed access to water with algal blooms, but where no alternative drinking water is available, the construction of simple barriers to keep the blooms away from the edge of the water is recommended.[4]

Human poisoning

There is a danger of poisoning from blue-green algae after drinking or accidentally swallowing water with algal blooms. This has been reported in several countries, and in Britain in 1989, two young men became ill after swallowing water during canoe exercises on a reservoir where *Microcystis aeruginosa* was abundant.[19] Their symptoms included vomiting, abdominal pain, blistering around the mouth, coughing, and consolidation of the lungs. Other symptoms recorded in human poisoning are skin rashes, irritation of the eyes, and muscle and joint pains.[2] The presence of algal toxins in the drinking water supply has been implicated in cases of poisoning (mainly gastroenteritis) in Australia, the USA, and southern Africa.[4]

Several methods of treatment have been attempted, but so far no specific treatment has been found, and symptomatic measures are all that can be taken.

Oscillatoria species

These are filamentous algae that do not form a surface bloom, and are normally present only on the sediment at the bottom of the water. However, mats of the algae sometimes become detached from the bottom, rise to the surface and are driven to the edge by wind and waves.

Poisonous principles

Oscillatoria species in culture release substantial amounts of microcystins, the same toxins as those found in *Microcystis aeruginosa*, but *Oscillatoria* also appears to produce potent neurotoxins, similar to saxitoxin in marine algae.

Animal poisoning

Toxins from *Oscillatoria* were considered to be the cause of death in four of six dogs that entered or drank water from a Scottish loch.[20] Clinical signs including hypersalivation, muscle twitching, convulsions, and coma developed rapidly. At the time of these incidents, mats of algae, which contained red as well as blue and green pigments and appeared brown, were present at the edge of the loch.

OTHER ALGAE

The algae (marine dinoflagellates) responsible for water blooms at sea (red tides), also produce toxins. Red tides around Britain have caused the death of marine animals, including sea birds and farmed salmon.[21] The toxins accumulate in shellfish, molluscs, and some fish and so can enter the human food chain and give rise to various types of poisoning:[5, 22] paralytic shellfish poisoning (caused by saxitoxins), neurotoxic shellfish poisoning (brevetoxins), diarrhoeic shellfish poisoning (okadaic acid derivatives), and amnesic shellfish poisoning (domoic acid). These types of poisoning occur after eating shellfish in many parts of the world, and may be fatal; paralytic shellfish poisoning has been reported in Britain.

1　*Allium ursinum*　Ramsons

2　*Narcissus* species Daffodils

3　*Nerium oleander* Oleander

4   *Ilex aquifolium* Holly

5   *Arum maculatum* Cuckoo pint (flowers)

6   *Arum maculatum* Cuckoo pint (fruits)

7   *Dieffenbachia* Dumb cane

8   *Hedera helix* Ivy

9   *Berberis* species Barberry

10   *Symphytum officinale* Comfrey

11   *Buxus sempervirens* Box

12   *Sambucus nigra* Elder

13   *Symphoricarpos alba* Snowberry

14   *Agrostemma githago* Corn cockle

15   *Euonymus europaeus* Spindle

16   *Chenopodium album* Fat hen

17   *Senecio jacobaea* Ragwort

18   *Convolvulus arvensis* Field bindweed

19   *Ipomoea* species Morning glory

20   *Armoracia rusticana* Horse radish

21   *Brassica napus* Rape

22   *Bryonia dioica* White bryony (flowers)

23   *Bryonia dioica* White bryony (fruits)

24   *Cupressus* species Cypress

25   *Pteridium aquilinum* Bracken

26   *Tamus communis* Black bryony (flowers)

27   *Tamus communis* Black bryony (fruits)

28 *Dryopteris filix-mas* Male fern

29 *Equisetum* species Horsetail

30 *Pieris* species Pieris

31   *Rhododendron ponticum*
Rhododendron

32   *Euphorbia peplus* Petty spurge

33   *Euphorbia pulcherrima* Poinsettia

34   *Mercurialis perennis* Dog's mercury

35   *Ricinus communis* Castor oil plant

36   *Ricinus communis* Castor oil plant (seeds)

37　*Fagus sylvatica* Beech

38　*Quercus robur* Oak

39　*Hypericum perforatum* Common St John's wort

41

40 *Aesculus hippocastanum*
Horse chestnut

41 *Iris pseudacorus*
Yellow flag

42   *Laburnum anagyroides* Laburnum (flowers)

43   *Laburnum anagyroides* Laburnum (fruits)

44   *Lupinus* species Lupin

46

45 *Robinia pseudoacacia*
False acacia

46 *Wisteria* species
Wisteria

47 *Colchicum autumnale*
Meadow saffron

48 *Convallaria majalis*
Lily of the valley

49   *Hyacinthoides non-scripta* Bluebell

50   *Narthecium ossifragum* Bog asphodel

51   *Fraxinus excelsior* Ash

52 *Ligustrum* species Privet (flowers)

53 *Ligustrum* species Privet (fruits)

54 *Oxalis acetosella* Wood sorrel

55 *Chelidonium majus* Greater celandine

56 *Papaver rhoeas* Field poppy

57 *Rheum rhabarbarum* Rhubarb

58 *Rumex acetosella* Sheep's sorrel

59 *Anagallis arvensis* Scarlet pimpernel

60 *Primula obconica* Poison primrose

61 *Anenome nemorosa* Wood anemone

62   *Clematis vitalba* Traveller's joy

63   *Helleborus foetidus* Stinking hellebore

64   *Ranunculus* species Buttercup

65   *Aconitum napellus* Monkshood

66 *Rhamnus cathartica* Purging buckthorn

67 *Prunus laurocerasus* Cherry laurel

68 *Ruta graveolens* Rue

69 *Digitalis purpurea* Foxglove

70   *Atropa belladonna* Deadly nightshade (flowers)

71   *Atropa belladonna* Deadly nightshade (fruits)

72   *Datura stramonium* Thorn apple

73   *Hyoscyamus niger* Henbane

74   *Solanum dulcamara* Woody nightshade (flowers)

75   *Solanum dulcamara* Woody nightshade (fruits)

76   *Solanum nigrum* Black nightshade (flowers)

77   *Solanum nigrum* Black nightshade (fruits)

78   *Solanum tuberosum* Potato (fruits)

79   *Taxus baccata* Yew

80   *Daphne laureola* Spurge laurel

81   *Daphne mezereum* Mezereon

82   *Conium maculatum* Hemlock

83   *Oenanthe crocata* Hemlock water dropwort

84   *Heracleum*
      mantegazzianum
      Giant hogweed

85   *Lantana camara*
      Lantana

86   *Viscum album*
      Mistletoe

87 *Amanita phalloides* Death cap

88 *Cortinarius speciosissimus* Cortinarius

89

90

91

89 *Gyromitra
    esculenta*
    False morel

90 *Amanita muscaria*
    Fly agaric

91 *Panaeolus
    subbalteatus*
    Panaeolus

92

94

92 *Psilocybe
    semilanceata*
    Liberty cap

93 *Clitocybe dealbata*
    Clitocybe

94 *Inocybe geophylla*
    Inocybe

95 *Coprinus atramentarius*
Common ink cap

96 *Agaricus xanthodermus*
Yellow-staining mushroom

97 *Hebeloma crustuliniforme*
Fairy cake hebeloma

98   *Hypholoma fasciculare*
     Sulphur tuft

99   *Paxillus involutus*
     Brown roll rim

100 *Russula emetica*
     Sickener

101 *Amanita rubescens* Blusher

102 *Lepista nebularis* Cloudy cap

103 *Claviceps purpurea* Ergot

Appendices

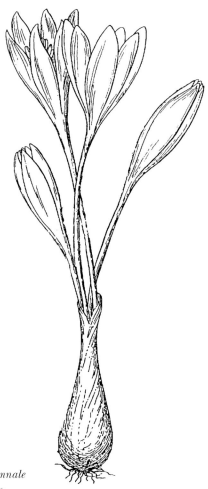

Colchicum autumnale
Meadow saffron

APPENDIX A

PLANTS AFFECTING MILK

It has been recognized for many years that the consumption of certain plants can cause a drop in yield, or even a temporary cessation of milk production. This is, however, difficult to assess accurately as loss of condition in a lactating animal, from whatever cause, including plant poisoning, may lead to a drop in milk yield. Whether or not yield is decreased, some plants, e.g. *Oxalis* species, can impart an unpleasant taste or odour to milk,[1-3] and change its physical composition, rendering it unsuitable for making butter or cheese. The plants incriminated belong to several different families, and the constituents responsible for the taint are not necessarily of the same type. Many of the plants causing milk taint are poisonous, while others are not, or only doubtfully so, e.g. the cresses (*Coronopus* species) and the pepperworts (*Lepidium* species). Taint can often be detected even when only small quantities of affected milk are added to bulk collections. Tasting is one of the routine tests performed on milk samples from individual farms and also from bulk tanks in this country. It has been established that, although they may not cause a taint, some plant and fungal toxins (e.g. from bracken, and aflatoxin) are present in the milk of animals that have eaten them.[1,4-6] The possibility of human poisoning resulting from drinking such milk, however, has not been proved conclusively and remains an open question.

From time to time lists and tables have been compiled of the plants that can have adverse effects on milk (see below). These are useful for reference, but the information contained in some of them is derived mainly from old reports,[7,8] and no recent, authoritative publication on this subject, applicable to Britain, is available. The following lists include only those plants mentioned, because of their toxicity, in the main text of this book; they do not necessarily cover all of the plants in Britain that could affect milk.

PLANTS THAT CAN REDUCE MILK YIELD

Aconitum napellus	Monkshood
Allium species	Onion and Garlic
Beta vulgaris	Beet
Bryonia dioica	White Bryony
Chenopodium album	Fat Hen
Cicuta virosa	Cowbane
Colchicum autumnale	Meadow Saffron
Conium maculatum	Hemlock
Crataegus monogyna	Hawthorn
Cupressus species	Cypresses
Cynoglossum officinale	Hound's Tongue
Equisetum species	Horsetails
Frangula alnus	Alder Buckthorn
Fraxinus excelsior	Ash
Hedera helix	Ivy
Hyacinthoides non-scripta	Bluebell
Hyoscyamus niger	Henbane

PLANTS THAT CAN REDUCE MILK YIELD (*continued*)

Hypericum perforatum	St John's Wort
Laburnum anagyroides	Laburnum
Mercurialis species	Annual and Dog's Mercury
Papaver species	Poppies
Pteridium aquilinum	Bracken
Quercus species	Oaks
Ranunculus species	Buttercups
Raphanus raphanistrum	Radish
Rhododendron ponticum	Rhododendron
Rhamnus species	Buckthorns
Ricinus communis	Castor Oil Plant
Rumex species	Docks and Sorrels
Scrophularia aquatica	Water Betony
Solanum tuberosum	Potato (green)
Taxus baccata	Yew
Trifolium species	Clovers

PLANTS THAT CAN TAINT MILK

Aethusa cynapium	Fool's Parsley
Allium species	Onion and Garlic
Beta vulgaris	Beet
Brassica campestris	Turnip
Capsella bursa-pastoris	Shepherd's Purse
Compositae family	Several plants
Conium maculatum	Hemlock
Coronopus species	Cresses
Equisetum species	Horsetails
Hedera helix	Ivy
Hyoscyamus niger	Henbane
Laburnum anagyroides	Laburnum
Lotus corniculatus	Bird's Foot Trefoil
Melilotus species	Sweet Clovers
Mentha species	Mints
Oxalis species	Wood Sorrels
Pisum species	Peas
Pteridium aquilinum	Bracken
Quercus species	Oaks
Ranunculus species	Buttercups
Raphanus raphanistrum	Radish
Solanum tuberosum	Potato (green)
Taxus baccata	Yew

PLANTS WHOSE TOXINS MAY BE FOUND IN MILK

Armoracia rusticana	Horse Radish
Brassica oleracea	Kale

274

PLANTS WHOSE TOXINS MAY BE FOUND IN MILK (*continued*)

Cannabis sativa	Hemp, Cannabis
Colchicum autumnale	Meadow Saffron
Conium maculatum	Hemlock
Cynoglossum species	Hound's Tongues
Echium species	Buglosses
Heliotropium species	Heliotropes
Helleborus species	Hellebores
Lupinus species	Lupins
Nerium oleander	Oleander
Pteridium aquilinum	Bracken
Senecio species	Ragworts
Symphytum officinale	Comfrey
Taxus baccata	Yew

APPENDIX B

ADVISORY SERVICES

In addition to textbooks and databases with information on poisonous plants, there are various organizations in Britain that have staff who have the relevant expertise and are able to give advice by answering specific enquiries. Such organizations include botanic gardens, the Ministry of Agriculture, Fisheries and Food, and the National Poisons Information Service (NPIS). The only enquiry service available to the public is that provided by the Royal Botanic Gardens, Kew; use of the others is generally restricted to the medical and veterinary professions. Poisonous plants have always featured among the enquiries made to Kew, but the present service, provided by the Centre for Economic Botany, was set up in 1988. Of the restricted-access services, the NPIS was established in 1963, and the veterinary part of that service (VPIS) in 1992. Details of the services provided by these organizations, and of a Computerized Identification System for poisonous plants, are given in the sections that follow.

Poisonous Plant Enquiry Service, Royal Botanic Gardens, Kew
James Morley BSc

The only enquiry service on poisonous plants available to the general public in the UK is provided by staff in the Centre for Economic Botany (CEB) at the Royal Botanic Gardens, Kew. The CEB exists as a focal point for Kew's research into economic and poisonous plants, housing, for example, the *Poisonous Plants in Britain and Ireland* on CD-ROM project (see pp. 279–281).

The unique nature of this enquiry service is reinforced by botanists in the Herbarium at Kew whose expertise enables the rapid and accurate identification of plants involved in poisoning incidents. Hospital accident and emergency departments use the service for advice, and also send samples for identification so that medical staff can give appropriate treatment. The Kew staff on 'poisons duty' carry a pager enabling rapid action to be taken.

The enquiries relate to a great diversity of plants with no single species being particularly prevalent. Cultivated ornamental plants form the largest category, but many enquiries also relate to wild plants. In addition, enquiries are often received from overseas, or relate to plant products that have been brought into the UK for sale. Thus an enormous breadth of knowledge and, more importantly, access to the most appropriate literature are essential.

Fortunately the majority of the enquiries received are not the result of a poisoning, but are calls from the public wishing to know if certain plants are poisonous. By providing correct information to individual enquirers, as well as increasing public awareness through the development of educational material, the CEB hopes to assist in reducing the number of actual poisonings that occur each year.

During the period 1993 to 1995 the number of enquiries received by the CEB more than doubled. In 1996 there has been a further increase and this trend looks set to continue. As might be expected there is a marked 'calendar' of events each year that is clearly reflected in the types of enquiries received. Early in the year enquiries from within the UK are restricted to house plants and a few evergreen garden plants such as laurel (usually this means *Prunus laurocerasus*) and *Mahonia* species. Spring is a highly variable time with, perhaps, the greatest diversity of enquiries of any season. Then during midsummer contact with plants increases as people spend more time out of doors. It is at this time that most of the enquiries relating to skin sensitivity, particularly from rue (*Ruta graveolens*), are received. The onset of the 'berry season' in early autumn sees enquiries relating to such plants as *Cotoneaster* and honeysuckle (*Lonicera*). The highly seasonal nature of the enquiries (over 50% occur during the period from July to October) stretches limited resources to the full. It is clear that funds will be needed so that this valuable service can continue to cope with the rising number of enquiries.

For more information please write to:

Centre for Economic Botany
Royal Botanic Gardens
Kew
Richmond
Surrey
TW9 3AE

The National Poisons Information Service, London

Frances Northall BSc, RGN and Nicholas Edwards BSc, MIInfSc

The National Poisons Information Service in London, NPIS(L), provides information to members of the medical profession to assist them in the treatment of poisoned or potentially poisoned patients. It is part of the Guy's & St Thomas' Hospital Trust and was established in 1963. It is now one of the busiest poisons information services in the world and offers its users a wide range of services.

The graduate information officers who work at the NPIS(L) provide a 24-hour emergency telephone information service for the medical profession with information on the toxicity of drugs, household products, industrial chemicals, plants, and animals. A wide variety of sources is used to provide enquirers with an assessment of the risk to the patient, advise on the clinical features that may occur, and recommend specific treatments where necessary. Medical staff are always available to deal with enquiries that require in-depth clinical knowledge. The service can also assist in identifying unknown tablets using a CD-ROM database called TICTAC.

The NPIS(L) receives many thousands of enquiries each year and can monitor any trends in them. Although it does not have calls from all hospitals in the country, the data collected at the NPIS(L) can be used by researchers, drug companies, and industries who wish to monitor the incidence of exposures to specified agents.

The NPIS(L) has access to extensive databases, both in-house and international, including the American POISINDEX and RTECS (Registry of Toxic Effects of Chemical Substances). The library has MEDLINE and a wide range of on-line databases. These resources, combined with the expert medical interpretation available within the NPIS(L), enable the service to answer non-emergency enquiries, especially those relating to unusual or chronic exposures. The medical staff hold a medical toxicology clinic to which patients who are suffering from the adverse effects of chemical exposure can be referred.

The NPIS(L) also works closely with the Royal Botanical Gardens at Kew on many aspects of plant toxicity. The two organizations have collaborated to develop the computerized identification system *Poisonous Plants in Britain and Ireland* (see pp.279–281).

National Poisons Information Service (London)
Medical Toxicology Unit
Avonley Road
London
SE14 5ER

There are another seven poisons units in Britain and Ireland that are available to the medical profession; none are public access services. Their addresses are:

- BELFAST   Regional Drug and Poisons Information Service, Royal Victoria Hospital, Grosvenor Road, Belfast BT12 6BA
- BIRMINGHAM   West Midlands Poisons Unit, Dudley Road Hospital, Winson Green, Birmingham B18 7QH
- CARDIFF   Welsh National Poisons Unit, Llandough Hospital, Penarth, South Glamorganshire CF64 2XX
- EDINBURGH   Scottish Poisons Information Bureau, The Royal Infirmary, Lauriston Place, Edinburgh EH3 9YW
- LEEDS   Poisons Information Service, Leeds General Infirmary, Pharmacy Department, Great George Street, Leeds L51 3EX
- NEWCASTLE   Newcastle Poisons Information Service, Wolfson Unit, Claremont Place, Newcastle-upon-Tyne NE1 4LP
- DUBLIN   Poisons Information Centre, Beaumont Hospital, PO Box 1297, Beaumont Road, Dublin 9

Veterinary Poisons Information Service

Alexander Campbell BSc

This service (the VPIS) was officially launched in the spring of 1992 by the London and Leeds centres of the National Poisons Information Service, in response to a sharply rising demand from veterinary practices for information on the hazards of various agents to animals, principally domestic pets. Its primary aim is the provision of information, on a 24-hour basis, to veterinarians and animal welfare organizations to aid their management of cases of acute poisoning in animals.

The information provided to enquirers usually includes an assessment of the toxicity of the agent involved in the specific case referred, details about the expected clinical effects and their time course, recommendations for treatments, and sometimes a prognostic indication. The laboratory facilities of the centres are also made available to authorized users on request.

Since 1992 the demand for information from the VPIS has increased steadily and the number of registered practices has also continued to rise. Some 11% of the enquiries made to the VPIS concern the ingestion of plant material by animals. In the first years of the service the plant enquiries usually involved domestic pets that had inadvertently eaten a bewildering array of house or garden plants. However, over the years there has been a rising number of enquiries concerning plant ingestion by livestock, with the increasing variety reflecting the agricultural and industrial settings of these incidents.

With the aim of improving the quality of the information provided, the VPIS routinely collects and collates data for the majority of the cases by means of follow-up questionnaires sent to the enquiring veterinarians. These case reports, together with information from various sources (veterinary toxicology textbooks, case reports from journals, results and findings of animal laboratory work performed during drug and product testing, human toxicology databases containing animal data, and our library of product datasheets provided, on a confidential basis, by manufacturers throughout the UK) has enabled the VPIS to build its own unique database of clinical veterinary toxicology. This has allowed more detailed, and often species-specific, advice to be offered. A significant number of entries in the database relate to ingestion of plant material.

Veterinarians and animal welfare organizations wishing to use the VPIS will need to be registered with the service. Details of the subscription charges will be provided by either centre on request.

VPIS (London)
Medical Toxicology Unit
Avonley Road
London
SE14 5ER

Tel. 0171-635 9195

VPIS (Leeds)
The General Infirmary
Great George Street
Leeds
L51 3EX

Tel. 0113-2430715

Computerized Identification System for Medical Professionals and the General Public

Elizabeth A. Dauncey BSc, PhD and Christine J. Leon MSc

The effective management by medical professionals of cases of suspected poisoning by plants and fungi is difficult if their identity is uncertain or unknown. Collaboration between the Poisons Unit of Guy's & St Thomas' Hospital Trust and the Royal Botanic Gardens, Kew, has sought to provide a solution in the form of a computerized method of plant and fungus identification. By taking advantage of relatively recent advances in information technology it has been possible to produce a fast and accurate interactive identification system, which runs under Windows on IBM-compatible computers. Its unique and innovative design received a prestigious 1994 Information Technology award from the British Computer Society.

The system, called *Poisonous Plants in Britain and Ireland*,* was published on CD-ROM by HMSO in 1995. It enables non-botanists to identify plants that are potentially hazardous to humans if eaten or touched. Also included are non-toxic and low-toxicity species that are eaten, perhaps because of their attractiveness to children, but whose harmless nature is not generally known by medical professionals, parents, etc. This ensures that any plant which is a common cause for concern is included in the system, enabling a positive identification to be made in the majority of cases of suspected poisoning. Over 240 plant groups, covering around 2000 plants of the home, garden, and countryside, can be identified.

Although the motive behind developing this system was to assist medical professionals in the speedy provision of appropriate treatment, its application in other circumstances is apparent. An educational version of the CD-ROM has also been published for use by anyone who is interested in learning which plants are potentially hazardous. Parents, grandparents, and child-minders can check that the plants in their home or garden are 'safe'. Garden centres can ensure that they are labelling plants correctly so that customers can make an informed choice. Furthermore, teachers will find that this is a new and exciting way to educate children about many aspects of plants, including their toxicity.

An identification is straightforward. A series of questions are asked about the plant and the answers given are used to reduce the list of suspects. The process is dynamic, with the software calculating the 'best' question to offer at each stage of the identification in order to achieve the fastest possible answer. The questions avoid botanical terminology and many are illustrated with simple line drawings. If the user is unsure which answer to give they can skip the question and an alternative will be offered. It is possible to change the answer given to any question at any stage of the identification by using the 'Review answers' facility. It is also possible to choose a question to answer from all those that are available, an option that can be useful if there is something distinctive about the plant.

When only five or fewer suspect plants remain, the user is prompted to look at photographic images in order to complete and confirm their identification. About ten images are used to illustrate each suspect plant, an advantage of publishing on CD-ROM. The images include close-ups of various plant parts so that the fine detail of leaves, fruit, etc. can be examined. Some plants can be quite variable, for example, species and cultivars of *Cotoneaster* may vary significantly in habit, leaf size, and fruit colour, and this variation is illustrated in the range of images. Each image can be 'zoomed' to almost full screen size to enable closer examination.

Once an identification has been made, the Latin name of the plant is provided, together with a list of vernacular names, full description, and toxicity details. The descriptions will help confirm the identification, and, in addition, are designed to be of educational value to non-botanists. The toxicity information provided in the medical version includes case details, toxins, and mechanisms. The educational version for the general public gives an indication of the degree of toxicity of the plant and is in line with the Horticultural Trades Association's 1994 Code[†] on the labelling of potentially harmful plants. The Code was based on a report produced by the Royal Botanic Gardens, Kew, the Poisons Unit of Guy's & St Thomas' Hospital Trust, and the Royal Horticultural Society.

An interactive identification system for *Poisonous Fungi in Britain and Ireland* is currently under development, and will be published in 1998. It will use the same software and operate in the same way as the plants identification system. The medical version will enable fungi to be identified from the patient's symptoms, or by answering questions about the cap, stem (stipe), etc. The latter method of identification will be of more use to the general public, enabling them to ascertain, before they eat them, whether the fungi that they have collected are edible or poisonous.

Medical Toxicology Unit
Guy's & St Thomas' Hospital Trust
Avonley Road
London
SE14 5ER

Centre for Economic Botany
Royal Botanic Gardens
Kew
Richmond
Surrey
TW9 3AE

Poisonous Plants in Britain and Ireland (second edition)will be available on CD-ROM from:

Publication Sales
Royal Botanic Gardens
Kew
Richmond
Surrey
TW9 3AB
Tel: 0181 332 5219; Fax: 0181 332 5646

†*Code of Recommended Retail Practice Relating to the Labelling of Potentially Harmful Plants.*
Horticultural Trades Association
Horticultural House
19 High Street
Theale
Reading
Berkshire RG7 5AH.

APPENDIX C

GLOSSARY

These definitions apply to the terms as used in this book, and are not necessarily complete.

abomasum	Fourth stomach of ruminants
abortion	Premature birth of non-viable foetus
achene	Single-seeded fruit that does not split open on ripening
acidosis	Increased acidity in the stomach contents and body fluids of ruminants
acute	Sudden and severe, referring to a disease
addiction	Habitual, compulsive intake, with adverse effects
agglutinate	Aggregate into clumps
alimentary	Relating to the digestive tract
alkalosis	Increased alkalinity in the stomach contents and body fluids of ruminants
allergen	Substance that induces an allergic (hypersensitive) reaction
allergic	Relating to the response to an allergen
allergy	Hypersensitivity (especially to food component or skin contact)
anaemia	Condition in which the number of red blood cells and the haemoglobin content of blood is decreased
analgesic	Pain-relieving drug
anthelmintic	Substance that destroys or expels parasitic (especially intestinal) worms
anther	Pollen-bearing part of flower
anticoagulant	Substance that impedes or prevents coagulation (especially of blood)
antidote	Substance that counteracts the adverse effects of another substance
anus	Terminal orifice of digestive tract
asphyxia	Cessation of breathing associated with inadequate blood levels of oxygen
astringent	Causing contraction of tissues, with reduction or cessation of their secretions
ataxia	Impaired control over body (especially locomotory) functions; incoordination
atony	Lack of the normal tension of a tissue or organ
awn	Bristle-like appendage of fruit of grasses
axil	Upper angle between leaf and stem of plant
axillary	Arising from the axil of a plant
biennial	Plant that produces flowers and usually dies in its second year
bifid	Deeply cleft into two parts

bilirubin	A red bile pigment
bloat	Distension of the rumen of cattle and sheep with gases
bract	Leaf-like structure at the base of an inflorescence
bracteole	Leaf-like structure at the base of a flower stalk
brisket	Fore and under part of the chest wall of cattle and sheep; sternal region
bulbil	Small axillary bulb of plant
caecum	Part of large intestine; the 'blind gut'
calcareous	Containing calcium carbonate, such as chalk or limestone
calcinosis	Deposition of calcium salts in body tissues where it does not normally occur
calyx	Outer portions (sepals) of some flowers often enclosing the flower bud
carcinogen	Substance that can induce tumour formation
cardiac	Relating to the heart
carpel	Unit of the female part of a flower
cerebrum	Largest part of the brain
cervix	Neck (of the uterus)
chromatography	Process for separating chemical substances by differential deposition in absorptive material
chronic	Of slow progress and long duration, referring to a disease
cirrhosis	Progressive fibrosis of the liver
colic	Severe, often spasmodic, abdominal pain
colon	Part of large intestine
coma	Prolonged unconsciousness
comatose	In a state of coma
congenital	Existing from birth (defect, etc.)
congestion	Presence of an abnormally large amount of blood in the blood vessels of a part of the body
conjunctiva	Lining of the eyelids and outer membrane of the eye
conjunctivitis	Inflammation of the conjunctiva; 'pink eye'
cultivar	Variety of plant produced by selective breeding
cyanosis	Bluish tinge of mucous membranes and skin, resulting from lack of oxygen in the blood, as occurs in cyanide poisoning
deciduous	(of trees) Shedding leaves annually
defaecation	Passing of faeces
delirium	Confused state of mind, often accompanied by agitation and incoherent speech
demulcent	Soothing medicament to relieve inflammation, particularly of the digestive tract
dermatitis	Inflammation of the skin
diuresis	Increased urination
diuretic	Substance that increases the volume of urine
duodenum	Part of small intestine, leading from the stomach
ecology	Study of living things in relation to their environment
eczema	Form of dermatitis, often with fissuring and itching

electrolyte	Compound which, in aqueous solution, readily dissociates into electrically charged particles (ions) and makes possible the conduction of an electric current through the solution
embryo	Organism in the early stages of prenatal development; an early foetus
emesis	Vomiting
emetic	Substance that induces vomiting
endemic	(of a disease) Regularly or consistently present in a region or among a group of individuals
ensilage	Preservation of green feed in a silo
enteric	Relating to the intestines
enzootic	Denoting an animal disease indigenous in an area
enzyme	Substance produced by living cells that catalyses biochemical reaction
epithelium	Layers of cells covering or lining interior and exterior body surfaces
euphoria	Feeling of well-being, often exaggerated and without justification
excretion	Process of elimination from the body of undigested material or waste products of metabolism
extremities	Parts of the body most remote from their points of attachment to the trunk
faeces	Waste matter eliminated from the digestive tract
family	Taxonomic group to which organisms of related genera belong
foetus	Unborn young after it has taken form in the uterus
fibrosis	Formation of fibrous tissue at abnormal sites
floret	Individual flower of a composite flower head
follicle	(of a plant) Dry fruit that splits open on one side when ripe
friable	Easily crumbled
frond	Leaf and stem of plant, especially of ferns
gallinaceous	Bird belonging to the order Galliformes, including the domestic fowl
gangrene	Necrosis of part of the body, usually as a result of obstruction of blood supply
gastritis	Inflammation of the stomach
gastroenteritis	Inflammation of the stomach and intestines
gastrointestinal	Relating to the stomach and intestines
generic	Relating to a genus
genus	Taxonomic group to which organisms of related species belong
gills	Thin, radiating structures on the underside of the cap of a fungus
glume	Bract of grass flower
goitre	Abnormally enlarged thyroid gland
goitrogen	Substance that induces goitre

habitat	Natural environment of plant or animal
haemagglutination	Aggregation of blood cells into clumps
haemagglutinins	Substances that cause haemagglutination
haematuria	Presence of blood or red blood cells in urine
haemodialysis	Separation of (especially toxic) substances from the blood by passage across a semipermeable membrane
haemoglobin	Red pigment in red blood cells
haemoglobinuria	Presence of haemoglobin in urine
haemolysis	Destruction of red blood cells with release of haemoglobin
haemolytic	Relating to haemolysis
haemoperfusion	Separation of (especially toxic) substances from the blood by passage through adsorbent material
haemorrhage	Bleeding
hallucination	Strongly perceived sense of illusory objects or events
hallucinogen	Substance that can induce hallucinations
hepatotoxic	Relating to toxic substances that damage the liver
herbaceous	Relating to non-woody plants
herbicide	Chemical substance whose application can kill vegetation
histology	Study of microscopic structure of cells, organs, and tissues
hock	Tarsal joint of the hind leg
hybrid	Plant resulting from the fertilization of one species (or subspecies) with another
hydrolysis	Chemical splitting of compounds to simpler compounds with the uptake of water
hypocalcaemia	Subnormal concentration of calcium in the blood
hypothermia	Subnormal body temperature
inflammation	A pathological process, affecting blood vessels and surrounding tissues and characterized by redness, warmth, swelling, and pain
inflorescence	Part of plant bearing the flowers
ingestion	Intake of food or drink
intraperitoneal	Within the peritoneal (abdominal) cavity
intravenous	Within a vein
jaundice	Pathological condition involving the passage of bile pigments into the blood, with consequent yellowish coloration of the skin and other tissues
ketosis	Metabolic disorder in which the ketone content of blood increases and that of glucose decreases
lacrimation	Secretion or flow of tears, especially when excessive
lactation	Milk secretion
lactic acidosis	Increased acidity of the rumen contents due to accumulation of lactic acid after feeding excess carbohydrate
laminitis	Inflammatory condition of the hoof
larynx	Part of the throat; 'voice box'
lassitude	Weariness; lack of desire to be active
latent	(of a disease) Present, but not currently apparent; potential

lavage	Washing-out of an organ (usually stomach)
lesion	Pathological change in tissues
leukocytosis	Abnormally large number of white blood cells
lymph	Fluid that flows in lymphatic vessels
lymph node	Gland of the lymphatic system
lymphocyte	Type of blood cell
macrophage	Large cell with single nucleus; ingests damaged or dead cells
malignant	Severe, progressive, and often not responsive to treatment (especially of a tumour)
metabolism	Chemical changes occurring in the functioning of the body
micturition	Passing of urine
monogastric	Having a single stomach
mucous membrane	Lining membrane, particularly of digestive and upper respiratory tracts
mucus	Clear, semi-fluid, viscid secretion from a mucous membrane
mutagen	Agent inducing a genetic change in cells
myocardium	Muscular wall of heart
narcotic	Inducing drowsiness, sleep, or state of unconsciousness
nausea	Inclination to vomit
necrosis	Death of cells or portion of tissue or organ
nectar	Sweet-tasting secretion of flowers
nephritis	Inflammation of the kidneys
neuro-	Relating to nerves or the nervous system
oedema	Swelling of tissue as a result of fluid accumulation
oesophagus	Portion of digestive tract leading from the throat to the stomach; gullet
oestrogen	Substance inducing female characteristics; female sex hormone
oestrus	(of animals) Stage in female sexual cycle when mating can occur; 'heat'
offal	Internal organs and parts removed from the carcass of animals at slaughter
omasum	Third compartment of the forestomach of ruminants
ophthalmic	Relating to the eye
oral	Relating to the mouth
papule	Small, raised pimple on the skin
paranoia	Mental disorder, characterized by delusions (often of persecution)
perennial	A plant that lives for several years even if the above-ground parts die down annually
peripheral	Relating to the outer part or surface
peritoneum	Thin layer of tissue that lines the abdominal cavity and covers most of the body parts within it
photosensitivity	Presence of a photosensitive agent in the skin

photosensitization	Light-induced reaction of skin to light, in the presence of a photosensitive agent
phytohaemagglutinins	Haemagglutinins of plant origin
placenta	Organ, attached to the inner wall of the uterus, by which the foetus is nourished
polymer	Substance of high molecular weight made up of a chain of identical units
polymorphic	Existing in several different forms
post-mortem examination	Examination of a body after death
prolapse	Displacement of an internal organ, such that part of it may be visible externally (especially digestive or female genital tracts)
psychedelic	Expanding or heightening consciousness and awareness
psychic	Relating to the mind
pulmonary	Relating to the lungs
purgative	Substance promoting evacuation of the bowel; laxative
rectum	Terminal portion of intestine
recumbent	Lying down
rehydration	Replacement of lost fluids
renal	Relating to the kidney
respiration	Breathing
retina	Light-sensitive layer on the inner surface of the eye
rhizome	Underground stem of plant
rickets	Skeletal deformity, especially of limb bones, resulting from deficiencies of calcium and vitamin D
rodenticide	Substance used to kill rodents
rumen	Large forestomach of ruminants; paunch
rumenotomy	Incision of the rumen
ruminal atony	Cessation of ruminal movement
rumination	Chewing the cud
salivation	Production of (excessive amounts of) saliva
scouring	Severe (usually watery) diarrhoea
sedative	Agent inducing state of calmness
sepal	One of the outer (usually green) parts of a flower, often enclosing the flower bud
septicaemia	Presence of disease-producing microorganisms in the blood
serum	Clear, watery, fluid portion of the blood
silage	Green feed preserved in a silo
spasm	Involuntary, temporary contraction of muscle
species	Taxonomic status of organism subordinate to genus and superior to variety
spore	Small, usually single-celled, reproductive portion of simple, non-seed-bearing plants
stamen	Part of flower consisting of the pollen-bearing anther and its filament
stigma	Pollen receptor of the female part of the flower
stimulant	Agent inducing increased activity

stipule	Scale-like or leaf-like portion present at the base of the leaf stalk of some plants
stomatitis	Inflammation of the mucous membranes of the mouth
style	Portion of female part of plant between the stigma and the ovary
subcutaneous	Beneath the skin
supportive	(of treatment) For the maintenance of essential body functions
symptomatic	(of treatment) Aimed at alleviating specific clinical signs
syndrome	Group of clinical signs that, collectively, are present in and indicative of a certain condition or disease
tap root	Simple, tapering, main root of a plant
taxonomy	Systematic classification, especially of living organisms
tenosynovitis	Inflammation of a tendon sheath
teratogen	Substance that can induce abnormal development (often malformation) of a foetus
therapy	Treatment
thorax	Chest
topical application	Local, external use of therapeutic substance
tranquillizer	Substance given to relieve a state of agitation
tremorgenic	Producing muscular tremors
tumour	Abnormal mass of tissue that grows continuously and excessively
tympany	Distension of the rumen with gases; bloat
uraemia	Accumulation of nitrogenous waste (mainly urea) in the blood
urethra	Canal through which urine is discharged from the bladder
vacuole	Minute cavity or space in cells or tissues
vacuolation	Formation of vacuoles
variety	Taxonomic unit of lower status than species
vasodilator	Substance that dilates blood vessels
veil	Thin membrane that stretches over the cap to the stalk of some fungi when young; may persist as a ring on the stalk and patches on the cap
vertigo	Sensation of dizziness
vesicle	Blister
volva	Residual cup at the base of some fungi, e.g. *Amanita* species
whorl	Three or more plant parts of the same kind, that arise at the same level (e.g. a ring of leaves on a stem)

Bibliography and References

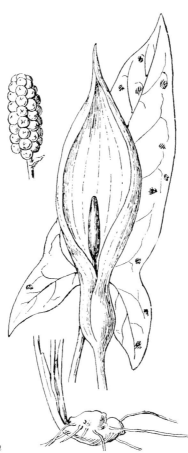

Arum maculatum
Cuckoo pint

BIBLIOGRAPHY (BOOKS): GENERAL

ALTMANN, H. *Poisonous Plants and Animals* (Chatto Nature Guides). Chatto & Windus, London, UK. 1980, 143 pp.

ARNOLD, R.E. *Poisonous Plants.* Terra Publishing Inc., Jefferstown, Kentucky, USA. 1978, 152 pp.

BARTÍK, M.; PISKAČ, A. (Editors) *Veterinary Toxicology.* Elsevier Scientific Publishing Co., Amsterdam, Netherlands. 1981, 346 pp.

BENTZ, H. (Editor) *Nutztiervergiftungen. Erkennung und Verhütung.* (in German) Gustav Fischer Verlag, Jena, Germany. 1969, 432 pp.

BOHOSIEWICZ, M. *Toksykologia Weterynaryjna.* (in Polish) Panstwowe Wydawnictwo Rolnicze i Leśne, Warsaw, Poland. 1970, 376 pp.

BRUMMITT, R.K. (Compiler) *Vascular Plant Families and Genera.* Royal Botanic Gardens, Kew, UK. 1992, 804 pp.

CHEEKE, P.R. (Editor) *Toxicants of Plant Origin. Volume I. Alkaloids.* CRC Press, Boca Raton, Florida, USA. 1989, 335 pp.

CHEEKE, P.R. (Editor) *Toxicants of Plant Origin. Volume II. Glycosides.* CRC Press, Boca Raton, Florida, USA. 1989, 277 pp.

CHEEKE, P.R. (Editor) *Toxicants of Plant Origin. Volume III. Proteins and Amino Acids.* CRC Press, Boca Raton, Florida, USA. 1989, 271 pp.

CHEEKE, P.R. (Editor) *Toxicants of Plant Origin. Volume IV. Phenolics.* CRC Press, Boca Raton, Florida, USA. 1989, 232 pp.

CHEEKE, P.R.; SHULL, L.R. *Natural Toxicants in Feeds and Poisonous Plants.* AVI Publishing Company, Westport, Connecticut, USA. 1985, 492 pp.

CLAPHAM, A.R.; TUTIN, T.G.; MOORE, D.M. *Flora of the British Isles.* Cambridge University Press, Cambridge, UK. 3rd Edition. 1987, 688 pp.

COLEGATE, S.M.; DORLING, P.R. (Editors) *Plant-associated Toxins. Agricultural, Phytochemical and Ecological Aspects.* CAB International, Wallingford, UK. 1994, 581 pp.

CONNOR, H.E. *The Poisonous Plants in New Zealand.* E.C. Keating, Government Printer, Wellington, New Zealand. 1977, 247 pp.

COOPER, M.R.; JOHNSON, A.W. *Poisonous Plants & Fungi. An Illustrated Guide.* HMSO, London, UK. 1988 (reprinted 1996), 134 pp.

COOPER, P. *Poisoning by Drugs and Chemicals, Plants and Animals.* Alchemist Publications, London, UK. 3rd Edition. 1974, 252 pp.

CORNEVIN, C. *Des Plantes Vénéneuses et des Empoisonnements qu'elles Déterminent.* (in French) Librairie de Firmin-Didot, 56 rue Jacob, Paris, France. 1887, 524 pp.

DE BRUYN, J.W.; SCHNEIDER, F. *Giftige Planten in en am Huis.* (in Dutch) A.A. Balkema, Rotterdam, Netherlands. 1976, 191 pp.

DERIVAUX, J.; LIÉGEOIS, F. *Toxicologie Vétérinaire.* (in French) Vigot Frères, Paris, France. Desoer, Liège, Belgium. 1962, 332 pp.

D'MELLO, J.P.F.; DUFFUS, C.M.; DUFFUS, J.H. (Editors) *Toxic Substances in Crop Plants.* Royal Society of Chemistry, Cambridge, UK. 1991, 339 pp.

EVERIST, S.L. *Poisonous Plants of Australia.* Angus & Robertson Publishers, Sydney, Australia. 2nd Edition. 1981, 966 pp.

FOSTER, S.; CARAS, R.A. *A Field Guide to Venomous Animals and Poisonous Plants. North America North of Mexico.* Houghton Mifflin Co., Boston, New York, USA. 1994, 244 pp.

FROHNE, D.; PFÄNDER, H.J. *A Colour Atlas of Poisonous Plants.* Wolfe Publishing Ltd, London, UK. 1984, 291 pp.

GUSYNIN, I.A. [*The Toxicology of Poisonous Plants.*] (in Russian) Gosudarstvennoe Izdatel'stvo Sel'skokhozyaistvennoi Literatury, Moscow, USSR. 3rd Edition. 1955, 330 pp.

HAILS, M.R. (Compiler) *Plant Poisoning in Animals. A Bibliography from the World Literature. No.2. 1980–1982.* CAB International, Farnham Royal, UK. 1986, 93 pp.

HAILS, M.R. (Compiler) *Plant Poisoning in Animals. A Bibliography from the World Literature. No.3. 1983–1992.* CAB International, Wallingford, UK. 1994, 302 pp.

HAILS, M.R.; CRANE, T.D. *Plant Poisoning in Animals, A Bibliography from the World Literature, 1960–1979.* Commonwealth Bureau of Animal Health, Weybridge, Surrey, UK. 1983, 158 pp.

HARBORNE, J.B.; BAXTER, H. (Editors) *Phytochemical Dictionary. A Handbook of Bioactive Compounds from Plants.* Taylor & Francis, London, UK. 1993, 791 pp.

HARBORNE, J.B.; BAXTER, H. (Editors) *Dictionary of Plant Toxins.* John Wiley & Sons, Chichester, UK. 1996, 523 pp.

HARDIN, J.W.; ARENA, J.M. *Human Poisoning from Native and Cultivated Plants.* Duke University Press, Durham, North Carolina, USA. 2nd Edition. 1974, 194 pp.

HENSLOW, G. *Poisonous Plants in Field and Garden.* Society for Promoting Christian Knowledge, London, UK. 1901, 189 pp.

HUMPHREYS, D.J. *Veterinary Toxicology.* Baillière Tindall, London, UK. 3rd Edition. 1988, 356 pp.

JAMES, L.F.; RALPHS, M.H.; NIELSEN, D.B. (Editors) *The Ecology and Economic Impact of Poisonous Plants on Livestock Production.* Westview Press, Bolder, Colorado, USA. 1988, 428 pp.

JEAN-BLAIN, C. *Les Plantes Vénéneuses.* (in French) La Maison Rustique, Librairie de l'Académie d'Agriculture, 26 rue Jacob, Paris, France. 1973, 140 pp.

JOHNSON, C.; JOHNSON, C.P.; SOWERBY, J.E. *British Poisonous Plants.* John Van Voorst, London, UK. 2nd Edition. 1861, 76 + 32 pp.

KEBLE MARTIN, W. *The New Concise British Flora.* Bloomsbury Books, London, UK. 1991, 247 pp.

KEELER, R.F.; VAN KAMPEN, K.R.; JAMES, L.F. *Effects of Poisonous Plants on Livestock.* Academic Press, New York and London. 1978, 600 pp.

KEELER, R.F.; TU, A.T. (Editors) *Handbook of Natural Toxins. Volume 6. Toxicology of Plant and Fungal Compounds.* Marcel Dekker, New York, USA. 1991, 672 pp.

KINGHORN, A.D. (Editor) *Toxic Plants.* Columbia University Press, New York, USA. 1979, 195 pp.

KINGSBURY, J.M. *Poisonous Plants of the United States and Canada.* Prentice-Hall Inc., New Jersey, USA. 1964, 626 pp.

KINGSBURY, J.M. *Deadly Harvest. A Guide to Common Poisonous Plants.* George Allen and Unwin Ltd, London, UK. 1967, 128 pp.

KLAASSEN, C.D. (Editor) *Casarett and Doull's Toxicology. The Basic Science of Poisons.* McGraw-Hill, New York, USA. 5th Edition. 1996, 1152 pp.

LAMPE, K.F.; FAGERSTRÖM, R. *Plant Toxicity and Dermatitis.* Williams and Wilkins Co., Baltimore, USA. 1968, 231 pp.

LAMPE, K.F.; McCANN, M. *AMA Handbook of Poisonous and Injurious Plants.* American Medical Association, Chicago, USA. 1985, 432 pp.

LANG, D.C. *The Complete Book of British Berries.* Threshold Books, London, UK. 1987, 223 pp.

LIENER, I.E. (Editor) *Toxic Constituents of Plant Foodstuffs.* Academic Press, New York and London. 2nd Edition. 1980, 502 pp.

LONG, H.C. *Plants Poisonous to Live Stock.* University Press, Cambridge, UK. 1917, 119 pp.

LOVELL, C.R. *Plants and the Skin.* Blackwell Scientific Publications, Oxford, UK. 1993, 272 pp.

MABBERLEY, D.J. *The Plant Book.* Cambridge University Press, Cambridge, UK. 1987 (reprinted 1989), 707 pp.

McBARRON, E.J. *Medical and Veterinary Aspects of Plant Poisons in New South Wales.* Department of Agriculture, New South Wales, Australia. 1976, 243 pp.

MORTON, A.G. *History of Botanical Science.* Academic Press, London and New York. 1981, 474 pp.

MUENSCHER, W.C. *Poisonous Plants of the United States.* Macmillan Co., New York, USA. 1939, 266 pp.

NICHOLSON, J.A. *Lander's Veterinary Toxicology.* Baillière, Tindall and Cox, London, UK. 3rd Edition. 1945, 329 pp.

NORTH, P.M. *Poisonous Plants and Fungi.* Blandford Press, London, UK. 1967, 161 pp.

PAMMEL, L.H. *Manual of Poisonous Plants.* Cedar Rapids, Iowa, USA. 1911, 977 pp.

PRATT, A. *The Poisonous, Noxious and Suspected Plants of our Fields and Woods.* Society for Promoting Christian Knowledge, London, UK. 1857, 208 pp.

RIEMANN, H. (Editor) *Food-borne Infections and Intoxications.* Academic Press, New York and London. 1969, 698 pp.

RIZK, A.F.M. (Editor) *Poisonous Plant Contamination of Edible Plants.* CRC Press, Boca Raton, Florida, USA. 1991, 183 pp.

ROSENTHAL, G.A.; BERENBAUM, M.R. (Editors) *Herbivores. Their Interactions with Secondary Plant Metabolites. Volume I: The Chemical Participants.* Academic Press, New York and London. 1991, 468 pp.

ROSENTHAL, G.A.; BERENBAUM, M.R. (Editors) *Herbivores. Their Interactions with Secondary Plant Metabolites. Volume II: Ecological and Evolutionary Processes.* Academic Press, New York and London. 1992, 493 pp.

SCHAUENBERG, P.; PARIS, F. *Guide to Medicinal Plants.* Lutterworth Press, Guildford and London, UK. 1977, 349 pp.

SCHELINE, R.R. *CRC Handbook of Mammalian Metabolism of Plant Compounds.* CRC Press, Boca Raton, Florida, USA. 1991, 514 pp.

SCHULTES, R.E.; HOFMANN, A. *The Botany and Chemistry of Hallucinogens.* Charles C. Thomas, Springfield, Illinois, USA. 2nd Edition. 1980, 437 pp.

SIMMONDS, N.W. *Evolution of Crop Plants.* Longman, London and New York. 1976, 339 pp.

STACE, C. *New Flora of the British Isles.* Cambridge University Press, Cambridge, UK. 1991, 1226 pp.

STEYN, D.G. *The Toxicology of Plants in South Africa.* Central News Agency, South Africa. 1934, 631 pp.

TURNER, N.J.; SZCZAWINSKI, A.F. *Common Poisonous Plants and Mushrooms of North America.* Timber Press, Portland, Oregon, USA. 1991 (reprinted 1995), 311 pp.

TUTIN, T.G. *Umbellifers of the British Isles.* (BSBI Handbook No.2). Botanical Society of the British Isles, London, UK. 1980, 197 pp.

VAHRMEIJER, J. *Poisonous Plants of South Africa that Cause Stock Losses.* Tafelberg Publishers Ltd, 28 Wales Street, Cape Town, South Africa. 1981, 168 pp.

VICKERY, M.L.; VICKERY, B. *Secondary Plant Metabolism.* Macmillan Press Ltd, London, UK. 1981, 335 pp.

VÖLKER, R. *Lehrbuch der Toxikologie für Tierärzte. (Fröhner).* (in German) Ferdinand Enke Verlag, Stuttgart, Germany. 6th Edition. 1950, 404 pp.

WATT, J.M.; BREYER-BRANDWIJK, M.G. *The Medicinal and Poisonous Plants of Southern and Eastern Africa.* E. & S. Livingstone Ltd, Edinburgh and London, UK. 2nd Edition. 1962, 1457 pp.

BIBLIOGRAPHY (BOOKS): FUNGI

BENJAMIN, D.R. *Mushrooms: Poisons and Panaceas. A Handbook for Naturalists, Mycologists, and Physicians.* W.H. Freeman and Company, New York, USA. 1995, 422 pp.

BRESINSKY, A.; BESL, H. *A Colour Atlas of Poisonous Fungi.* Wolfe Publishing Ltd, London, UK. 1990, 295 pp.

JORDAN, M. *The Encyclopedia of Fungi of Britain and Europe.* David & Charles, Newton Abbot, UK. 1995, 384 pp.

LANGE, M.; HORA, F.B. *Collins Guide to Mushrooms and Toadstools.* Collins, London, UK. 1963, 257 pp.

LINCOFF, G.; MITCHEL, D.H. *Toxic and Hallucinogenic Mushroom Poisoning. A Handbook for Physicians and Mushroom Hunters.* Van Nostrand Reinhold Co., New York, USA. 1977, 267 pp.

OLDRIDGE, S.G.; PEGLER, D.N.; SPOONER, B.M. *Wild Mushroom and Toadstool Poisoning.* Royal Botanic Gardens, Kew, UK. 1989, 24 pp.

PEGLER, D. *Field Guide to the Mushrooms & Toadstools of Britain and Europe.* Kingfisher Books, London, UK. 1990 (reprinted 1994), 192 pp.

PEGLER, D.; SPOONER, B. *The Mushroom Identifier.* Apple Press, London, UK. 1992 (reprinted 1994), 144 pp.

REID, D. *Mushrooms and Toadstools.* Kingfisher Books, Ward Lock Ltd, London, UK. 1980, 124 pp.

SMITH, J.E.; HENDERSON, R.S. (Editors) *Mycotoxins and Animal Foods.* CRC Press, Boca Raton, Florida, USA. 1991, 875 pp.

SPOERKE, D.G.; RUMACK, B.H. (Editors) *Handbook of Mushroom Poisoning. Diagnosis and Treatment.* CRC Press, Boca Raton, Florida, USA. 1994, 456 pp.

WAKEFIELD, E.M.; DENNIS, R.W.G. *Common British Fungi.* Saiga Publishing Co. Ltd, Hindhead, Surrey, UK. 2nd Edition. 1981, 216 pp.

WATLING, R. *Children and Toxic Fungi: the Essential Medical Guide to Fungal Poisoning in Children.* Royal Botanic Garden, Edinburgh, UK. 1995, 54 pp.

REFERENCES

The references for each of the plant families (arranged alphabetically) are in separate groups, numbered in the order in which they appear in the appropriate section of the text. The sections on fungi and algae follow those on the plants. Square brackets enclosing a title indicate that the original is not in English; most of such papers have English abstracts.

POISONOUS PLANTS

ALLIACEAE

1 MIYATA, D. Isolation of a new phenolic compound from the onion (*Allium cepa* L. onion) and its oxidative effect on erythrocytes. *Japanese Journal of Veterinary Research* 1990, 38, 65.

2 FENWICK, G.R.; HANLEY, A.B. The genus *Allium* – part 3. *Critical Reviews in Food Science and Nutrition* 1985, 23, 1–73.

3 DIN, Z.Z.; AHMAD, Y.; ELSON, C.E.; QURESHI, A.A. Inhibition of lipid metabolism by garlic and its fractions in chicken liver. *Federation Proceedings* 1982, 41, 544.

4 YAMOTO, O.; MAEDE, Y. Susceptibility to onion-induced hemolysis in dogs with hereditary high erythrocyte reduced glutathione and potassium concentrations. *American Journal of Veterinary Research* 1992, 53, 134–137.

5 GILL, P.A.; SERGEANT, E.S.G. Onion poisoning in a bull. *Australian Veterinary Journal* 1981, 57, 484.

6 VERHOEFF, J.; HAJER, R.; VAN DEN INGH, T.S.G.A.M. Onion poisoning of young cattle. *Veterinary Record* 1985, 117, 497–498.

7 LINCOLN, S.D.; HOWELL, M.E.; COMBS, J.J.; HINMAN, D.D. Hematologic effects and feeding performance in cattle fed cull domestic onions (*Allium cepa*). *Journal of the American Veterinary Medical Association* 1992, 200, 1090–1094.

8 HOTHI, D.S.; ARNEJA, J.S.; CHAWLA, J.S. Onion (*Allium cepa*) poisoning in bullocks. *Indian Veterinary Journal* 1980, 57, 690–692.

9 HUTCHISON, T.W.S. Onions as a source of Heinz body anaemia and death in cattle. *Canadian Veterinary Journal* 1977, 18, 358–360.

10 LAZARUS, A.E.; RAJAMANI, S. Poisoning due to onion spoilage in cattle. *Indian Veterinary Journal* 1968, 45, 877–880.

11 THAKUR, D.K. Onion poisoning in cow. (A case report.) *Livestock Adviser* 1983, 8, No.5, 37–38.

12 KIRK, J.H.; BULGIN, M.S. Effect of feeding cull domestic onions (*Allium cepa*) to sheep. *American Journal of Veterinary Research* 1979, 40, 397–399.

13 FRANKEN, P.; VAN BEUKELEN, P.; BLOK, G. [Onions: not a horse feed.] *Tijdschrift voor Diergeneeskunde* 1980, 105, 529–534.

14 FORSYTH, A.A. *British Poisonous Plants*. HMSO, London, UK. Ministry of Agriculture, Fisheries and Food Bulletin 161, 1968, 105 (amended 1979, 106).

15 IMADA, O. [Experimental work on onion poisoning in dogs – relationship between the quantity of onion supplied and the onset of disease.] *Bulletin of Azabu University of Veterinary Medicine* 1980, 1, 271–287.

16 WILLIAMS, H.H.; ERICKSON, B.N.; BEACH, E.F.; MACY, I.G. Biochemical studies of the blood of dogs with *n*-propyl disulphide anemia. *Journal of Laboratory and Clinical Medicine* 1941, 29, 996–1008.

17 SPICE, R.N. Hemolytic anemia associated with ingestion of onions in a dog. *Canadian Veterinary Journal* 1976, 17, 181–183.

18 SOLTER, P.; SCOTT, R. Onion ingestion and subsequent Heinz body anemia in a dog: a case report.

Journal of the American Animal Hospital Association 1987, 23, 544–546.

19 STALLBAUMER, M. Onion poisoning in a dog. *Veterinary Record* 1981, 108, 523–524.

20 SMITH, C.H.; ELLISON, R.S. Concurrent onion poisoning and haematuria in a dog. *New Zealand Veterinary Journal* 1986, 34, 77–78.

21 HARVEY, J.W.; RACKEAR, D. Experimental onion-induced hemolytic anemia in dogs. *Veterinary Pathology* 1985, 22, 387–392.

22 KOBAYASHI, K. Onion poisoning in the cat. *Feline Practice* 1981, 11, No.1, 22–27.

23 CHRISTOPHER, M.M. Relation of endogenous Heinz bodies to disease and anemia in cats: 120 cases (1978–1987). *Journal of the American Veterinary Medical Association* 1989, 194, 1089–1095.

24 SPISNI, D.; FRATESCHI, T.L.; MARIANI, A.P.; MARTELLI, F. [Effect of methionine treatment on rabbits made anaemic by feeding on onions.] *Annali della Facoltà di Medicina Veterinaria di Pisa* 1971, 24, 35–46.

25 COWAN, J.W.; SAGHIR, A.R.; SALJI, J.P. Antithyroid activity of onion volatiles. *Australian Journal of Biological Sciences* 1967, 20, 683–685.

26 WATT, J.M.; BREYER-BRANDWIJK, M.G. *The Medicinal and Poisonous Plants of Southern and Eastern Africa.* E. & S. Livingstone Ltd, Edinburgh and London, UK. 2nd Edition, 1962, 670–679.

27 FENWICK, G.R.; HANLEY, A.B. *Allium* species poisoning. *Veterinary Record* 1985, 116, 28.

28 STEVENS, H. Suspected wild garlic poisoning in sheep. *Veterinary Record* 1984, 115, 363.

29 LEWIS, G. Personal communication.

30 LUND, L.J.; GIBSON, G.M.; TURNER, R.G. Leek taint in beef carcases. *Veterinary Record* 1991, 128, 263–264.

31 MIYAZAWA, K.; ITO, M.; OHSAKI, K. An equine case of urticaria associated with dry garlic feeding. *Journal of Veterinary Medical Science* 1991, 53, 747–748.

32 PIERCE, K.R.; JOYCE, J.R.; ENGLAND, R.B.; JONES, L.P. Acute hemolytic anemia caused by wild onion poisoning in horses. *Journal of the American Veterinary Medical Association* 1972, 160, 323–327.

33 VAN KAMPEN, K.R.; JAMES, L.F.; JOHNSON, A.E. Hemolytic anemia in sheep fed wild onion (*Allium validum*). *Journal of the American Veterinary Medical Association* 1970, 156, 328–332.

34 LOVELL, C.R. *Plants and the Skin.* Blackwell Scientific Publications, Oxford, UK. 1993, 217–220.

35 FARRELL, A.M.; STAUGHTON, R.C.D. Garlic burns mimicking herpes zoster. *Lancet* 1996, 347, 1195.

AMARYLLIDACEAE

1 HONNEGER, R.E.; FURRER, J. [Some noteworthy causes of death in reptiles.] *Salamandra* 1975, 11, 179–181.

2 NIEUWLAND, I.C.H. [The use of bulbs as cattle feed.] *Tijdschrift voor Diergeneeskunde* 1941, 68, 359–368.

3 NATIONAL POISONS INFORMATION SERVICE, London, UK. Personal communication.

4 LITOVITZ, T.L.; FAHEY, B.A. Please don't eat the daffodils. *New England Journal of Medicine* 1982, 306, 547.

5 VIGNEAU, C.H.; TSAO, J.; CHAMAILLARD, C.; GALZOT, J. Accidental absorption of daffodils (*Narcissus jonquilla*): two common intoxications. *Veterinary and Human Toxicology* 1982, 24, Supplement, 133–135.

6 HARDIN, J.W.; ARENA, J.M. *Human Poisoning from Native and Cultivated Plants.* Duke University Press, Durham, North Carolina, USA. 1969, 39–40.

7 LOVELL, C.R. *Plants and the Skin.* Blackwell Scientific Publications, Oxford, UK. 1993, 220–222.

APOCYNACEAE

1   GALEY, F.D.; HOLSTEGE, D.M.; PLUMLEE, K.H.; TOR, E.; JOHNSON, B.; ANDERSON, M.L.; BLANCHARD, P.C.; BROWN, F. Diagnosis of oleander poisoning in livestock. *Journal of Veterinary Diagnostic Investigation* 1996, 8, 358–364.

2   ANONYMOUS. Oleander poisoning in equines. *Journal of the Royal Army Veterinary Corps* 1971, 42, 8–9.

3   VERMUNT, J. Oleander – decorative and very poisonous. *New Zealand Veterinary Journal* 1987, 35, 138–139.

4   DE PINTO, J.; PALERMO, D.; MILILLO, M.A.; IAFFALDANO, D. [Outbreak of oleander (*Nerium oleander*) poisoning.] *Clinica Veterinaria* 1981, 104, 15–18.

5   MAHIN, L.; MARZOU, A.; HUART, A. A case report of *Nerium oleander* poisoning in cattle. *Veterinary and Human Toxicology* 1984, 26, 303–304.

6   REZAKHANI, A.; MAHAM, M. Oleander poisoning in cattle of the Fars Province, Iran. *Veterinary and Human Toxicology* 1992, 34, 549.

7   REZAKHANI, A.; MAHAM, M. Cardiac manifestations of oleander poisoning in cattle and donkeys. In: *Plant-associated Toxins. Agricultural, Phytochemical and Ecological Aspects.* Edited by S.M. Colegate and P.R. Dorling. CAB International, Wallingford, UK. 1994, 534–537.

8   MAHAM, M.; REZAKHANI, A. Treatment of oleander poisoning in cattle and donkeys. In: *Plant-associated Toxins. Agricultural, Phytochemical and Ecological Aspects.* Edited by S.M. Colegate and P.R. Dorling. CAB International, Wallingford, UK. 1994, 538–540.

9   ARMIÉN, A.G.; PEIXOTO, P. V.; BARBOSA, J.D.; TOKARNIA, C.H. [Experimental poisoning of sheep by *Nerium oleander* (Apocynaceae).] *Pesquisa Veterinária Brasileira* 1994, 14, 85–93.

10 MAYER, H.; WACKER, R.; DALCHOW, W. [Plant poisoning from chestnut, oleander, acorns and autumn crocus in zoo and wild animals.] *Tierärztliche Umschau* 1986, 41, 169–178.

11 ALFONSO, H.A.; SANCHEZ, L.M.; MERINO, N.; GOMEZ, B.C. Intoxication due to *Nerium oleander* in geese. *Veterinary and Human Toxicology* 1994, 36, 47.

12 SHROPSHIRE, C.M.; STAUBER, E.; ARAI, M. Evaluation of selected plants for acute toxicosis in budgerigars. *Journal of the American Veterinary Medical Association* 1992, 200, 936–939.

13 ARAI, M.; STAUBER, E.; SHROPSHIRE, C.M. Evaluation of selected plants for their toxic effects in canaries. *Journal of the American Veterinary Medical Association* 1992, 200, 1329–1331.

14 SHUMAIK, G.M.; WU, A.W.; PING, A.C. Oleander poisoning: treatment with digoxin-specific Fab antibody fragments. *Annals of Emergency Medicine* 1988, 17, 732–735.

15 ROMANO, G.A.; MOMBELLI, G. [Poisoning with oleander leaves.] *Schweizerische Medizinische Wochenschrift* 1990, 120, 596–597.

16 GOERRE, S.; FRÖHLI, P. [Poisoning with digitoxin-like glycosides following eating of oleander leaves.] *Schweizerische Rundschau für Medizin Praxis* 1993, 82, 121–122.

17 MACK, R.B. "To see a world in a grain of sand and a heaven in a wild flower" - oleander poisoning. *North Carolina Medical Journal* 1984, 45, 729–730.

18 NATIONAL POISONS INFORMATION SERVICE, London, UK. Personal communication.

19 HAYNES, B.E.; BESSEN H.A.; WIGHTMAN, W.D. Oleander tea: herbal draught of death. *Annals of Emergency Medicine* 1985, 14, 350–353.

20 OSTERLOH, J.; HEROLD, S.; POND, S. Oleander interference in the digoxin radioimmunoassay in a fatal ingestion. *Journal of the American Medical Association* 1982, 247, 1596–1597.

21 MITCHELL, J.; ROOK, A. *Botanical Dermatology. Plants and Plant Products Injurious to the Skin.* Greengrass Ltd, Vancouver, Canada. 1979, 104–105.

22   APTED, J. Oleander dermatitis. *Contact Dermatitis* 1983, 9, 321.

23   CLARK, R.F.; SELDEN, B.S.; CURRY, S.C. Antidigoxin-Fab fragments in the treatment of a canine model of oleander toxicity. *Veterinary and Human Toxicology* 1990, 32, 353.

AQUIFOLIACEAE

1   FINANCE, B. [Holly (*Ilex aquifolium*) poisoning in two Comtois foals.] *Pferdeheilkunde* 1987, 3, 43–44.

2   SIMPSON, V.R. '*Ilex* choke' in lambs. *In Practice* 1992, 14, 39.

3   STANDRING, G.; GOULDING, R. Poisonous plants. *Nursing Times* 1969, August 7, 1009–1011.

4   RODRIGUES, T.D.; JOHNSON, P.N.; JEFFREY, L.P. Holly berry ingestion: case report. *Veterinary and Human Toxicology* 1984, 26, 157–158.

5   SCHILLING, R.; SPEAKER. J. Incidence of plant poisoning in Philadelphia noted as poison information calls. *Veterinary and Human Toxicology* 1980, 22, 148–150.

6   O'LEARY, S.B. Poisoning in man from eating poisonous plants. *Archives of Environmental Health* 1964, 9, 216–242.

ARACEAE

1   OEHME, F.W. The hazard of plant toxicities in the human population. In: *Effects of Poisonous Plants on Livestock*. Edited by R.F. Keeler, K.R. Van Kampen and L.F. James. Academic Press, New York and London. 1978, 67–81.

2   O'MOORE, L.B. *Arum maculatum* poisoning in cattle. *Irish Veterinary Journal* 1955, 9, 146–147.

3   KYLE, R.A.M. Poisoning of sheep by lords and ladies. *Veterinary Record* 1983, 113, 23.

4   GLYN, M. An unknown equine condition. *Veterinary Record* 1968, 82, 554.

5   DABIJA, G.; DOMILESCU, C.; NEMŢEANU, S. [Toxicity of *Arum maculatum* for animals.] *Archiva Veterinaria* 1968, 4, 157–168.

6   STANDRING, G.; GOULDING, R. Poisonous plants. *Nursing Times* 1969, August 7, 1009–1011.

7   NATIONAL POISONS INFORMATION SERVICE, London, UK. Personal communication.

8   ALTMANN, H. *Poisonous Plants and Animals*. Chatto and Windus, London, UK. 1980, 112.

9   SCHURZ, J. [Wild arum.] *Kosmos* 1976, 72, 74–75.

10 KECK, G.; JAUSSAUD, P. [A case of *Dieffenbachia* poisoning.] *Notes de Toxicologie Vétérinaire* 1981, 4, 88.

11 ARDITTI, J.; RODRIGUEZ, E. *Dieffenbachia*: uses, abuses and toxic constituents. *Journal of Ethnopharmacology* 1982, 5, 293–302.

12 IPPEN, H.; WERETA-KUBEK, M.; ROSE, U. [Skin and mucous membrane reactions from house plants of the genus *Dieffenbachia*.] *Dermatosen in Beruf und Umwelt* 1986, 34, 93–101.

13 EVANS, C.R.H. Oral ulceration after contact with the houseplant *Dieffenbachia*. *British Dental Journal* 1987, 162, 467–468.

14 JÍCHA, J.; VOSTATEK, M.; TOMAN, J. [*Dieffenbachia* and toxicological problems.] *Československá Pediatrie* 1989, 44, 305–307.

15 OTTOSEN, C.O.; IRGENS-MØLLER, L. [Eye injuries can be due to the pot plant *Dieffenbachia*.] *Ugeskrift for Læger* 1984, 146, 3927–3928.

16 VÁCHA, J.; BODNÁR, M. [*Dieffenbachia* and the eye.] *Československá Oftalmologie* 1988, 44, 453–455.

17 LAMPE, K.F.; MCCANN, M. *AMA Handbook of Poisonous and Injurious Plants*. American Medical Association, Chicago, USA. 1985.

18 SELLERS, S.J.; KING, M.; ARONSON, C.E.; MARDEROSIAN, A.D. Toxicologic assessment of *Philodendron oxycardium* Schott (Araceae) in domestic cats. *Veterinary and Human Toxicology* 1978, 20, 92–96.

19 McINTYRE, M.S.; GUEST, J.R.; PORTERFIELD, J.F. *Philodendron* – an infant death. *Clinical Toxicology* 1990, 28, 177–183.

20 MRVOS, R.; DEAN, B.S.; KRENZELOK, E.P. *Philodendron/Dieffenbachia* ingestions: are they a problem? *Veterinary and Human Toxicology* 1990, 32, 369.

ARALIACEAE

1 BOHOSIEWICZ, M. *Toksykologia Weterynaryjna.* Panstwowe Wydawnictwo Rolnicze i Leśne, Warsaw, Poland. 1970, 270.

2 FORSYTH, A.A. *British Poisonous Plants.* HMSO, London, UK. Ministry of Agriculture, Fisheries and Food Bulletin 161, 1968, 67–68 (amended 1979, 68–69).

3 BRÖMEL, J.; ZETTL, K. [Ivy poisoning in a roe deer.] *Praktische Tierarzt* 1986, 67, 967–968.

4 NATIONAL POISONS INFORMATION SERVICE, London, UK. Personal communication.

5 MAHE-QUINIO, M.; ROSSINYOL, G.; FOUCAUD, A. [Fatal poisoning of chickens by ivy seeds.] *Plantes Médicinales et Phytothérapie* 1975, 9, 182–186.

6 CORNEVIN, C. *Des Plantes Vénéneuses.* Librairie de Firmin-Didot, Paris, France. 1887, 402–403.

7 LOVELL, C.R. *Plants and the Skin.* Blackwell Scientific Publications, Oxford, UK. 1993, 143–145.

8 GOLDMAN, L.; PRESTON, R.H.; MUEGEL, H.R. Dermatitis venenata from English ivy (*Hedera helix*). *Archives of Dermatology* 1956, 74, 311–312.

9 BOYLE, J.; HARMAN, R.M.H. Contact dermatitis to *Hedera helix* (common ivy). *Contact Dermatitis* 1985, 12, 111–112.

BERBERIDACEAE

1 FROHNER, D.; PFÄNDER, H.J. *A Colour Atlas of Poisonous Plants.* Wolfe Publishing Ltd, London, UK. 1984, 69–72.

2 NATIONAL POISONS INFORMATION SERVICE, London, UK. Personal communication.

3 MITCHELL, J.; ROOK, A. *Botanical Dermatology. Plants and Plant Products Injurious to the Skin.* Greengrass Ltd, Vancouver, Canada. 1979, 131–132.

BORAGINACEAE

1 GREATOREX, J.C. Some unusual cases of plant poisoning in animals. *Veterinary Record* 1966, 78, 725–727.

2 MANDRYKA, I.I. [*Cynoglossum officinale* (hound's tongue) as a poisonous plant.] *Veterinariya, Moscow* 1979, No.9, 69–70.

3 BAKER, D.C.; SMART, R.A.; RALPHS, M.; MOLYNEUX, R.J. Hound's tongue (*Cynoglossum officinale*) poisoning in a calf. *Journal of the American Veterinary Medical Association* 1989, 194, 929–930.

4 BAKER, D.C.; PFISTER, J.A.; MOLYNEUX, R.J.; KECHELE, P. *Cynoglossum officinale* toxicity in calves. *Journal of Comparative Pathology* 1991, 104, 403–410.

5 KNIGHT, A.P.; KIMBERLING, C.V.; STERMITZ, F.R.; ROBY, M.R. *Cynoglossum officinale* (hound's tongue) – a cause of pyrrolizidine alkaloid poisoning in horses. *Journal of the American Veterinary Medical Association* 1984, 185, 647–650.

6 STEGELMEIER, B.L.; GARDNER, D.R.; MOLYNEUX, R.J.; PFISTER, J.A.; JAMES, L.F. The clinicopathologic changes of *Cynoglossum officinale* (houndstongue) intoxication in horses. In: *Plant-associated Toxins. Agricultural, Phytochemical and Ecological Aspects.* Edited by S.M. Colegate and P.R. Dorling. CAB International, Wallingford, UK. 1994, 297–302.

7 CULVENOR, C.C.J. Paterson's curse and toxic alkaloids. *Search* 1985, 16, 219–223.

8 SHARROCK, A.C. Pyrrolizidine alkaloid poisoning in a horse in New South Wales. *Australian*

Veterinary Journal 1969, 45, 388.

9   SEAMAN, J.T. Pyrrolizidine alkaloid poisoning of horses. *Australian Veterinary Journal* 1978, 54, 150.

10   MÉNDEZ, M.DEL C.; RIET-CORREA, F.; SCHILD, A.L.; GARCIA, J.T.C. [Poisoning by *Echium plantigineum* (Boraginaceae) in cattle in southern Brazil.] *Pesquisa Veterinária Brasileira* 1985, 5, 57–64.

11   ST. GEORGE-GRAMBAUER, T.D. Hepatogenous chronic copper poisoning in sheep in South Australia due to the consumption of *Echium plantagineum* L. (Salvation Jane). *Australian Veterinary Journal* 1962, 38, 288–293.

12   SEAMAN, J.T. Hepatogenous chronic copper poisoning in sheep associated with grazing *Echium plantagineum*. *Australian Veterinary Journal* 1985, 62, 247–248.

13   SEAMAN, J.T. Pyrrolizidine alkaloid poisoning of sheep in New South Wales. *Australian Veterinary Journal* 1987, 64, 164–167.

14   CULVENOR, C.C.J.; JAGO, M.V.; PETERSON, J.E.; SMITH, L.W.; PAYNE, A.L.; CAMPBELL, D.G.; EDGAR, J.A.; FRAHN, J.L. Toxicity of *Echium plantagineum* (Paterson's curse). I. Marginal toxic effects in Merino wethers from long-term feeding. *Australian Journal of Agricultural Research* 1984, 35, 293–304.

15   PETERSON, J.E.; JAGO, M.V. Toxicity of *Echium plantagineum* (Paterson's curse). II. Pyrrolizidine alkaloid poisoning in rats. *Australian Journal of Agricultural Research* 1984, 35, 305–315.

16   MITCHELL J.; ROOK, A. *Botanical Dermatology. Plants and Plant Products Injurious to the Skin.* Greengrass Ltd, Vancouver, Canada, 1979, 140–141.

17   LOVELL, C.R. *Plants and the Skin.* Blackwell Scientific Publications, Oxford, UK. 1993, 43.

18   MATTOCKS, A.R. Toxic pyrrolizidine alkaloids in comfrey. *Lancet* 1980, II, 1136–1137.

19   KEINDORF, A.; KEINDORF, H.J. [Nitrate–nitrite poisoning in pigs caused by the intake of comfrey (*Symphytum asperum*).] *Monatshefte für Veterinärmedizin* 1978, 33, 425–427.

20   ROHRBACH, J.A. Tongue ulcers in cats.*Veterinary Record* 1977, 101, 292.

21   GONNERMANN, H. [Kytta preparations used by veterinary practitioners.] *Tierärztliche Umschau* 1976, 31, 402 and 404.

22   SHIPOCHLIEV, T.A. Pharmacological investigations of some extracts of *Symphytum officinale*. *20th World Veterinary Congress, Thessaloniki, Greece,* 1975, Summaries vol. 1, 166.

23   SCHAUENBERG, P.; PARIS, F. *Guide to Medicinal Plants.* Lutterworth Press, Guildford and London, UK. 1977, 54.

24   JORDAN, M. *A Guide to Wild Plants.* Millington Books Ltd, London, UK. 1976, 106–107.

25   HILLS, L.D. *Comfrey Report. The story of the world's fastest protein builder.* Henry Doubleday Research Association, Bocking, Braintree, Essex, UK. 1975, 98 pp.

26   HIRONO, I.; MORI, H.; HAGA, M. Carcinogenic activity of *Symphytum officinale*. *Journal of the National Cancer Institute* 1978, 61, 865–869.

27   RIDKER, P.M.; McDERMOTT, W.V. Comfrey herb tea and hepatic veno-occlusive disease. *Lancet* 1989, I, 657–658.

28   WINSHIP, K.A. Toxicity of comfrey. *Adverse Drug Reactions and Toxicological Reviews* 1991, 10, 47–59.

29   RIDKER, P.M.; OHKUMA, S.; McDERMOTT, W.V.; TREY, C.; HUXTABLE, R.J. Hepatic venocclusive disease associated with the consumption of pyrrolizidine-containing dietary supplements. *Gastroenterology* 1985, 88, 1050–1054.

30   YEONG, M.L.; SWINBURN D.; KENNEDY, M.; NICHOLSON, G. Hepatic veno-occlusive disease associated with comfrey ingestion. *Journal of Gastroenterology and Hepatology* 1990, 5, 211–214.

31   WESTON, C.F.M.; COOPER, B.T.; DAVIES, J.D.; LEVINE, D.F. Veno-occlusive disease of the liver secondary to ingestion of comfrey. *British Medical Journal* 1987, 295, 183.

32   ROITMAN, J.N. Comfrey and liver damage. *Lancet* 1981, I, 944.

33   HUXTABLE, R.J. Human health implications of pyrrolizidine alkaloids and herbs containing them. In: *Toxicants of Plant Origin. Volume I. Alkaloids.* Edited by P.R. Cheeke. CRC Press Inc., Boca

Raton, Florida, USA. 1989, 57–61.

34 YEONG, M.L.; CLARK, S.P.; WARING, J.M.; WILSON, R.D.; WAKEFIELD, ST J. The effects of comfrey derived pyrrolizidine alkaloids on rat liver. *Pathology* 1991, 23, 35–38.

35 MINISTRY OF AGRICULTURE, FISHERIES AND FOOD. Food Safety Directorate. News Release, 2 March, 1993.

36 MINISTRY OF AGRICULTURE, FISHERIES AND FOOD. Food Safety Directorate. Foodsense Factsheet 1993, No.14.

37 BRAUCHLI, J.; LÜTHY, J.; ZWEIFEL, U.; SCHLATTER, C. Pyrrolizidine alkaloids from *Symphytum officinale* L. and their percutaneous absorption in rats. *Experientia* 1982, 38, 1085–1087.

38 MITCHELL, J.; ROOK, A. *Botanical Dermatology. Plants and Plant Products Injurious to the Skin.* Greengrass Ltd, Vancouver, Canada. 1979, 140.

39 LOVELL, C.R. *Plants and the Skin.* Blackwell Scientific Publications, Oxford, UK. 1993, 43.

40 BULL, L.B.; ROGERS, E.S.; KEAST, J.C.; DICK, A.T. *Heliotropium* poisoning in cattle. *Australian Veterinary Journal* 1961, 37, 37–43.

41 HARPER, P.A.W.; WALKER, K.H.; KRAHENBUHL, R.E.; CHRISTIE, B.M. Pyrrolizidine alkaloid poisoning in calves due to contamination of straw by *Heliotropium europeum. Australian Veterinary Journal* 1985, 62, 382–383.

42 BULL, L.B.; DICK, A.T.; KEAST, J.C.; EDGAR, G. An experimental investigation of the hepatotoxic and other effects on sheep of consumption of *Heliotropium europaeum* L.: heliotrope poisoning of sheep. *Australian Journal of Agricultural Research* 1956, 7, 281–332.

43 SHLOSBERG, A.; EGYED, M.N.; NOBEL, T.A.; KLOPFER, U.; PERL, S.; YAKOBSON, B.; ABRAHAMSON, M.; WEINBERG, H. First cases in Israel of chronic poisoning in calves caused by ingestion of *Heliotropium europaeum.* 1. Epidemiological investigations. *Refuah Veterinarith* 1982, 39, 63–64.

44 BRUCKSTEIN, S.; TROMP, A.M.; PERL, S. *Heliotropium* poisoning. *Israel Journal of Veterinary Medicine* 1996, 51, 75–77.

45 GAUL, K.L.; GALLAHER, P.F.; REYES, D.; STASI, S.; EDGAR, J. Poisoning of pigs and poultry by stock feed contaminated with heliotrope seed. In: *Plant-associated Toxins. Agricultural, Phytochemical and Ecological Aspects.* Edited by S.M. Colegate and P.R. Dorling. CAB International, Wallingford, UK. 1994, 137–142.

BUXACEAE

1 VÖLKER, R. *Lehrbuch der Toxikologie für Tierärzte.* (Fröhner). Ferdinand Enke Verlag, Stuttgart, Germany. 6th Edition, 1950, 322–323.

2 FROHNE, D.; PFÄNDER, H.J. *A Colour Atlas of Poisonous Plants.* Wolfe Publishing Ltd, London, UK. 1984, 74–75.

3 FORSYTH, A.A. *British Poisonous Plants.* HMSO, London, UK. Ministry of Agriculture, Fisheries and Food Bulletin 161, 1968, 57–58 (amended 1979, 59–60).

4 VAN SOEST, H.; GOTINK, W.M.; VAN DEN VOOREN, L.J. [Box poisoning in pigs and cattle.] *Tijdschrift voor Diergeneeskunde* 1965, 90, 387–389.

5 BASTIEN, A.; GRISVARD, M.; JEAN-BLAIN, C.; ROUX, M. [Poisoning of young cattle by box.] *Bulletin de la Societé des Sciences Vétérinaires et de Médecine Comparée de Lyon* 1973, 75, 289–290.

6 CAMY, G.; LEVEILLE, J.L.; NEVERS, B. [Case report. Poisoning of cattle with box (*Buxus sempervirens*).] *Point Vétérinaire* 1986, 18, 203–204.

7 KRÜGER, A.; MATSCHULLAT, G. [Box poisoning in pigs.] *Praktische Tierarzt* 1970, 51, 235–236.

8 SPOERKE, D.G.; SMOLINSKE, S.C. *Toxicity of Houseplants.* CRC Press Inc., Boca Raton, Florida, USA. 1990, 86–87.

CACTACEAE

1   SCHULTES, R.E.; HOFMANN, A. *The Botany and Chemistry of Hallucinogens.* Charles C. Thomas, Springfield, Illinois, USA. 1980, 192–222.

2   TURNER, N.J.; SZCZAWINSKI, A.F. *Common Poisonous Plants and Mushrooms of North America.* Timber Press, Portland, Oregon, USA. 1991 (reprinted 1995), 127–128.

CAMPANULACEAE

1   DOLLAHITE, J.W.; ALLEN, T.J. Poisoning of cattle, sheep and goats with *Lobelia* and *Centaurium* species. *Southwestern Veterinarian* 1962, 15, 126–130.

2   CORNEVIN, C. *Des Plantes Vénéneuses.* Librairie de Firmin-Didot, Paris, France. 1887, 486–487.

3   LAMPE, K.F.; McCANN, M.A. *AMA Handbook of Poisonous and Injurious Plants.* American Medical Association, Chicago, USA. 1985, 108–109.

4   MITCHELL, J.; ROOK, A. *Botanical Dermatology. Plants and Plant Products Injurious to the Skin.* Greengrass Ltd, Vancouver, Canada. 1979, 150–151.

5   TURNER, N.J.; SZCZAWINSKI, A.F. *Common Poisonous Plants and Mushrooms of North America.* Timber Press, Portland, Oregon, USA. 1991 (reprinted 1995), 114–115, 184–185.

CANNABACEAE

1   FLORENCE, A. (Chairman of meeting). Should cannabis be prescribed on the NHS? *Pharmaceutical Journal* 1996, 256, 457.

2   CARDASSIS, J. [Poisoning of horses by *Cannabis indica.*] *Recueil de Médecine Vétérinaire* 1951, 127, 971–973.

3   FRYE, F.L. Acute cannabis intoxication in a pup. *Journal of the American Veterinary Medical Association* 1968, 152, 472.

4   MERIWETHER, W.F. Acute marijuana toxicity in a dog. (A case report). *Veterinary Medicine* 1969, 64, 577–578.

5   JONES, D.L. A case of canine cannabis ingestion. *New Zealand Veterinary Journal* 1978, 26, 135–136.

6   GODBOLD, J.C.; HAWKINS, B.J.; WOODWARD, M.G. Acute oral marijuana poisoning in the dog. *Journal of the American Veterinary Medical Association* 1979, 175, 1101–1102.

7   CROW, S.E.; SOKOLOWSKI, V. Marijuana intoxication. *Journal of the American Veterinary Medical Association* 1980, 176, 388.

8   FROST, R.C. Marijuana toxaemia. *Veterinary Record* 1983, 112, 441.

9   HENNEY, S.N.; COLEMAN, M.J. Canine cannabis intoxication. *Veterinary Record* 1984, 114, 436.

10 VALENTINE, J. Unusual poisoning in a dog. *Veterinary Record* 1992, 130, 307.

11 GODWIN, R.L.G. Unusual poisoning in a dog. *Veterinary Record* 1992, 130, 335.

12 DUMONCEAUX, G.A.; BEASLEY, V.R. Emergency treatments for police dogs used for illicit drug detection. *Journal of the American Veterinary Medical Association* 1990, 197, 185–187.

13 THOMPSON, G.R.; ROSENKRANTZ, H.; SCHAEPPI, U.H.; BRAUDE, M.C. Comparison of acute oral toxicity of cannabinoids in rats, dogs and monkeys. *Toxicology and Applied Pharmacology* 1973, 25, 363–372.

14 NATIONAL POISONS INFORMATION SERVICE, London, UK. Personal communication.

15 NICHOLI, A.M. The nontherapeutic use of psychoactive drugs. *New England Journal of Medicine* 1983, 308, 925–933.

16 MAYKUT, M.O. Health consequences of acute and chronic marihuana use. *Progress in Neuropsychopharmacology & Biological Psychiatry* 1985, 9, 209–238.

17 NAHAS, G.; LATOUR, C. The human toxicity of marijuana. *Medical Journal of Australia* 1992, 156,

495–497.

18 PEREZ-REYES, M.; WALL, M.E. Presence of Δ^9-tetrahydrocannibinol in human milk. *New England Journal of Medicine* 1982, 307, 819–820.

19 ASHTON, C.H.; YOUNG, A.H. Decriminalisation of cannabis. (Correspondence). *Lancet* 1995, 346, 1708–1709.

20 McEVEDY, C.; McPHILLIPS, M.A. Decriminalisation of cannabis. (Correspondence). *Lancet* 1995, 346, 1709.

21 JOHNSON, D.; CONRADI, A.; McGUIGAN, M. Hashish ingestion in toddlers. *Veterinary and Human Toxicology* 1991, 33, 393.

CAPRIFOLIACEAE

1 NATIONAL POISONS INFORMATION SERVICE, London, UK. Personal communication.

2 MITCHELL, J.; ROOK, A. *Botanical Dermatology. Plants and Plant Products Injurious to the Skin.* Greengrass Ltd, Vancouver, Canada. 1979, 158.

3 FROHNE. D.; PFÄNDER, H.J. *A Colour Atlas of Poisonous Plants.* Wolfe Publishing Ltd, London, UK. 1984, 76–80.

4 RÎPEANU, M. [Observations on some important cases of poisoning in animals.] *Revista de Zootehnie şi Medicină Veterinară* 1963, 13, No.12, 67–68.

5 KINGSBURY, J.M. *Poisonous Plants of the United States and Canada.* Prentice-Hall, Inc., New Jersey, USA. 1964, 389–390.

6 CORNEVIN, C. *Des Plantes Vénéneuses.* Librairie de Firmin-Didot, Paris, France. 1887, 406.

7 KUNITZ, S.; MELTON, R.J.; UPDYKE, T.; BREEDLOVE, D.; WERNER, S.B. Poisoning from elderberry juice. *Journal of the American Medical Association* 1984, 251, 2075.

8 POGORZELSKI, E. Formation of cyanide as a product of decomposition of cyanogenic glycosides in the treatment of elderberry fruit(*Sambucus nigra*). *Journal of the Science of Food and Agriculture* 1982, 33, 496–498.

9 SZAUFER, M.; KOWALEWSKI, Z.; PHILLIPSON, J.D. Chelidonine from *Symphoricarpos albus*. *Phytochemistry* 1978, 17, 1446–1447.

10 RUYLE, G.B.; BONN, J.E. Forage use by cattle and sheep grazing separately and together on summer range in southwestern Utah. *Journal of Range Management* 1985, 38, 299–302.

11 SIEGERS, C.P. [Poisonous plants in our environment. I. Poisonings by plants.] *Zeitschrift für Allgemeinmedizin* 1978, 54, 1151–1158.

12 AMYOT, T.E. Poisoning by snowberries. *British Medical Journal* 1885, 1, 986.

13 LEWIS, W.H. Snowberry (*Symphoricarpos*) poisoning in children. *Journal of the American Medical Association* 1979 242, 2663.

CARYOPHYLLACEAE

1 CORNEVIN, C. *Des Plantes Vénéneuses.* Librairie de Firmin-Didot, Paris, France. 1887, 248–261.

2 FORSYTH, A.A. *British Poisonous Plants.* HMSO, London, UK. Ministry of Agriculture, Fisheries and Food Bulletin 161, 1968, 47 (amended 1979, 47–50).

3 BUBIEŃ, Z.; KOTZ, J. [Corn cockle poisoning in domestic animals.] *Medycyna Weterynaryjna* 1965, 21, 458–460.

4 KOTZ, J. [Morphology and pathogenesis of corn cockle poisoning in poultry. I. History.] *Medycyna Weterynaryjna* 1964, 20, 200–204.

5 KOTZ, J. [Morphology and pathogenesis of corn cockle poisoning in poultry. II. III. IV.] *Medycyna Weterynaryjna* 1965, 21, 143–150, 520–524, 730–734.

6 BALLARINI, G. [*Agrostemma githago* poisoning in cattle.] *Atti della Società Italiana de Buiatria* 1985,

17, 187–190.

7   BIRK, Y.; PERI, I. Saponins. In: *Toxic Constituents of Plant Foodstuffs*. Edited by I.E. Liener. Academic Press, New York and London. 2nd Edition. 1980, 161–182.

8   PAMMEL, L.H. *A Manual of Poisonous Plants*. Torch Press, Cedar Rapids, Iowa, USA. 1911 (reprinted 1992), 442–444.

9   LONG, H.C. *Plants Poisonous to Live Stock*. Cambridge University Press, Cambridge, UK. 1917, 101–102.

CELASTRACEAE

1   CORNEVIN, C. *Des Plantes Vénéneuses*. Librairie de Firmin-Didot, Paris, France. 1887, 271–272.

2   ANHARS'KA, M.A.; BEZRUK, P.H. [Some data on the general pharmacology of glycoside SK.] *Farmatsevtychnyi Zhurnal* 1968, 23, 68–72.

3   FORSYTH, A.A. *British Poisonous Plants*. HMSO, London, UK. Ministry of Agriculture, Fisheries and Food Bulletin 161, 1968, 56–57 (amended 1979, 58–59).

4   GESSNER, O. [Fatal poisoning of horses by *Euonymus europaeus* L.] *Berliner und Münchener Tierärztliche Wochenschrift* 1943, 7/8, 47–48.

5   VAN OETTINGEN, W.F. *Poisoning. A Guide to Clinical Diagnosis and Treatment*. W.B. Saunders Company, Philadelphia and London. 2nd Edition, 1958, 361.

6   MAITAI, C.K. The toxicity of the plant *Catha edulis* in rats. *Toxicon* 1977, 15, 363–366.

CHENOPODIACEAE

1   SIMESEN, M.G.; KONGGARD, S.P. [Experimental investigations on fodder beet poisoning in cattle.] *Nordisk Veterinær Medizin* 1970, 22, 174–185.

2   WILLIAMS, V.J.; COUP, M.R. Preliminary studies on the toxicity of fodder beet to sheep. *New Zealand Veterinary Journal* 1959, 7, 8–14.

3   PINKIEWICZ, E.; MADEJ, E.; SAMOREK, M. [Fresh fodder beet as a cause of bovine ketosis.] Proceedings of the 17th World Veterinary Congress, Hannover 1963, 2, 1377–1378.

4   POP, M. [Mass poisoning of cattle with sugar beet tops.] *Lucrarile Stiintifice Institutul Agronomic Cluj, Serie Medicine Veterinaria Zootehnia* 1965, 21, 105–110.

5   ALEKSEEV, N.P. [The parathyroids in mineral metabolism of bulls fattened on beet pulp.] *Sel'skokhozyaistvennaya Biologiya* 1976, 11, 96–102.

6   O'MOORE, L.B. The nitrate hazard in freshly lifted mangolds. *Irish Veterinary Journal* 1955, 9, 292–293.

7   MINISTRY OF AGRICULTURE, FISHERIES AND FOOD. Bulky feeds for dairy cows. Advisory Leaflet No.524, 1977, 15 pp.

8   KINGSBURY, J.M. *Poisonous Plants of the United States and Canada*. Prentice-Hall Inc., New Jersey, USA. 1964, 233.

9   SAVAGE, A. Nitrate poisoning from sugar beet tops. *Canadian Journal of Comparative Medicine* 1949, 13, 9–10.

10 FORSYTH, A.A. *British Poisonous Plants*. HMSO, London, UK. Ministry of Agriculture, Fisheries and Food Bulletin 161, 1968, 52 (amended 1979, 54).

11 KORUKOV, G.; POPOV, L. [Poisoning of hens by beet.] *Veterinarna Sbirka* 1984, 82, No.7, 31–32.

12 JAMES, L.F. Oxalate poisoning in livestock. In: *Effects of Poisonous Plants on Livestock*. Academic Press, New York and London. 1978, 139–145.

13 CONNOR, H.E. *The Poisonous Plants in New Zealand*. Bulletin 99, New Zealand Department of Scientific and Industrial Research. 2nd Edition. 1977, 25–26.

14 GORIŠEK, J. [Metabolic disorders in dairy cows due to the feeding of sugar beet leaves.]

Proceedings of the 17th World Veterinary Congress, Hannover 1963, 2, 1343–1344.

15 GORIŠEK, J. [Blood coagulation and calcium content of blood and urine in cows fed sugar beet leaves.] *Veterinarski Arhiv* 1960, 30, 300–306.

16 GARCIA PARTIDA, P.; ALONSO, A.; PRIETO MONTAÑA, F. [Haematuria in cattle from ingesting sugar beet tops.] Proceedings of the 13th World Congress on Diseases of Cattle, Durban, South Africa 1984, 2, 691–694.

17 JONAS, K. [Feeding of heavily mildewed beet leaves to dairy cows and breeding sows.] *Monatshefte für Veterinärmedizin* 1986, 41, 341–344.

18 SUKHONOS, V.P.; PETRENKO, O.F. [Composition of articular cartilage in young bulls fattened on beet pulp.] *Veterinaria, Moscow* 1987, No.11, 65–69.

19 ZDELAR, F.; MITIN, V.; BIŠĆAN, J.; TRANGER, M. [Goitre of cattle in Croatia. IV. Effect of fresh sugar beet leaves on thyroid function in dairy cows.] *Veterinarski Arhiv* 1967, 37, 208–218.

20 MOCSY, J. [Poisoning of horses by old sugarbeet tops.] *Állatorvosok Közleményei* 1936, 33, 23–25.

21 HIBBS, C.M. Cyanide and nitrate toxicoses of cattle. *Veterinary and Human Toxicology* 1979, 21, 401–403.

22 LIEBENOW, H. [*Solanum nigrum* L. and other weeds as nitrate-containing plants – their nitrate content.] *Wissenschaftliche Zeitschrift der Humboldt-Universität zu Berlin* 1970, 19, 73–80.

23 MADDEN, F.J. The effect of fat hen (*Chenopodium album*) on young lambs in dry conditions. *Institute of Inspectors of Stock of New South Wales Year Book* 1943, 25.

24 HERWEIJER, C.H.; DEN HOUTER, L.F. Poisoning due to fat hen (*Chenopodium album*) in sheep. *Netherlands Journal of Veterinary Science* 1971, 4, 52–54.

25 PEARCE, O.D. Drought in the West. (*Brassica campestris* and *Chenopodium album* poisoning in cattle). *Veterinary Record* 1975, 97, 60.

26 ANONYMOUS. Oxalate poisoning in cows (*Chenopodium album*). New Zealand Department of Agriculture. Annual Report for 1950–51, 53–54.

27 GRZYBOWSKI, M.D. A peculiar, pellagra-like skin sensitisation to light in starving persons. *British Journal of Dermatology* 1948, 60, 410–415.

28 SEBASTYŃSKI, T. [A case of a pellagra-like condition after consumption of *Chenopodium*.] *Polski Tygodnik Lekarski* 1960, 15, 688–689.

29 SCHEUER-KARPIN, R. Poisoning by food plants. *Lancet* 1948, I, 574–575.

COMPOSITAE

1 THIVIERGE, G. Granular stomatitis in dogs due to burdock. *Canadian Veterinary Journal* 1973, 14, 96–97.

2 STOJANOVIĆ, D. [Burdock – cause of mortality in a pheasantry in the Požarevac region.] *Veterinarski Glasnik* 1971, 25, 707.

3 RHOADS, P.M.; TONG, T.G.; BANNER, W.; ANDERSON, R. Anticholinergic poisonings associated with commercial burdock root tea. *Journal of Toxicology. Clinical Toxicology* 1984, 22, 581–584.

4 CRAIG, A.M.; BLYTHE, L.L.; ROY, D.N.; SPENCER, P.S. Detection and isolation of neurotoxins from yellow star thistle (*Centaurea solstitialis*), the cause of nigropallidial encephalomalacia. In: *Plant-associated Toxins. Agricultural, Phytochemical and Ecological Aspects*. Edited by S.M. Colegate and P.R. Dorling. CAB International, Wallingford, UK. 1994, 257–262.

5 CORDY, D.R. *Centaurea* species and equine nigropallidal encephalomalacia. In: *Effects of Poisonous Plants on Livestock*. Edited by R.F. Keeler, K.R. Van Kampen and L.F. James. Academic Press, New York and London. 1978, 327–336.

6 CLAPHAM, A.R.; TUTIN, T.G.; MOORE, D.M. *Flora of the British Isles*. Cambridge University Press, Cambridge, UK. 3rd Edition, 1987, 490.

7 BUBIEŃ, Z.; WACHNIK, Z.; ZUCHOWSKI, A. [Chicory root poisoning in heifers.] *Medycyna Weterynaryjna* 1962, 18, 603–605.

8 FRITZSCH, R. [Food poisoning in cattle from fodder plants: sunflower, beet leaves, *Glyceria aquatica.*] *Monatshefte für Veterinärmedizin* 1966, 21, 327–331.

9 TOMOV, A. [Poisoning of cattle with wild *Helianthus* species.] *Veterinariya, Moscow* 1965, 42, No.2, 113.

10 GARBULIŃSKI, T.; BUBIEŃ, Z.; WEGRZYNOWICZ, R.; KOTZ, J. [Toxicity of helanin from *Inula helenium*, for laboratory animals.] *Zeszyty Naukowe Wyzszej Szkoly Rolniczej we Wroclawiu, Weterynaria* 1963, 15, 207–214.

11 ULBRICH, M.; LORENZ, H.; RITTENBACH, P.; ROSSOW, N.; VOIGT, O. [*Inula conyza* as a cause of mass poisoning among cattle.] *Monatshefte für Veterinärmedizin* 1966, 21, 896–902.

12 VOCKRODT, H. [Plant poisoning in farm animals (*Senecio jacobaea* and *Inula conyza*) and its prevention.] *Monatshefte für Veterinärmedizin* 1973, 28, 59–62.

13 MEADLY, G.R.W. Weeds of Western Australia. Stinkwort (*Inula graveolens* Desf.). *Journal of the Department of Agriculture, Western Australia* 1965, 6, 434–437.

14 MATTOCKS, A.R. *Chemistry and Toxicology of Pyrrolizidine Alkaloids.* Academic Press, London, UK. 1986, 393 pp.

15 ANONYMOUS. *Veterinary Investigation Diagnostic Analysis III 1992 and 1985–92.* Central Veterinary Laboratory, Weybridge, Surrey, UK. 1993.

16 ANONYMOUS. *Veterinary Investigation Diagnostic Analysis III 1994 and 1987–94.* Central Veterinary Laboratory, Weybridge, Surrey, UK. 1995.

17 MOLYNEUX, R.J.; JOHNSON, A.E.; STUART, L.D. Delayed manifestation of *Senecio*-induced pyrrolizidine alkaloidosis in cattle: case reports. *Veterinary and Human Toxicology* 1988, 30, 201–205.

18 TILT, S.E. Ragwort toxicosis in a heifer. *Canadian Veterinary Journal* 1969, 10, 302–306.

19 STOCKMAN, S. Poisoning of cattle with British ragwort. *Journal of Comparative Pathology and Therapeutics* 1917, 30, 131–134.

20 CANDRIAN, U.; LÜTHY, J.; SCHMID, P.; SCHLATTER, C.; GALLASZ, E. Stability of pyrrolizidine alkaloids in hay and silage. *Journal of Agricultural and Food Chemistry* 1984, 32, 935–937.

21 LEWANDOWSKI, L.; KUTROWSKI, W. [*Senecio jacobaea* poisoning in heifers.] *Medycyna Weterynaryjna* 1957, 15, 518.

22 CHEEKE, P.R. Toxicity and metabolism of pyrrolizidine alkaloids. *Journal of Animal Science* 1988, 66, 2343–2350.

23 MORTIMER, P.H.; WHITE, E.P. Toxicity of some composite (*Senecio*) weeds. In: *Proceedings of the 28th New Zealand Weed and Pest Control Conference* 1975, 88–91.

24 HARDING, J.D.J.; LEWIS, G.; DONE, J.T.; ALLCROFT, R. Experimental poisoning by *Senecio jacobaea* in pigs. *Pathologia Veterinaria* 1964, 1, 204–220.

25 CRAIG, A.M.; BLYTHE, L.L.; LASSEN, E.D.; SLIZESKI, M.L. Resistance of sheep to pyrrolizidine alkaloids. *Israel Journal of Veterinary Medicine* 1986, 42, 376–384.

26 BETTERIDGE, K.; COSTALL, D.A.; HUTCHING, S.M.; DEVANTIER, B.P.; LIU, Y. Ragwort (*Senecio jacobaea*) control by sheep in a hill country bull beef system. In: *Proceedings of the Forty Seventh New Zealand Plant Protection Conference, Waitangi, New Zealand.* 1994, 53–57.

27 DEAN, R.E.; WINWARD, A.H. An investigation into the possibility of tansy ragwort poisoning of black-tailed deer. *Journal of Wildlife Diseases* 1974, 10, 166–169.

28 PIERSON, M.L.; CHEEKE, P.R.; DICKINSON, E.O. Resistance of the rabbit to dietary pyrrolizidine (*Senecio*) alkaloid. *Research Communications in Chemical Pathology and Pharmacology* 1977, 16, 561–564.

29 SWICK, R.A. *Senecio jacobaea*: toxicity and effects on mineral metabolism in animals. *Dissertation*

Abstracts International 1982, 43, 3B.

30 DUBY, G.D. Tansy ragwort: a toxic threat to livestock. *Modern Veterinary Practice* 1975, 56, 185–188.

31 PEARSON, E.G. Clinical manifestations of tansy ragwort poisoning. *Modern Veterinary Practice* 1977, 58, 421–424.

32 ELCOCK, L.; OEHME, F.W. *Senecio* poisoning in horses: a summary. *Veterinary and Human Toxicology* 1982, 24, 122–123.

33 McGINNESS, J.P. *Senecio jacobaea* as a cause of hepatic encephalopathy. *California Veterinarian* 1980, 34, 20–22.

34 FORD, E.J.H. Clinical aspects of ragwort poisoning in horses. *Veterinary Annual* 1973, 14, 86–88.

35 JOHNSON, A.E. Tolerance of cattle to tansy ragwort (*Senecio jacobaea*). *American Journal of Veterinary Research* 1978, 39, 1542–1544.

36 GILES, C.J. Outbreak of ragwort (*Senecio jacobaea*) poisoning in horses. *Equine Veterinary Journal* 1983, 15, 248–250.

37 LEYLAND, A. Ragwort poisoning in horses. *Veterinary Record* 1985, 117, 479.

38 MILNE, E.M.; POGSON, D.M.; DOXEY, D.L. Secondary gastric impaction associated with ragwort poisoning in three ponies. *Veterinary Record* 1990, 126, 502–504.

39 JOHNSON, A.E.; SMART, R.A. Effects on cattle and their calves of tansy ragwort (*Senecio jacobaea*) fed in early gestation. *American Journal of Veterinary Research* 1983, 44, 1215–1219.

40 SYNGE, B.A.; STEPHEN, F.B. Delayed ragwort poisoning associated with lactation stress in cows. *Veterinary Record* 1993, 132, 327.

41 LESSARD, P.; WILSON, W.D.; OLANDER, H.J.; ROGERS, Q.R.; MENDEL, V.E. Clinicopathologic study of horses surviving pyrrolizidine alkaloid (*Senecio vulgaris*) toxicosis. *American Journal of Veterinary Research* 1986, 47, 1776–1780.

42 HOOPER, P.T. Spongy degeneration in the central nervous system of domestic animals. III. Occurrence and pathogenesis – hepatocerebral disease caused by hyperammonaemia. *Acta Neuropathologica* 1975, 31, 343–351.

43 FORSYTH, A.A. *British Poisonous Plants*. HMSO, London, UK. Ministry of Agriculture, Fisheries and Food Bulletin 161, 1968, 97–101 (amended 1979, 98–102).

44 GOEGER, D.E.; CHEEKE, P.R.; SCHMITZ, J.A.; BUHLER, D.R. Toxicity of tansy ragwort (*Senecio jacobaea*) to goats. *American Journal of Veterinary Research* 1982, 43, 252–254.

45 CHEEKE, P.R. A review of the functional and evolutionary roles of the liver in the detoxification of poisonous plants, with special reference to pyrrolizidine alkaloids. *Veterinary and Human Toxicology* 1994, 36, 240–247.

46 ANONYMOUS. Ovine bacteria protect against ragwort toxins. *Veterinary Record* 1996, 139, 104.

47 GOPINATH, C.; FORD, E.J.H. The effect of ragwort (*Senecio jacobaea*) on the liver of the domestic fowl (*Gallus domesticus*): a histopathological and enzyme histochemical study. *British Poultry Science* 1977, 18, 137–141.

48 MENDEL, V.E.; WITT, M.R.; GITCHELL, B.S.; GRIBBLE, D.N.; ROGERS, Q.R.; SEGALL, H.J.; KNIGHT, H.D. Pyrrolizidine alkaloid-induced liver disease in horses: an early diagnosis. *American Journal of Veterinary Research* 1988, 49, 572–578.

49 CRAIG, A.M.; PEARSON, E.G.; MEYER, C.; SCHMITZ, J.A. Serum liver enzyme and histopathologic changes in calves with chronic and chronic-delayed *Senecio jacobaea* toxicosis. *American Journal of Veterinary Research* 1991, 52, 1969–1978.

50 BUCKMASTER, G.W.; CHEEKE, P.R.; SHULL, L.R. Pyrrolizidine alkaloid poisoning in rats: protective effects of dietary cysteine. *Journal of Animal Science* 1976, 43, 464–473.

51 DICKINSON, J.O.; COOKE, M.P.; KING, R.R.; MOHAMED, P.A. Milk transfer of pyrrolizidine alkaloids in cattle. *Journal of the American Veterinary Medical Association* 1976, 169, 1192–1196.

52 MIRANDA, C.L.; CHEEKE, P.R.; GOEGER, D.E.; BUHLER, D.R. Effect of consumption of milk from

goats fed *Senecio jacobaea* on hepatic drug metabolising enzyme activities in rats. *Toxicology Letters* 1981, 8, 343–347.

53 DEINZER, M.L.; THOMSON, P.A.; BURGETT, D.M.; ISAACSON, D.L. Pyrrolizidine alkaloids: their occurrence in honey from tansy ragwort (*Senecio jacobaea* L.). *Science, USA* 1977, 195, 497–499.

54 HOWES, F.N. *Plants and Beekeeping.* Faber and Faber, London, UK. 1979, 25.

55 FORBES, J.C. Ragwort survey in north-east Scotland. The Scottish Agricultural Colleges Research and Development Note No.5, 1982.

56 MINISTRY OF AGRICULTURE, FISHERIES AND FOOD. Weed control – Ragwort. AW51. HMSO, London, UK. 1976 (amended 1978).

57 IRVINE, H.M.; FORBES, J.C.; DRAPER, S.R. Effect of 2,4-D on the water-soluble carbohydrate content of ragwort (*Senecio jacobaea* L.) leaves. *Weed Research* 1977, 17, 169–172.

58 MACADAM, J.F. Some poisonous plants of the north-west (of New South Wales). *Agricultural Gazette, New South Wales* 1966, 77, 73–78.

59 URROZ, I.G.; MERLO, I.; LAKSMAN, G.M.; GALLO, G.G. [Toxicity of milk thistle (*Silybum marianum*) for cattle.] *Revista de la Facultad de Ciencias Veterinarias de La Plata* 1960, 2, 93–103.

60 REYNOSO CASTRO, H.W.; SELFERO AUDICO, N. [Poisoning of cattle by the thistle *Silybum marianum*: use of methylene blue in high concentration.] *Gaceta Veterinaria* 1963, 25, 429–434.

61 STUART, B.P.; COLE, R.J.; GOSSER, H.S. Cocklebur (*Xanthium strumarium*, L. var. *strumarium*) intoxication in swine: review and redefinition of the toxic principle. *Veterinary Pathology* 1981, 18, 368–383.

62 KINGSBURY, J.M. *Poisonous Plants of the United States and Canada.* Prentice-Hall Inc., New Jersey, USA. 1964, 440–442.

63 OELKERS, S.; OEHME, F. Cocklebur poisoning in swine. *Bovine Practice* 1982, 3, 11–14.

64 KRUSTEV, E. [An outbreak of *Xanthium strumarium* L. poisoning in pigs.] *Izvestiya na Instituta za Nezarazni Bolesti i Zookhigiena, Sofia* 1962, 2, 133–135.

65 MARTIN, T.; STAIR, E.L.; DAWSON, L. Cocklebur poisoning in cattle. *Journal of the American Veterinary Medical Association* 1986, 189, 562–563.

66 MARTIN, T.; JOHNSON, B.J.; SANGIAH, S.; BURROWS, G.E. Experimental cocklebur (*Xanthium strumarium*) intoxication in calves. In: *Poisonous Plants. Proceedings of the Third International Symposium.* Edited by L.F. James et al. Iowa State University Press, Ames, USA. 1992, 489–494.

67 GOODWIN, M.A.; MALLINSON, E.T.; BROWN, J.; PLAYER, E.C.; LATIMER, K.S.; DALE, N.; SHAFF, W.V.; DICKSON, T.G. Toxicological pathology of cockleburs (*Xanthium* spp.) for broiler chickens. *Avian Diseases* 1992, 36, 444–446.

68 HIBBS, C.M. Cyanide and nitrate toxicoses of cattle. *Veterinary and Human Toxicology* 1979, 21, 401–403.

69 LOVELL, C.R. *Plants and the Skin.* Blackwell Scientific Publications, Oxford, UK. 1993, 148–181.

CONVOLVULACEAE

1 TRAUB-DARGATZ, J.L.; SCHULTHEISS, P.C.; KIPER, M.L.; STASHAK, T.S.; WRIGLEY, R.; SCHLIPF, J.; APPLEHANS, F.M. Intestinal fibrosis with partial obstruction in five horses and two ponies. *Journal of the American Veterinary Medical Association* 1992, 201, 603–607.

2 SCHULTHEISS, P.C.; KNIGHT, A.P.; TRAUB-DARGATZ, J.L.; TODD, F.G.; STERMITZ, F.R. Toxicity of field bindweed (*Convolvulus arvensis*) to mice. *Veterinary and Human Toxicology* 1995, 37, 452–454.

3 TODD, F.G.; STERMITZ, F.R.; SCHULTHEISS, P.; KNIGHT, A.P.; TRAUB-DARGATZ, J. Tropane alkaloids and toxicity of *Convolvulus arvensis. Phytochemistry* 1995, 39, 301–303.

4 AZARYAN, Kh.A. [*Cuscuta* poisoning in horses and control measures.] *Veterinariya, Moscow* 1955, 32, No.6, 75–76.

5   IBRAGIMOV, Kh.Z.; KHABIEV, M.S.; BABAEV, P.B.; TOVMASYAN, D.A. [*Plant poisoning of farm animals in Uzbekistan.*] Izdatel'stvo "Fan", Tashkent, USSR. 1979, 59–61.

6   FRIEDMAN, M.; DAO, L.; GUMBMANN, M.R. Ergot alkaloids and chlorogenic acid content in different varieties of morning-glory (*Ipomoea* spp.) seeds. *Journal of Agricultural and Food Chemistry* 1989, 37, 708–712.

7   TIRKEY, K.; YADAVA, K.P.; MANDAL, T.K.; BANERJEE, N.C. Pharmacological study of *Ipomoea carnea*. *Indian Veterinary Journal* 1988, 65, 206–210.

8   TIRKEY, K.; YADAVA, K.P.; JHA, G.J.; BANERJEE, N.C. Effect of feeding *Ipomoea carnea* leaves on goats. *Indian Journal of Animal Sciences* 1987, 57, 863–866.

9   DAMIR, H.A.; ADAM, S.E.I.; TARTOUR, G. The effects of *Ipomoea carnea* on goats and sheep. *Veterinary and Human Toxicology* 1987, 29, 316–319.

10   DUGAN, G.M.; GUMBMANN, M.R Toxicological evaluation of morning glory seed: subchronic 90-day feeding study. *Food and Chemical Toxicology* 1990, 28, 553–559.

11   NATIONAL POISONS INFORMATION SERVICE, London, UK. Personal communication.

12   TAMPION, J. *Dangerous Plants*. David and Charles, Newton Abbot, UK. 1977, 35.

CRASSULACEAE

1   CLARKE, E.G.C.; CLARKE, M.L. *Veterinary Toxicology*. Baillière Tindall, London, UK. 1975, 294.

2   CORNEVIN, C. *Des Plantes Vénéneuses*. Librairie de Firmin-Didot, Paris, France.1887, 400–402.

3   VÉGH, E. [Ornamental plant (*Sedum spectabile*) poisoning in pigs.] *Magyar Állatorvosok Lapja* 1985, 40, 505–506.

4   MCBARRON, E.J. *Medical and Veterinary Aspects of Plant Poisons in New South Wales*. Department of Agriculture, New South Wales, Australia. 1976, 127.

CRUCIFERAE

1   TOOKEY, H.L.; VANETTEN, C.H.; DAXENBICHLER, M.E. Glucosinolates. In: *Toxic Constituents of Plant Foodstuffs*. Edited by I.E. Liener. Academic Press, New York and London. 2nd Edition. 1980, 103–142.

2   VANETTEN, C.H.; TOOKEY, H.L. Chemistry and biological effects of glucosinolates. In: *Herbivores. Their Interaction with Secondary Plant Metabolites*. Edited by G.A. Rosenthal and D.H. Janzen. Academic Press, New York and London. 1979, 471–500.

3   CROSBY, D.G. Natural toxic background in the food of man and his animals. *Journal of Agricultural and Food Chemistry* 1969, 17, 532–538.

4   MINISTRY OF AGRICULTURE, FISHERIES AND FOOD. Poisoning of animals in Britain (1975–1977). *Animal Disease Report* 1978, 2, No.2, 9–12.

5   FORSYTH, A.A. *British Poisonous Plants*. HMSO, London, UK. Ministry of Agriculture, Fisheries and Food Bulletin 161, 1968, 42–43 (amended 1979, 43–44).

6   HILL, R. A review of the 'toxic' effects of rapeseed meals with observations on meal from improved varieties. *British Veterinary Journal* 1979, 135, 3–16.

7   WHITTLE, P.J.; SMITH, R.H.; MCINTOSH, A. Estimation of S-methylcysteine sulphoxide (kale anaemia factor) and its distribution among brassica forage and root crops. *Journal of the Science of Food and Agriculture* 1976, 27, 633–642.

8   COTE, F.T. Rape poisoning in cattle. *Canadian Journal of Comparative Medicine* 1944, 8, 38–41.

9   PRACHE, S. Haemolytic anaemia in ruminants fed forage brassicas: a review. *Veterinary Research* 1994, 25, 497–520.

10   SCHOFIELD, F.W. The constant occurrence of macrocytic anemia in cattle feeding on rape. *Report of the Ontario Veterinary College* 1947, No.29, 122–125.

11 GUTZWILLER, A. [Effect of selenium status in the goat on erythrocyte susceptibility to oxidative damage.] *Schweizer Archiv für Tierheilkunde* 1991, 133, 157–161.

12 BÄCKGREN, A.W.; JÖNSSON, G. Blood and bone marrow studies in cattle feeding on *Brassica* species. *Acta Veterinaria Scandinavica* 1969, 10, 309–318.

13 GREGOR, A. Rye-grass staggers. Rape poisoning. Feeding of beet tops. Dietetic haematuria. Selenium poisoning. *Report of Proceedings, Conference on Metabolic Disorders and Other Problems Related to Grassland and Fodder Crops and Innovations in Animal Husbandry.* British Veterinary Association, London, UK. 1952, 132–141.

14 STAMP, J.T.; STEWART, J. Haemolytic anaemia with jaundice in sheep. *Journal of Comparative Pathology and Therapeutics.* 1953, 63, 48–52.

15 PERRETT, D.R. Suspected rape poisoning in cattle. *Veterinary Record* 1947, 59, 674.

16 HUNGERFORD T.G. *Diseases of Livestock.* McGraw-Hill Book Co., Sydney, Australia. 9th Edition, 1990, 1630.

17 SCHMID, A.; SCHMID, H. [Rape poisoning in wild herbivores.] *Tierärztliche Praxis* 1992, 20, 321–325.

18 CRAWSHAW, H.A. Rape blindness. *Veterinary Record* 1953, 65, 254.

19 DALTON, P.J. Rape blindness. *Veterinary Record* 1953, 65, 298.

20 O'DRISCOLL, J. Rape poisoning in cattle. *Irish Veterinary Journal* 1958, 12, 82.

21 HUEY, I.B. Rape poisoning in cattle. *Irish Veterinary Journal* 1958, 12, 83.

22 MICHAEL, D.T. Rape or cole: some observations on its management in relation to the health of sheep grazing on it. *Veterinary Record* 1953, 65, 231–232.

23 VERMUNT, J.J.; WEST, D.M. Rape poisoning in sheep. *New Zealand Veterinary Journal* 1993, 41, 151–152.

24 GRIFFITH, G. AP; JOHNSTON, T.D. The nitrate-nitrogen content of herbage. III. The mineral nitrate content of rape and kale. *Journal of the Science of Food and Agriculture* 1961, 12, 348–352.

25 BRUERE, A.N. Nitrite/nitrate poisoning on second-growth rape. *New Zealand Veterinary Journal* 1956, 4, 128.

26 BARNOUIN, J.; PACCARD, P. [Nutritional risk factors for liver damage in French dairy herds.] *Canadian Veterinary Journal* 1988, 29, 915–920.

27 CONNOR, H.E. *The Poisonous Plants in New Zealand.* E.C. Keating, Government Printers, Wellington, New Zealand. 1977, 67–69.

28 RUSSEL, A.J.F. A note on goitre in lambs grazing rape (*Brassica napus*). *Animal Production* 1967, 9, 131–133.

29 FALES, S.F.; GUSTINE, D.L.; BOSWORTH, S.C.; HOOVER, R.J. Concentrations of glucosinolates and S-methylcysteine sulfoxide in ensiled rape (*Brassica napus* L.). *Journal of Dairy Science* 1987, 70, 2402–2405.

30 VERMOREL, M.; HEANEY, R.K.; FENWICK, G.R. Antinutritional effects of the rapeseed meals Darmor and Jet Neuf, and progoitrin together with myrosinase, in the growing rat. *Journal of the Science of Food and Agriculture* 1988, 44, 321–334.

31 AHLIN, K.Å.; EMANUELSON, M.; WIKTORSSON, H. Rapeseed products from double-low cultivars as feed for dairy cows: effects of long-term feeding on thyroid function, fertility and animal health. *Acta Veterinaria Scandinavica* 1994, 35, 37–53.

32 HALL, S.A. Lysis of hepatic reticulin. An unusual lesion in laying fowls, possibly associated with rapeseed meal. *Veterinary Record* 1972, 91, 495.

33 JACKSON, N. Toxicity of rapeseed meal and its use as a protein supplement in the diet of two hybrid strains of caged laying hens. *Journal of the Science of Food and Agriculture* 1969, 20, 734–740.

34 WIGHT, P.A.L.; SCOUGALL, R.K.; SHANNON, D.W.F.; WELLS, J.W.; MAWSON, R. Role of glucosinolates in the causation of liver haemorrhages in laying hens fed water-extracted or heat-treated rapeseed cakes. *Research in Veterinary Science* 1987, 43, 313–319.

35 FENWICK, G.R.; CURTIS, R.F. Rapeseed meal and its use in poultry diets. A review. *Animal Feed Science and Technology* 1980, 5, 255–298.

36 TIMMS, L.M. Influence of a 12.5 per cent rapeseed diet and an avian reovirus on the production of leg abnormalities in male broiler chickens. *Research in Veterinary Science* 1985, 38, 69–76.

37 MARANGOS, A.; HILL, R. The use of rapeseed meal as a protein supplement in poultry and pig diets. *Veterinary Record* 1975, 96, 377–380.

38 LEE, P.A.; HILL, R.; ROSS, E.J. Studies on rapeseed meal from different varieties of rape in the diets of gilts. II. Effects on farrowing performance of gilts, performance of their piglets to weaning and subsequent conception of the gilts. *British Veterinary Journal* 1985, 141, 592–602.

39 ETIENNE, M.; DOURMAD, J.Y. Effects of zearalenone or glucosinolates in the diet on reproduction in sows: a review. *Livestock Production Science* 1994, 40, 99–113.

40 BUTLER, E.J.; PEARSON, A.W.; FENWICK, G.R. Problems which limit the use of rapeseed meal as a protein source in poultry diets. *Journal of the Science of Food and Agriculture* 1982, 33, 866–875.

41 ANONYMOUS. Toxic effects of rapeseed meal. Report of the Houghton Poultry Research Station, Huntingdon, UK. 1979–1980, 77–79.

42 PEARSON, A.W.; BUTLER, E.J.; CURTIS, R.F.; FENWICK, G.R.; HOBSON-FROHOCK, A.; LAND, D.G. Rapeseed meal and egg taint: demonstration of the metabolic defect in male and female chicks. *Veterinary Record* 1979, 104, 318–319.

43 PEARSON, A.W.; GREENWOOD, N.M.; BUTLER, E.J.; FENWICK. G.R. Low glucosinolate rapeseed meals and egg taint. *Veterinary Record* 1980, 106, 560.

44 WHEELER, J.L.; PARK, R.J.; SPURWAY, R.A.; FORD, A.L. Variation in the effects of forage rape on meat flavour in sheep. *Journal of Agricultural Science, UK* 1974, 83, 569–571.

45 SEIGLER, D.S. Toxic seed lipids. In: *Herbivores. Their Interaction with Secondary Plant Metabolites.* Edited by G.A. Rosenthal and D.H. Janzen. Academic Press, New York and London. 1979, 449–470.

46 MINISTRY OF AGRICULTURE, FISHERIES AND FOOD. Kale as a feeding stuff. Advisory Leaflet 1975, No.408 (amended), 1–5.

47 MINISTRY OF AGRICULTURE, FISHERIES AND FOOD. Bulky feeds for dairy cows. Advisory Leaflet 1977, No.524 (revised), 1–16.

48 SMITH, R.H. Kale poisoning: the brassica anaemia factor. *Veterinary Record* 1980, 107, 12–15.

49 VANETTEN, C.H.; TOOKEY, H.L. Chemistry and biological effects of glucosinolates. In: *Herbivores. Their Interaction with Secondary Plant Metabolites.* Edited by G.A. Rosenthal and D.H. Janzen. Academic Press, New York and London. 1979, 471–500.

50 PAXMAN, P.J.; HILL, R. The goitrogenicity of kale and its relation to thiocyanate content. *Journal of the Science of Food and Agriculture* 1974, 25, 329–337.

51 VANETTEN, C.H.; DAXENBICHLER, M.E.; WOLFF, I.A. Natural glucosinolates (thioglucosides) in foods and feeds. *Journal of Agricultural and Food Chemistry* 1969, 17, 483–491.

52 MCDONALD, R.C.; MANLEY, T.R.; BARRY, T.N.; FORSS, D.A.; SINCLAIR, A.G. Nutritional evaluation of kale (*Brassica oleracea*) diets. 3. Changes in plant composition induced by soil fertility practices, with special reference to SMCO and glucosinolate concentrations. *Journal of Agricultural Science* 1981, 97, 13–23.

53 EARL, C.R.A.; SMITH, R.H. Dimethyl disulphide in the blood of cattle fed on brassicas. *Journal of the Science of Food and Agriculture* 1982, 34, 23–28.

54 CLEGG, F. Haemoglobinuria of cattle associated with the feeding of kale and other brassicae species. *Proceedings, IVth International Meeting of the World Association for Buiatrics, Zurich, Switzerland, 4–9 August 1966*, 184–195.

55 MACWILLIAMS, P.S.; SEARCY, G.P.; BELLAMY, J.E.C. Bovine parturient hemoglobinuria: a review of the literature. *Canadian Veterinary Journal* 1982, 23, 309–312.

56 GREENHALGH, J.F.D.; AITKEN, J.N.; GUNN, J.B. Kale anaemia. III. A survey of kale feeding practices and anaemia in cattle on dairy farms in England and Scotland. *Research in Veterinary Science* 1972, 13, 15–21.

57 SMITH, R.H.; KAY, M.; MATHESON, N.A.; LAWSON, W. S-methylcysteine sulphoxide, the ruminant kale anaemia factor. *Journal of the Science of Food and Agriculture* 1978, 29, 414–416.

58 WHITTLE, P.J.; SMITH, R.H.; MACINTOSH, A. Estimation of S-methylcysteine sulphoxide (kale anaemia factor) and its distribution among brassica forage and root crops. *Journal of the Science of Food and Agriculture* 1976, 27, 633–642.

59 MAXWELL, M.H. Production of a Heinz body anaemia in the domestic fowl after ingestion of dimethyl disulphide: a haematological and ultrastructural study. *Research in Veterinary Science* 1981, 30, 233–238.

60 WRIGHT, E.; SINCLAIR, D.P. The goitrogenic effect of thousand-headed kale on adult sheep and rabbits. *New Zealand Journal of Agricultural Research* 1958, 1, 477–485.

61 WILLIAMS, H.L.; HILL, R.; ALDERMAN, G. The effects of feeding kale to breeding ewes. *British Veterinary Journal* 1965, 121, 2–17.

62 WRIGHT, E.; SINCLAIR, D.P. The concentration of radioiodine by the foetal thyroid gland and its relation to congenital goitre in sheep. *New Zealand Journal of Agricultural Research* 1959, 2, 933–937.

63 HUNGERFORD, T.G. *Diseases of Livestock*. McGraw-Hill Book Co., Sydney, Australia. 8th Edition, 1975, 151 and 408.

64 PAXMAN, P.J.; HILL, R. Thiocyanate content of kale. *Journal of the Science of Food and Agriculture* 1974, 25, 323–328.

65 SINCLAIR, D.P.; ANDREWS, E.W. Goitre in new-born lambs. *New Zealand Veterinary Journal* 1954, 2, 72–79.

66 RADOSTITS, O.M.; BLOOD, D.C.; GAY, C.C. *Veterinary Medicine*. Baillière Tindall, London, UK. 8th Edition, 1994, 1395–1398.

67 DAVID, J.S.E. The effect of prolonged kale feeding on the thyroid glands of sheep. *Journal of Comparative Pathology* 1976, 86, 235–241.

68 BOYD, H.; REED, H.C.B. Investigations into the incidence and cause of infertility in dairy cattle – influence of kale feeding, milk production and management factors associated with 'farming intensity'. *British Veterinary Journal* 1961, 117, 192–200.

69 MELROSE, D.R.; BROWN, B.B. Some observations on the possible effect of kale feeding on fertility in dairy cattle. *Journal of Reproduction and Fertility* 1962, 4, 232.

70 CLEGG, F.G.; EVANS, R.K. Haemoglobinaemia of cattle associated with the feeding of brassicae species. *Veterinary Record* 1962, 74, 1169–1176.

71 MALLARD, C. [Toxicity of Cruciferae and pregnancy disorders in a herd of goats.] *Bulletin des Groupements Techniques Vétérinaires* 1981, No.3, 23–25.

72 PICKARD, D.W.; CRIGHTON, D.B. An investigation into the possible oestrogenic effect of kale. *British Veterinary Journal* 1967, 123, 64–69.

73 DEAS, D.W.; MELROSE, D.R.; REED, H.C.B.; VANDEPLASSCHE, M.; PIDDUCK, H. Other non-infectious abnormalities. In: *Fertility and Infertility in Domestic Animals*. Edited by J.A. Laing. Baillière Tindall, London, UK. 3rd Edition, 1979, 137–159.

74 WRIGHT, E. Goitrogen of milk produced on kale. *Nature, London* 1958, 181, 1602–1603.

75 CLEMENTS, F.W.; WISHART, J.W. A thyroid-blocking agent in the etiology of endemic goiter. *Metabolism* 1956, 5, 623–639.

76 BACHELARD, H.S.; McQUILLAN, M.T.; TRIKOJUS, V.M. Studies on endemic goitre. III. An investigation of the anti-thyroid activities of isothiocyanates and derivatives with observations on fractions of milk from goitrous areas. *Australian Journal of Biological Sciences* 1963, 16, 177–191.

77 NIKOLAEV, K. [Toxicity of the wild radish, *Raphanus raphanistrum.*] *Veterinarnomeditsinski Nauki, Sofia* 1964, 1, No.10, 31–35.

78 HALE, O.M.; UTLEY, P.R. Effects of feeding wheat contaminated with wild radish (*Raphanus raphanistrum*) to growing pigs. *Journal of Animal Science* 1985, 61, 1172–1177.

79 TROUCHE. [Poisoning in a flock of lambs by wild radish (*Raphanus raphanistrum*).] *Revue Vétérinaire*, 1936, 88, 682–683.

80 FORSYTH, A.A. *British Poisonous Plants.* HMSO, London, UK. Ministry of Agriculture, Fisheries and Food Bulletin 161, 1968, 41–42 (amended 1979, 42–43).

81 GALLIE, J.G.E.; PATERSON, J.D. Charlock poisoning of lambs. *Veterinary Record* 1945, 57, 198–199.

82 JAHN, S.; SEFFNER, W. [Results of feeding sheep on mustard cake.] *Archiv für Tierernährung* 1962, 12, 11–16.

83 EATON, G. Suspected poisoning of bullocks by white mustard. *Veterinary Record* 1941, 53, 146.

84 HOLMES, R.G. A case of suspected poisoning of dairy cows by white mustard seeds (*Sinapis alba*). *Veterinary Record* 1965, 77, 480–481.

85 ALIKUTTY, K.M. Mustard seed toxicity in cattle. *Indian Veterinary Journal* 1976, 53, 962–964.

86 TROXLER, J. [Fatal poisoning of 19 heifers by white mustard (*Sinapis alba* L.).] *Schweizer Archiv für Tierheilkunde* 1981, 123, 495–497.

87 LANSON, R.K.; ABDULLA, A. Effect of feeding mustard seed to immature chickens and laying hens. *Poultry Science* 1963, 42, 1283–1284.

88 NIKOLAEV, K. [Toxicological studies on *Sinapis arvensis* L. I. The amount of active principle in the plant. II. Fowls. III. Sheep.] *Izvestiya Veterinarniya Institut Nezarazni Bolestii Zookhigiena, Sofia* 1962, 2, 101–105; 1963, 3, 91–96, 97–101.

89 KOVALEV, A.A. [Poisoning of horses by 'field mustard' *Sinapis arvensis.*] *Sovetskaya Veterinariya* 1937, No.10, 28–31.

90 MIHAILOV, M. [Charlock (*Sinapis arvensis*) poisoning in horses.] *Veterinarski Glasnik* 1961, 15, 681–683.

91 MAKARYAN, O.A. [Poisoning of cattle with *Sinapis arvensis* (charlock).] *Veterinariya, Moscow* 1973, No.11, 95–96.

92 GREENHALGH, J.F.D. Problems of animal disease. In: *The Future of Brassica Fodder Crops.* Edited by J.F.D. Greenhalgh and M. Hamilton. Occasional Publication, Rowett Research Institute 1971, No.2, 56–64.

93 TALJAARD, T.L. Cabbage poisoning in ruminants. *Journal of the South African Veterinary Association* 1993, 64, 96–100.

94 SMITH, R.H. Kale and brassica poisoning. *Veterinary Annual* 1977, 17, 28–33.

95 YOUNG, N.E.; AUSTIN, A.R.; ORR, R.J.; NEWTON, J.E.; TAYLOR, R.J. A comparison of a hybrid stubble turnip (cv. Appin) with other cruciferous catch crops for lamb fattening. 2. Animal performance and toxicological evaluation. *Grass and Forage Science* 1982, 37, 39–46.

96 BARBERAN, M.; VALDERRÁBANO, J. Pathological features in thymus and thyroids of lambs fed on turnips. *Veterinary Record* 1987, 120, 367–368.

97 WIKSE, S.E.; LEATHERS, C.W.; PARISH, S.M. Diseases of cattle that graze turnips. *Compendium on Continuing Education for the Practicing Veterinarian* 1987, 9, F112–F121.

98 O'HARA, P.J.; FRAZER, A.J. Nitrate poisoning in cattle grazing crops. *New Zealand Veterinary Journal* 1975, 23, 45–53.

99 MINISTRY OF AGRICULTURE, FISHERIES AND FOOD. Veterinary Investigation Division. Dramatic incident of nitrate/nitrite poisoning in cattle grazing stubble turnips. *Veterinary Record* 1996, 138,76.

100 DEBACKERE, M.; HOORENS, J.; HAUSTRAETE, K.H. [Poisoning of cows by linseed cake contaminated with rape and turnip seed.] *Vlaams Diergeneeskundig Tijdschrift* 1966, 35, 393–399.

CUCURBITACEAE

1 CORNEVIN, C. *Des Plantes Vénéneuses.* Librairie de Firmin-Didot, Paris, France. 1887, 360–363.

2 FORSYTH, A.A. *British Poisonous Plants.* HMSO, London, UK. Ministry of Agriculture, Fisheries and Food Bulletin 161, 1968, 72–73 (amended 1979, 73–74).

3 KYLE, R.A.M. Oxford, UK. Personal communication.

4 DERIVAUX, J.; LIÉGEOIS, F. *Toxicologie Vétérinaire.* Vigot Frères, Paris, France. 1962, 232–233.

5 WHUR, P. White bryony poisoning in a dog. *Veterinary Record* 1986, 119, 411.

6 RIPEANU, M. [Observations on some important cases of poisoning in animals.] *Revista de Zootehnie și Medicină Veterinară* 1963, 13, No.12, 67–68.

7 JORDAN, M. *A Guide to Wild Plants.* Millington Books, London, UK. 1976, 192–194.

8 FROHNE, D.; PFÄNDER, H.J. *A Colour Atlas of Poisonous Plants.* Wolfe Publishing Ltd, London, UK. 1984, 93.

CUPRESSACEAE

1 NATIONAL POISONS INFORMATION SERVICE, London, UK. Personal communication.

2 LOVELL, C.R. *Plants and the Skin.* Blackwell Scientific Publications, Oxford, UK. 1993, 242–245.

3 LONG, H.C. *Plants Poisonous to Live Stock.* Cambridge University Press, Cambridge, UK. 1917, 73.

4 MACDONALD, J. Macrocarpa poisoning. *New Zealand Veterinary Journal* 1956, 4, 30.

5 GOULD, C.M. Cypress poisoning. *Veterinary Record* 1962, 74, 743.

6 O'SCANALL, T. Suspected cypress poisoning in a cow. *Irish Veterinary Journal* 1986, 40, 156.

7 SLOSS, V.; BRADY, J.W. Abnormal births in cattle following ingestion of *Cupressus macrocarpa* foliage. *Australian Veterinary Journal* 1983, 60, 223.

8 MASON, R.W. Foetal cerebral leucomalacia associated with *Cupressus macrocarpa* abortion in cattle. *Australian Veterinary Journal* 1974, 50, 419.

9 MASON, R.W. Attempted induction of premature birth in sheep fed *Cupressus macrocarpa.* *Australian Veterinary Journal* 1984, 61, 192–193.

10 BARTÍK, M.; PISKAČ, A. (Editors) *Veterinary Toxicology.* Elsevier, Amsterdam, Netherlands. 1981, 220–223.

11 BENTZ, H. *Nutztiervergiftungen. Erkennung und Verhütung.* VEB Gustav Fischer Verlag, Jena, Germany. 1969, 327.

12 FORSYTH, A.A. *British Poisonous Plants.* HMSO, London, UK. Ministry of Agriculture, Fisheries and Food Bulletin 161, 1968, 29 (amended 1979, 31).

CYPERACEAE

1 SCHAUENBERG, P.; PARIS, F. *Guide to Medicinal Plants.* Lutterworth Press, Guildford and London, UK. 1977, 199.

2 ROSCA, V.; PAVEL, A. [Hydrocyanic acid poisoning of cattle with sedges of the genus *Carex.*] *Revista de Zootehnie și Medicină Veterinară* 1969, 19, No.11, 81–85.

DENNSTAEDTIACEAE

1 PAKEMAN, R.J.; MARRS, R.H.; HOWARD, D.C.; BARR, C.J. Predicting the effects of climate and land-use change on the spread of bracken. In: *Bracken: an Environmental Issue. (Bracken Conference, Aberystwyth, 1994.)* Edited by R.T. Smith and J.A. Taylor. School of Geography, University of Leeds, UK. 1995, 69–72.

2 TAYLOR, J.A. The bracken problem: a global perspective. In: *Bracken Biology and Management.* Edited by J.R. Thomson and R.T. Smith. Australian Institute of Agricultural Science, Wahroonga,

New South Wales, Australia. 1990, 3–19.

3   COOPER-DRIVER, G.A.; SWAIN, T. Cyanogenic polymorphism in bracken in relation to herbivore predation. *Nature, London* 1976, 260, 604.

4   PARKER, W.H.; McCREA, C.T. Bracken (*Pteris aquilina*) poisoning of sheep in the North York Moors. *Veterinary Record* 1965, 77, 861–866.

5   WATSON, W.A.; TERLECKI, S.; PATTERSON, D.S.P.; SWEASEY, D.; HEBERT, C.N.; DONE, J.T. Experimentally produced retinal degeneration (bright blindness) in sheep. *British Veterinary Journal* 1972, 128, 457–469.

6   ALLSUP, T.N.; GRIFFITHS, W.R. Progressive retinal degeneration in sheep in South Wales. *Veterinary Record* 1978, 103, 268.

7   KELLEWAY, R.A.; GEOVJIAN, L. Acute bracken fern poisoning in a 14-month-old horse. *Veterinary Medicine and Small Animal Clinician* 1978, 73, 295–296.

8   THOMAS, A.J. Bracken poisoning in animals. *Biochemical Journal* 1963, 88, 56P–57P.

9   EVANS, W.C. Bracken thiaminase-mediated neurotoxic syndromes. *Botanical Journal of the Linnean Society* 1976, 73, 113–131.

10   KONISHI, T.; ICHIJO, S. [Experimentally induced equine bracken poisoning by thermostable antithiamine factor (SF factor) extracted from dried bracken.] *Journal of the Japan Veterinary Medical Association* 1984, 37, 730–734.

11   HINTZ, H.F. Bracken fern. *Equine Practice* 1990, 12, No.6, 6–7.

12   FENWICK, G.R. Bracken (*Pteridium aquilinum*) – toxic effects and toxic constituents. *Journal of the Science of Food and Agriculture* 1988, 46, 147–173.

13   CAMPO, M.S.; JARRETT, W.F.H.; BARRON, R.; O'NEILL, B.W.; SMITH K.T. Association of bovine papillomavirus type 2 and bracken fern with bladder cancer in cattle. *Cancer Research* 1992, 52, 6898–6904.

14   CAMPO, M.S.; JARRETT, W.F.H.; O'NEILL, W.; BARRON, R.J. Latent papillomavirus infection in cattle. *Research in Veterinary Science* 1994, 56, 151–157.

15   CAMPO, M.S.; O'NEILL, W.; BARRON, R.J.; JARRETT, W.F.H. Experimental reproduction of the papilloma-carcinoma complex of the alimentary canal in cattle. *Carcinogenesis* 1994, 15, 1597–1601.

16   HIRONO, I.; KONO, Y.; TAKAHASHI, K.; YAMADA, K.; NIWA, H.; OJIKA, M.; KIGOSHI, H.; NIIYAMA, K.; UOSAKI, Y. Reproduction of acute bracken poisoning in a calf with ptaquiloside, a bracken constituent. *Veterinary Record* 1984, 115, 375–378.

17   HIRONO, I.; ITO, M.; YAGYU, S.; HAGA, M.; WAKAMATSU, K.; KISHIKAWA, T.; NISHIKAWA, O.; YAMADA, K.; OJIKA, M.; KIGOSHI, H. Reproduction of progressive retinal degeneration (bright blindness) in sheep by administration of ptaquiloside contained in bracken. *Journal of Veterinary Medical Science* 1993, 55, 979–983.

18   NGOMUO, A.J.; JONES, R.S. Cytotoxicity studies of quercetin, shikimate, cyclohexanecarboxylate and ptaquiloside. *Veterinary and Human Toxicology* 1996, 38, 14–18.

19   NGOMUO, A.J.; JONES, R.S. Genotoxicity studies of quercetin and shikimate in vivo in the bone marrow of mice and gastric mucosal cells of rats. *Veterinary and Human Toxicology* 1996, 38, 176–180.

20   DINIZ, J.M.F.; BASILE, J.R.; DE CAMARGO, N.J. [Natural poisoning of mules with *Pteridium aquilinum* in Brazil.] *Arquivo Brasileiro de Medicina Veterinária e Zootechnia* 1984, 36, 512–522.

21   FERNANDES, W.R.; GARCIA, R.C.M.; MEDEIROS, R.M.A.; BIRGAL, E.H. [Experimental *Pteridium aquilinum* poisoning in horses.] *Arquivos da Escola de Medicina Veterinaria da Universidade Federal da Bahia* 1990, 13, 112–124.

22   HARDING, J.D.J. Bracken poisoning in pigs. *Agriculture* 1972, 79, 313–314.

23   EVANS, W.C.; WIDDOP, B.; HARDING, J.D.J. Experimental poisoning by bracken rhizomes in pigs.

Veterinary Record 1972, 90, 471–475.

24 EDWARDS, B.L. Poisoning by *Pteridium aquilinum* in pregnant sows. *Veterinary Record* 1983, 112, 459–460.

25 EVANS, W.C.; EVANS, I.A.; HUMPHREYS, D.J.; LEWIN, B.; DAVIES, W.E.J.; AXFORD, R.F.E. Induction of thiamine deficiency in sheep, with lesions similar to those of cerebrocortical necrosis. *Journal of Comparative Pathology* 1975, 85, 253–267.

26 PENBERTHY, J. Vegetable poisoning (?) simulating anthrax in cattle. *Journal of Comparative Pathology and Therapeutics* 1893, 6, 266–275.

27 ALMOND, N. In: Fern poisoning (editorial). *Journal of Comparative Pathology and Therapeutics* 1894, 7, 165–167.

28 EVANS, W.C.; EVANS, E.T.R. Studies on the biochemistry of pasture plants – No.3. The effects of bracken (*Pteris aquilina*) in the diet of rats, and the problem of bracken poisoning in farm animals. *British Veterinary Journal* 1949, 105, 175–186.

29 STATE VETERINARY SERVICE. Effect of the drought of 1976 on the health of cattle, sheep and other farm livestock in England and Wales. *Veterinary Record* 1982, 111, 407–411.

30 HOPKINS, A. Bracken (*Pteridium aquilinum*); its distribution and animal health implications. *British Veterinary Journal* 1990, 146, 316–326.

31 HOPKINS, A. Factors influencing cattle bracken-poisoning in Great Britain. In: *Bracken: an Environmental Issue. (Bracken Conference, Aberystwyth, 1994.)* Edited by R.T. Smith and J.A. Taylor. School of Geography, University of Leeds, UK. 1995, 120–123.

32 ANONYMOUS. *Veterinary Investigation Diagnostic Analysis III 1994 and 1987–94.* Central Veterinary Laboratory, Weybridge, Surrey, UK. 1995.

33 ANONYMOUS. *Veterinary Investigation Diagnostic Analysis III 1992 and 1985–92.* Central Veterinary Laboratory, Weybridge, Surrey, UK. 1993.

34 TUSTIN, R.C.; ADELAAR, T.F.; MELDAL-JOHNSON, C.M. Bracken poisoning in cattle in the Natal midlands. *Journal of the South African Veterinary Medical Association* 1968, 39, No.3, 91–99.

35 PERSSON, L.; JOHANSSON, L.E.; KRISTIANSSON, L. [Bracken – the probable cause of poisoning of cattle at pasture.] *Svensk Veterinärtidning* 1993, 45, 179–180.

36 EVANS, W.C.; EVANS, I.A.; AXFORD, R.F.E.; THRELFALL, G.; HUMPHREYS, D.A.; THOMAS, A.J. Studies on bracken poisoning in cattle. VII. The toxicity of bracken rhizomes. *Veterinary Record* 1961, 73, 852–853.

37 EVANS, W.C. Bracken poisoning of farm animals. *Veterinary Record* 1964, 76, 365–372.

38 YAMANE, O.; HAYASHI, T.; SAKO, S.; TATEMATSU, S.; TAKEDA, K.; FUKUSHIMA, H. Studies on the haemorrhagic diathesis of experimental bovine bracken poisoning. II. Heparin-like substance level in blood. *Japanese Journal of Veterinary Science* 1975, 37, 341–347.

39 EVANS, W.C. The acute disease caused by bracken in animals. In: *Bracken, Ecology, Land Use and Control Technology.* Edited by R.T. Smith and J.A. Taylor. Parthenon Publishing Group, Carnforth, UK. 1986, 121–132.

40 HANNAM, D.A.R. Bracken poisoning in farm animals with special reference to the North York Moors. In: *Bracken, Ecology, Land Use and Control Technology.* Edited by R.T. Smith and J.A. Taylor. Parthenon Publishing Group, Carnforth, UK. 1986, 133–138.

41 SUNDERMAN, F.M. Bracken poisoning in sheep. *Australian Veterinary Journal* 1987, 64, 25–26.

42 VON ROSENBERGER, G. Nature, manifestations, cause and control of chronic enzootic haematuria in cattle. *Veterinary Medical Review* 1971, No.2/3, 189–206.

43 HOPKINS, N.C.G. Aetiology of enzootic haematuria. *Veterinary Record* 1986, 118, 715–717.

44 VON ROSENBERGER, G.; HEESCHEN, W. [Bracken, the cause of bovine enzootic haematuria.] *Deutsche Tierärztliche Wochenschrift* 1960, 67, 201–207.

45 MCCREA, C.T.; HEAD, K.W. Sheep tumours in North East Yorkshire. II. Experimental induction

of tumours. *British Veterinary Journal* 1981, 137, 21–30.

46 HIRONO, I.; OGINO, H.; FUJIMOTO, M.; YAMADA, K.; YOSHIDA, Y.; IKAGAWA, M.; OKUMURA, M. Induction of tumors in ACI rats given a diet containing ptaquiloside, a bracken carcinogen. *Journal of the National Cancer Institute* 1987, 79, 1143–1149.

47 YOSHIDA, M.; SAITO, T. Acute toxicity of braxin C, a bracken toxin, in guinea pigs. *Journal of Toxicological Sciences* 1994, 19, 17–23.

48 YOSHIDA, M.; SAITO, T. Non-urotoxic induction of hemorrhagic cystitis by braxin C, a bracken toxin, in guinea pigs. *Journal of Toxicological Sciences* 1994, 19, 55–59.

49 MOURA, J.W.; STOCCO DOS SANTOS, R.C.; DAGLI, M.L.Z.; D'ANGELINO, J.L.; BIRGEL, E.H.; BEÇAK, W. Chromosome aberrations in cattle raised on bracken fern pasture. *Experientia* 1988, 44, 785–788.

50 PEAUROI, J.R.; MOHR, F.C.; FISHER, D.J.; MISHEFF, M.; GRINDLEY, G.J.; CAMPO, M.S. Anemia, hematuria, and multicentric urinary neoplasia in a llama (*Lama glama*) exposed to bracken fern. *Journal of Zoo and Wildlife Medicine* 1995, 26, 315–320.

51 WATSON, W.A.; BARLOW, R.M.; BARNETT, K.C. Bright blindness – a condition prevalent in Yorkshire hill sheep. *Veterinary Record* 1965, 77, 1060–1069.

52 WATSON, W.A.; BARNETT, K.C.; TERLECKI, S. Progressive retinal degeneration (bright blindness) in sheep: a review. *Veterinary Record* 1972, 91, 665–670.

53 FORSYTH, A.A. *British Poisonous Plants*. HMSO, London, UK. Ministry of Agriculture, Fisheries and Food Bulletin 161, 1979, 28–30.

54 JARRETT, W.F.H.; McNEIL, P.E.; GRIMSHAW, W.T.R.; SELMAN, I.E.; McINTYRE, W.I.M. High incidence area of cattle cancer with a possible interaction between an environmental carcinogen and a papilloma virus. *Nature, London* 1978, 274, 215–217.

55 MACLEOD, A. The bracken problem in the Highlands and Islands. *Proceedings of the Royal Society of Edinburgh* 1982, 81B, 11–18.

56 VILLALOBOS-SALAZAR, J.; MORA, J.; MENESES, A.; PASHOV, B. The carcinogenic effects of bracken spores. In: *Bracken: an Environmental Issue. (Bracken Conference, Aberystwyth, 1994.)* Edited by R.T. Smith and J.A. Taylor. School of Geography, University of Leeds, UK. 1995, 102–103.

57 EVANS, I.A. The carcinogenic, mutagenic and teratogenic toxicity of bracken. In: *Bracken: an Environmental Issue. (Bracken Conference, Aberystwyth, 1994.)* Edited by R.T. Smith and J.A. Taylor. School of Geography, University of Leeds, UK. 1995, 139–146.

58 PAKEMAN, R.J. Bracken. *Biologist* 1993, 40, 105–109.

59 POTTER, D.M.; PITMAN, R.M. The extraction and characterisation of carcinogens from bracken and the effect of composting. In: *Bracken: an Environmental Issue. (Bracken Conference, Aberystwyth, 1994.)* Edited by R.T. Smith and J.A. Taylor. School of Geography, University of Leeds, UK. 1995, 110–115.

60 PITMAN, R. Bracken compost: a substitute for peat? In: *Bracken: an Environmental Issue. (Bracken Conference, Aberystwyth, 1994.)* Edited by R.T. Smith and J.A. Taylor. School of Geography, University of Leeds, UK. 1995, 191–196.

61 PAMUKCU, A.M.; CHING YUNG WANG; HATCHER, J.; BRYAN, G.T. Carcinogenicity of tannin and tannin-free extracts of bracken fern (*Pteridium aquilinum*) in rats. *Journal of the National Cancer Institute* 1980, 65, 131–136.

62 MARLIÈRE, C.A.; SANTOS, R.C.; GALVÃO, M.A.M.; SILVA, M.L.C.; KAWAMOTO, M.; CASTRO, M.C.F.M.; SOARES, J.F.; VON KRUGER, E.R.; BARRETO, J.M.A.; GOMES, R.Q.F. Gastric and oesophageal cancer related to bracken (*Pteridium aquilinum*) ingestion: a case control study from Ouro Preto, Minas Gerais, Brazil. In: *Bracken: an Environmental Issue. (Bracken Conference, Aberystwyth, 1994.)* Edited by R.T. Smith and J.A. Taylor. School of Geography, University of Leeds, UK. 1995, 99–101.

63 EVANS, I.A., JONES, R.S.; MAINWARING-BURTON, R. Passage of bracken fern toxicity into milk. *Nature, London* 1972, 237, 107–108.

64 ALONSO-AMELOT, M.E.; CASTILLO, U.; DE JONGH, F. Passage of the bracken fern carcinogen ptaquiloside into bovine milk. *Lait* 1993, 73, 323–332.

65 ALONSO-AMELOT, M.E.; CASTILLO, U.; SMITH, B.L.; LAUREN, D.R. Bracken ptaquiloside in milk. *Nature, London* 1996, 382, 587.

66 VILLALOBOS-SALAZAR, J.; MENESES, A.; SALAS, J. Carcinogenic effects in mice of milk from cows fed on bracken fern *Pteridium aquilinum*. In: *Bracken Biology and Management*. Edited by J.R. Thomson and R.T. Smith. Australian Institute of Agricultural Science, Wahroonga, New South Wales, Australia. 1990, 247–251.

67 SMITH, B.L.; SEAWRIGHT, A.A. Bracken fern (*Pteridium* spp.) carcinogenicity and human health – a brief review. *Natural Toxins* 1995, 3, 1–5.

68 GALPIN, O.P.; WHITAKER, C.J.; WHITAKER, R.; KASSAB, J.Y. Gastric cancer in Gwynedd. Possible links with bracken. *British Journal of Cancer* 1990, 61, 737–740.

69 VILLALOBOS-SALAZAR, J.; MENESES, A.; ROJAS, J.L.; MORA, J.; PORRAS, R.E.; HERRERO, M.V. Bracken derived carcinogens as affecting animal health and human health in Costa Rica. In: *Bracken Toxicity and Carcinogenicity as related to Animal and Human Health*. Edited by J.A. Taylor. International Bracken Group Special Publication, Institute of Earth Studies, University College of Wales, Aberystwyth, UK. 1989, 40–51.

DIOSCOREACEAE

1 JORDAN, M. *A Guide to Wild Plants*. Millington Books Ltd, London, UK. 1976, 226–228.

2 SCHMIDT, R.J.; MOULT, S.P. The dermatitic properties of black bryony (*Tamus communis* L.). *Contact Dermatitis* 1983, 9, 390–396.

3 CORNEVIN, C. *Des Plantes Vénéneuses*. Librairie de Firmin-Didot, Paris, France. 1887, 127–131.

4 BLACKWELL, W.E. Horses poisoned by bryony. *Veterinary Record* 1931, 11, 911–912.

5 VALE, J.A.; MEREDITH, T.J. Poisonous plants. *Hospital Update* 1980 (June), 543–555.

6 CAPASSO, F.; MASCOLO, N.; AUTORE, G.; DE SIMONE, F.; SENATORE, F. Anti-inflammatory and analgesic activity in alcoholic extract of *Tamus communis* L. *Journal of Ethnopharmacology* 1983, 8, 321–325.

7 COOPER, H.C. Personal communication.

8 KASHCHENKO, V.B.; KOZHUKHAR', G.S. [Toxidermatosis caused by *Tamus communis*.] *Vestnik Dermatologii i Venerologii* 1986, No.5, 50–51.

DRYOPTERIDACEAE

1 MURRAY, V. Suspected poisoning by common buckle fern (*Dryopteris* family). *Irish Veterinary Journal* 1966, 20, 122–124.

2 EDGAR, J.T.; THIN, I.M. Plant poisoning involving male fern. *Veterinary Record* 1968, 82, 33–34.

3 MACLEOD, N.S.M.; GREIG, A.; BONN, J.M.; ANGUS, K.W. Poisoning in cattle associated with *Dryopteris filix-mas* and *D. borreri*. *Veterinary Record* 1978, 102, 239–240.

4 MITCHELL, G.B.B.; WAIN, E.B. Suspected male fern poisoning in cattle. *Veterinary Record* 1983, 113, 188.

5 ROSEN, E.S.; EDGAR, J.T.; SMITH, J.L.S. Male fern retro-bulbar neuropathy in cattle. *Journal of Small Animal Practice* 1970, 10, 619–625.

6 KELLY, W.R. *Veterinary Clinical Diagnosis*. Baillière Tindall, London, UK. 1984, 369.

EQUISETACEAE

1 FROHNE, D.; PFÄNDER, H.J. *A Colour Atlas of Poisonous Plants*. Wolfe Publishing Ltd, London, UK. 1984, 103–104.

2   EVANS, E.T.R.; EVANS, W.C.; ROBERTS, H.E. Studies on bracken poisoning in the horse. *British Veterinary Journal* 1951, 107, 364–371, 399–411.

3   FORSYTH, A.A. *British Poisonous Plants*. HMSO, London, UK. Ministry of Agriculture, Fisheries and Food Bulletin 161, 1968, 25–26 (amended 1979, 26–27).

4   KINGSBURY, J.M. *Poisonous Plants of the United States and Canada*. Prentice-Hall, New Jersey, USA. 1964, 114–118.

5   MCLEAN, A.; NICHOLSON, H.H. Stock poisoning plants of the British Columbia Ranges. Canada Department of Agriculture 1958, Publication 1037, 23–24.

6   FORENBACHER, S. [Horsetail poisoning of horses – a B₁ avitaminosis.] *Schweizer Archiv für Tierheilkunde* 1952, 94, 153–171.

7   BOCOS, E.I. [Observations on *Equisetum* poisoning in animals.] *Revista Zootehnie și Medicină Veterinară* 1971, 21, No.8, 57–59.

8   HUDSON, R. Poisoning by horsetail (*Equisetum arvense*). *Veterinary Journal* 1924, 80, 40.

9   GUSYNIN, I.A. [*The Toxicology of Poisonous Plants*.] Gosudarstvennoe Izdatel'stvo Sel'skokhozyaistvennoi Literatury, Moscow, USSR. 1955, 109–112.

10 LINDT, S. [Horsetail poisoning in calves.] *Schweizer Archiv für Tierheilkunde* 1959, 101, 461–464.

11 DERIVAUX, J.; LIÉGEOIS, F. *Toxicologie Vétérinaire*. Vigot Frères, Paris, France.1962, 231–232.

12 LOTT, D.G. The use of thiamin in mare's tail poisoning of horses. *Canadian Journal of Comparative Medicine* 1951, 15, 274–276.

ERICACEAE

1   SMITH, M.C. Japanese pieris poisoning in the goat. *Journal of the American Veterinary Medical Association* 1978, 173, 78–79.

2   HOLLANDS, R.D.; HUGHES, M.C. *Pieris formosanum* poisoning in the goat. *Veterinary Record* 1986, 118, 407–408.

3   VISSER, I.J.R.; VAN DEN HOVEN, R. ; VOS, J.H.; VAN DEN INGH, T.S.G.A.M. [*Pieris japonica* poisoning in two goats.] *Tijdschrift voor Diergeneeskunde* 1988, 113, 185–189.

4   PLUMLEE, K.H.; VANALSTINE, W.G.; SULLIVAN, J. M. Japanese pieris toxicosis of goats. *Journal of Veterinary Diagnostic Investigation* 1992, 4, 363–364.

5   SMITH, M.C. Fetal mummification in a goat due to Japanese pieris (*Pieris japonica*) poisoning. *Cornell Veterinarian* 1979, 69, 85–87.

6   POWER, S.B.; O'DONNELL, P.G.; QUIRK, E.G. *Pieris* poisoning in sheep. *Veterinary Record* 1991, 128, 599–600.

7   GILLIS, W.T.; BALL, W.; BALL, W. *Pieris* poisoning in zoo animals. *Michigan State University Veterinarian* 1961, 22, 24–26.

8   BRAHM, E.; BUNTENKÖTTER, S.; SIMANOWSKI, W. [Poisoning of llamas, alpacas, goats and wolves by Ericaceae at Dortmund Zoo.] *Erkrankungen der Zootiere. Verhandlungsbericht des XV. Internationalen Symposiums*. Akademie-Verlag, Berlin. 1973, 125–130.

9   NATIONAL POISONS INFORMATION SERVICE, London, UK. Personal communication.

10 TSCHEKUNOW, H.; KLUG, S.; MARCUS, S. "Symptomatic poisoning" from ingestion of *Pieris japonica*: a case report. *Veterinary and Human Toxicology* 1989, 31, 360.

11 GEROULANOS, S.; ATTINGER, B.; ÇAKMAKÇI, M. [Honey-induced poisoning.] *Schweizerische Rundschau für Medizin Praxis* 1992, 81, 535–540.

12 BOLTON, J.F. Rhododendron poisoning. *Veterinary Record* 1955, 67, 138–139.

13 HIGNETT, P.G. A case of presumed rhododendron poisoning in sheep. *Veterinary Record* 1951, 63, 346–347.

14 VAN LEENGOED, L.A.M.G.; AMERONGEN, J.J. [Rhododendron poisoning: clinical signs, treatment

and course in a sheep flock.] *Tijdschrift voor Diergeneeskunde* 1983, 108, 41–42.

15 EDLER, M.; GLADH, A.; HANSSON, K.; HÖJER, K.; INGEMANSSON, E.; MELLGRENN, M.; WIDMARK, K. [Case of rhododendron poisoning in sheep.] *Svensk Vetererinärtidning* 1984, 36, 411–412.

16 HIGGINS, R.J.; HANNAM, D.A.R.; HUMPHREYS, D.J.; STODULSKI, J.B.J. Rhododendron poisoning in sheep. *Veterinary Record* 1985, 116, 294–295.

17 SHANNON, D. Rhododendron poisoning in sheep. *Veterinary Record* 1985, 116, 451.

18 HOSIE, B.D.; MULLEN, C.M.; GILLESPIE, I.D.; COCHRANE, G.W. Rhododendron poisoning in lambs. *Veterinary Record* 1986, 118, 110.

19 BLACK, D.H. Rhododendron poisoning in sheep. *Veterinary Record* 1991, 128, 363–364.

20 KOHANAWA, M.; IKEDA, K.; OGUMA, K.; SASAKI, N. [Emetic effects of grayanotoxin isolated from *Rhododendron hymenanthes*, Makino on goats.] *Annual Report of the National Veterinary Assay Laboratory, Japan* 1973, 10, 53–57.

21 GHENNE, P.; MEES, G. [Rhododendron poisoning in a goat.] *Annales de Médecine Vétérinaire* 1968, 112, 25–29.

22 MILNES, J.N. Rhododendron poisoning in the goat. *Veterinary Record* 1953, 65, 211.

23 HUMPHRIES, D.J.; STODULSKI, J.B.J.; STOCKER, J.G. Rhododendron poisoning in goats. *Veterinary Record* 1983, 113, 503–504.

24 GREGORY, N.F. "Delayed" rhododendron poisoning. *Goat Veterinary Society Journal* 1990, 11, 41.

25 MASHETER, J.W.H. Rhododendron "poisoning" in cattle. *Veterinary Journal* 1941, 97, 223–225.

26 WOODS, S.B. Personal communication.

27 THIEMANN, A. Rhododendron poisoning. *Veterinary Record* 1991, 128, 411.

28 PUROHIT, K. Rhododendron poisoning in animals. *Indian Veterinary Journal* 1960, 37, 631–633.

29 SCHALLER, K. [Rhododendron poisoning in circus elephants.] *Kleintierpraxis* 1983, 28, 53–56.

30 BOGATKO, W. [Poisoning of coypu with rhododendron.] *Medycyna Weterynaryjna* 1968, 24, 417–418.

31 FRAPE, D.; WARD, A. Suspected rhododendron poisoning in dogs. *Veterinary Record* 1993, 132, 515–516.

32 CASTEEL, S.; WAGSTAFF, J. *Rhododendron macrophyllum* poisoning in a group of goats and sheep. *Veterinary and Human Toxicology* 1989, 31, 176–177.

33 MACGREGOR, J.L. Poisoning of bees by rhododendron nectars. *British Bee Journal* 1960, 88, 76–78, 88–89.

34 MATSCHULLAT, G. [Rhododendron poisoning in sheep.] *Praktische Tierarzt* 1974, 55, 624 and 626.

35 HUMPHREYS, D.J.; STODULSKI, J.B.J. Detection of andromedotoxins for the diagnosis of rhododendron poisoning in animals. *Journal of Applied Toxicology* 1986, 6, 121–122.

36 ARENA, J.M. Pretty poisonous plants. *Veterinary and Human Toxicology* 1979, 21, 108–111.

37 CHAMBERS, A.M. Warning – rhododendrons may damage your health! *Scottish Medical Journal* 1984, 29, 107–108.

38 MEIER, K.H.; HEMMICK, R.S. Bradycardia and complete heart block after ingestion of rhododendron tea. *Veterinary and Human Toxicology* 1992, 34, 351.

39 SCOTT, P.M.; COLDWELL, B.B.; WIBERG, G.S. Grayanotoxins, occurrence and analysis in honey and a comparison of toxicities in mice. *Food and Cosmetics Toxicology* 1971, 9, 179–184.

40 GOSSINGER, H.; HRUBY, K.; HAUBENSTOCK, A.; POHL, A.; DAVOGG, S. Cardiac arrhythymias in a patient with grayanotoxin-honey poisoning. *Veterinary and Human Toxicology* 1983, 25, 328–329.

41 GOSSINGER, H.; HRUBY, K.; POHL, A.; DAVOGG, S.; SUTTERLUTTI, G.; MATHIS, G. [Poisoning with andromedotoxin-containing honey.] *Deutsche Medizinische Wochenschrift* 1983, 108, 1555–1558.

42 YAVUZ, H.; ÖZEL, A.; AKKUS, I.; ERKUL, I. Honey poisoning in Turkey. *Lancet* 1991, 337, 789–790.

43 KERKVLIET, J.D. Analysis of a toxic rhododendron honey. *Journal of Apicultural Research* 1981, 20, 249–253.

44 CRANE, E. (Editor). *Honey. A Comprehensive Survey.* Heinemann, London, UK. 1975, 61.

45 HOWES, F.N. *Plants and Beekeeping.* Faber & Faber, London, UK. 1979, 23–24.

46 KLEIN-SCHWARTZ, W.; LITOVITZ, T. Azalea toxicity: an overrated problem? *Clinical Toxicology* 1985, 23, 91–101.

EUPHORBIACEAE

1 FORSYTH, A.A. *British Poisonous Plants.* HMSO, London, UK. Ministry of Agriculture, Fisheries and Food Bulletin 161, 1968, 74–76 (amended 1979, 75–77).

2 SHARAF, A.E.A. A pharmacological study of the Egyptian plant, *Euphorbia peplus. Veterinary Journal* 1948, 104, 313–318.

3 SHARAF, A.E.A. Chemical investigation of the Egyptian plant, *Euphorbia peplus. British Veterinary Journal* 1949, 105, 128–135.

4 VLACHOS, P., POULOS, L., KOUTSELINIS, A.; PAPADATOS, K. *Euphorbia* poisoning (case reports). *IRCS Medical Science: Library Compendium* 1978, 6, 104.

5 MITCHELL, J.; ROOK, A. *Botanical Dermatology. Plants and Plant Products Injurious to the Skin.* Greengrass Ltd, Vancouver, Canada. 1979, 269.

6 CALNAN, C.D. Petty spurge (*Euphorbia peplus* L.) *Contact Dermatitis* 1975, 1, 128.

7 RÖSSLER, G. [*Euphorbia* conjunctivitis.] *Klinische Monatsblätter für Augenheilkunde* 1985, 186, 380–381.

8 ANTCLIFF, R.J.; HODGKINS, P.R.; BOWMAN, R.; KEAST-BUTLER, J. *Euphorbia lathyrus* latex keratoconjunctivitis. *Eye* 1994, 8, 696–698.

9 EKE, T. Acute kerato-uveitis associated with topical self-administration of the sap of petty spurge (*Euphorbia peplus*). *Eye* 1994, 8, 694–696.

10 HORNFELDT, C.S. Confusion over toxicity of poinsettia. *Journal of the American Veterinary Medical Association* 1989, 194, 1004.

11 NATIONAL POISONS INFORMATION SERVICE, London UK. Personal communication.

12 FROHNE, D.; PFÄNDER, H.J. *A Colour Atlas of Poisonous Plants.* Wolfe Publishing Ltd, London, UK. 1984, 119.

13 KLUG, S.; SALEEM, G.; HONCHARUK, L.; MARCUS, S. Toxicity potential of poinsettia, is the plant really toxic? *Veterinary and Human Toxicology* 1990, 32, 368.

14 WINEK, C.L.; BUTALA, J.; SHANOR, S.P.; FOCHTMAN, F.W. Toxicology of poinsettia. *Clinical Toxicology* 1978, 13, 27–45.

15 RUNYON, R. Toxicity of fresh poinsettia (*Euphorbia pulcherrima*) to Sprague-Dawley rats. *Clinical Toxicology* 1980, 16, 167–173.

16 ROCK, J.F. The poisonous plants of Hawaii. *Hawaiian Forester and Agriculturist* 1920, 17, 61.

17 EDWARDS, N. Local toxicity from a poinsettia plant: a case report. *Journal of Pediatrics* 1983, 102, 404–405.

18 SANTUCCI, B.; PICARDO, M.; CRISTAUDO, A. Contact dermatitis from *Euphorbia pulcherrima. Contact Dermatitis* 1985, 12, 285–286.

19 D'ARCY, W.G. Severe contact dermatitis from poinsettia – status of poinsettia as a toxic agent. *Archives of Dermatology* 1974, 109, 909–910.

20 CHEVALIER, H. [Study of the main plant poisonings in Maine-Anjou.] Thesis, École Nationale Vétérinaire d'Alfort, France. 1974, 11–15.

21 POLIDORI, F.; MAGGI, M. [Nutritional problems in animals. Some cases of *Mercurialis annua* poisoning in cattle. Experimental studies on differences in the toxicity of the fresh and dried plant.] *Nuova Veterinaria* 1954, 30, 146–150.

22 LONG, H.C. *Plants Poisonous to Live Stock.* Cambridge University Press, Cambridge, UK. 1917, 67–69.

23 BAKER, J.R.; FAULL, W.B. Dog's mercury (*Mercurialis perennis* L.) poisoning in sheep. *Veterinary Record* 1968, 82, 485–489.

24 WELCHMAN, D. DE B.; GIBBENS, J.C.; GILES, N.; PIERCY, D.W.T.; SKINNER, P.H. Suspected annual mercury (*Mercurialis annua*) poisoning of lambs grazing fallow arable land. *Veterinary Record* 1995, 137, 592–593.

25 LANDAU, M.; EGYED, M.N.; FLESH, D. *Mercurialis annua* poisoning in housed sheep. *Refuah Veterinarith* 1973, 30, 131–135.

26 SENF, W.; SEFFNER, W. [*Mercurialis annua* poisoning in sheep.] *Monatshefte für Veterinärmedizin* 1965, 20, 622–625.

27 BIZZETI, M.; DE LUCIA, P.G.; CORAZZA, M.; SANTINI, P.P. [*Mercurialis annua* poisoning in sheep.] *Annali della Facoltà di Medicina Veterinaria di Pisa* 1987, 60, 165–175.

28 ŞENDIL, Ç. [Clinical features and treatment of experimentally induced *Mercurialis annua* poisoning in sheep and calves.] *Veteriner Fakültesi Dergisi, Ankara Üniversitesi* 1987, 25, 480–499.

29 BISMARCK, R.; FLOEHR, W. [Dog's mercury poisoning in a dairy herd at pasture.] *Deutsche Tierärztliche Wochenschrift* 1974, 81, 433–434.

30 DELATOUR, P.; JEAN-BLAIN, C. [*Mercurialis* poisoning in cattle.] *Notes de Toxicologie Vétérinaire* 1977, No.2, 65–68.

31 ANONYMOUS. [*Mercurialis* poisoning in cattle.] *Notes de Toxicologie Vétérinaire* 1979, No.6, 348–349.

32 HOLLBERG, W.; WINKELMANN, J. [Enzootic haemoglobinuria in a dairy herd as a result of *Mercurialis* poisoning.] *Tierärztliche Umschau* 1989, 44, 162–164.

33 BEN SAID, M.S.; REKHIS, J.; AMARA, A.; BOUTOURIA, M.; MALEK, A.; ZMERLI, K. [Poisoning of cattle by *Mercurialis annua.*] *Revue de Médecine Vétérinaire* 1995, 146, 89–91.

34 DEPREZ, P.; SUSTRONCK, B.; MIJTEN, P.; VANDE VYVERE, B.; MUYLLE, E. [Two outbreaks of *Mercurialis annua* poisoning in cattle.] *Vlaams Diergeneeskundig Tijdschrift* 1996, 65, 92–96.

35 BOKORI, J.; KOVÁCS, F.; HARASZTI, E. [*Mercurialis annua* poisoning in horses.] *Magyar Állatorvosok Lapja* 1955, 10, 191–196.

36 HARTLEY, W.J.; HAKIOGLU, F. Investigation of an outbreak of icterohaemoglobinuria in goats. *Pendik Veteriner Kontrol Arastirma Enstitusi Dergisi* 1970, 2, No.2, 67–89.

37 ALZIEU, J.P.; ALZIEU, C.; DORCHIES, P. [*Mercurialis* poisoning in cattle: value of haematological studies in differential diagnosis from bovine piroplasmosis.] *Bulletin des GTV* 1993, No.3, 29–36.

38 JELINKOVA, V.; VESELY, Z. [Toxicity of castor beans.] *Veterinární Medicína* 1960, 5, 827–838.

39 CORWIN, A.H. Toxic constituents of the castor bean. *Journal of Medicinal and Pharmaceutical Chemistry* 1961, 4, 483–496.

40 LIN, T.T.S.; LI, S.S.L. Purification and physicochemical properties of ricins and agglutinins from *Ricinus communis. European Journal of Biochemistry* 1980, 105, 453–459.

41 LIST, G.R.; SPENCER, G.F.; HUNT, W.H. Toxic weed contaminants in soybean processing. *Journal of the American Oil Chemists' Society* 1979, 56, 706–710.

42 FARAH, M.O.; HASSAN, A.B.; HASHIM, M.M.; ATTA, A.H. Phytochemical and pharmacological studies on the leaves of *Ricinus communis* L. *Egyptian Journal of Veterinary Science* 1987, 24, 169–179.

43 WALLER, G.R.; EBNER, K.E.; SCROGGS, R.A.; DAS GUPTA, B.R.; CORCORAN, J.B. Studies on the toxic action of ricin. *Proceedings of the Society for Experimental Biology and Medicine* 1966, 121, 685–691.

44 KNIGHT, B. Ricin – a potent homicidal poison. *British Medical Journal* 1979, 1, 350–351.

45 TIANO, F. [Castor oil cake poisoning in the dog.] *Notes de Toxicologie Vétérinaire* 1977, No.2, 109–111.

46 GEARY, T. Castor bean poisoning. *Veterinary Record* 1950, 62, 472–473.

47 LENSCH, J. [Ricin poisoning in cattle.] *Tierärztliche Praxis* 1966, 21, 21–22.

48 SEIGLER, D.S. Toxic seed lipids. In: *Herbivores. Their Interaction with Secondary Plant Metabolites.*

Edited by G.A. Rosenthal and D.H. Janzen. Academic Press, New York and London. 1979, 449–470.

49 Fox, M.W. Castor seed residue poisoning in dairy cattle. *Veterinary Record* 1961, 73, 885–886.

50 Mel'nik, I.L.; Koltun, E.M. [Castor oil cake (*Ricinus*), a cause of illness in newborn calves.] *Veterinariya, Moscow* 1973, No.1, 98–99.

51 Anderson, T.S. Castor poisoning in Ayrshire cattle. *Veterinary Record* 1948, 60, 28.

52 Clemens, E. [Toxicity and tolerance of *Ricinus* seed oil meal by different animals.] *Landwirtschaftliche Forschung* 1963, Sonderheft 17, 202–211.

53 Purushotham, N.P.; Raghavan, G.V.; Rao, M.S.; Reddy, M.R.; Mahendar, M. Studies on the pathology of experimental feeding of castor bean meal (*Ricinus communis*) in sheep. *Indian Veterinary Journal* 1985, 62, 116–118.

54 Purushotham, N.P.; Raghavan, G.V.; Rao, M.S.; Reddy, M.R.; Mahendar, M. Pathology of thyroid gland of sheep fed on castor bean meal (*Ricinus communis*). *Indian Journal of Veterinary Pathology* 1985, 9, 70–73.

55 Lapcević, E.; Kozić, L.; Paunović, S. [The clinical picture of castor bean poisoning in the horse.] *Veterinarski Glasnik* 1960, 14, 883–886.

56 McCunn, J.; Andrew, H.; Clough, G.W. Castor-bean poisoning in horses. *Veterinary Journal* 1945, 101, 136–138.

57 Anonymous. Castor-oil bean toxicity. *Veterinary Record* 1982, 111, 172.

58 Krieger-Huber, S. [Fatal poisoning by ricin in dogs following intake of the biological fertiliser "Oscorna animalin".] *Kleintierpraxis* 1980, 25, 281–286.

59 National Poisons Information Service, London, UK. Personal communication.

60 Golosnitskii, A.K.; Kozyrev, V.M. [Changes in the blood of horses poisoned with *Ricinus communis* seeds.] *Trudy Novocherkasskogo Zootekhnichesko-Veterinarnogo Instituta* 1961, 13, 104–108.

61 Albin, R.C.; Harbaugh, F.G.; Zinn, D.W. Castor bean meal of three ricin levels for cattle. *Journal of Animal Science* 1968, 27, 288.

62 Clarke, E.G.C.; Jackson, J.H. The use of immune serum in the treatment of ricin poisoning. *British Veterinary Journal* 1956, 112, 57–62.

63 Jensen, W.I.; Allen, J.P. Naturally occurring and experimentally induced castor bean (*Ricinus communis*) poisoning in ducks. *Avian Diseases* 1981, 25, 184–194.

64 Figueredo, M. de los Angeles; Currente, H.; Rodríguez, J.; Tablada, R. [Clinical and pathological changes in geese poisoned with *Ricinus communis* (castor oil seeds.)] *Revista de Salud Animal* 1991, 13, 30–34.

65 Shrivastava, H.P.; Prasad, M.C.; Sadagopan, V.R. Hepatorenal changes in chicks fed diets containing raw and treated castor meals. *Indian Journal of Veterinary Pathology* 1988, 12, 49–53.

66 El Badwi, S.M.A.; Adam, S.E.I.; Hapke, H.J. Experimental *Ricinus communis* poisoning in chicks. *Phytotherapy Research* 1992, 6, 205–208.

67 Okoye, J.O.A.; Enunwaonye, C.A.; Okorie, A.U.; Anugwa, F.O.I. Pathological effects of feeding roasted castor bean meal (*Ricinus communis*) to chicks. *Avian Pathology* 1987, 16, 283–290.

68 Lampe, K.F. Systemic plant poisoning in children. *Pediatrics* 1974, 54, 347–351.

69 *The Times*, 29 June 1993, pp. 2 and 17.

70 O'Leary, S.B. Poisoning in man from eating poisonous plants. *Archives of Environmental Health* 1964, 9, 216–242.

71 Rauber, A.; Heard, J. Castor bean toxicity re-examined: a new perspective. *Veterinary and Human Toxicology* 1985, 27, 498–502.

72 Cooper, W.C.; Perone, V.B.; Scheel, L.D.; Keenan, R.G. Occupational hazards from castor bean pomace: tests for toxicity. *American Industrial Hygiene Association Journal* 1964, 25, 431–438.

73 Jenkins, F.P. Allergenic and toxic components of castor bean meal: review of the literature and

studies of the inactivation of these components. *Journal of the Science of Food and Agriculture* 1963, 14, 773–780.

74 LAMPE, K.F.; FAGERSTRÖM, R. *Plant Toxicity and Dermatitis.* Williams and Wilkins Co., Baltimore, USA. 1968, 62.

75 MITCHELL, J.; ROOK, A. *Botanical Dermatology. Plants and Plant Products Injurious to the Skin.* Greengrass Ltd, Vancouver, Canada. 1979, 296–297.

76 LOVELL, C.R. *Plants and the Skin.* Blackwell Scientific Punlications, Oxford, UK. 1993, 206–207.

FAGACEAE

1 CORNEVIN, C. *Des Plantes Vénéneuses.* Librairie de Firmin-Didot, Paris, France. 1887, 137–139.

2 BOHOSIEWICZ, M. [*Veterinary Toxicology.*] Panstwowe Wydawnictwo Rolnicze i Leśne, Warsaw, Poland. 1970, 214.

3 WILKENS, W.M.; CRANWELL, M.P. Beechmast poisoning in ponies. *Veterinary Record* 1990, 127, 435.

4 VÖLKER, R. *Lehrbuch der Toxikologie für Tierärzte. (Fröhner).* Ferdinand Enke Verlag, Stuttgart, Germany. 6th Edition. 1950, 325–326.

5 COOPER, P. *Poisoning by Drugs and Chemicals, Plants and Animals.* Alchemist Publications, London, UK. 3rd Edition. 1974, 102.

6 JEAN-BLAIN, A.; JEAN-BLAIN, M. [Pathogenesis of acorn poisoning in Bovidae.] *Economie et Médecine Animales* 1975, 16, 213–226.

7 SHI, Z.C. Identification of the phenolic substances in bovine urine associated with oak leaf poisoning. *Research in Veterinary Science* 1988, 45, 152–155.

8 SHI, Z.C. Research on the pathogenesis of oak leaf poisoning in cattle. In: *Poisonous Plants. Proceedings of the Third International Symposium.* Edited by L.F. James, R.F. Keeler, E.M. Bailey, P.R. Cheeke and M.P. Hegarty. Iowa State University Press, Ames, Iowa, USA. 1992, 509–516.

9 ZHU, J.; FILIPPICH, L.J.; NG, J. Rumen involvement in sheep tannic acid metabolism. *Veterinary and Human Toxicology* 1995, 37, 436–440.

10 JERRETT, I.V.; McCAUSLAND, I.P.; THOMAS, K.W.; HANDSON, P.D. Acorn poisoning in cattle, experimental reproduction and proposed pathogenesis. In: *XXII World Veterinary Congress, Abstracts Booklet.* Perth, Australia. 1983, 77.

11 WEBER-KIRCHNER, C. [Acorn poisoning in cattle. Observations on naturally affected animals and on two experimental animals.] Inaugural Dissertation, Tierärztliche Hochschule, Hannover, Germany. 1978, 88 pp.

12 BROUGHTON, J.E. Acorn poisoning. *Veterinary Record* 1976, 99, 403–404.

13 DANIELS, M.G. Acorn poisoning. *Veterinary Record* 1976, 99, 465–466.

14 LLEWELLYN, C.A. A case of chronic oak poisoning. *Veterinary Record* 1962, 74, 1238.

15 FORSYTH, A.A. *British Poisonous Plants.* HMSO, London, UK. Ministry of Agriculture, Fisheries and Food Bulletin 161, 1968, 81–83 (amended 1979, 82–84).

16 PANCIERA, R.J. Oak poisoning in cattle. In: *Effects of Poisonous Plants on Livestock.* Edited by R.F. Keeler, K.R. Van Kampen and L.F. James. Academic Press, New York and London. 2nd Edition. 1978, 499–506.

17 SPIER, S.J.; SMITH, B.P.; SEAWRIGHT, A.A.; NORMAN, B.B.; OSTROWSKI, S.R.; OLIVER, M.N. Oak toxicosis in cattle in northern California: clinical and pathological findings. *Journal of the American Veterinary Medical Association* 1987, 191, 958–964.

18 GARG, S.K.; MAKKAR, H.P.S.; NAGAL, K.B.; SHARMA, S.K.; WADHWA, D.R.; SINGH, B. Oak (*Quercus incana*) leaf poisoning in cattle. *Veterinary and Human Toxicology* 1992, 34, 161–164.

19 DOLLAHITE, J.W. Shin oak (*Quercus havardi*) poisoning in cattle. *Southwestern Veterinarian* 1960–1961, 14, 198–201.

20 WISEMAN, A.; THOMPSON, H. Acorn poisoning. *Veterinary Record* 1984, 115, 605.

21 MINISTRY OF AGRICULTURE, FISHERIES AND FOOD. Poisoning of animals in Britain. *Animal Disease Report* 1978, 2, No.2, 9–12.

22 SLAUGHTER, T.S. On acorn poisoning in cattle. *Veterinary Medicine and Small Animal Clinician* 1964, 59, 227–230.

23 DIXON, P.M.; MCPHERSON, E.A.; ROWLAND, A.C.; MACLENNAN, W. Acorn poisoning in cattle. *Veterinary Record* 1979, 104, 284–285.

24 WARREN, C.G.B.; VAUGHAN, S.M. Acorn poisoning. *Veterinary Record* 1985, 116, 82.

25 OSTROWSKI, S.R.; SMITH, B.P.; SPIER, S.J.; NORMAN, B.B.; OLIVER, M.N. Compensatory weight gain in steers recovered from oak bud toxicosis. *Journal of the American Veterinary Medical Association* 1989, 195, 481–484.

26 HOLLIMAN, A. Acorn poisoning in ruminants. *Veterinary Record* 1985, 116, 546.

27 NATIONAL POISONS INFORMATION SERVICE, London, UK. Personal communication.

28 EDWARDS, C.M. Some observations on plant poisoning in grazing animals. *Veterinary Record* 1949, 61, 864–865.

29 WAGNER, H. [Fatal poisoning of sheep by green acorns.] *Berliner und Münchener Tierärztliche Wochenschrift* 1935, 51, 452–453.

30 TUDOR, G. [Green acorn poisoning in sheep.] *Revista de Zootehnie și Medicină Veterinară* 1971, 21, No.8, 60–62.

31 KINDE, H.; BRITT, J.O.; MOLLER, G.; GIACOPUZZI, R.K. Oak poisoning in a pet pygmy goat. *California Veterinarian* 1989, 43, No.3, 9–10.

32 AKAR, F.; FILAZI, A. [Oak poisoning in goats.] *Veteriner Hekimler Derneği Dergisi* 1992, 63, No.3/4, 27–30.

33 WHARMBY, M.J. Acorn poisoning. *Veterinary Record* 1976, 99, 343.

34 BATU, A.; NADAS, Ü.G.; GÜREL, A. [Experiments on the use of calcium hydroxide for the treatment and prevention of oak leaf poisoning in rabbits.] *Pendik Veteriner Bakteriyoloji ve Seroloji Enstitusu Dergisi* 1978, 10, 93–100.

35 DOLLAHITE, J.W.; HOUSHOLDER, G.T.; CAMP, B.J. Effect of calcium hydroxide on the toxicity of post oak (*Quercus stellata*) in calves. *Journal of the American Veterinary Medical Association* 1966, 148, 908–912.

FUMARIACEAE

1 KINGSBURY, J.M. *Poisonous Plants of the United States and Canada*. Prentice-Hall Inc., New Jersey, USA. 1964, 154–156.

2 BLACK, O.F.; EGGLESTON, W.W.; KELLY, J.W.; TURNER, H.C. Poisonous properties of *Bikukulla cucullaria* (Dutchman's breeches) and *B. canadensis* (squirrel-corn). *Journal of Agricultural Research* 1923, 23, 69–77.

3 ARENA, J. M. Pretty poisonous plants. *Veterinary and Human Toxicology* 1979, 21, 108–111.

4 LOVELL, C.R. *Plants and the Skin*. Blackwell Scientific Publications, Oxford, UK. 1993, 127–128.

GERANIACEAE

1 HURST, E. *The Poison Plants of New South Wales*. Snelling Printing Works Pty Ltd, 52-54 Bay Street, Sydney, Australia. 1942, 200–201.

2 FORD, G.E. Photosensitivity due to *Erodium* spp. *Australian Veterinary Journal* 1965, 41, 56.

3 CONNOR, H.E. *The Poisonous Plants in New Zealand*. E.C. Keating, Government Printer, Wellington, New Zealand. 1977, 81–82.

4 SPOERKE, D.G.; SMOLINSKE, S.C. *Toxicity of Houseplants*. CRC Press, Boca Raton, Florida, USA. 1990, 182.

GRAMINEAE

1   SIDHU, K.S.; HARGUS, W.A.; PFANDER, W.H. Metabolic inhibitor(s) in fractions of orchardgrass (*Dactylis glomerata* L.) detected by *in vitro* rumen fermentation technique. *Proceedings of the Society for Experimental Biology and Medicine* 1967, 124, 1038–1041.

2   KÖHLER, H. [Calcinosis in cattle and the current state of research.] *Deutsche Tierärztliche Wochenschrift* 1977, 84, 98–100.

3   RAMBECK, W.A.; WETZEL, A.; ZUCKER, H. [Plant-induced calcinosis in cattle: a steroid hormone derived from vitamin D, demonstrated in *Trisetum flavescens*.] *Revue de Médecine Vétérinaire* 1989, 140, 703–705.

4   SPEDDING, C.R.W.; DIEKMAHNS, E.C. (Editors). *Grasses and Legumes in British Agriculture.* Bulletin 49 Commonwealth Bureau of Pastures and Field Crops. Commonwealth Agricultural Bureaux, Farnham Royal, UK. 1972, 273.

5   RIPEANU, M. [Observations on some cases of poisoning in animals.] *Revista de Zootehnie și Medicină Veterinară* 1963, 13, No.12, 63–64.

6   LONG, H.C. *Plants Poisonous to Live Stock.* Cambridge University Press, Cambridge, UK. 1917, 82–84.

7   KINGSBURY, J.M. *Poisonous Plants of the United States and Canada.* Prentice-Hall Inc., New Jersey, USA. 1964, 484–486.

8   AINSWORTH, G.C.; AUSTWICK, P.K.C. *Fungal Diseases of Animals.* Commonwealth Agricultural Bureaux, Farnham Royal, UK. 1st Edition. 1959, 52.

9   WATT, J.M.; BREYER-BRANDWIJK, M.G. *Medicinal and Poisonous Plants of Southern and Eastern Africa.* E. & S. Livingstone Ltd, Edinburgh and London, UK. 2nd Edition. 1962, 475–476.

10 STEYN, D.G. *The Toxicology of Plants in South Africa.* Central News Agency Ltd, South Africa. 1934, 493–497.

11 CUNNINGHAM, I.J. Non-toxicity to animals of ryegrass endophyte fungi and other endophyte fungi of New Zealand grasses. *New Zealand Journal of Agricultural Research* 1958, 1, 489–497.

12 URBAIN, A.; NOUVEL, J. [Darnel poisoning of wild animals in captivity.] *Bulletin de l'Académie Vétérinaire de France* 1939, 12, 77–82.

13 MUNRO, I.B. Photosensitisation and neurological disorders in grazing cattle and sheep in S.E. England. In: *Proceedings of the 5th Meeting on Mycotoxins in Animal & Human Health, Edinburgh, 1984.* Edited by M.O. Moss and M. Frank. University of Surrey, Guildford, UK. 1985, 145–146.

14 BREEZE, R.G.; PIRIE, H.M.; SELMAN, I.E.; WISEMAN, A. Fog fever (acute pulmonary emphysema) in cattle in Britain. *Veterinary Bulletin* 1976, 46, 243–251.

15 ROBERTS, H.E.; BENSON, J.A.; JONES, D.G.H. "Fog fever" (acute bovine pulmonary emphysema) in Mid-Wales, 1971: features of occurrence. *Veterinary Record* 1973, 92, 558–561.

16 SELMAN, I.E.; WISEMAN, A.; PIRIE, H.M.; BREEZE, R.G. Fog fever in cattle: clinical and epidemiological features. *Veterinary Record* 1974, 95, 139–146

17 POTCHOIBA, M.J.; CARLSON, J.R.; NOCERINI, M.R.; BREEZE, R.G. Effect of monensin and supplemental hay on ruminal 3-methylindole formation in adult cows after abrupt change to lush pasture. *American Journal of Veterinary Research* 1992, 53, 129–133.

18 TOR-AGBIDYE, J.; BLYTHE, L.L.; CRAIG, A.M. Correlation of quantities of ergovaline and lolitrem B toxins to clinical cases of tall fescue toxicosis and perennial ryegrass staggers. In: *Plant-associated Toxins, Agricultural, Phytochemical and Ecological Aspects.* Edited by S.M. Colegate and P.R. Dorling. CAB International, Wallingford, UK. 1994, 369–374.

19 PRITCHARD, G.C.; LEWIS, G.C. Ryegrass staggers. *Veterinary Record* 1995, 137, 471–472.

20 FOOT, J.Z.; WOODBURN, O.J.; WALSH, J.R.; HEAZLEWOOD, P.G. Responses in grazing sheep to toxins from perennial ryegrass/endophyte associations. In: *Plant-associated Toxins. Agricultural,*

Phytochemical and Ecological Aspects. Edited by S.M. Colegate and P.R. Dorling. CAB International, Wallingford, UK. 1994, 375–380.

21 DAVIES, E.G.; ASHTON, W.M. Coumarin and related compounds of *Anthoxanthum puelli* and *Melilotus alba* and dicoumarol formation in spoilt sweet vernal and sweet clover hay. *Journal of the Science of Food and Agriculture* 1964, 15, 733–738.

22 SCHEEL, C.D. The toxicology of sweet clover and coumarin anticoagulants. In: *Mycotoxic Fungi, Mycotoxins, Mycotoxicoses. An Encyclopedic Handbook.* Edited by T.D. Wyllie and L.G. Morehouse. Marcel Dekker Inc., New York, USA. Vol. 2, 1978, 121–142.

23 PRITCHARD, D.G.; MARKSON, L.M.; BRUSH, P.J.; SAWTELL, J.A.A.; BLOXHAM, P.A. Haemorrhagic syndrome of cattle associated with the feeding of sweet vernal (*Anthoxanthum odoratum*) hay containing dicoumarol. *Veterinary Record* 1983, 113, 78–84.

24 CRANWELL, M.P. Acute fatal haemorrhagic syndrome in dairy cows. *Veterinary Record* 1983, 112, 486.

25 RAISBEK, M.F.; ROTTINGHAUS, G.E.; KENDALL, J.D. Effects of naturally occurring mycotoxins on ruminants. In: *Mycotoxins and Animal Foods.* Edited by J.E. Smith and R.S. Henderson. CRC Press Inc., Boca Raton, Florida, USA. 1991, 647–677.

26 STRICKLAND, J.R.; OLIVER, J.W.; CROSS, D.L. Fescue toxicosis and its impact on animal agriculture. *Veterinary and Human Toxicology* 1993, 35, 454–464.

27 ORSKOV, E.R. Whole grain feeding for ruminants. *Veterinary Record* 1980, 106, 399–401.

28 MULLEN, P.A. Intensive beef production – barley beef. *Veterinary Bulletin* 1972, 42, 119–124.

29 SIMONSSON, A.; BJORKLUND, N.E. Some effects of the fineness of ground barley on gastric lesions and gastric contents in growing pigs. *Swedish Journal of Agricultural Research* 1978, 8, 97–106.

30 DOBSON, K.J.; DAVIES, R.L.; CARGILL, C.F. Ulceration of the pars oesophagia in pigs. *Australian Veterinary Journal* 1978, 54, 601–602.

31 IBRAHIM, T.M.; SHAKER, M.; KAMEL, S.H. Cyanide content in growing corn. *Veterinary Medical Journal, Giza* 1969, 16, 127–134.

32 DUNLOP, R.H. Pathogenesis of ruminant lactic acidosis. *Advances in Veterinary Science and Comparative Medicine* 1972, 16, 259–302.

33 WARD, A.T.; MARQUARDT, R.R. Antinutritional activity of a water-soluble pentosan-rich fraction from rye grain. *Poultry Science* 1987, 66, 1665–1674.

34 ELAM, C.J. Acidosis in feedlot cattle: practical observations. *Journal of Animal Science* 1976, 43, 898–901.

35 HUBER, T.L. Physiological effects of acidosis on feedlot cattle. *Journal of Animal Science* 1976, 43, 902–909.

36 McMANUS, W.R.; LEE, G.J.; ROBINSON, V.N.E. Micro-lesions of rumen papillae of sheep fed diets of wheat grain. *Research in Veterinary Science* 1977, 22,135–137.

37 LEE, G.J. Changes in composition and pH of digesta along the gastrointestinal tract of sheep in relation to scouring induced by wheat engorgement. *Australian Journal of Agricultural Research* 1977, 28, 1075–1082.

38 NAGARAJA, T.J.; BARTLEY, E.E.; FINA, L.R.; ANTHONY, H.D. Relationship of rumen gram-negative bacteria and free endotoxin to lactic acidosis in cattle. *Journal of Animal Science* 1978, 47, 1329–1337.

39 CLARKE, M.L.; HARVEY, D.G.; HUMPHREYS, D.J. *Veterinary Toxicology.* Baillière Tindall, London, UK. 2nd Edition. 1981, 225–227.

40 FRIGG, M.; BRUBACHER, G. Biotin deficiency in chicks fed a wheat-based diet. *International Journal for Vitamin and Nutrition Research* 1976, 46, 314–321.

GUTTIFERAE

1   HUDSON, J.B.; TOWERS, G.H.N. Benefits of plant phototoxins: antiviral properties. In: *Plant-associated Toxins. Agricultural, Phytochemical and Ecological Aspects.* Edited by S.M. Colegate and P.R. Dorling. CAB International, Wallingford, UK. 1994, 517–522.

2   ARAYA, O.S.; FORD, E.J.H. An investigation of photosensitisation caused by ingestion of St John's wort (*Hypericum perforatum*) by calves. *Journal of Comparative Pathology* 1981, 91, 135–141.

3   MARSH, C.D.; CLAWSON, A.B. Toxic effect of St John's wort (*Hypericum perforatum*) on cattle and sheep. United States Department of Agriculture Technical Bulletin No.202, 1930, 23 pp.

4   RAY, G. [Note on the toxic effects of leaves of *Hypericum crispum.*] *Recueil de Médecine Vétérinaire* 1914, 68, 39–42.

5   CUNNINGHAM, I.J. Photosensitivity diseases in New Zealand. V. Photosensitisation by St John's wort (*Hypericum perforatum*). *New Zealand Journal of Science and Technology* 1947, 29A, 207–213.

6   DODD, S. St. John's wort and its effects on livestock. *Agricultural Gazette of New South Wales* 1920, 31, 265–272.

7   KÜMPER, H. [*Hypericum* poisoning in sheep.] *Tierärztliche Praxis* 1989, 17, 257–261.

8   CLARE, N.T. *Photosensitization in Diseases of Domestic Animals.* Review Series No.3, Commonwealth Bureau of Animal Health. Commonwealth Agricultural Bureaux, Farnham Royal, UK. 1952, 11–15.

9   HOLMES, J.W.H. Simultaneous cases of photosensitisation. *Veterinary Record* 1963, 75, 1223–1224.

10 SALGUES, R. [New chemical and toxicological studies on the genus *Hypericum* L. (Tourn).] *Qualitas Plantarum et Materiae Vegetabiles* 1961, 8, 38–64.

11 KAKO, M.D.N.; AL-SULTAN, I.I.; SALEEM, A.M. Studies of sheep experimentally poisoned with *Hypericum perforatum. Veterinary and Human Toxicology* 1993, 35, 298–300.

12 TURNER, N.J.; SZCZAWINSKI, A.F. *Common Poisonous Plants and Mushrooms of North America.* Timber Press, Portland. Oregon, USA. 1991, 136–137.

HIPPOCASTANACEAE

1   CONNOR, H.E. *The Poisonous Plants in New Zealand.* E.C. Keating, Government Printer, Wellington, New Zealand, 1977, 96.

2   SCOTT, H.G. Poisonous plants and animals. In: *Food-borne Infections and Intoxications.* Edited by H. Riemann. Academic Press, New York and London. 1969, 543–604.

3   REYNARD, G.B.; NORTON, J.B.S. Poisonous plants of Maryland in relation to livestock. *University of Maryland Agricultural Experiment Station Technical Bulletin A10,* 1942, 270.

4   KORNHEISER, K.M. Buckeye poisoning in cattle. *Veterinary Medicine and Small Animal Clinician* 1983, 78, 769–770.

5   MAGNUSSON, R.A.; WHITTIER, W.D.; VEIT, H.P.; EASLEY, K.J.; MELDRUM, J.B.; JORTNER, B.S.; CHICKERING, W.R. Yellow buckeye (*Aesculus octandra* Marsh) toxicity in calves. *Bovine Practitioner* 1983, No.18, 195–199.

6   MUENSCHER, W.C. *Poisonous Plants of the United States.* Macmillan, New York, USA. 1939, 157–159.

7   NATIONAL POISONS INFORMATION SERVICE, London, UK. Personal communication.

8   WILLIAMS, M.C.; OLSEN, J.D. Toxicity of seeds of three *Aesculus* spp to chicks and hamsters. *American Journal of Veterinary Research* 1984, 45, 539–542.

9   LAMPE, K.F.; FAGERSTRÖM, R. *Plant Toxicity and Dermatitis.* Williams and Wilkins Co., Baltimore, USA. 1968, 23.

HYDRANGEACEAE

1   KINGSBURY, J.M. *Poisonous Plants of the United States and Canada*. Prentice-Hall Inc., Englewood Cliffs, New Jersey, USA. 1964, 370–371.

2   HURST, E. *The Poison Plants of New South Wales*. Snelling Printing Works Pty Ltd, 52–54 Bay Street, Sydney, Australia. 1942, 138.

3   TURNER, N.J.; SZCZAWINSKI, A.F. *Common Poisonous Plants and Mushrooms of North America*. Timber Press, Portland, Oregon, USA. 1991, 168.

4   SPOERKE, D.G.; SMOLINSKE, S.C. *Toxicity of Houseplants*. CRC Press, Boca Raton, Florida, USA. 1990, 156–157.

5   LOVELL, C.R. *Plants and the Skin*. Blackwell Scientific Publications, Oxford, UK. 1993, 137–138.

IRIDACEAE

1   CORNEVIN, C. *Des Plantes Vénéneuses*. Librairie de Firmin-Didot, Paris, France. 1887, 131.

2   HENSLOW, G. *Poisonous Plants in Field and Garden*. Society for Promoting Christian Knowledge, London, UK. 1901, 165.

3   KINGSBURY, J.M. *Deadly Harvest*. George Allen and Unwin Ltd, London, UK. 1967, 114.

4   JORDAN, M. *A Guide to Wild Plants*. Millington Books Ltd, London, UK. 1976, 225–226.

5   BOHOSIEWICZ, M. *Toksykologia Weterynaryjna*. Panstwowe Wydawnictwo Rolnicze Leśne, Warsaw, Poland. 1970, 311.

6   BRUCE, E.A. Iris poisoning of calves. *American Veterinary Journal* 1919-1920, 56, New Series 9, 72–74.

7   BODDIE, G.F. Toxicological problems in veterinary practice. *Veterinary Record* 1947, 59, 471–486.

8   FORSYTH, A.A. *British Poisonous Plants*. HMSO, London, UK. Ministry of Agriculture, Fisheries and Food Bulletin 161, 1968, 107–108 (amended 1979, 108–109).

9   LAMPE, K.F.; McCANN, M.A. *AMA Handbook of Poisonous and Injurious Plants*. American Medical Association, Chicago, USA. 1985, 98.

10 LOVELL, C.R. *Plants and the Skin*. Blackwell Scientific Publications, Oxford, UK. 1993, 226–227.

11 SCHAUENBERG, P.; PARIS, F. *Guide to Medicinal Plants*. Lutterworth Press, Guildford and London, UK. 1977, 238.

12 NATIONAL POISONS INFORMATION SERVICE, London, UK. Personal communication.

13 MELI, F.; BRACA, G.; RICHETTI, A.; CATARSINI, O. [Outbreak of spontaneous poisoning by *Gladiolus segetum* Ker-Gall in cattle at pasture.] *Atti della Società Italiana di Buiatria* 1983, 14, 365–377.

JUNCACEAE

1   ALBISTON, H.E. The joint leaf rush (*Juncus holoschoenus*): a cyanogenetic plant. *Australian Veterinary Journal* 1937, 13, 200.

2   MOGG, A.O.D. Vlei poisoning. *South African Journal of Science* 1927, 24, 269–277.

3   MINISTRY OF AGRICULTURE, FISHERIES AND FOOD. *Grass and Grassland*. HMSO, London, UK. 1966, Bulletin No.154, 15.

4   MINISTRY OF AGRICULTURE, FISHERIES AND FOOD. *Grass and Grassland*. HMSO, London, UK. 1966, Bulletin No.154, 90.

5   FORSYTH, A.A. *British Poisonous Plants*. HMSO, London, UK. Ministry of Agriculture, Fisheries and Food Bulletin 161, 1968, 106 (amended 1979, 106–107).

JUNCAGINACEAE

1 CONN, E.E. Cyanogenic glycosides. *Journal of Agricultural and Food Chemistry* 1969, 17, 519–526.

2 CONN, E.E. Cyanogenesis, the production of hydrogen cyanide by plants. In: *Effects of Poisonous Plants on Livestock.* Edited by R.F. Keeler, K.R. Van Kampen and L.F. James. Academic Press, New York and London. 1978, 301–310.

3 KINGSBURY, J.M. *Poisonous Plants of the United States and Canada.* Prentice-Hall Inc., New Jersey, USA. 1964, 501–503.

4 ANONYMOUS. *16 plants poisonous to livestock in Western States.* United States Department of Agriculture Farmer's Bulletin No.2106, 1958, 2–4.

5 HIBBS, C.M. Cyanide and nitrate toxicoses of cattle. *Veterinary and Human Toxicology* 1979, 21, 401–403.

6 JUBB, K.V.F.; KENNEDY, P.C.; PALMER, N. *Pathology of Domestic Animals.* Vol. 1. Academic Press, New York and London. 3rd Edition. 1985, 250.

7 CLAWSON, A.B.; MORAN, E.A. Toxicity of arrowgrass for sheep and remedial treatment. United States Department of Agriculture Technical Bulletin No.580, 1937, 16 pp.

8 BURROWS, G.E. Cyanide intoxication in sheep: therapeutics. *Veterinary and Human Toxicology* 1981, 23, 22–27.

LABIATAE

1 FORSYTH, A.A. *British Poisonous Plants.* HMSO, London, UK. Ministry of Agriculture, Fisheries and Food Bulletin 161, 1968, 96 (amended 1979, 97).

2 FROLKIN, M. [Poisoning of horses and pigs with seeds of hemp-nettle (*Galeopsis*).] *Veterinariya, Moscow* 1965, 42, No.9, 68.

3 VON HAZSLINSZKY, B. [Poisoning of horses by *Glechoma.*] *Deutsche Tierärztliche Wochenschrift* 1935, 43, 708–709.

4 VON NICOLAU, A.; BÂRZĂ, H.; DUCA, H.; CRETEANU, C.; MAY, H.; POPOVICIU, A. [Acute emphysema of the lungs in horses caused by ingestion of ground ivy (*Glechoma hederacea*).] *Monatshefte für Veterinärmedizin* 1956, 11, 534–538.

5 RICHTER, H.E. [Damage caused by the etheric oils of *Mentha longifolia* (abortion in cows).] *Wiener Tierärztliche Monatsschrift* 1966, 53, 201–202.

6 LOVELL, C.R. *Plants and the Skin.* Blackwell Scientific Publications, Oxford, UK. 1993, 198–199.

LEGUMINOSAE

1 JAMES, L.F.; KEELER, R.F.; JOHNSON, A.E.; WILLIAMS, M.C.; CRONIN, E.H.; OLSEN, J.D. Plants poisonous to livestock in the Western States. United States Department of Agriculture, Agriculture Information Bulletin No.415, 1980, 41–43.

2 PASS, M.A. Toxicity of plant-derived aliphatic nitrotoxins. In: *Plant-associated Toxins. Agricultural, Phytochemical and Ecological Aspects.* Edited by S.M. Colegate and P.R. Dorling. CAB International, Wallingford, UK. 1994, 541–545.

3 DORLING, P.R.; COLEGATE, S.M.; HUXTABLE, C.R. Swainsonine: a toxic indolizidine alkaloid. In: *Toxicants of Plant Origin. Volume I. Alkaloids.* Edited by P.R. Cheeke. CRC Press, Boca Raton, Florida, USA. 1989, 237–256.

4 JAMES, L.F.; HARTLEY, W.F.; PANTER, K.E.; STEGELMEIER, B.L.; GOULD, D.; MAYLAND, H.F. *Selenium* poisoning in cattle. In: *Plant-associated Toxins. Agricultural, Phytochemical and Ecological Aspects.* Edited by S.M. Colegate and P.R. Dorling. CAB International, Wallingford, UK. 1994, 416–420.

5 SHERWOOD, R.T.; SHAMMA, M.; MONIOT, J.L.; KROSCHEWSKY, J.R. Flavone C-glycosides from *Coronilla*

varia. Phytochemistry 1973, 12, 2275–2278.

6   SHENK, J.S.; WANGSNESS, P.J.; LEACH, R.M.; GUSTINE, D.L.; GOBBLE, J.L.; BARNES, R.F. Relationship between β-nitropropionic acid content of crown vetch and toxicity in nonruminant animals. *Journal of Animal Science* 1976, 42, 616–621.

7   GUSTINE, D.L.; MOYER, B.G.; WANGSNESS, P J.; SHENK, J.S. Ruminal metabolism of 3-nitropropanoyl-D-glucopyranoses from crown vetch. *Journal of Animal Science* 1977, 44, 1107–1111.

8   SÁLYI, G.; SZTOJKOV, V.; HILBERTNÉ MIKLOVICS, M. [Crown vetch (*Coronilla varia* L.) poisoning in coypu.] *Magyar Állatorvosok Lapja* 1988, 43, 313–316.

9   BARTÍK, M.; PISKAČ, A. (Editors) *Veterinary Toxicology.* Elsevier, Amsterdam, Netherlands. 1981, 250.

10 SCHAUENBERG, P.; PARIS, F. *Guide to Medicinal Plants.* Lutterworth Press, Guildford and London, UK. 1977, 50.

11 NICHOLSON, J.A. *Lander's Veterinary Toxicology.* Baillière, Tindall and Cox, London, UK. 1945, 216.

12 KÖHLER, H. [Examination of *Galega* species for their toxin content by biological methods. I. Toxicity of goat's rue (*Galega officinalis*) for warm-blooded animals.] *Biologisches Zentralblatt* 1969, 88, 165–177.

13 PUYT, J.D.; FALIU, L.; KECK, G.; GEDFRAIN, J.C.; PINAULT, L.; TAINTURIER, D. Fatal poisoning of sheep by *Galega officinalis* (French honeysuckle). *Veterinary and Human Toxicology* 1981, 23, 410–411.

14 FALIU, L.; PUYT, J.D.; TAINTURIER, D. [Goat's rue (*Galega officinalis*), a very dangerous legume for sheep.] *Recueil de Médecine Vétérinaire* 1981, 157, 419–426.

15 PUYT, J.D.; FALIU, L. [Poisoning of sheep by *Galega officinalis* in France.] Proceedings of the 13th World Congress on Diseases of Cattle, Durban, South Africa. 1984, 2, 670–674.

16 RIPEANU, M. [Observations on some important cases of poisoning in animals.] *Revista de Zootehnie și Medicină Veterinară* 1963, 13, No.12, 61–69.

17 CONNOR, H.E. *The Poisonous Plants in New Zealand.* E.C. Keating, Government Printer, Wellington, New Zealand. 1977, 107.

18 NUTTALL, W.O.; THOMPSON, K.G. Goat's rue toxicity in a goat. *Surveillance, New Zealand* 1986, 13, No.2, 19.

19 GRESHAM, A.C.J.; BOOTH, K. Poisoning of sheep by goat's rue. *Veterinary Record* 1991, 129, 197–198.

20 MORQUER, R.; RIVAS, P.; ANDRAL, L. [*Galega officinalis*: a dangerous plant for livestock.] *Revue de Médecine Vétérinaire* 1952, 103, 327–342.

21 KUDRNA, V.; RENDLA, J.; MARKALOUS, E. [Stimulation of milk production by feeding *Galega officinalis.*] *Sborník Jihočeská Univerzita Zemědělská Fakulta, České Budějovice. Fytotechnická Řada* 1992, 9, 254.

22 KEELER, R.F.; BAKER, D.C.; PANTER, K.E. Concentration of galegine in *Verbesina encelioides* and *Galega officinalis* and the toxic and pathologic effects induced by the plants. *Journal of Environmental Pathology, Toxicology and Oncology* 1992, 11, No.2, 11–18.

23 KEELER, R.F.; JOHNSON, A.E.; STUART, L.D.; EVANS, J.O. Toxicosis from and possible adaptation to *Galega officinalis* in sheep and the relationship to *Verbesina encelioides* toxicosis. *Veterinary and Human Toxicology* 1986, 28, 309–315.

24 KEELER, R.F.; BAKER, D.C.; EVANS, J.O. Individual animal susceptibility and its relationship to induced adaptation or tolerance in sheep to *Galega officinalis* L. *Veterinary and Human Toxicology* 1988, 30, 420–423.

25 GRANT, G. Lectins. In: *Toxic Substances in Crop Plants.* Edited by J.P.F. D'Mello, C.M. Duffus and J.H. Duffus. Royal Society of Chemistry, Cambridge, UK. 1991, 49–67.

26 DUFFUS, C.M.; SMITH, P.M. Legumes and their toxins. *Span* 1981, 24, 63–65.

27 ROMBOLI, I.; FINZI, A. [The antithyroid factors in soya.] *Rivista di Zootecnia e Veterinaria* 1974, No.2, 123–137.

28 FEDELI AVANZI, C. [Thyroid-inhibiting effects of soya beans.] *Agricoltura Italiana, Pisa* 1972, 72, 293–296.

29 LIENER, I.E. Antinutritional factors related to proteins and amino acids. In: *Foodborne Disease Handbook. Volume 3.* Edited by Y.H. Hui, J.R. Gorham, K.D. Murrell and D.O. Oliver. Marcel Dekker, Inc., New York, USA. 1994, 261–309.

30 HOVE, E.L.; KING, S.; HILL, G.D. Composition, protein quality and toxins of seeds of the grain legumes *Glycine max, Lupinus* spp., *Phaseolus* spp., *Pisum sativum,* and *Vicia faba. New Zealand Journal of Agricultural Research* 1978, 21, 457–462.

31 BOOTH, A.N.; ROBBINS, D.J.; RIBELIN, W.E.; DEEDS, F. Effect of raw soybean meal and amino acids on pancreatic hypertrophy. *Proceedings of the Society for Experimental Biology and Medicine* 1960, 104, 681–683.

32 SAXENA, H.C.; JENSEN, L.S.; McGINNIS, J.; LAUBER, J.K. Histo-physiological studies on chick pancreas as influenced by feeding raw soybean meal. *Proceedings of the Society for Experimental Biology and Medicine* 1963, 112, 390–393.

33 STOCKMAN, S. Cases of poisoning in cattle by feeding a meal from soya bean after extraction of the oil. *Journal of Comparative Pathology and Therapeutics* 1916, 29, 95–107.

34 STEWART, G.H.G.; LAWRENCE, J.A. An outbreak of hepatosis dietetica in Rhodesia. *Rhodesian Veterinary Journal* 1978, 8, 80–86.

35 MOUNTS, T.L.; DUTTON, H.J.; EVANS, C.D.; COWAN, J.C. Chick edema factor: removal from soybean oil. *Journal of the American Oil Chemists' Society* 1976, 53, 105–107.

36 KINGSBURY, J.M. *Poisonous Plants of the United States and Canada.* Prentice-Hall Inc., New Jersey, USA. 1964, 320–322.

37 BORNSTEIN, S.; LIPSTEIN, B. The influence of age of chicks on their sensitivity to raw soybean oil meal. *Poultry Science* 1963, 42, 61–70.

38 FINZI, A.; ROMBOLI, I. [Congenital blindness in chicks as a result of prolonged administration of raw soya bean meal to laying hens.] *Rivista Italiana delle Sostanze Grasse* 1972, 49, 252–253.

39 COOPER, P. *Poisoning by Drugs and Chemicals, Plants and Animals.* Alchemist Publications, London, UK. 3rd Edition. 1974, 69–70.

40 FORSYTH, A.A. *British Poisonous Plants.* HMSO, London, UK. Ministry of Agriculture, Fisheries and Food Bulletin 161, 1968, 60–61 (amended 1979, 62–63).

41 AUCHTERLONE, L. Laburnum poisoning. *Veterinary Record* 1948, 60, 633.

42 CONNOLLY, F. Laburnum poisoning in cattle. *Irish Veterinary Journal* 1949, 3, 266–268.

43 KEELER, R.F.; BAKER, D.C. Myopathy in cattle induced by alkaloid extracts from *Thermopsis montana, Laburnum anagyroides* and a *Lupinus* sp. *Journal of Comparative Pathology* 1990, 103, 169–182.

44 CLARKE, M.L.; CLARKE, E.G.C.; KING, T. Fatal laburnum poisoning in a dog. *Veterinary Record* 1971, 88, 199–200.

45 LEYLAND, A. Laburnum (*Cytisus laburnum*) poisoning in two dogs. *Veterinary Record* 1981, 109, 287.

46 NATIONAL POISONS INFORMATION SERVICE, London, UK. Personal communication.

47 CORNEVIN, C. *Des Plantes Vénéneuses.* Librarie de Firmin-Didot, Paris, France. 1887, 288–307.

48 BRAMLEY, A.; GOULDING, R. Laburnum "poisoning". *British Medical Journal* 1981, 283, 1220–1221.

49 MITCHELL, R.G. Laburnum poisoning in children. Report on ten cases. *Lancet* 1951, II, 57–58.

50 HAUPT, H. [Poisonous and less poisonous plants. Part 8. *Laburnum anagyroides.*] *Kinderkrankenschwester* 1993, 12, 258.

51 MOŘKOVSKÝ, O.; KUČERA, J. [Outbreak of poisoning by seeds of *Laburnum anagyroides* in children in a kindergarten.] *Československá Pediatrie* 1980, 35, 284–285.

52 FURET, Y.; ERNOUF, D.; BRECHOT, J.F.; AUTRET, E.; BRETEAU, M. [Outbreak of poisoning by laburnum flowers.] *Presse Médicale* 1986, 15, 1103–1104.

53 RICHARDS, H.G.H.; STEPHENS, A. A fatal case of laburnum seed poisoning. *Medical Science and*

the Law 1970, 10, 260–266.

54 FORRESTER, R.M. "Have you eaten laburnum?" *Lancet* 1979, I, 1073.

55 ROY, D.N.; SPENCER, P.S. Lathyrogens. In: *Toxicants of Plant Origin. Volume III. Proteins and Amino Acids.* CRC Press, Boca Raton, Florida, USA. 1989, 169–201.

56 LAMBEIN, F.; DE VOS, B. Lathyrism in young chicks induced by isoxazolin-5-ones from *Lathyrus odoratus* seedlings. *Archives Internationales de Physiologie et de Biochimie* 1981, 89, No.2 , B66–B67.

57 BARROW, M.V.; SIMPSON, C.F.; MILLER, E.J. Lathyrism: a review. *Quarterly Journal of Biology* 1974, 49, 101–128.

58 ROY, D.N. Toxic amino acids and proteins from *Lathyrus* plants and other leguminous species: a literature review. *Nutrition Abstracts and Reviews, Series A* 1981, 51, 691–707.

59 LEVENE, C.I. Collagen and lathyrism. *Proceedings of the Royal Society of Medicine* 1966, 59, 757–758.

60 ANONYMOUS. Lathyrism – an ancient disease, odoratism – an experimental model. *Nutrition Reviews* 1959, 17, 272–274.

61 DASTUR, D.K.; IYER, C.G. Lathyrism versus odoratism. *Nutrition Reviews* 1959, 17, 33–36.

62 FORSYTH, A.A. *British Poisonous Plants.* HMSO London, UK. Ministry of Agriculture, Fisheries and Food Bulletin 161, 1968, 62–63 (amended 1979, 64–65).

63 SUGG, R.S.; SIMMS, B.T.; BAKER, K.G. Studies of toxicity of wild winter peas (*Lathyrus hirsutus*) for cattle. *Veterinary Medicine* 1944, 39, 308–311.

64 GIBBONS, W.J. Forage poisoning. Part Two. *Modern Veterinary Practice* 1959, 40, No.16, 43–47.

65 BURROWS, G.E.; TATE, L.H.; TRIPP, M.L.; WHITENACK, D.; EDWARDS, W.C. Suspected intoxications due to *Lathyrus. Veterinary and Human Toxicology* 1993, 35, 262–263.

66 ANONYMOUS. Lathyrism in sheep. *Surveillance* 1981, 8, 22.

67 CONNOR, H.E. *The Poisonous Plants in New Zealand.* E.C. Keating, Government Printer, Wellington, New Zealand. 1977, 105.

68 RASMUSSEN, M.A.; ALLISON, M.J.; FOSTER, J.G. Flatpea intoxication in sheep and indications of ruminal adaptation. *Veterinary and Human Toxicology* 1993, 35, 123–127.

69 ROWE, L.D.; IVIE, G.W.; DELOACH, J.R.; FOSTER, J.G. The toxic effects of mature flatpea (*Lathyrus sylvestris* L cv Lathco) on sheep. *Veterinary and Human Toxicology* 1993, 35, 127–133.

70 CHOWDHURY, S.D.; DAVIS, R.H. Comparison of the effects of two lathyrogens on the reproductive system of the laying hen. *Veterinary Record* 1989, 124, 240–242.

71 GREATOREX, J.C. Some unusual cases of plant poisoning in animals. *Veterinary Record* 1966, 78, 725–727.

72 LIPPEGAUS, K.; KÄHN, B.; SCHOON, H.A. [Neurolathyrism in two horses after consumption of seeds of *Lathyrus latifolius*.] *Pferdeheilkunde* 1992, 8, 181–186.

73 KINGSBURY, J. M. *Poisonous Plants of the United States and Canada.* Prentice-Hall, New Jersey, USA. 1964, 326–331.

74 PRODANOV, P.; ZHELEZOVA, B. [Studies on the cyanogenic properties of *Lotus corniculatus* (bird's foot trefoil) in Bulgaria.] *Izvestiya na Instituta po Sravnitelna Patologiya na Domashnite Zhivotni, Sofia* 1960, 8, 281–287.

75 DOBES, F.; JŮZA, J. [Investigation of the HCN content of leaves, flowers and pods of bird's foot trefoil (*Lotus corniculatus*.] *Rostlinná Výroba* 1972, 18, 1097–1104.

76 BIRK, Y.; PERI, I. Saponins. In: *Toxic Constituents of Plant Foodstuffs.* Edited by I.E. Liener. Academic Press, New York and London. 2nd Edition. 1980, 161–182.

77 DOUGHERTY, R.W.; CHRISTENSEN, R.B. In vivo absorption of hydrocyanic acid of plant juice origin. *Cornell Veterinarian* 1953, 43, 481–486.

78 SHKLYAR, B.L. [Hydrocyanic acid poisoning by bird's foot trefoil (*Lotus corniculatus*).] *Veterinariya, Moscow* 1956, 33, No.6, 79.

79 RICHTER, H.E. [Influence of certain indigenous Austrian plants on milk quality. II. Taint and

smell.] *Wiener Tierärztliche Monatsschrift* 1964, 51, 266–280.

80 GLADSTONES, J.S. Lupins as crop plants. *Field Crop Abstracts* 1970, 23, 123–148.

81 HOVE, E.L.; KING, S. Trypsin inhibitor contents of lupin seeds and other grain legumes. *New Zealand Journal of Agricultural Research* 1979, 22, 41–42.

82 SCHULTZ, G.; ELGHAMRY, M.I. Isolation of biochanin A from *Lupinus termis* and estimation of its estrogenic activity. *Naturwissenschaften* 1971, 58, 98.

83 GARDINER, M.R. Lupinosis. *Advances in Veterinary Science* 1967, 11, 85–138.

84 KEELER, R.F. Lupin alkaloids from teratogenic and nonteratogenic lupins. III. Identification of anagyrine as the probable teratogen in feeding trials. *Journal of Toxicology and Environmental Health* 1976, 1, 889–898.

85 KEELER, R.F. Alkaloid teratogens from *Lupinus, Conium, Veratrum* and related genera. In: *Effects of Poisonous Plants on Livestock.* Edited by R.F. Keeler, K.R. Van Kampen and L.F. James. Academic Press, New York and London. 1978, 397–408.

86 GARDNER, D.R.; PANTER, K.E. Anagyrine and ammodendrine alkaloid levels in the blood of cattle, sheep and goats fed teratogenic lupin species. In: *Plant-associated Toxins. Agricultural, Phytochemical and Ecological Aspects.* Edited by S.M. Colegate and P.R. Dorling. CAB International, Wallingford, UK. 1994, 173–177.

87 KEELER, R.F.; PANTER, K.E. Induction of crooked calf disease by the piperidine alkaloid-containing plant *Lupinus formosus.* In: *Poisonous Plants. Proceedings of the Third International Symposium.* Edited by L.F. James, R.F. Keeler, E.M. Bailey, P.R. Cheeke and M.P. Hegerty. Iowa State University Press, Ames, Iowa, USA. 1992, 239–243.

88 CRAIGMILL, A.L.; CROSBY, D.; KILGORE, W., POPPEN, N.; HEDRICK, K. Passage of toxic alkaloids into goats milk. *Proceedings of the Third International Conference on Goat Production and Disease, Tucson, Arizona, 1982.* Dairy Goat Journal Publishing Co., Scottsdale, Arizona, USA. 1982, 567.

89 ALLEN, J.G. Recent advances with cultivated lupins with emphasis on toxicological aspects. In: *Poisonous Plants. Proceedings of the Third International Symposium.* Edited by L.F. James, R.F. Keeler, E.M. Bailey, P.R. Cheeke and M.P. Hegerty. Iowa State University Press, Ames, Iowa, USA. 1992, 229–233.

90 GARDINER, M.R.; PETTERSON, D.S. Pathogenesis of mouse lupinosis induced by a fungus (*Cytospora* sp.) growing on dead lupins. *Journal of Comparative Pathology* 1972, 82, 5–13.

91 VAN WARMELO, K.T.; MARASAS, W.F.O.; ADELAAR, T.F.; KELLERMAN, T.S.; VAN RENSBERG, I.B.J.; MINNE, J.A. Experimental evidence that lupinosis of sheep is a mycotoxicosis caused by the fungus *Phomopsis leptostromiformis* (Kühn) Bubák. *Journal of the South African Veterinary Medical Association* 1970, 41, 235–247.

92 WOOD, P.McR., BROWN, A.G.P.; PETTERSON, D.S. Production of lupinosis mycotoxin by *Phomopsis russiana. Australian Journal of Experimental Biology and Medical Science* 1973, 51, 557–558.

93 COCKRUM, P.A.; PETTERSON, D.S.; EDGAR, J.A. Identification of novel phomopsins in lupin seed extracts. In: *Plant-associated Toxins. Agricultural, Phytochemical and Ecological Aspects.* Edited by S.M. Colegate and P.R. Dorling. CAB International, Wallingford, UK. 1994, 232–237.

94 ZÜRN, F.A. [Mass outbreak of disease in sheep caused by consumption of infected lupins.] *Vorträge für Thierärzte* 1879, Series II, 7, 3–29.

95 ALLEN, J.G. An evaluation of lupinosis in cattle in Western Australia. *Australian Veterinary Journal* 1981, 57, 212–215.

96 MEDREA, N.; DONCEA, V.; AVRAM, E.; SÎRBU, Z.; SZÖCKE, E. [An outbreak of accidental lupin poisoning in sheep.] *Zootehnie și Medicină Veterinară* 1990, 40, No.7–9, 20–22.

97 BÁNHIDI, G.; EPERJESI, I.; SÁLYI, G. [Occurrence of acute poisoning by bitter lupins in a pig herd.] *Magyar Állatorvosok Lapja* 1991, 46, 540–541.

98 ARAI, M.; STAUBER, E.; SHROPSHIRE, C.M. Evaluation of selected plants for their toxic effects in

canaries. *Journal of the American Veterinary Medical Association* 1992, 200, 1329–1331.

99 FROHNE, D.; PFÄNDER, H.J. *A Colour Atlas of Poisonous Plants.* Wolfe Publishing Co., London, UK. 1984, 129.

100 NORTH, P.M. *Poisonous Plants and Fungi.* Blandford Press, London, UK. 1967, 127–128.

101 MARQUEZ, R.L.; GUTIERREZ-RAVE, M.; MIRANDA, F.I. Acute poisoning by lupine seed debittering water. *Veterinary and Human Toxicology* 1991, 33, 265–267.

102 MORRISON, J. Lucerne (*Medicago sativa*). In: *Grasses and Legumes in British Agriculture.* Edited by C.R.W. Spedding and E.C. Diekmahns. Commonwealth Agricultural Bureaux, Farnham Royal, UK. 1972, 387–403.

103 LE BARS, J.; LE BARS, P.; BRICE, G. [Occurrence, accumulation and fate of coumestrol in lucerne and in feed products containing it.] *Recueil de Médecine Vétérinaire* 1990, 166, 463–469.

104 ADAMS, N.R. Phytoestrogens. In: *Toxicants of Plant Origin. Volume IV. Phenolics.* Edited by P.R. Cheeke. CRC Press, Boca Raton, Florida, USA. 1989, 23–51.

105 BARBERAN, M.; VALDERRABANO, J.; BASCUAS, J.A. Histopathological changes in ewe lambs exposed to prolonged diet on lucerne. *Annales de Recherches Vétérinaires* 1990, 21, 161–166.

106 PUTNAM, M.R.; QUALLS, C.W.; RICE, L.E.; DAWSON, L.J.; EDWARDS, W.C. Hepatic enzyme changes in bovine hepatogenous photosensitivity caused by water-damaged alfalfa hay. *Journal of the American Veterinary Medical Association* 1986, 189, 77–82.

107 CASTEEL, S.W.; ROTTINGHAUS, G.E.; JOHNSON, G.C.; GOSSER, H.S.; BRAUN, W.F.; WICKLOW, D.T. Hepatotoxicosis in cattle induced by consumption of alfalfa-grass hay. In: *Plant-associated Toxins. Agricultural, Phytochemical and Ecological Aspects.* Edited by S.M. Colegate and P.R. Dorling. CAB International, Wallingford, UK. 1994, 307–312.

108 BYRNE, K.V. Dermatitis in white pigs due to photosensitisation. *Australian Veterinary Journal* 1937, 13, 74–75.

109 AUSTIN, A.R.; RESTALL, D. Variation in blood coagulation in animals fed legume forages. Grassland Research Institute, Maidenhead, UK. Annual Report 1980 (published 1981), 103.

110 SCHEEL, C.D. The toxicology of sweet clover and coumarin anticoagulants. In: *Mycotoxic Fungi, Mycotoxins, Mycotoxicoses.* An Encyclopedic Handbook. Edited by T.D. Wyllie and L.G. Morehouse. Marcel Dekker Inc., New York, USA. Vol. 2, 1978, 121–142.

111 RADOSTITS, O.M.; SEARCY, G.P.; MITCHALL, K.G. Moldy sweet clover poisoning in cattle. *Canadian Veterinary Journal* 1980, 21, 155–158.

112 RIZK, A.F.M.; KAMEL, A. Chemistry and toxicity of *Melilotus* species. In: *Poisonous Plant Contamination of Edible Plants.* Edited by A.F.M. Rizk. CRC Press, Boca Raton, Florida, USA. 1991, 107–116.

113 ALSTAD, A.D.; CASPER, H.H.; JOHNSON, L.J. Vitamin K treatment of sweet clover poisoning in calves. *Journal of the American Veterinary Medical Association* 1985, 187, 729–731.

114 CONNOR, H.E. *The Poisonous Plants in New Zealand.* E.C. Keating, Government Printer, Wellington, New Zealand, 1977, 117–118.

115 DUFFUS, C.M.; SMITH, P.M. Legumes and their toxins. *Span* 1981, 24, 63–65.

116 JAFFÉ, W.G.; SIDEL, D.S. Toxicology of plant lectins. In: *Food Poisoning. Handbook of Natural Toxins. Volume 7.* Edited by A.T. Tu. Marcel Dekker Inc., New York, USA. 1992, 263–290.

117 HUISMAN, J.; JANSMAN, A.J.M. Dietary effects and some analytical aspects of antinutritional factors in peas (*Pisum sativum*), common beans (*Phaseolus vulgaris*) and soyabeans (*Glycine max* L.) in monogastric farm animals. A literature review. *Nutrition Abstracts and Reviews. Series B.* 1991, 61, 901–921.

118 XAVIER-FILHO, J.; CAMPOS, F.A.P. Proteinase inhibitors. In: *Toxicants of Plant Origin. Volume III. Proteins and Amino Acids.* Edited by P.R. Cheeke. CRC Press, Boca Raton, Florida, USA. 1989, 1–27.

119 Pusztai, A. Nutritional toxicity of the kidney bean (*Phaseolus vulgaris*). *Rowett Research Institute Annual Report of Studies in Animal Nutrition and Allied Sciences* 1980, 36, 110–118.

120 Pusztai, A.; Clarke, E.M.W.; Grant, G.; King, T.P. The toxicity of *Phaseolus vulgaris* lectins. Nitrogen balance and immunochemical studies. *Journal of the Science of Food and Agriculture* 1981, 32, 1037–1046.

121 Pusztai, A. Lectins. In: *Toxicants of Plant Origin. Volume III. Proteins and Amino Acids*. Edited by P.R. Cheeke. CRC Press, Boca Raton, Florida, USA. 1989, 29–71.

122 Aletor, V.A.; Fetuga, B.L. The interactive effects of lima bean (*Phaseolus lunatus*) trypsin inhibitor, hemagglutinin and cyanide on some hepatic dehydrogenases, ornithine carbamoyltransferase and intestinal disaccharidases in weanling rats. *Veterinary and Human Toxicology* 1988, 30, 540–544.

123 Grant, G.; More, L.J.; McKenzie, N.H.; Stewart, J.C.; Pusztai, A. A survey of the nutritional and haemagglutination properties of legume seeds generally available in the UK. *British Journal of Nutrition* 1983, 50, 207–214.

124 Venter, F.S.; Thiel, P.G. Red kidney beans – to eat or not to eat? *South African Medical Journal* 1995, 85, 250–252.

125 Myer, R.O.; Froseth, J.A.; Coon, C.N. Protein utilization and toxic effects of raw beans (*Phaseolus vulgaris*) for young pigs. *Journal of Animal Science* 1982, 55, 1087–1098.

126 Kamphues, J.; Coenen, M.; Wolf, P.; Hahn, H. [Decreased feed intake and digestive disturbances in pig herds after using mixed feeds with French beans (*Phaseolus* species).] *Monatshefte für Veterinärmedizin* 1994, 49, 275–280.

127 Jaffé, W.G. Hemagglutinins (lectins). In: *Toxic Constituents of Plant Foodstuffs*. Edited by I.E. Liener. Academic Press, New York and London. 2nd Edition. 1980, 73–102.

128 King, T.P.; Begbie, R.; Cadenhead, A. Nutritional toxicity of raw kidney beans in pigs. Immunocytochemical and cytopathological studies on the gut and the pancreas. *Journal of the Science of Food and Agriculture* 1983, 34, 1404–1412.

129 Kik, M.J.L.; Huisman, J.; Van Der Poel, A.F.B.; Mouwen, J.M.V.M. Pathologic changes of the small intestinal mucosa of pigs after feeding *Phaseolus vulgaris* beans. *Veterinary Pathology* 1990, 27, 329–334.

130 Huisman, J.; Van Der Poel, A.F.B.; Van Leeuwen P.; Verstegen, M.W.A. Comparison of growth, nitrogen metabolism and organ weights in piglets and rats fed on diets containing *Phaseolus vulgaris* beans. *British Journal of Nutrition* 1990, 64, 743–753.

131 Noah, N.D.; Bender, A.E.; Reaidi, G.B.; Gilbert, R.J. Food poisoning from raw red kidney beans. *British Medical Journal* 1980, 281, 236–237.

132 Anonymous. Unusual outbreak of food poisoning. *British Medical Journal* 1976, 2, 1268.

133 Rodhouse, J.C.; Haugh, C.A.; Roberts, D.; Gilbert, R.J. Red kidney bean poisoning in the UK: an analysis of 50 suspected incidents between 1976 and 1989. *Epidemiology and Infection* 1990, 105, 485–491.

134 Haidvogl, M.; Fritsch, G.; Grubbauer, H.M. [Poisoning by raw garden beans (*Phaseolus vulgaris* and *Phaseolus coccineus*) in children.] *Pädiatrie und Pädologie* 1979, 14, 293–296.

135 Tuxen, M.K.; Nielsen, H.V.; Biergens, H. [Poisoning by kidney beans (*Phaseolus vulgaris*).] *Ugeskrift for Læger* 1991, 153, 3628–3629.

136 Grant, G.; More, L.J.; McKenzie, N.H.; Pusztai, A. The effect of heating on the haemagglutinating activity and nutritional properties of bean (*Phaseolus vulgaris*) seeds. *Journal of the Science of Food and Agriculture* 1982, 33, 1324–1326.

137 Pusztai, A. Lectins. In: *Toxicants of Plant Origin. Volume III. Proteins and Amino Acids*. Edited by P.R. Cheeke. CRC Press, Boca Raton, Florida, USA. 1989, 58.

138 Salmon, W.D.; Sewell, W.E. Lameness in hogs produced by Austrian pea (*Pisum arvense*).

47th Annual Report of the Agricultural Experiment Station, Polytechnic Institute, Auburn, Alabama, USA. 1936, 17–18.

139 WHITING, F.; CONNELL, R.; PLUMMER, P.J.G.; CLARK, R.D. Incoordination (cerebellar ataxia) among lambs from ewes fed peavine silage. *Canadian Journal of Comparative Medicine and Veterinary Science* 1957, 21, 77–84.

140 MORRISON, F.B. *Feeds and Feeding.* Morrison Publishing Company, Iowa, USA. 1959, 328–329.

141 KIENHOLZ, E.W.; JENSEN, L.S.; McGINNIS, J. Evidence for chick growth inhibitors in several legume seeds. *Poultry Science* 1962, 41, 367–371.

142 KINGSBURY, J.M. *Poisonous Plants of the United States and Canada.* Prentice-Hall, Inc., New Jersey, USA. 1968, 351–353.

143 KELLER, H.; DEWITZ, W. [Poisoning of nine horses by the bark of false acacia (*Robinia pseudoacacia*).] *Deutsche Tierärztliche Wochenschrift* 1969, 76, 115–116.

144 ZAREMBA, S.; DONIEC, H. Histological changes in the chick liver following phytohaemagglutinin administration. *Folia Biologica, Krakow* 1977, 25, 55–61.

145 LAMPE, K.F.; FAGERSTRÖM, R. *Plant Toxicity and Dermatitis.* Williams and Wilkins Co., Baltimore, USA. 1968, 71.

146 ARTERO SIVERA, A.; ARNEDO PENA, A.; PASTOR CUBO, A. [Clinical epidemiological study of accidental poisoning by *Robinia pseudoacacia* L. in school children.] *Annales Espanoles de Pediatria* 1989, 30, 191–194.

147 COSTA BOU, X.; SOLER I ROS, J.M.; SECULI PALACIOS, J.L. [*Robinia pseudoacacia* poisoning.] *Annales Espanoles de Pediatria* 1990, 32, 68–69.

148 VELASCO BERNADO, R.; CRESPO, E.; MONTALVO, N.; ORTIZ, P.; ALONSO, L.; ALONSO MARTIN, J.A. [*Robinia pseudoacacia* poisoning.] *Annales Espanoles de Pediatria* 1990, 33, 404.

149 FILANDRINOS, D.T.; SIORIS, L.J. Transient elevation of liver function tests following ingestion of black locust beans. *Veterinary and Human Toxicology* 1992, 34, 351.

150 MORRISON, J. White clover (*Trifolium repens*). In: *Grasses and Legumes in British Agriculture.* Edited by C.R.W. Spedding and E.C. Diekmahns. Commonwealth Agricultural Bureaux, Farnham Royal, UK. 1972, 347–369.

151 MORRISON, J. Red clover (*Trifolium pratense*). In: *Grasses and Legumes in British Agriculture.* Edited by C.R.W. Spedding and E.C. Diekmahns. Commonwealth Agricultural Bureaux, Farnham Royal, UK. 1972, 370–386.

152 COX, R.I. Plant estrogens affecting livestock in Australia. In: *Effects of Poisonous Plants on Livestock.* Edited by R.F. Keeler, K.R. Van Kampen and L.F. James. Academic Press, New York and London. 1978, 451–464.

153 ADAMS, N.R. Permanent infertility in ewes exposed to plant oestrogens. *Australian Veterinary Journal* 1990, 67, 197–201.

154 NWANNENNA, A.I.; MADEJ, A.; LUNDH, T.J.O.; FREDRIKSSON, G. Effects of oestrogenic silage on some clinical and endocrinological parameters in ovarioectomized heifers. *Acta Veterinaria Scandinavica* 1994, 35, 173–183.

155 KALLELA, K.; HEINONEN, K.; SALONIEMI, H. Plant oestrogens: the cause of decreased fertility in cows. A case report. *Nordisk Veterinærmedicin* 1984, 36, 124–129.

156 SABA, N.; DRANE, H.M.; HEBERT, C.M.; HOLDSWORTH, R.J. Seasonal variation in oestrogenic activity, coumestrol and formononetin content of white clover. *Journal of Agricultural Science* 1974, 83, 505–510.

157 WARD, W.R. The aetiology of 'ringwomb' or partial dilatation of the cervix. *Veterinary Annual* 1975, 15, 75–78.

158 ADAMS, N.R.; NAIRN, M.E. The nature of dystokia in ewes after grazing oestrogenic subterranean clover. *Australian Veterinary Journal* 1983, 60, 124–125.

159 WHITMAN, R.J. Herbivore feeding and cyanogenesis in *Trifolium repens* L. *Heredity* 1973, 30, 241–245.

160 GURNEY, M.P.; JONES, W.T.; MERRALL, M.; REID, C.S.W. Cyanide poisoning in cattle: two unusual cases. *New Zealand Veterinary Journal* 1977, 25, 128–130.

161 FORSYTH, A.A. *British Poisonous Plants*. HMSO, London, UK. Ministry of Agriculture, Fisheries and Food Bulletin 161, 1968, 62 (amended 1979, 64).

162 AUSTIN, A.R.; RESTALL, D. Variation in blood coagulation in animals fed legume forages. Grassland Research Institute, Maidenhead, UK. Annual Report 1980 (published 1981), 103.

163 FINCHER, M.G.; FULLER, H.K. Photosensitisation-trifoliosis-light sensitisation. *Cornell Veterinarian* 1942, 32, 95–98.

164 MORRILL, C.C. Clover sickness, or trifoliosis. *North American Veterinarian* 1943, 24, 731–732.

165 ØSTERGAARD, H. [An outbreak of photosensitization in horses.] *Dansk Veterinærtidsskrift* 1992, 75, 49.

166 SCHOFIELD, F.W. Liver disease of horses (big liver) caused by the feeding of Alsike clover. Veterinary College, Ontario Department of Agriculture, Circular No. 52, 1933, 1–4.

167 NATION, P.N. Alsike clover poisoning: a review. *Canadian Veterinary Journal* 1989, 30, 410–415.

168 NATION, P.N. Hepatic disease in Alberta horses: a retrospective study of "alsike clover poisoning" (1973–1988). *Canadian Veterinary Journal* 1991, 32, 602–607.

169 BLOOD, D.C.; HENDERSON, J.A.; RADOSTITS, O.M. *Veterinary Medicine*. Baillière Tindall, London, UK. 5th Edition, 1979, 993–995.

170 HAGLER, W.M.; CROOM, W.J. Slaframine: occurrence, chemistry, and physiological activity. In: *Toxicants of Plant Origin. Volume I. Alkaloids*. Edited by P.R. Cheeke. CRC Press, Boca Raton, Florida, USA. 1989, 257–279.

171 CLAPHAM, A.R.; TUTIN, T.G.; MOORE, D.M. *Flora of the British Isles*. Cambridge University Press, Cambridge, UK. 1987, 190.

172 MARQUARDT, R.R. Vicine, convicine, and their aglycones – divicine and isouramil. In: *Toxicants of Plant Origin. Volume II. Glycosides*. Edited by P.R. Cheeke. CRC Press, Boca Raton, Florida, USA. 1989, 161–200.

173 JANSMAN, A.J.M.; ENTING, H.; VERSTEGEN, M.W.A.; HUISMAN, J. Effect of condensed tannins in hulls of faba beans (*Vicia faba* L.) on the activities of trypsin (EC 2.4.21.4) and chymotrypsin (EC 2.4.21.1) in digesta collected from the small intestine of pigs. *British Journal of Nutrition* 1994, 71, 627–641.

174 GRIFFITHS, D.W. Some anti-nutritive factors in *Vicia faba*. Newsletter. *Faba Bean Information Service* 1983, No.6, 1–3.

175 SOBRINI, F.J.; MARTINEZ, J.A.; ILUNDAIN, A.; LARRALDE, J. The effects of '*Vicia faba* L.' polyphenols on absorption, growth and metabolism in the rat. *Qualitas Plantarum. Plant Foods for Human Nutrition* 1983, 33, 231–235.

176 AHERNE, F.X.; LEWIS, A.J.; HARDIN, R.T. An evaluation of faba beans (*Vicia faba*) as a protein supplement for swine. *Canadian Journal of Animal Science* 1977, 57, 321–328.

177 STRYCZEK, J. [Outbreak of *Vicia faba* poisoning in swine.] *Medycyna Weterynaryjna* 1981, 37, 549.

178 NABER, E.C.; VOGT, H.; HARNISH, S.; KRIEG, R.; UEBERSCHAER, K.H.; RAUCH, H.W. Reproductive performance of hens fed field beans and potential relationships to vicine metabolism. *Poultry Science* 1988, 67, 455–462.

179 ORTIZ VERA, L.T. [Effect of faba bean tannins on enzyme activity and growth of chickens.] *Avances en Alimentacíon y Mejora Animal* 1994, 34, 83–87.

180 MAGER, J.; CHEVION, M.; GLASER, G. Favism. In: *Toxic Constituents of Plant Foodstuffs*. Edited by I.E. Liener. Academic Press, New York and London. 2nd Edition. 1980, 265–294.

181 SENIOR, B.; BRAUDO, J.L. Favism. Report of a case occurring in Johannesburg. *South African*

Medical Journal 1955, 29, 1264–1266.

182 GESSNER, O. *Die Gift- und Arzneipflanzen von Mitteleuropa.* Carl Winter, Heidelberg, Germany. 1953, 667.

183 GARDNER, C.A.; BENNETTS, H.W. *The Toxic Plants of Western Australia.* West Australian Newspapers Periodicals Division, Perth, Australia. 1956, 114.

184 SMITH, A. Other legumes. In: *Grasses and Legumes in British Agriculture.* Edited by C.R.W. Spedding and E.C. Diekmahns. Commonwealth Agricultural Bureaux, Farnham Royal, UK. 1972, 414–422.

185 RUBY, E.S.; BEASLEY, J.; STEPHENSON, E.L. Prussic acid poisoning in common vetch (*Vicia sativa*) seed. *Proceedings of the Arkansas Academy of Sciences* 1955, 18–20.

186 CONN, E.E. Cyanogenic glycosides. *Journal of Agricultural and Food Chemistry* 1969, 17, 519–526.

187 HIBBS, C.M. Cyanide and nitrate toxicoses of cattle. *Veterinary and Human Toxicology* 1979, 21, 401–403.

188 RESSLER, C. Isolation and identification from common vetch of the neurotoxin β-cyano-L-alanine, a possible factor in neurolathyrism. *Journal of Biological Chemistry* 1962, 237, 733–735.

189 VÖLKER, R. *Lehrbuch der Toxikologie für Tierärzte. (Fröhner).* Ferdinand Enke Verlag, Stuttgart, Germany. 6th Edition. 1950, 272–273.

190 ARSCOTT, G.H.; HARPER, J.A. Evidence for a difference in toxicity between common and hairy vetch seed for chicks. *Poultry Science* 1964, 43, 271–273.

191 HARPER, J.A.; ARSCOTT, G.H. Toxicity of common and hairy vetch seed for poults and chicks. *Poultry Science* 1962, 41, 1968–1974.

192 CLAUGHTON, W.P.; CLAUGHTON, H.D. Vetch seed poisoning. *Auburn Veterinarian* 1954, 10, 125–126.

193 PANCIERA, R.J. Hairy vetch (*Vicia villosa* Roth) poisoning in cattle. In: *Effects of Poisonous Plants on Livestock.* Edited by R.F. Keeler, K.R. Van Kampen and L.F. James. Academic Press, New York and London. 1978, 555–563.

194 KERR, L.A., EDWARDS, W.C. Hairy vetch poisoning of cattle. *Veterinary Medicine and Small Animal Clinician* 1982, 77, 257–258.

195 BURROUGHS, G.W.; NESER, J.A.; KELLERMAN, T.S.; VAN NIEKERK, F.A. Suspected hybrid vetch (*Vicia villosa* crossed with *Vicia dasycarpa*) poisoning of cattle in the Republic of South Africa. Proceedings of the 13th World Congress on Diseases of Cattle, Durban, South Africa. 1984, 2, 681–685.

196 ANDERSON, C.A.; DIVERS, T.J. Systemic granulomatous inflammation in a horse grazing hairy vetch. *Journal of the American Veterinary Medical Association* 1983, 183, 569–570.

197 GESSNER, O. *Die Gift- und Arzneipflanzen von Mitteleuropa.* Carl Winter, Heidelberg, Germany. 1953, 318–319.

198 CORNEVIN, C. *Des Plantes Vénéneuses.* Librairie de Firmin-Didot, Paris, France. 1887, 309–310.

199 LAMPE, K.F. Pharmacology of poisonous plants of Florida. *Journal of the Florida Medical Association* 1978, 65, 171–174.

200 LAMPE, K.F.; FAGERSTRÖM, R. *Plant Toxicity and Dermatitis.* Williams and Wilkins, Baltimore, USA. 1968, 19.

201 KINGSBURY, J. *Poisonous Plants of the United States and Canada.* Prentice-Hall, Inc., New Jersey, USA. 1964, 364.

202 PIOLA, C.; RAVAGLIA, M.; ZOLI, M.P. [Poisoning by *Wisteria sinensis* seeds. Two clinical cases.] *Bollettino Società Italiana di Farmacia Ospitaliera* 1983, 29, 333–337.

203 RONDEAU, E.S. *Wisteria* toxicity. *Journal of Toxicology. Clinical Toxicology* 1993, 31, 107–112.

LILIACEAE

1 SPOERKE, D.G.; SMOLINSKE, S.C. *Toxicity of Houseplants.* CRC Press, Boca Raton, Florida, USA. 1990, 104–105.

2   DELATOUR, P. [*Colchicum autumnale.*] *Notes de Toxicologie Vétérinaire* 1977, No.1, 23–24.

3   TRIBUNSKII, M.P. [*Colchicum autumnale* poisoning in lambs.] *Veterinariya, Moscow* 1970, 6, 71–72.

4   VON SCHULZ, O.; HOMMEL, H. [*Colchicum autumnale* poisoning in cattle.] *Monatshefte für Veterinärmedizin* 1975, 30, 333–334.

5   CHAREYRE, S.; MERAM, D.; PULCE, C.; DESCOTES, J. Acute poisoning of cows by autumnal crocus. *Veterinary and Human Toxicology* 1989, 31, 261–262.

6   DEBARNOT, A. [*Colchicum autumnale* (meadow saffron) poisoning.] Thesis, École Nationale Vétérinaire, Alfort, Paris, France. 1968, 66 pp.

7   SHERGIN, Y, K.; TRIBUNSKII, M.P. [Pathology of *Colchicum* (Kesselring variety) poisoning in lambs.] *Veterinariya, Moscow* 1971, No.5, 88–89.

8   PANARITI, E. Meadow saffron (*Colchicum autumnale*) intoxication in a nomadic Albanian sheep flock. *Veterinary and Human Toxicology* 1996, 38, 227–228.

9   KAMPHUES, J.; MEYER, H. [Autumn crocus (*Colchicum autumnale*) in hay and equine colic.] *Tierärztliche Praxis* 1990, 18, 273–275.

10   LOHNER, E.; GINDELE, H.R. [Colchicine poisoning in pigs. Clinical and pathological changes after intake of autumn crocus.] *Tierärztliche Umschau* 1989, 44, 314–317.

11   HILL, F.W.G. Malabsorption in dogs induced with oral colchicine. *British Veterinary Journal* 1972, 128, 372–378.

12   MAYER, H.; WACKER, R.; DALCHOW, W. [Poisoning by chestnut, oleander, acorns and autumn crocus in various zoo and wild animals.] *Tierärztliche Umschau* 1986, 41, 169–178.

13   PANARITI, E. Tissue distribution and milk transfer of colchicine in a lactating sheep following a single dose intake. *Deutsche Tierärztliche Wochenschrift* 1996, 103, 128–129.

14   RICHTER, H.E. [Influence of certain Austrian plants on milk quality. I. Excretion of plant poisons in milk.] *Wiener Tierärztliche Monatsschrift* 1963, 50, 692–699.

15   KASIM, M.; LANGE, H. [Toxicological diagnosis of *Colchicum autumnale* poisoning in ruminants. Method for determining colchicine.] *Archiv für Experimentelle Veterinärmedizin* 1973, 27, 601–603.

16   STAHL, N.; WEINBERGER, A.; BENJAMIN, D.; PINKHAS, J. Fatal colchicine poisoning in a boy with familial Mediterranean fever. *American Journal of the Medical Sciences* 1979, 278, 77–81.

17   MCINTYRE, I.M.; RUSZKIEWICZ, A.R.; CRUM, K.; DRUMMER, O.H. Death following colchicine poisoning. *Journal of Forensic Sciences* 1994, 39, 280–286.

18   LAMPE, K.F.; MCCANN, M.A. *AMA Handbook of Poisonous and Injurious Plants.* American Medical Association, Chicago, USA. 1985, 59–60.

19   SCHERRMANN, J.M.; SABOURAUD, A.; URTIZBEREA, M.; ROUZIOUX, J.; LANG, J.; BAUD, F.; BISMUTH, C. Clinical use of colchicine-specific Fab fragments in colchicine poisoning. *Veterinary and Human Toxicology* 1992, 34, 334.

20   MOXLEY, R.A.; SCHNEIDER, N.R.; STEINEGGER, D.H.; CARLSON, M.P. Apparent toxicosis associated with lily-of-the-valley (*Convallaria majalis*) ingestion in a dog. *Journal of the American Veterinary Medical Association* 1989, 195, 485–487.

21   LAMPE, K.F. Systemic plant poisoning in children. *Pediatrics* 1974, 54, 347–351.

22   O'LEARY, S.B. Poisoning in man from eating poisonous plants. *Archives of Environmental Health* 1964, 9, 216–242.

23   NATIONAL POISONS INFORMATION SERVICE, London, UK. Personal communication.

24   FORSYTH, A.A. *British Poisonous Plants.* HMSO, London, UK. Ministry of Agriculture, Fisheries and Food Bulletin 161, 1968, 103–104 (amended 1979, 104–105).

25   THURSBY-PELHAM, R.H.C. Suspected *Scilla nonscripta* (bluebell) poisoning in cattle. *Veterinary Record* 1967, 80, 709–710.

26   VETERINARY INVESTIGATION SERVICE. Metabolic diseases afflict cattle in wet spring. *Veterinary Record* 1983, 113, 28.

27 MITCHELL, J.; ROOK, A. *Botanical Dermatology. Plants and Plant Products Injurious to the Skin.*
Greengrass Ltd, Vancouver, Canada. 1979, 445.

28 NIEUWLAND, C.H. [The use of bulbs as cattle feed.] *Tijdschrift voor Diergeneeskunde* 1941, 68,
359–368.

29 HARDIN, J.W.; ARENA, J.M. *Human Poisoning from Native and Cultivated Plants.* Duke University
Press, Durham, North Carolina, USA. 1969, 38.

30 MITCHELL, J.; ROOK, A. *Botanical Dermatology. Plants and Plant Products Injurious to the Skin.*
Greengrass Ltd, Vancouver, Canada. 1979, 443.

31 CEH, L.; HAUGE, J.G. Alveld-producing saponins. I. Chemical studies. *Acta Veterinaria Scandinavica*
1981, 22, 391–402.

32 LAKSESVELA, B.; DISHINGTON, I.W. PESTALOZZI, M.; OVERÅS, H., HAMAR, T.O. [Alveld
(photosensitization due to *Narthecium ossifragum*) in lambs.] *Norsk Veterinærtidsskrift* 1977, 89,
199–209.

33 ENDER, F. Aetiological studies on 'alveld', a disease in lambs caused by grazing *Narthecium
ossifragum. Proceedings of the Eighth International Grassland Congress, Reading, UK.* 1960, 664–667.

34 FLÅØYEN, A.; TØNNESEN, H.H.; GRØNSTØL, H.; KARLSEN, J. Failure to induce toxicity in lambs by
administering saponins from *Narthecium ossifragum. Veterinary Research Communications* 1991, 15,
483–487.

35 FLÅØYEN, A.; JENSEN, E.G. Microsomal enzymes in lambs and adult sheep, and their possible
relationship to alveld. *Veterinary Research Communications* 1991, 15, 271–278.

36 FLÅØYEN, A.; SKAARE, J.U.; BRÅTEN, K. Glutathione transferase activity in livers from lambs of
three different breeds of Norwegian sheep, and its possible relationship to alveld. *Veterinary
Research Communications* 1992, 16, 199–203.

37 FLÅØYEN, A. A difference in susceptibility of two breeds of sheep to the 'alveld toxin'. *Veterinary
Research Communications* 1991, 15, 455–457.

38 AAS, O.; ULVUND, M.J. Do microfungi help to induce the phototoxic disease alveld in Norway?
Veterinary Record 1989, 124, 563.

39 DI MENNA, M.E.; FLÅØYEN, A.; ULVUND, M.J. Fungi on *Narthecium ossifragum* leaves and their
possible involvement in alveld disease of Norwegian lambs. *Veterinary Research Communications*
1992, 16, 117–124.

40 FLÅØYEN, A.; BORREBÆK, B.; NORDSTOGA, K. Glycogen accumulation and histological changes in
the livers of lambs with alveld and experimental sporidesmin intoxication. *Veterinary Research
Communications* 1991, 15, 443–453.

41 FLÅØYEN, A. Studies on the aetiology and pathology of alveld, with some comparisons to
sporidesmin intoxication. Thesis. College of Veterinary Medicine, Oslo, Norway. 1993, 128 pp.

42 FLÅØYEN, A.; DI MENNA, M.E.; COLLIN, R.G.; SMITH, B.L. *Cladosporium magnusianum* (Jaap) M.B.
Ellis is probably not involved in alveld. *Veterinary Research Communications* 1993, 17, 241–245.

43 MALONE, F.E.; KENNEDY, S.; REILLY, G.A.C.; WOODS, F.M. Bog asphodel (*Narthecium ossifragum*)
poisoning in cattle. *Veterinary Record* 1992, 131, 100–103.

44 FJØLSTAD, M.; BRATBERG, B. [Poisoning of cattle at pasture in the summer of 1992 – *Narthecium
ossifragum* poisoning?] *Norsk Veterinærtidsskrift* 1993, 105, 645–647.

45 FLÅØYEN, A.; BRATBERG, B.; FRØSLIE, A.; GRØNSTØL, H. Nephrotoxicity and hepatotoxicity in calves
apparently caused by experimental feeding with *Narthecium ossifragum. Veterinary Research
Communications* 1995, 19, 63–73.

46 FLÅØYEN, A.; BINDE, M.; BRATBERG, B.; DJØNNE, B.; FJØLSTAD, M.; GRØNSTØL, H.; HASSAN, H.;
MANTLE, P.G.; LANDSVERK, T.; SCHÖNHEIT, J.; TØNNESEN, M.H. Nephrotoxicity of *Narthecium
ossifragum* in cattle in Norway. *Veterinary Record* 1995, 137, 259–263.

47 FLÅØYEN, A. [Alveld – a historical review from 1940.] *Norsk Veterinærtidsskrift* 1992, 104, 737–742.

341

48 FLÅØYEN, A.; MILES, C.O.; SMITH, B.L. Alveld in lambs in Norway. In: *Plant-associated Toxins. Agricultural, Phytochemical and Ecological Aspects.* Edited by S.M. Colegate and P.R. Dorling. CAB International, Wallingford, UK. 1994, 293–296.

49 ENDER, F. [Aetiological studies on 'alveld' – a disease involving photosensitization and icterus in lambs.]. *Nordisk Veterinærmedicin* 1955, 7, 329–377.

50 FLÅØYEN, A.; JÓHANSEN, J.; OLSEN, J. *Narthecium ossifragum* associated photosensitization in sheep in the Faroe Islands. *Acta Veterinaria Scandinavica* 1995, 36, 277–278.

51 SANDERS, K.J. Loss of ears in lambs. *Veterinary Record* 1981, 109, 320.

52 LAMONT, H.G. Loss of ears in lambs. *Veterinary Record* 1981, 109, 368.

53 FORD, E.J.H. A preliminary investigation of photosensitisation in Scottish sheep. *Journal of Comparative Pathology and Therapeutics* 1964, 74, 37–44.

54 SUZUKI, K.; KOBAYASHI, M.; ITO, A.; NAKGAWA, M. *Narthecium asiaticum* Maxim. poisoning of grazing cattle: observations on spontaneous and experimental cases. *Cornell Veterinarian* 1985, 75, 348–365.

55 FLÅØYEN, A.; BRATBERG, B.; FJØLSTAD, M.; GRØNSTØL, H.; LANDSVERK, T.; SCHÖNHEIT, J. A pasture-related nephrotoxicosis of cattle in Norway: clinical signs and pathological findings. In: *Plant-associated Toxins. Agricultural, Phytochemical and Ecological Aspects.* Edited by S.M. Colegate and P.R. Dorling. CAB International, Wallingford, UK. 1994, 557–560.

56 FLÅØYEN, A.; BRATBERG, B.; GRØNSTØL, H. Nephrotoxicity in lambs apparently caused by experimental feeding with *Narthecium ossifragum. Veterinary Research Communications* 1995, 19, 75–79.

57 ANONYMOUS. *Glasshouse Crops and Horticultural Trades Journal* 1977, 182, No.7, 12.

58 WATT J.M.; BREYER-BRANDWIJK, M.G. *The Medicinal and Poisonous Plants of Southern and Eastern Africa.* E. & S. Livingstone Ltd, Edinburgh and London, UK. 2nd Edition. 1962, 710.

59 VAHRMEIJER, J. *Poisonous Plants of Southern Africa that cause Stock Losses.* Tafelberg Publishers Ltd, Cape Town, South Africa. 1981, 20.

60 DERIVAUX, J., LIÉGEOIS, F. *Toxicologie Vétérinaire,* Vigot Frères, Paris, France. 1962, 254.

61 GUSYNIN, I.A. [*The toxicology of poisonous plants.*] Gosudarstvennoe Izdatel'stvo Sel'skokhozyaistvennoi Literatury, Moscow, USSR. 1955, 202–203.

62 SCHURZ, J. [Herb paris.] *Kosmos* 1976, 72, 236–237.

63 BAXTER, C.P. Solomon's seal poisoning in a dog. *Veterinary Record* 1983, 113, 247–248.

64 FROHNE, D.; PFÄNDER, H.J. *A Colour Atlas of Poisonous Plants.* Wolfe Publishing Ltd, London, UK. 1984, 149.

65 MARETIĆ, Z.; RUSSELL, F.E.; LADAVAC, J. Tulip bulb poisoning. *Periodicum Biologorum* 1978, 80 (Supplement 1), 141–143.

66 PEPERKAMP, N.H.M.T.; GRUYS, E.; JOOSTEN, A.; PEETERS, H.; SYBESMA, J.; NOTERMANS, S.H.W.; HAAGSMA, J. [Death of cattle after feeding with mouldy flower bulbs.] *Tijdschrift voor Diergeneeskunde* 1992, 117, 165–168.

67 LAHTI, A. Contact urticaria and respiratory symptoms from tulips and lilies. *Contact Dermatitis* 1986, 14, 317–319.

68 GETTE, M.T.; MARKS, J.E. Tulip fingers. *Archives of Dermatology* 1990, 126, 203–205.

69 CASSINA, G.; VALSECCHI, R.; LEGHISSA, P.; FERRARI, M.T.; PIAZZOLLA, S. [Allergic contact dermatitis and oculorhinitis due to tulips.] *Giornale Italiano di Medicina del Lavoro* 1989, 11, 241–242.

70 HAUSEN, B.M. Airborne contact dermatitis caused by tulip bulbs. *Journal of the American Academy of Dermatology* 1982, 7, 500–503.

71 TER-POGOSOV, S. [Toxicity of rhododendron and white hellebore.] In: *Profilaktika i Lechenie Nezaranykh Boleznei.* Edited by I.R. Mozgov et al. Izdatel'stvo Kolos, Moscow, USSR. 1964, 106–109.

72 FRANTOVÁ, E.; OFÚKANY, L.; HALAŠA, M. [Problems of poisoning of farm animals with toxic

plants.] *Veterinářství* 1983, 33, 71–73.

73 HRUBY, K.; LENZ, K.; KRAUSLER, J. [*Veratrum album* poisoning.] *Wiener Klinische Wochenschrift* 1981, 93, 517–519.

74 GARNIER, R.; CARLIER, P.; HOFFELT, J.; SAVIDAN, A. [Acute poisoning by ingestion of white hellebore (*Veratrum album* L.). Clinical and analytical data. Five cases.] *Annales de Médecine Interne* 1985, 136, 125–128.

75 CRUMMETT, D.; BRONSTEIN, D.; WEAVER, Z. Accidental *Veratrum viride* poisoning in three "ramp" foragers. *North Carolina Medical Journal* 1985, 46, 469–471.

76 JAFFE, A.M.; GEPHARDT, D.; COURTEMANCHE, L. Poisoning due to ingestion of *Veratrum viride* (false hellebore). *Journal of Emergency Medicine* 1990, 8, 161–167.

77 GARNIER, R.; HOFFELT, J.; CARLIER, P.; RIBOULET-DELMAS, G.; KARCHEN, G.; THIMON, D.; FOURNIER, E. *Veratrum* poisoning with home-made gentian wine: clinical and analytical findings. *Veterinary and Human Toxicology* 1982, 24, Supplement, 138–141.

78 QUATREHOMME, G.; BERTRAND, F.; CHAUVET, C.; OLLIER, A. Intoxication from *Veratrum album*. *Human & Experimental Toxicology* 1993, 12, 111–115.

79 CARLIER, P.; EFTHYMIOU, M.L.; GARNIER, R.; HOFFELT, J.; FOURNIER, E. Poisoning with *Veratrum*-containing sneezing powders. *Human Toxicology* 1983, 2, 321–325.

80 FOGH, A.; KULLING, P.; WICKSTROM, E. *Veratrum* alkaloids in sneezing powder a potential danger. *Journal of Toxicology. Clinical Toxicology* 1983, 20, 175–179.

LINACEAE

1 BURTON, D.; HANENSON, I.B. Plant toxins. In: *Quick Reference to Clinical Toxicology*. Edited by I.B. Hanenson. J.B. Lippincott, Philadelphia, USA. 1980, 242–251.

2 JAMES, L.F.; JOHNSON, A.E. Some major plant toxicities of the Western United States. *Journal of Range Management* 1976, 29, 356–363.

3 BISHARA, H.N.; WALKER, H.F. The vitamin B_6 status of pigs given a diet containing linseed meal. *British Journal of Nutrition* 1977, 37, 321–331.

4 BRIOUX, C.; RICHART, A. [Hydrocyanic acid in linseed cake. Toxicity of some oilseed cakes.] *Bulletin de l'Académie Vétérinaire de France* 1928, 1 (New Series), 134–146.

5 VILLET, C. [Alimentary toxicology of linseed cake in cattle.] Thesis. École Nationale Vétérinaire de Lyon, France. 1965, 69 pp.

6 PERROT, M. [Poisoning of sheep by linseed cake.] *Recueil de Médecine Vétérinaire* 1928, 104, 15–18.

7 COLIN, M.A.M. [Toxicity of linseed cake for sheep.] Thesis. École Nationale Vétérinaire d'Alfort, France. 1937, 51 pp.

8 MORRISON, F.B. *Feeds and Feeding*. Morrison Publishing Co., Iowa, USA. 22nd Edition, 1959, 485–489.

9 McBARRON, E.J. *Medical and Veterinary Aspects of Plant Poisons in New South Wales*. Department of Agriculture, New South Wales, Australia. 1976, 179.

10 BAKHIET, A.O.; ADAM, S.E.I. Response of Bovans chicks to low dietary levels of *Linum usitatissimum* seeds. *Veterinary and Human Toxicology* 1995, 37, 534–536.

11 CAIUS, J.F. *The Medicinal and Poisonous Plants of India*. Scientific Publishers, Jodhpur, India. Reprinted 1992, 379.

12 FORSYTH, A.A. *British Poisonous Plants*. HMSO, London, UK. Ministry of Agriculture, Fisheries and Food Bulletin 161, 1968, 57 (amended 1979, 57).

MALVACEAE

1 DODD, S.; HENRY, M. Staggers or shivers in live stock. *Journal of Comparative Pathology, and Therapeutics* 1922, 35, 41–61.

2 GORDON, McL. H. Some field observations on various diseases of sheep. *Australian Veterinary Journal* 1936, 12, 29–31.

3 HENNING, M.W. Krimpsiekte. 11th and 12th Reports of the Director of Veterinary Education and Research, Onderstepoort, South Africa, 1926, 331–365.

4 MARSH, C.D.; CLAWSON, A.B.; ROE, G.C. Four species of range plants not poisonous to livestock. United States Department of Agriculture, Technical Bulletin No.93. 1928, 9 pp.

5 CONNOR, H.E. *The Poisonous Plants in New Zealand.* E.C. Keating, Government Printer, Wellington, New Zealand. 1977, 124.

6 MACFARLANE, J.J.; SHENSTONE, F.S.; VICKERY, J.R. Malvalic acid and its structure. *Nature, London* 1957, 179, 830–831.

7 SHENSTONE, F.S.; VICKERY, J.R. A biologically active fatty-acid in Malvaceae. *Nature, London* 1956, 177, 94.

8 SHENSTONE, F.S.; VICKERY, J.R. Substances in plants of the order Malvale causing pink whites in stored eggs. *Poultry Science* 1959, 38, 1055–1070.

OLEACEAE

1 FORSYTH, A.A. *British Poisonous Plants.* HMSO, London, UK. Ministry of Agriculture, Fisheries and Food Bulletin 161, 1968, 85–86 (amended 1979, 86–87).

2 REEVES, R.J.C. Cattle poisoning from ash leaves and fruits. *Veterinary Record* 1966, 79, 580.

3 BOHOSIEWICZ, M. *Toksykologia Weterynaryjna.* Panstwowe Wydawnictwo Rolnicze i Leśne, Warsaw, Poland. 1970, 293.

4 FORRESTER, R.M. Ash as fodder. *Lakeland Gardener* 1985, Spring, 18–24.

5 MITCHELL, J.; ROOK, A. *Botanical Dermatology. Plants and Plant Products Injurious to the Skin.* Greengrass Ltd, Vancouver, Canada. 1979, 493.

6 TURNER, T.W. Some interesting cases. *Veterinary Record* 1904, 17, 319–320.

7 ANONYMOUS. Accidental poisonings of stock. *New Zealand Journal of Agriculture* 1939, 59, 429–431.

8 REYNARD, G.B.; NORTON, J.B.S. Poisonous plants of Maryland in relation to livestock. University of Maryland Agricultural Experiment Station. Technical Bulletin No.A10, 1942, 273.

9 PARKINSON, S.C.J. Suspected privet poisoning. *Veterinary Record* 1986, 119, 483–484.

10 NATIONAL POISONS INFORMATION SERVICE, London, UK. Personal communication.

11 FROHNE, D.; PFÄNDER, H.J. *A Colour Atlas of Poisonous Plants.* Wolfe Publishing Ltd, London, UK. 1984, 157–158.

12 KOZLOV, V.A.; GULYAEVA, T.N. [Poisoning by berries of privet (*Ligustrum vulgare*).] *Sudebno-Meditsinskaya Ekspertisa* 1983, 26, No.3, 56–57.

13 MITCHELL, J.; ROOK, A. *Botanical Dermatology. Plants and Plant Products Injurious to the Skin.* Greengrass Ltd, Vancouver, Canada. 1979, 494.

OXALIDACEAE

1 MATHAMS, R.H.; SUTHERLAND, A.K. The oxalate content of some Queensland pasture plants. *Queensland Journal of Agricultural Science* 1952, 9, 317–334.

2 BULL, L.B. Poisoning of sheep by soursobs (*Oxalis cernua*): chronic oxalic acid poisoning. *Australian Veterinary Journal* 1929, 5, 60–69.

3 WALKER, D.J. Poisoning of sheep by *Oxalis corniculata*. Institute of Inspectors of Stock of New

South Wales 1939, 49–52.

4   LEONI, A.; NIEDDU, A.M. [Oxalic acid poisoning in Sardinian sheep at pasture.] *Summa* 1985, 2, 171–174.

5   MANUNTA, G.; NAITANA, S. [Experimental *Oxalis cernua* poisoning in sheep: hormonal and chemical changes in blood and urine.] *Atti della Società Italiana delle Scienze Veterinarie* 1984, 38, 221–224.

6   REKHIS, J.; AMARA, A. [*Oxalis cernua* poisoning in two goats.] *Revue de Médecine Vétérinaire* 1990, 141, 633–636.

7   MANUNTA, G.; FLORIS, B. [Experimental *Oxalis cernua* poisoning in sheep: protein electrophoresis and blood alkaline reserve.] *Atti della Società Italiana delle Scienze Veterinarie* 1984, 38, 224–227.

8   MANUNTA, G.; NAITANA, S.; FLORIS, B.; GALLUS, M.; SCALA, A. [Parathyroid hormone, thyrocalcitonin, Ca, P, Mg, Zn, Cu, alkaline phosphatase and chloride in blood and bone from sheep experimentally fed *Oxalis cernua.*] *Clinica Veterinaria* 1985, 108, 185–206.

9   MANUNTA, G.; NAITANA, S.; FLORIS, B.; NIEDDU, A.M.; GIOI, F.; SCALA, A. [Electrophoretic picture of the blood, alkaline state, renal deposition of calcium salts and their lysis in sheep fed *Oxalis cernua* or maize.] *Clinica Veterinaria* 1985, 108, 207–218.

10 LONG, H.C. *Plants Poisonous to Live Stock.* Cambridge University Press, Cambridge, UK. 1917, 23.

PAEONIACEAE

1   SCHILLING, R.; SPEAKER, J. Incidence of plant poisonings in Philadelphia noted as poison information calls. *Veterinary and Human Toxicology* 1980, 22, 148–150.

2   GUSYNIN, I.A. [*The toxicology of poisonous plants.*] Gosudarstvennoe Izdatel'stvo Sel'skokhozyaistvennoi Literatury, Moscow, USSR. 3rd Edition. 1955, 255.

PAPAVERACEAE

1   SCHAUENBERG, P.; PARIS, F. *Guide to Medicinal Plants.* Lutterworth Press, Guildford and London, UK. 1977, 29.

2   REEKS, H.C. Poisoning of cattle by common celandine. *Journal of Comparative Pathology and Therapeutics* 1903, 16, 367–371.

3   FORSYTH, A.A. *British Poisonous Plants.* HMSO, London, UK. Ministry of Agriculture, Fisheries and Food Bulletin 161, 1968, 40 (amended 1979, 42).

4   MITCHELL, J.; ROOK, A. *Botanical Dermatology. Plants and Plant Products Injurious to the Skin.* Greengrass Ltd, Vancouver, Canada. 1979, 507–508.

5   FROHNER, D.; PFÄNDER, H.J. *A Colour Atlas of Poisonous Plants.* Wolfe Publishing Ltd, London, UK. 1984, 160–162.

6   PINTO GARCÍA, V.; VICENTE, R.R.; BAREZ, A.; SOTO, I.; CANDAS, M.A.; COMA, A. [Haemolytic anaemia induced by *Chelidonium majus.*] *Sangre, Barcelona* 1990, 35, 401–403.

7   DE MALMANCHE, I. Suspected *Papaver nudicaule* (Iceland poppy) poisoning in two horses. *New Zealand Veterinary Journal* 1970, 18, 96.

8   TERBLANCHE, M.; ADELAAR, I.F. A note on the toxicity of *Papaver nudicaule* L. (Iceland poppy). *Journal of the South African Veterinary Medical Association* 1964, 35, 383–384.

9   MCLENNAN, G.C. Poisoning of sheep by ingestion of Iceland poppies (*Papaver nudicaule*). *Australian Veterinary Journal* 1929, 5, 117.

10 MCLENNAN, G.C. Iceland poppy poisoning. *Australian Veterinary Journal* 1930, 6, 40.

11 ANONYMOUS. Poisoning with Iceland poppies (*Papaver nudicaule*). Annual Report, New Zealand Department of Agriculture 1960, 190.

12 CORNEVIN, C. *Des Plantes Vénéneuses.* Librairie de Firmin-Didot, Paris, France. 1887, 234–237.

13 LAGNEAU, F.; GALLARD, P. [Poisoning of cattle by poppies (*Papaver somniferum*).] *Recueil de Médecine Vétérinaire* 1946, 122, 310–313.

14 LÉZY. [Poisoning of cattle by poppy capsules (*Papaver somniferum*).] *Recueil de Médecine Vétérinaire* 1946, 122, 23–24.

15 ODENDAAL, J.S.J. [Suspected opium poisoning in two young dogs.] *Journal of the South African Veterinary Association* 1986, 57, 113–114.

16 BERRIDGE, V.; EDWARDS, G. *Opium and the People. Opiate Use in Nineteenth-century England.* Yale University Press, New Haven, USA, and Allen Lane, UK. 1987.

17 FROHNE, D.; PFÄNDER, H.J. *A Colour Atlas of Poisonous Plants.* Wolfe Publishing Ltd, London, UK. 1984, 164–165.

18 BEER, J.H.; VOGT, A.; BERNHARD, W. Gourmet restaurant syndrome. *Lancet* 1994, 343, 1302.

PHYTOLACCACEAE

1   KINGSBURY, J.M. *Poisonous Plants of the United States and Canada.* Prentice-Hall Inc., New Jersey, USA. 1964, 225–227.

2   WATT, J.M.; BREYER-BRANDWIJK, M.G. *The Medicinal and Poisonous Plants of Southern and Eastern Africa.* E. & S. Livingstone Ltd, Edinburgh and London, UK. 2nd Edition. 1962, 834–841.

3   SCOTT, H.G. Poisonous plants and animals. In: *Foodborne Infections and Intoxications.* Edited by H. Riemann. Academic Press, New York and London. 1969, 543–604.

4   HANSEN, A.A. The poisonous plant situation in Indiana. *American Veterinary Journal* 1924, 66, 351–362.

5   PATTERSON, F.D. Pokeweed causes heavy losses in swine herd. *Veterinary Medicine* 1929, 24, 114.

6   BARNETT, B.D. Toxicity of pokeberries (fruit of *Phytolacca americana* Large) for turkey poults. *Poultry Science* 1975, 54, 1215–1217.

7   CATTLEY, R.C.; BARNETT, B.D. The effect of pokeberry ingestion on immune response in turkeys. *Poultry Science* 1977, 56, 246–248.

8   DUNCAN, A.A. Inkweed is a potentially dangerous weed. *New Zealand Journal of Agriculture* 1962, 105, 17 and 19.

9   O'LEARY, S.B. Poisoning in man from eating poisonous plants. *Archives of Environmental Health* 1964, 9, 216–242.

10 LAMPE, K.F.; FAGERSTRÖM, R. *Plant Toxicity and Dermatitis.* Williams and Wilkins, Baltimore, USA. 1968, 32.

11 LAWRENCE, R.A. The clinical effect of pokeweed root ingestion upon 32 adults. *Veterinary and Human Toxicology* 1990, 32, 369.

12 ANONYMOUS. Pokeweed poisoning – Passiac County. *Communication, Food Production and Inspection Branch, Agriculture, Canada* 1981, 28, 25.

13 JAECKLE, K.A.; FREEMAN, F.R. Pokeweed poisoning. *Southern Medical Journal* 1981, 74, 639–640.

14 HAMILTON, R.J.; SHIH, R.D.; HOFFMAN, R.S. Mobitz type I heart block after pokeweed ingestion. *Veterinary and Human Toxicology* 1995, 37, 66–67.

15 MITCHELL, J.; ROOK, A. *Botanical Dermatology. Plants and Plant Products Injurious to the Skin.* Greengrass Ltd, Vancouver, Canada. 1979, 513–514.

16 BARKER, B.E.; FARNES, P. Histochemistry of blood cells treated with pokeweed mitogen. *Nature, London* 1967, 214, 787–789.

PINACEAE

1   JAMES, L.F.; SHORT, R.E.; PANTER, K.E.; MOLYNEUX, R.J.; STUART, L.D.; BELLOWS, R.A. Pine needle abortion in cattle: a review and report of 1973–1984 research. *Cornell Veterinarian* 1989, 79, 39–52.

2   GARDNER, D.R.; MOLYNEUX, R.J.; JAMES, L.F.; PANTER, K.E.; STEGELMEIER, B.L. Ponderosa pine needle-induced abortion in beef cattle: identification of isocupressic acid as the principal active component. *Journal of Agricultural and Food Chemistry* 1994, 42, 756–761.

3   GARDNER, D.R.; MOLYNEUX, R.J.; JAMES, L.F.; PANTER, K.E.; STEGELMEIER, B.L. Studies on the abortifacient principle of ponderosa pine needles (*Pinus ponderosa* Laws). In: *Plant-associated Toxins. Agricultural, Phytochemical and Ecological Aspects*. Edited by S.M. Colegate and P.R. Dorling. CAB International, Wallingford, UK. 1994, 339–344.

4   CHRISTENSON, L.K.; SHORT, R.E.; FORD, S.P. Effects of ingestion of ponderosa pine needles by late-pregnant cows on uterine blood flow and steroid secretion. *Journal of Animal Science* 1992, 70, 531–537.

5   WIEDMEIER, R.D.; PFISTER, J.A.; ADAMS, D.C.; BAIR, J.R.; SISSON, D.V. Effects of ponderosa pine needle consumption on ruminal microflora in cattle. In: *Poisonous Plants. Proceedings of the Third International Symposium*. Edited by L.F. James, R.F. Keeler, E.M. Bailey, P.R. Cheeke and M.P. Hegarty. Iowa State University Press, Ames, Iowa, USA. 1992, 382–386.

6   LOVELL, C.R. *Plants and the Skin*. Blackwell Scientific Publications, Oxford, UK. 1993, 236–242.

POLYGONACEAE

1   CLARE, N.T. *Photosensitisation in Diseases of Domestic Animals*. Review Series No.3, Commonwealth Bureau of Animal Health. Commonwealth Agricultural Bureaux, Farnham Royal, UK. 1952, 15–16.

2   CLARE, N.T. Photosensitisation in animals. *Advances in Veterinary Science* 1955, 2, 182–211.

3   WATT, J.M.; BREYER-BRANDWIJK, M.G. *The Medicinal and Poisonous Plants of Southern and Eastern Africa*. E. & S. Livingstone Ltd, Edinburgh and London, UK. 2nd Edition. 1962, 857–859.

4   FORSYTH, A.A. *British Poisonous Plants*. HMSO, London, UK. Ministry of Agriculture, Fisheries and Food Bulletin 161, 1968, 79–80 (amended 1979, 80–81).

5   KINGSBURY, J.M. *Poisonous Plants of the United States and Canada*. Prentice-Hall Inc., New Jersey, USA. 1964, 228–230.

6   SALGUES, R. [Polygonaceae. Chemical and toxicological studies.] *Qualitas Plantarum et Materiae Vegetabiles* 1961, 8, 367–395.

7   GUSYNIN, I.A. [*The Toxicology of Poisonous Plants*.] Gosudarstvennoe Izdatel'stvo Sel'skokhozyaistvennoi Literatury, Moscow, USSR. 1955, 236–237.

8   CHEREMISINOV, G.A. [Persistence of photodynamic substances in white sheep fed on buckwheat.] *Veterinariya, Moscow* 1956, No.6, 78.

9   PRIOUZEAU, M.M. [Fagopyrism in cattle.] *Recueil de Médecine Vétérinaire* 1942, 118, 160–168.

10 NAUDIN, L. [Poisoning of a goat by rhubarb leaves.] *Recueil de Médecine Vétérinaire* 1932, 109, 91–92.

11 BUCHANAN, J.M. Three cases of poisoning by plants. *Veterinary Record* 1933, 13, 927.

12 HANSEN, A.A. Indiana plants injurious to livestock. Purdue University Agricultural Experiment Station Circular No.175, 1930, 24.

13 NATIONAL POISONS INFORMATION SERVICE, London, UK. Personal communication.

14 ROBB, H.F. Death from rhubarb leaves due to oxalic acid poisoning. *Journal of the American Medical Association* 1919, 73, 627–628.

15 LEFFMAN H. Death from rhubarb leaves due to oxalic acid poisoning. *Journal of the American Medical Association* 1919, 73, 928–929.

16 ANONYMOUS. Poisoning by rhubarb leaves. *Lancet* 1917, I, 847.

17 STREICHER, E. [Acute kidney failure and icterus after poisoning with rhubarb leaves.] *Deutsche Medizinische Wochenschrift* 1964, 89, 2379.

347

18 TALLQVIST, H.; VAANANEN, I. Death of a child from oxalic acid poisoning due to eating rhubarb leaves. *Annales Paediatriae Fenniae* 1960, 6, 144–147.

19 FASSETT, D.W. Oxalates. In: *Toxicants Occurring Naturally in Foods.* National Academy of Sciences, Washington, USA. 2nd Edition. 1973, 346–362.

20 CONNOR, H.E. *The Poisonous Plants in New Zealand.* E.C. Keating, Government Printer, Wellington, New Zealand. 1977, 139–141.

21 COWARD, T.G. Acute, fatal poisoning in sheep due to ingestion of common sorrel (*Rumex acetosa*). *Veterinary Record* 1949, 46, 765–766.

22 PANCIERA, R.J.; MARTIN, T.; BURROWS, G.E.; TAYLOR, D.S.; RICE, L.E. Acute oxalate poisoning attributable to ingestion of curly dock (*Rumex crispus*) in sheep. *Journal of the American Veterinary Medical Association* 1990, 196, 1981–1984.

23 CRAIG, J.F.; KEHOE, D. Investigations as to the poisonous nature of common sorrel (*Rumex acetosa* Linn.) for cattle. *Journal of Comparative Pathology and Therapeutics* 1921, 34, 27–47.

24 CORNEVIN, C. *Des Plantes Vénéneuses.* Librairie de Firmin-Didot, Paris, France. 1887, 150–151.

25 FARRÉ, M.; XIRGU, J.; SALGADO, A.; PERACAULA, R.; REIG, R.; SANZ, P. Fatal oxalic acid poisoning from sorrel soup. *Lancet* 1989, II, 1524.

26 REIG, R.; SANZ, P.; BLANCHE, C.; FONTARNAU, R.; DOMINGUEZ, A.; CORBELLA, J. Fatal poisoning by *Rumex crispus* (curled dock): pathological findings and application of scanning electron microscopy. *Veterinary and Human Toxicology* 1990, 32, 468–470.

27 FORSYTH, A.A. *British Poisonous Plants.* HMSO, London, UK. Ministry of Agriculture, Fisheries and Food Bulletin 161, 1968, 79 (amended 1979, 80).

28 KNIGHT, P.R. Suspected nitrite toxicity in horses associated with the ingestion of wireweed (*Polygonum aviculare*). *Australian Veterinary Practitioner* 1979, 9, 175–177.

29 LLOYD, M. Personal communication.

PRIMULACEAE

1 CORNEVIN, C. *Des Plantes Vénéneuses.* Librairie de Firmin-Didot, Paris, France. 1887, 429–430.

2 WATT, J.M.; BREYER-BRANDWIJK, M.G. *Medicinal and Poisonous Plants of Southern and Eastern Africa.* E. & S. Livingstone Ltd, Edinburgh and London, UK. 2nd Edition. 1962, 870.

3 REYNARD, G.B.; NORTON, J.B.S. Poisonous plants of Maryland in relation to livestock. University of Maryland Agricultural Experiment Station Technical Bulletin A10, 1942, 292.

4 FORSYTH, A.A. *British Poisonous Plants.* HMSO, London, UK. Ministry of Agriculture, Fisheries and Food Bulletin 161, 1968, 84–85 (amended 1979, 85–86).

5 PULLAR, E.M. Studies on five suspected poisonous plants. *Australian Veterinary Journal* 1939, 15, 19–23.

6 SCHNEIDER, D.J. Fatal ovine nephrosis caused by *Anagallis arvensis. Journal of the South African Veterinary Association* 1978, 49, 321–324.

7 ROTHWELL, J.T.; MARSHALL, D.J. Suspected poisoning of sheep by *Anagallis arvensis* (scarlet pimpernel). *Australian Veterinary Journal* 1986, 63, 316.

8 MITCHELL, J.; ROOK, A. *Botanical Dermatology. Plants and Plant Products Injurious to the Skin.* Greengrass Ltd, Vancouver, Canada. 1979, 544.

9 LOVELL, C.R. *Plants and the Skin.* Blackwell Scientific Publications, Oxford, UK. 1993, 182–185.

10 SPOERKE, D.G.; SMOLINSKE, S.C. *Toxicity of Houseplants.* CRC Press, Boca Raton, Florida, USA. 1990, 189–191.

11 NATIONAL POISONS INFORMATION SERVICE, London, UK. Personal communication.

RANUNCULACEAE

1 BONORA, A.; DALL'OLIO, G.; DONINI, A.; BRUNI, A. An HPLC screening of some Italian Ranunculaceae for the lactone protoanemonin. *Phytochemistry* 1987, 26, 2277–2279.

2 SHEARER, G.D. Some observations on the poisonous properties of buttercups. *Veterinary Journal* 1938, 94, 22–32.

3 FORSYTH, A.A. *British Poisonous Plants.* HMSO, London, UK. Ministry of Agriculture, Fisheries and Food Bulletin 161, 1968, 32–39 (amended 1979, 33–40).

4 MOORE, R.H.S. Poisoning by old man's beard (*Clematis vitalba*). *Veterinary Record* 1971, 89, 569–570.

5 LOVELL, C.R. *Plants and the Skin.* Blackwell Scientific Publications, Oxford, UK. 1993, 52, 57–59.

6 FROHNER, D.; PFÄNDER, H.J. *A Colour Atlas of Poisonous Plants.* Wolfe Publishing Ltd, London, UK. 1984, 172–182.

7 BERSELLI, L. [Green hellebore poisoning in cattle.] *Nuova Veterinaria* 1936, 14, 197–198.

8 JOHNSON, C. T.; ROUTLEDGE, J.K. Suspected *Helleborus viridis* poisoning of cattle. *Veterinary Record* 1971, 89, 202.

9 HOLLIMAN, A.; MILTON, D. *Helleborus foetidus* poisoning of cattle. *Veterinary Record* 1990, 127, 339–340.

10 BLASZYK, P. [Disease of cattle after application of growth regulators to pasture.] *Gesunde Pflanzen* 1969, 21, 33–36.

11 HEGGSTAD, E. [A fatal combination: fat cattle in late pregnancy on poor pasture with buttercups.] *Norsk Veterinærtidsskrift* 1989, 101, 935–936.

12 THERREIN, H.P.; HIDIROGLOU, M.; CHARETTE, L.A. Note on the toxicity of tall buttercup (*Ranunculus acris* L.) to cattle. *Canadian Journal of Animal Science* 1962, 42, 123–124.

13 HIDIROGLOU, M.; KNUTTI, H.J. The effects of green tall buttercup on the growth and health of beef cattle and sheep. *Canadian Journal of Animal Science* 1963, 43, 68–71.

14 MIRKOVIĆ, M. [Some cases of poisoning in cattle by Ranunculaceae.] *Jugoslovenski Veterinarski Glasnik* 1936, 16, 544–545.

15 TEHON, L.R.; MORRILL, C.C.; GRAHAM, R. Illinois plants poisonous to livestock. Illinois College of Agriculture Extension Service Bulletin 599, 1946, 37–40.

16 WINTERS, J.B. Severe urticarial reaction in a dog following ingestion of tall field buttercup. *Veterinary Medicine and Small Animal Clinician* 1976, 71, 307.

17 GUNNING, O.V. Suspected buttercup poisoning in a Jersey cow. *British Veterinary Journal* 1949, 105, 393.

18 KELCH, W.J.; KERR, L.A.; ADAIR, H.S. Suspected buttercup (*Ranunculus bulbosus*) toxicosis with secondary photosensitization in a Charolais heifer. *Veterinary and Human Toxicology* 1992, 34, 238–239.

19 RAMISZ, A. [Poisoning of two cows by the celery-leaved buttercup (*Ranunculus sceleratus*).] *Medycyna Weterynaryjna* 1971, 27, 411–412.

20 RIPEANU, M. [Observations on some important cases of poisoning in animals.] *Revista de Zootehnie și Medicină Veterinară* 1963, 13, No.12, 61–69.

21 PIEKARZ, J. [Buttercup poisoning in a horse.] *Medycyna Weterynaryjna* 1981, 37, 658.

22 RAISON, A.V. Poisons in your backyard. *Canadian Pharmaceutical Journal* 1968, 101, 4–8.

23 GERBAUD, O. [Aconites.] *Notes de Toxicologie Vétérinaire* 1980, No.8, 453–456.

24 CORNEVIN, C. *Des Plantes Vénéneuses.* Librairie de Firmin-Didot, Paris, France. 1887, 211–220.

25 NATIONAL POISONS INFORMATION SERVICE, London, UK. Personal communication.

26 COOPER, P. *Poisoning by Drugs and Chemicals, Plants and Animals.* Alchemist Publications, London, UK. 3rd Edition. 1974, 4–5.

27 FELDKAMP, A.; KÖSTERS, B.; WEBER, H.P. [Fatal poisoning caused by monkshood (*Aconitum napellus*).] *Monatsschrift für Kinderheilkunde* 1991, 139, 366–367.

28 BUT, P.P.H.; TAI, Y.T.; YOUNG, K. Three fatal cases of herbal aconite poisoning. *Veterinary and Human Toxicology* 1994, 36, 212–215.

29 Personal communication.

30 MANNERS, G.D.; PANTER, K.E.; RALPHS, M.H.; PFISTER, J.A.; OLSEN, J.D.; JAMES, L.F. Toxicity and chemical phenology of norditerpenoid alkaloids in the tall larkspurs (*Delphinium* species). *Journal of Agricultural and Food Chemistry* 1993, 41, 96–100.

31 OLSEN, J.D.; MANNERS, G.D. Toxicology of diterpene alkaloids in rangeland larkspur (*Delphinium* spp.). In: *Toxicants of Plant Origin. Volume I. Alkaloids.* Edited by P.R. Cheeke. CRC Press, Boca Raton, Florida, USA. 1989, 291–326.

32 OLSEN, J.D. Larkspur poisoning: as we know it and a glimpse of the future. *Bovine Practitioner* 1994, 28, 157–163.

33 WILLIAMS, M.C.; CRONIN, E.H. Five poisonous range weeds – when and why they are dangerous. *Journal of Range Management* 1968, 19, 274–279.

34 JAMES, L.F.; KEELER, R.F.; JOHNSON, A.E.; WILLIAMS, M.C.; CRONIN, E.H.; OLSEN, J.D. Plants Poisonous to Livestock in the United States. United States Department of Agriculture, Agriculture Information Bulletin No.415, 1980, 31–34.

35 NATION, P.N.; BENN, M.H.; ROTH, S.H.; WILKENS, J.L. Clinical signs and studies of the site of action of purified larkspur alkaloid, methyllycaconitine, administered parenterally to calves. *Canadian Veterinary Journal* 1982, 23, 264–266.

36 PFISTER, J.A.; PANTER, K.E.; MANNERS, G.D.; CHENEY, C.D. Reversal of tall larkspur (*Delphinium barbeyi*) poisoning in cattle with physostigmine. *Veterinary and Human Toxicology* 1994, 36, 511–514.

37 MILNE, J.A. A case of *Delphinium* poisoning in rams. *New Zealand Veterinary Journal* 1966, 14, 127.

38 ELPHICK, E.E. Sheep poisoned as a result of eating larkspur (*Delphinium consolidum*). *Veterinary Record* 1931, 43, 512–513.

RHAMNACEAE

1 SÖDERMARK, N. [*Frangula* poisoning in cattle.] *Skandinavisk Veterinärtidskrift* 1942, 32, 458.

2 VAN DEN DIKKENBERG, M.I.; HOLTKAMP, B.M. [Alder buckthorn poisoning in horses.] *Tijdschrift voor Diergeneeskunde* 1987, 112, 340–341.

3 VÖLKER, R. *Lehrbuch der Toxikologie fur Tierärzte.* (Fröhner). Ferdinand Enke Verlag, Stuttgart, Germany. 6th Edition. 1950, 300.

4 CORNEVIN, C. *Des Plantes Vénéneuses.* Librairie de Firmin-Didot, Paris, France. 1887, 274.

5 LAMPE, K.F.; FAGERSTRÖM, R. *Plant Toxicity and Dermatitis.* Williams and Wilkins Co., Baltimore, USA. 1968, 56, 58.

6 BANACH, K. [Acute poisoning with anthraquinone compounds caused by ingestion of buckthorn berries.] *Wiadomści Lekarskie* 1980, 33, 405–408.

7 COOPER, P. *Poisoning by Drugs and Chemicals, Plants and Animals.* Alchemist Publications, London, UK. 3rd Edition. 1974, 106.

ROSACEAE

1 MAJAK, W.; MCDIARMID, R.E.; HALL, J.W. The cyanide potential of Saskatoon serviceberry (*Amelanchier alnifolia*) and chokecherry (*Prunus virginiana*). *Canadian Journal of Animal Science* 1981, 61, 681–686.

2 HANSEN, A.A. The poison plant situation in Indiana. *American Veterinary Journal* 1924, 66,

351–362.

3   STAUFFER, V.D. Hydrocyanic acid poisoning from chokecherry leaves. *Journal of the American Veterinary Medical Association* 1970, 157, 1324.

4   JACKSON, T. Cyanide poisoning in two donkeys. *Veterinary and Human Toxicology* 1995, 37, 567–568.

5   CARDASSIS, J.; GIANNAKOULAS, D. Hydrocyanic acid poisoning from plum stones in pigs. *Hellenike Kteniatrike, Thessaloniki* 1961, 4, 136–141.

6   NATIONAL POISONS INFORMATION SERVICE, London, UK. Personal communication.

7   AUSTVOLL, A. Plumstones in pig swill. *Veterinary Record* 1954, 66, 681.

8   MUENSCHER, W.C. *Poisonous Plants of the United States*. Macmillan, New York, USA. 1939, 109–113.

9   GLODEK, S. [Plum poisoning in cows and pigs.] *Medycyna Weterynaryjna* 1965, 21, 44.

10 THOLHUYSEN, L.J.T. [Lethal intoxication of two heifers by bitter almonds.] *Tijdschrift voor Diergeneeskunde* 1960, 85, 1243–1244.

11 SARGISON, N.D.; WILLIAMSON, D.S.; DUNCAN, J.R.; MCCANCE, R.W. *Prunus padus* (bird cherry) poisoning in cattle. *Veterinary Record* 1996, 138, 188.

12 SHAW, J.M. Suspected cyanide poisoning in two goats caused by ingestion of crab apple leaves and fruits. *Veterinary Record* 1986, 119, 242–243.

13 JEAN-BLAIN, C. [Cherry laurel.] *Notes de Toxicologie Vétérinaire* 1978, No.4, 222–223.

14 HIBBS, C.M. Cyanide and nitrate toxicoses of cattle. *Veterinary and Human Toxicology* 1979, 21, 401–403.

15 LASCH, E.E.; EL RAGHDA, S. Multiple cases of cyanide poisoning by apricot kernels in children from Gaza. *Pediatrics* 1981, 68, 5–7.

16 SAYRE, J.W.; KAYMAKCALAN, S. Cyanide poisoning from apricot seeds among children in central Turkey. *New England Journal of Medicine* 1964, 270, 1113–1115.

17 RUBINO, M.J.; DAVIDOFF, F. Cyanide poisoning from apricot seeds. *Journal of the American Medical Association* 1979, 241, 355.

18 KINGSBURY, J.M. *Poisonous Plants of the United States and Canada*. Prentice-Hall Inc., New Jersey, USA. 1964, 364–370.

19 VALE, J.A.; PROUDFOOT, A.T.; MEREDITH, T.J. Poisoning by inhalational agents. Cyanide. In: *Oxford Textbook of Medicine*. Edited by D.J. Wetherall, J.C.G. Ledingham and D.A. Warrell. Oxford University Press, Oxford, UK. 3rd Edition. 1996, 1097–1098.

20 CONN, E.E. Cyanogenesis, the production of hydrogen cyanide, by plants. In: *Effects of Poisonous Plants on Livestock*. Edited by R.F. Keeler, K.R. Van Kampen and L.F. James. Academic Press, New York and London. 1978, 301–310.

21 MORAN, E.A. Cyanogenetic compounds in plants and their significance in animal industry. *American Journal of Veterinary Research* 1954, 15, 171–176.

22 ROBB, W.; CAMPBELL, D. Poisoning of sheep by the consumption of laurel leaves. *Veterinary Record* 1941, 53, 93–95.

23 WILSON, D.R.; GORDON, W.J. Laurel poisoning in sheep. *Veterinary Record* 1941, 53, 95–97.

24 FROHNE, D.; PFÄNDER, H.J. *A Colour Atlas of Poisonous Plants*. Wolfe Publishing Ltd, London, UK. 1984, 193–194.

25 ST. JOHN, T.N. Urine discolouration. *Veterinary Record* 1976, 99, 21.

26 FROHNE, D.; PFÄNDER, H.J. *A Colour Atlas of Poisonous Plants*. Wolfe Publishing Ltd, London, UK. 1984, 199–200.

RUTACEAE

1   LOVELL, C.R. *Plants and the Skin.* Blackwell Scientific Publications, Oxford, UK. 1993, 93.

2   HESKEL, N.S.; AMON, R.B.; STORRS, F.J.; WHITE, C.R. Phytophotodermatitis due to *Ruta graveolens.*
     Contact Dermatitis 1983, 9, 278–280.

3   HANSLIAN, L.; KADLEC, K. Bullous dermatitis after contact with common rue (*Ruta graveolens* L.).
     Československá Farmacie 1968, 17, 293–295.

4   GAWKRODGER, D.J.; SAVIN, J.A. Phytophotodermatitis due to common rue (*Ruta graveolens*).
     Contact Dermatitis 1983, 9, 224.

5   PETHER, J.V.S. Ruing rue. *Lancet* 1985, II, 957.

SCROPHULARIACEAE

1   ARENA, J.M. A guide to poisonous plants. *Veterinary and Human Toxicology* 1979, 21, 108–111.

2   COOPER, P. *Poisoning by Drugs and Chemicals, Plants and Animals.* Alchemist Publications, London,
     UK. 3rd Edition. 1974, 85.

3   SINGH, R.B. The foxglove 1785–1985. *Acta Cardiologica* 1985, 40, 357–363.

4   WILKINS, M.R.; KENDALL, M.J.; WADE, O.L. William Withering and digitalis, 1785–1985. *British
     Medical Journal* 1985, 290, 7–8.

5   HOLLMAN, A. Plants and cardiac glycosides. *British Heart Journal* 1985, 54, 258–261.

6   CORRIGALL, W.; MOODY, R.R.; FORBES, J.C. Foxglove (*Digitalis purpurea*) poisoning in farmed red
     deer (*Cervus elaphus*). *Veterinary Record* 1978, 102, 119–122.

7   CARMICHAEL, M.A. Suspected foxglove poisoning in a dog. *Veterinary Record* 1987, 120, 375.

8   THOMAS, D.L.; QUICK, M.P.; MORGAN, R.P. Suspected foxglove (*Digitalis purpurea*) poisoning in a
     dairy cow. *Veterinary Record* 1987, 120, 300–301.

9   McCLEAN, A. Suspected foxglove poisoning in sheep. *Veterinary Record* 1966, 79, 817–818.

10   BARNIKOL, H.; HOFFMANN, W. [*Digitalis* poisoning in pigs.] *Tierärztliche Umschau* 1973, 28, 612–614,
     616.

11   NATIONAL POISONS INFORMATION SERVICE, London, UK. Personal communication.

12   TSCHIRCH, W.; JORGA, W. [*Digitalis purpurea* poisoning in guinea pigs in a zoo.]
     Verhandlungsbericht des Internationalen Symposiums über die Erkrankungen der Zoo- und Wildtiere 1989,
     No.31, 459–461.

13   PARKER, W.H. Foxglove (*Digitalis purpurea*) poisoning in turkeys. *Veterinary Record* 1951, 63, 416.

14   ARAI, M.; STAUBER, E.; SHROPSHIRE, C.M. Evaluation of selected plants for their toxic effects in
     canaries. *Journal of the American Veterinary Medical Association* 1992, 200, 1329–1331.

15   GERBAUD, O. [Foxglove, *Digitalis purpurea.*]. *Notes de Toxicologie Vétérinaire* 1980, No.8, 450–452.

16   LAMPE, K.F. Systemic plant poisoning in children. *Pediatrics* 1974, 54, 347–351.

17   SIMPKISS, M.; HOLT, D. *Digitalis* poisoning due to the accidental ingestion of foxglove leaves.
     Therapeutic Drug Monitoring 1983, 5, 217.

18   DICKSTEIN, E.S.; KUNKEL, F.W. *Digitalis purpurea* poisoning in man. *American Journal of Medicine*
     1980, 69, 167–169.

19   BAIN, R.J. Accidental digitalis poisoning due to drinking herbal tea. *British Medical Journal* 1985,
     290, 1624.

20   CHAMBERLAIN, D.A. Digitalis: where are we now? *British Heart Journal* 1985, 54, 227–233.

21   LE WINN, E.B. The steroidal actions of digitalis. *Perspectives in Biology and Medicine* 1984, 27,
     183–199.

22   PILTZ, J.R.; WERTENBAKER, C.; LANCE, S.E.; SLAMOVITS, T.; LEEPER, H.F. Digoxin toxicity.
     Recognizing the varied visual presentations. *Journal of Clinical Neuro-ophthalmology* 1993, 13,
     275–280.

23 Landauer, J.A. Magnesium deficiency and digitalis toxicity. *Journal of the American Medical Association* 1984, 251, 730.

24 Lee, T.C. Van Gogh's vision. Digitalis intoxication? *Journal of the American Medical Association* 1981, 245, 727–729.

25 Antman, E.M.; Wenger, T.L.; Butler, V.P.; Haber, E.; Smith, T.W. Treatment of 150 cases of life-threatening digitalis intoxication with digoxin-specific Fab antibody fragments. Final report of a multicenter study. *Circulation* 1990, 81, 1744–1752.

26 Ujhelyi, M.R.; Robert, S.; Cummings, D.M.; Colucci, R.D.; Green, P.J.; Sailsted, J.; Vlasses, P.H.; Zarowitz, B.J. Influence of digoxin immune Fab therapy and renal dysfunction on the disposition of total and free digoxin. *Annals of Internal Medicine* 1993, 119, 273–277.

27 Phillips, S.D. Digoxin immune Fab therapy for digoxin toxicity. *Annals of Internal Medicine* 1994, 120, 247.

28 Cornevin, C. *Des Plantes Vénéneuses.* Librairie de Firmin-Didot, Paris, France. 1887, 504–505.

29 Kamel, S.H. [Chemical and toxicological study of an Egyptian plant: *Orobanche minor* Sutton.]. *Revue d'Élevage et de Médecine Vétérinaire des Pays Tropicaux* 1956, 9, 43–48.

30 Long, H.C. *Plants Poisonous to Live Stock.* Cambridge University Press, Cambridge, UK. 1917, 95.

31 Ewart, R.H. Poisoning in young cattle by a member of the Scrophulariaceae. *Veterinary Record* 1937, 49, 1514.

SOLANACEAE

1 Fodor, G. Tropane alkaloids. In: *Chemistry of Alkaloids.* Edited by S.W. Pelletier. Van Nostrand Reinhold Company, New York, USA. 1970, 431–467.

2 *Merck Index,* Merck & Co. Inc., Whitehouse Station, New Jersey, USA. 12th Edition. 1996, 148–149.

3 Frohne, D.; Pfänder, H.J. *A Colour Atlas of Poisonous Plants,* Wolfe Publishing Ltd, London, UK. 1984, 201–222.

4 Scott, H.G. Poisonous plants and animals. In: *Food-borne Infections and Intoxications.* Edited by H. Riemann, Academic Press, New York and London. 1969, 561.

5 Forsyth, A.A. *British Poisonous Plants.* HMSO, London, UK. Ministry of Agriculture, Fisheries and Food Bulletin 161, 1968, 88–90 (amended 1979, 89–90).

6 Smith, H.C.; Taussig, R.A.; Peterson, P.C. Deadly nightshade poisoning in swine. *Journal of the American Veterinary Medical Association* 1956, 129, 116–117.

7 Ogilvie, D.D. Atropine poisoning in the goat. *Veterinary Record* 1935, 15, 1415–1417.

8 Sawin, P.B.; Glick, D. Atropinesterase, a genetically determined enzyme in the rabbit. *Proceedings of the National Academy of Science* 1943, 29, 55–59.

9 Galizia. E.J. Clinical curio: hallucinations in elderly tea drinkers. *British Medical Journal* 1983, 287, 979.

10 Anonymous. Food poisoning and *Salmonella* surveillance in England and Wales: 1983. *British Medical Journal* 1985, 291, 394–396.

11 Pestalozzi, B.C.; Caduff, F. [Group poisoning with belladonna tea.] *Schweizerische Medizinische Wochenschrift* 1986, 116, 924–926.

12 National Poisons Information Service, London, UK. Personal communication.

13 Trabattoni, G.; Visintini, D.; Terzano, G.M.; Lechi, A. Accidental poisoning with deadly nightshade berries: a case report. *Human Toxicology* 1984, 3, 513–516.

14 Testasecca, D.; Caputi, C.; Pavoni, P.A. [A case of poisoning by belladonna berries.] *Clinica Terapeutica, Rome* 1978, 86, 277–280.

15 Lange, A.; Toft, P. [Poisoning with nightshade, *Atropa belladonna.*] *Ugeskrift for Læger* 1990, 152,1096.

16 WORTH, D.P.; DAVISON, A.M.; ROBERTS, T.G.; LEWINS, A.M. Ineffectiveness of haemodialysis in atropine poisoning. *British Medical Journal* 1983, 286, 2023–2024.

17 McBARRON, E.J. *Medical and Veterinary Aspects of Plant Poisons in New South Wales.* Department of Agriculture, New South Wales, Australia. 1976, 83.

18 KEHAR, N.D.; RAU, K.G. Poisoning of livestock by *Datura stramonium. Indian Journal of Veterinary Science and Animal Husbandry* 1944, 14, 112–114.

19 FRIEDMAN, M.; LEVIN, C.E. Composition of jimson weed (*Datura stramonium*) seeds. *Journal of Agricultural and Food Chemistry* 1989, 37, 998–1005.

20 HIGHTOWER, C.E. Plants that kill and cure. *Veterinary and Human Toxicology* 1979, 21, 360–361.

21 BARNEY, G.H.; WILSON, B.J. A rare toxicity syndrome in ponies. *Veterinary Medicine* 1963, 58, 419–421.

22 WILLIAM, S.; SCOTT, P. The toxicity of *Datura stramonium* (thorn apple) to horses. *New Zealand Veterinary Journal* 1984, 32, 47.

23 SÁLYI, G.; ABONYÍ, T. [Poisoning by *Datura stramonium* seeds in horses.] *Magyar Állatorvosok Lapja* 1994, 49, 658–662.

24 SINGH, R.C.P.; SINGH, R.P. A suspected case of *Datura* poisoning in a cow. *Indian Veterinary Journal* 1971, 48, 194–196.

25 OFÚKANÝ, L.; FRANTOVÁ, E.; TUROŇ, J. [Mass poisoning of cattle with *Datura.*] *Veterinářství* 1983, 33, 316–317.

26 WATT, J.M.; BREYER-BRANDWIJK, M.G. *Medicinal and Poisonous Plants of Southern and Eastern Africa.* E. & S. Livingstone Ltd, Edinburgh and London, UK. 2nd Edition. 1962, 946–953.

27 ANONYMOUS. *Datura stramonium* poisoning in sheep. Edinburgh School of Agriculture Annual Report 1978, 129–130.

28 EL DIRDIRI, N.I.; WASFI, I.A.; ADAM, S.E.I.; EDDS, G.T. Toxicity of *Datura stramonium* to sheep and goats. *Veterinary and Human Toxicology* 1981, 23, 241–246.

29 BEHRENS, H.; HORN, M. [Tolerance of pigs to *Datura stramonium* seeds.] *Praktische Tierarzt* 1962, No.2, 43–44.

30 LEIPOLD, W.; OEHME, F.W.; COOK, J.E. Congenital arthrogryposis associated with ingestion of jimsonweed by pregnant sows. *Journal of the American Veterinary Medical Association* 1973, 162, 1059–1060.

31 NELSON, P.D.; MERCER, H.D.; ESSIG, H.W.; MINYARD, J.P. Jimson weed seed toxicity in cattle. *Veterinary and Human Toxicology* 1982, 24, 321–325.

32 WORTHINGTON, T.R.; NELSON, E.P.; BRYANT, M.J. Toxicity of thornapple (*Datura stramonium* L.) seeds to the pig. *Veterinary Record* 1981, 108, 208–211.

33 JANSSENS, G.; DE WILDE, R. [Toxicity of thornapple (*Datura stramonium* and/or ferox) in slaughter pig diets.] *Vlaams Diergeneeskundig Tijdschrift* 1989, 58, 84–86.

34 DAY, E.J.; DILWORTH, B.C. Toxicity of jimson weed seed and cocoa shell meal to broilers. *Poultry Science* 1984, 63, 466–468.

35 FLUNKER, L.K.; DAMRON, B.L.; SUNDLOF, S.F. Jimsonweed seed contamination of broiler chick and White Leghorn hen diets. *Nutrition Reports International* 1987, 36, 551–556.

36 LIST, G.R.; SPENCER, G.F. Fate of jimsonweed seed alkaloids in soybean processing. *Journal of the American Oil Chemists' Society* 1976, 53, 535–536.

37 FANGAUF, R.; VOGT, H. [Toxicity trials in laying hens and chicks with *Datura stramonium* seeds, a common contaminant of soya bean consignments.] *Archiv für Geflügelkunde* 1961, 25, 167–171.

38 HESSELBARTH. [Results of feeding experiments in cattle and pigs with *Datura stramonium* feeds.] *Praktische Tierarzt* 1962, No.7, 266–267 and No.8, 304–305.

39 TAHA, S.A.; MAHDI, A.H. *Datura* intoxication in Riyadh. *Transactions of the Royal Society of Tropical Medicine and Hygiene* 1984, 78, 134–135.

40 STROBEL, M.; CHEVALIER, J.; DE LAVARELLE, B. [Febrile coma with granulocytosis caused by *Datura stramonium* poisoning.] *Presse Médicale* 1991, 20, 2214.

41 SIEGEL, R.K. Herbal intoxication, psychoactive effects from herbal cigarettes, tea and capsules. *Journal of the American Medical Association* 1976, 236, 473–476.

42 MEBS, D.; SCHMIDT, K.; RAUDONAT, H.W.; JANZEN, R.W.; MAIKOWSKI, A.; WERNER, M. [Thornapple poisoning.] *Deutsche Medizinische Wochenschrift* 1986, 111, 762.

43 COREMANS, P.; LAMBRECHT, G.; SCHEPENS, P; VANWELDEN, J.; VERHAEGEN, H. Anticholinergic intoxication with commercially available thorn apple tea. *Journal of Toxicology. Clinical Toxicology* 1994, 32, 589–592.

44 MICHALODIMITRAKIS, M.; KOUTSELINIS, A. Discussion of "*Datura stramonium*: a fatal poisoning". *Journal of Forensic Sciences* 1984, 29, 961–962.

45 PATEL, T. Dangerous datura. *New Scientist* 1992, 135, 5.

46 KLEIN-SCHWARTZ, W.; ODERDA, G.M. Jimsonweed intoxication in adolescents and young adults. *American Journal of Diseases of Children* 1984, 138, 737–739.

47 GUHAROY, S.R.; BARAJAS, M. Atropine intoxication from the ingestion and smoking of jimson weed (*Datura stramonium*). *Veterinary and Human Toxicology* 1991, 33, 588–589.

48 VANDERHOFF, B.T.; MOSSER, K.H. Jimson weed toxicity: management of anticholinergic plant ingestion. *American Family Physician* 1992, 46, 526–530.

49 RODGERS, G.C.; VON KANEL, R.L. Conservative treatment of jimsonweed ingestion. *Veterinary and Human Toxicology* 1993, 35, 32–33.

50 RWIZA, H.T. Jimson weed food poisoning. An epidemic at Usangi Rural Government Hospital. *Tropical and Geographical Medicine* 1991, 43, 85–89.

51 VAN MEURS, A.; COHEN, A.; EDDELBROEK, P. Atropine poisoning after eating chapattis contaminated with *Datura stramonium* (thorn apple). *Transactions of the Royal Society of Tropical Medicine and Hygiene* 1992, 86, 221.

52 PEREIRA, C.A.; NISHIOKA, S. DE A. Poisoning by the use of *Datura* leaves in a homemade toothpaste. *Journal of Toxicology. Clinical Toxicology* 1994, 32, 329–331.

53 WILHELM, H.; WILHELM, B.; SCHIEFER, U. [Mydriasis caused by plant contact.] *Fortschritte der Ophthalmologie* 1991, 88, 588–591.

54 VOLTZ, R.; HOHLFELD, R.; LIEBLER, M.; HERTEL, H. Gardener's mydriasis. *Lancet* 1992, 339, 752.

55 SCHILLING, R.; SPEAKER, J. Incidence of plant poisonings in Philadelphia noted as poisons information calls. *Veterinary and Human Toxicology* 1980, 22, 148–150.

56 CRANE, E. (Editor). *Honey: A Comprehensive Survey*. William Heinemann Ltd, London, UK. 1975, 204.

57 SCHAUENBERG, P.; PARIS, F. *Guide to Medicinal Plants*. Lutterworth Press, Guildford and London, UK. 1977, 39.

58 CORNEVIN, C. *Des Plantes Vénéneuses*. Librairie de Firmin-Didot, Paris, France. 1887, 470–473.

59 MIĘDZOBRODZKI, K. [Poisoning in cows with henbane (*Hyoscyamus niger*).] *Medycyna Weterynaryjna* 1962, 18, 536–537.

60 GUSYNIN, I.A. [*Toxicology of Poisonous Plants.*] Gosudarstvennoe Izdatel'stvo Sel'skokhozyaistvennoi Literatury, Moscow, USSR. 1955, 61–62.

61 WELSBY, J.R. Henbane poisoning. *Veterinary Record* 1903, 16, 181.

62 *Merck Index*, Merck & Co., Whitehouse Station, New Jersey, USA, 12th Edition. 1996, 835.

63 FORSYTH, A.A. *British Poisonous Plants*. HMSO, London, UK. Ministry of Agriculture, Fisheries and Food Bulletin 161, 1968, 87–88 (amended 1979, 88–89).

64 LONG, H.C. *Plants Poisonous to Live Stock*. Cambridge University Press, Cambridge, UK. 1917, 51–52.

65 SPOERKE, D.G.; HALL, A.H.; DODSON, C.D.; STERMITZ, F.R.; SWANSON, C.H.; RUMACK, B.H. Mystery

root ingestion. *Journal of Emergency Medicine* 1987, 5, 385–388.

66 FORSYTH, A.A. *British Poisonous Plants.* HMSO, London, UK. Ministry of Agriculture, Fisheries and Food Bulletin 161, 1968, 92–93 (amended 1979, 93–94).

67 CROWE, M.W. Skeletal abnormalities in pigs associated with tobacco. *Modern Veterinary Practice* 1969, 50, No.13, 54–55.

68 KEELER, R.F.; CROWE, M.W. Anabasine, a teratogen from the *Nicotiana* genus. In: *Plant Toxicology. Proceedings of the Australia–U.S.A. Poisonous Plants Symposium, Brisbane, Australia, May 14–18, 1984.* Edited by A.A. Seawright, M.P. Heggerty, L.F. James and R.F. Keeler. Queensland Department of Primary Industries, Animal Research Institute, Yeerongpilly, Australia. 1985, 324–333.

69 KEELER, R.F.; SHUPE, J.L.; CROWE, M.W.; OLSON, A.; BALLS, L.D. *Nicotiana glauca*-induced congenital deformities in calves: clinical and pathologic aspects. *American Journal of Veterinary Research* 1981, 42, 1231–1234.

70 KEELER, R.F.; CROWE, M.W. Teratogenicity and toxicity of wild tree tobacco, *Nicotiana glauca* in sheep. *Cornell Veterinarian* 1984, 74, 50–59.

71 SANECKI, R.; GUPTA, R.C.; KADEL, W.L. Lethal nicotine intoxication in a group of mules. *Journal of Veterinary Diagnostic Investigation* 1994, 6, 503–504.

72 VIG, M.V. Nicotine poisoning in a dog. *Veterinary and Human Toxicology* 1990, 32, 573–575.

73 McGEE, D.; PICCIOTTI, M.; SPEVACK, T. Two year review of tobacco ingestions. *Veterinary and Human Toxicology* 1991, 33, 370.

74 SISSELMAN, S.G.; MOFENSON, H.C.; CARACCIO, T.R. Childhood poisonings from ingestion of cigarettes. *Lancet* 1996, 347, 200–201.

75 McKEY, D. The distribution of secondary compounds within plants. In: *Herbivores. Their Interaction with Secondary Plant Metabolites.* Edited by G.A. Rosenthal and D.H. Janzen. Academic Press, New York and London. 1979, 55–133.

76 CORNEVIN, C. *Des Plantes Vénéneuses.* Librairie de Firmin-Didot, Paris, France. 1887, 455.

77 CRAIG, J.F.; KEHOE, D. Plant poisoning. *Veterinary Record* 1925, 5, 795–825.

78 YATES, G. Poisoning by woody nightshade. *Veterinary Record* 1915, 28, 269–270.

79 BARRAT, M. [Poisoning by bittersweet.] *Journal de Médecine Vétérinaire et de Zootechnie, Lyons* 1926, 72, 545–552.

80 ALEXANDER, R.F.; FORBES, G.B.; HAWKINS, E.S. A fatal case of solanine poisoning. *British Medical Journal* 1948, 2, 518–519.

81 BORYS, D.J.; HERRICK, M.E.; KRENZELOK, E.P.; REISDORF, J.J.; SPILLER, H.A.; BOBBINK, S.R.; GUEVARA, D.S. The clinical effects of *Solanum dulcamara* (deadly nightshade) in pediatric patients. *Veterinary and Human Toxicology* 1992, 34, 351.

82 HORNFELDT, C.S.; COLLINS, J.E. Toxicity of nightshade berries (*Solanum dulcamara*) in mice. *Clinical Toxicology* 1990, 28, 185–192.

83 SENGER, E.; BAROUX, D. [Herbicides and resistance – toxicological significance.] *Notes de Toxicologie Vétérinaire* 1980, No.8, 444–445.

84 WELLER, R.F.; PHIPPS, R.H. A review of black nightshade (*Solanum nigrum* L.). *Protection Ecology* 1979, 1, 121–139.

85 KERY, A.; AL-JEBOORY, A.; SHAREFI, K.A. Qualitative and quantitative phytochemical studies on alkaloids of *Solanum* species grown in Iraq. I. *Solanum nigrum* L. *Journal of Biological Sciences Research* 1984, 15, No.2, 13–24.

86 KEELER, R.F. Alkaloid teratogens from *Lupinus, Conium, Veratrum* and related genera. In: *Effects of Poisonous Plants on Livestock.* Edited by R.F. Keeler, K.R. Van Kampen and L.F. James. Academic Press, New York and London. 1978, 397–408.

87 LIEBENOW, H. [*Solanum nigrum* L. as a nitrate-containing plant and the determination of its alkaloid content.] *Wissenschaftliche Zeitschrift der Humboldt-Universität zu Berlin* 1970, 19, 59–71.

88 BROBERG, G. Observations of the action of extracts of *Glium lotoides* on the miracidia of *Fasciola gigantica* and *Schistosoma mansoni. Suomen Eläinlääkärilehti* 1980, 86, 146–147.

89 CORNEVIN, C. *Des Plantes Vénéneuses*. Librairie de Firmin-Didot, Paris, France. 1887, 456.

90 *Encyclopaedia Britannica* 1929, 16, 447.

91 HUBBS, J.C. Belladonna poisoning in pigs. *Veterinary Medicine* 1947, 42, 428–429.

92 FORSYTH, A.A. *British Poisonous Plants*. HMSO, London, UK. Ministry of Agriculture, Fisheries and Food Bulletin 161, 1968, 92 (amended 1979, 91–92).

93 FAWCETT, R.S.; JENNINGS, V.M. Today's weed. Black nightshade (*Solanum nigrum* L.). *Weeds Today* 1979, 10, 21.

94 GUNNING, O.V. Poisoning in goats by black nightshade (*Solanum nigrum*). *British Veterinary Journal* 1949, 105, 473–474.

95 KWATRA, M.S.; HOTHI, D.S.; SINGH, A.; CHAWLA, R.S. Arteriosclerosis with metastatic calcification in Corriedale sheep in Punjab. *Atherosclerosis* 1974, 19, 521–528.

96 SENGER, E.; BAROUX, D. [Cases of poisoning after consumption of maize.] *Notes de Toxicologie Vétérinaire* 1980, No.8, 468–474.

97 VOGEL, R.; GUTZWILLER, A. [Black nightshade in maize silage: caution.] *Revue Suisse d'Agriculture* 1993, 25, 315–321.

98 WATT, J.M.; BREYER-BRANDWIJK, M.G. *The Medicinal and Poisonous Plants of Southern and Eastern Africa*. E. & S. Livingstone Ltd, Edinburgh and London, UK. 2nd Edition. 1962, 996–1000.

99 JADHAV, S.J.; SALUNKHE, D.K. Formation and control of chlorophyll and glycoalkaloids in tubers of *Solanum tuberosum* L. and evaluation of glycoalkaloid toxicity. *Advances in Food Research* 1975, 21, 307–354.

100 CHAUBE, S.; SWINYARD, C.A. Teratological and toxicological studies of alkaloidal and phenolic compounds from *Solanum tuberosum* L. *Toxicology and Applied Pharmacology* 1976, 36, 227–237.

101 NICHOLSON, J.W.G.; ALLEN, J.G. The distribution of trypsin and chymotrypsin inhibitors in potato tubers. *Canadian Journal of Animal Science* 1989, 69, 513–515.

102 VAN GELDER, W.M.J. Chemistry, toxicology, and occurrence of steroidal glycoalkaloids: potential contaminants of the potato (*Solanum tuberosum* L.). In: *Poisonous Plant Contamination of Edible Plants*. Edited by A.F.M. Rizk. CRC Press, Boca Raton, Florida, USA. 1991, 117–156.

103 COXON, D.T. The glycoalkaloid content of potato berries. *Journal of the Science of Food and Agriculture* 1981, 32, 412–414.

104 NICHOLSON, J.W.G.; YOUNG, D.A.; MCQUEEN, R.E.; DEJONG, H.; WOOD, F.A. The feeding potential of potato vines. *Canadian Journal of Animal Science* 1978, 58, 559–569.

105 OGILVIE, D.D. Solanin poisoning in pigs. *Veterinary Record* 1943, 55, 249.

106 LEWANDOWSKI, L.; BĄK, T.; MIĘDZOBRODSKI, K. [Solanine poisoning in swine.] *Zeszyty Naukowe Wyzszej Szkoly Rolniczej we Wroclawiu, Zootechnika* 1963, 11, 203–207.

107 BUCZEK, A.; MAJERAN, W. [A rare complication after solanin poisonings in pigs.] *Medycyna Weterynaryjna* 1969, 25, 507–508.

108 MILLIGAN, J.B. Suspected potato poisoning in cattle. *Veterinary Record* 1941, 53, 512.

109 KOTOWSKI, K. [Cases of poisoning in cattle due to excessive feeding with potatoes.] *Medycyna Weterynaryjna* 1967, 23, 736–737.

110 FORSYTH, A.A. *British Poisonous Plants*. HMSO, London, UK. Ministry of Agriculture, Fisheries and Food Bulletin 161, 1968, 92–93 (amended 1979, 92–93).

111 SOMVANSHI, R.; BISWAS, J.C.; SASTRY, M.S. Potato plant (*Solanum tuberosum*) induced dermatitis in Indian buffaloes. *Indian Journal of Animal Sciences* 1992, 62, 639–641.

112 BOLIN, F.M. Green potatoes can kill sheep. *North Dakota Farm Research* 1962, 22, No.7, 15.

113 GUNNING, O.V. Suspected potato poisoning in a mare. *British Veterinary Journal* 1950, 106, 32–33.

114 OWEN, R. AP R. Potato poisoning in a horse. *Veterinary Record* 1985, 117, 246.

115 BLOUNT, W.P. Potato poisoning in the adult dog. *Veterinary Record* 1928, 8, 924–925.

116 AZIM, A.; SHAIKH, H.A.; AHMAD, R. Effect of feeding green potatoes on different visceral organs and blood plasma of rabbits. *Journal of the Science of Food and Agriculture* 1982, 33, 1275–1279.

117 TEMPERTON, H. The effects of feeding green and sprouted potatoes to laying pullets. *Veterinary Record* 1943, 55, 359.

118 KLINE, B.E.; ELBE, H.; DAHLE, N.A.; KUPCHAN, S.M. Toxic effect of potato sprouts and of solanine fed to pregnant rats. *Proceedings of the Society for Experimental Biology and Medicine* 1961, 107, 807–809.

119 GAFFIELD, W.; KEELER, R.F.; BAKER, D.C.; STAFFORD, A.E. Studies on the *Solanum tuberosum* sprout teratogen. In: *Poisonous Plants. Proceedings of the Third International Symposium*. Edited by L.F. James, R.F. Keeler, E.M. Bailey, P.R. Cheeke and M.P. Heggerty. Iowa State University Press, Ames, Iowa, USA. 1992, 418–422.

120 BUSHWAY, R.J.; McGANN, D.F.; BUSHWAY, A.A. Gas chromatographic method for the determination of solanidine and its application to a study of feed-milk transfer in the cow. *Journal of Agricultural and Food Chemistry* 1984, 32, 548–551.

121 WILLIMOTT, S.G. An investigation of solanine poisoning. *Analyst* 1933, 58, 431–438.

122 WILSON, G.S. A small outbreak of solanine poisoning. *Monthly Bulletin of the Ministry of Health and the Public Health Laboratory Service* 1958, 17, 207–210.

123 McMILLAN, M.; THOMPSON, J.C. An outbreak of suspected solanine poisoning in schoolboys. *Quarterly Journal of Medicine* 1979, New Series 48, 190, 227–243.

124 RENWICK, J.H. Anencephaly and spina bifida are usually preventable by avoidance of a specific but unidentifed substance present in some potato tubers. *British Journal of Preventive and Social Medicine* 1972, 26, 67–88.

125 BROWN, D.; KEELER, R.F. Structure-activity relation of steroid teratogens. 2. N-substituted jervines. *Journal of Agricultural and Food Chemistry* 1978, 26, 564–566.

126 SHLOSBERG, A.; BELLAICHE, M.; HANJI, V.; ERSHOV, E.; BOGIN, E.; AVIDAR, Y.; PERL, S.; SHORE, L.; SHEMESH, M.; GAVRIELL, R.; GUTMAN, M. The effect of feeding dried tomato vines to beef cattle. *Veterinary and Human Toxicology* 1996, 38, 135–136.

127 LOVELL, C.R. *Plants and the Skin*. Blackwell Scientific Publications, Oxford, UK. 1993, 192–193.

TAXACEAE

1   WILLIAMSON, R. *The Great Yew Forest, the Natural History of Kingsley Vale*. Macmillan, London, UK. 1978.

2   Personal communication.

3   ALDEN, C.L.; FOSNAUGH, C.J.; SMITH, J.B.; MOHAN, R. Japanese yew poisoning of large domestic animals in the Midwest. *Journal of the American Veterinary Medical Association* 1977, 170, 314–316.

4   PUYT, J.D.; FALIU, L.; JEAN-BLAIN, C. [Yew. Poisonous plant no. 2.] *Point Vétérinaire* 1982, 13, 86–87.

5   SZABADOS, A. [Severe cases of poisoning in horses due to *Taxus baccata*.] *Magyar Állatorvosok Lapja* 1976, 31, 69.

6   LOWE, J.E.; HINTZ, H.P.; SCHRYVER, H.F.; KINGSBURY, J.M. *Taxus cuspidata* (Japanese yew) poisoning in horses. *Cornell Veterinarian* 1970, 60, 36–39.

7   KARNS, P.A. Intoxication in horses due to ingestion of Japanese yew (*Taxus cuspidata*). *Equine Practice* 1983, 5, 12 and 14–15.

8   PERSSON, L.; KOLMODIN, C.G.; THORNBERG, C.G.; VESTERLUND, S. [Yew poisoning. Sudden death in horses and cattle.] *Svensk Veterinärtidning* 1988, 40, 27–28.

9   ROOK, J.S. Japanese yew toxicity. *Veterinary Medicine* 1994, 89, 950–951.

10 KNOWLES, I.W. Yew poisoning in cattle. *Veterinary Record* 1949, 61, 421–422.

11 BOUTHIÈRE, G.; DELATOUR, P.; JEAN-BLAIN, C.; LORGUE, G.; RANCIEN, P. [Collective poisoning of cattle by yew.] *Bulletin de la Société des Sciences Vétérinaires et de Médecine Comparée de Lyon* 1973, 75, 163–164.

12 CASTEEL, S.W.; COOK, W.O. Japanese yew poisoning in ruminants. *Modern Veterinary Practice* 1985, 66, 875–877.

13 VEATCH, J.K.; REID, F.M.; KENNEDY, G.A. Differentiating yew poisoning from other toxicoses. *Veterinary Medicine* 1988, 83, 298–300.

14 OGDEN, L. *Taxus* (yews) – a highly toxic plant. *Veterinary and Human Toxicology* 1988, 30, 563–564.

15 HOLTE, P. [Yew poisoning in cattle.] *Svensk Veterinärtidning* 1992, 44, 659.

16 PANTER, K.E.; MOLYNEUX, R.J.; SMART, R.A.; MITCHELL, L.; HANSEN, S. English yew poisoning in 43 cattle. *Journal of the American Veterinary Medical Association* 1993, 202, 1476–1477.

17 ORR, A.B. Poisoning in domestic animals and birds. *Veterinary Record* 1952, 64, 339–343.

18 SCOTTISH VETERINARY INVESTIGATION SERVICE. Lean ewes and twin lamb disease common. Yew poisoning. *Veterinary Record* 1986, 118, 473.

19 ZETTL, K.; BRÖMEL, J. [Yew poisoning in sheep and goats.] *Praktische Tierarzt* 1986, 67, 317–321.

20 SMIT, M.P. [*Taxus baccata* poisoning in lambs, and meat inspection.] *Tijdschrift voor Diergeneeskunde* 1992, 117, 697–699.

21 RAE, C.A.; BINNINGTON, B.D. Yew poisoning in sheep. *Canadian Veterinary Journal* 1995, 36, 446.

22 MAXIE, G. Another case of Japanese yew poisoning. *Canadian Veterinary Journal* 1991, 32, 370.

23 COENEN, M.; BAHRS, F. [Fatal yew poisoning in goats as a result of ingestion of foliage from garden prunings.] *Deutsche Tierärztliche Wochenschrift* 1994, 101, 364–367.

24 KÖHLER, H.; GRÜNBERG, W. [Yew poisoning in kangaroos.] *Archiv für Experimentelle Veterinärmedizin* 1960, 14, 1149–1162.

25 WACKER, R. [Yew (*Taxus baccata*) poisoning in fallow deer.] *Tierärztliche Umschau* 1983, 38, 264 and 267–268.

26 DIETZ, H.H.; HØST, O.; WIESE, C. [Yew poisoning in fallow deer in Denmark.] *Dansk Veterinærtidsskrift* 1994, 77, 404–405.

27 EVANS, K.L.; COOK, J.R. Japanese yew poisoning in a dog. *Journal of the American Animal Hospital Association* 1991, 27, 300–302.

28 FIEDLER, H.H.; PERRON, R.M. [Yew poisoning in Australian emus (*Dromaius novaehollandiae*, Latham).] *Berliner und Münchener Tierärztliche Wochenschrift* 1994, 107, 50–52.

29 JORDAN, W.J. Yew (*Taxus baccata*) poisoning in pheasants (*Phasianus colchicus*). *Tijdschrift voor Diergeneeskunde* 1964, 89, Supplement No.1, 187–188.

30 SCOTTISH VETERINARY INVESTIGATION SERVICE. Bovine respiratory disease common. Birds. *Veterinary Record* 1984, 114, 180–181.

31 ARAI, M.; STAUBER, E.; SHROPSHIRE, C.M. Evaluation of selected plants for their toxic effects in canaries. *Journal of the American Veterinary Medical Association* 1992, 200, 1329–1331.

32 CORNEVIN, C. *Des Plantes Vénéneuses*. Librairie de Firmin-Didot, Paris, France. 1887, 43–63.

33 ANONYMOUS. [Yew.] Notes de Toxicologie Vétérinaire 1977, No.3, 157–158.

34 KYLE, R.A.M. Oxford, UK. Personal communication.

35 FORSYTH, A.A. *British Poisonous Plants*. HMSO, London, UK. Ministry of Agriculture, Fisheries and Food Bulletin 161, 1968, 29–31 (amended 1979, 31–33).

36 HUMPHREYS, D.J. *Veterinary Toxicology*. Baillière Tindall, London, UK. 3rd Edition. 1988, 276–277.

37 PORTER, K.A.M.; KROLL, S. Yew berry ingestion. *British Medical Journal* 1982, 284, 116.

38 NATIONAL POISONS INFORMATION SERVICE, London, UK. Personal communication.

39 MATYUNAS, N.J.; RODGERS, G.C. Evaluation of *Taxus* berry ingestion in children. *Veterinary and Human Toxicology* 1985, 28, 298.

40 SCHULTE, T. [Fatal poisoning by yew (*Taxus baccata*).] *Archives of Toxicology* 1975, 34, 153–158.

41 CUMMINS, R.O.; HAULMAN, J.; QUAN, L.; REID-GRAVES, J.; PETERSON, D.; HORAN, S. Near-fatal yew berry intoxication treated with external cardiac pacing and digoxin-specific Fab antibody fragments. *Annals of Emergency Medicine* 1990, 19, 38–43.

42 VON DER WERTH, J.; MURPHY, J.J. Cardiovascular toxicity associated with yew leaf ingestion. *British Heart Journal* 1994, 72, 92–93.

43 YERSIN, B.; FREY, J.G.; SHALLER, M.D.; NICOD, P.; PERRET, C. Fatal cardiac arrhythmias and shock following yew leaves ingestion. *Annals of Emergency Medicine* 1987, 16, 1396–1397.

44 JANSSEN, J.; PELTENBURG, H. [A classical way of committing suicide: with *Taxus baccata.*] *Nederlands Tijdschrift voor Geneeskunde* 1985, 129, 603–605.

45 SINN, L.E.; PORTERFIELD, J.F. Fatal taxine poisoning from yew leaf ingestion. *Journal of Forensic Sciences* 1991, 36, 599–601.

46 VAN INGEN, G.; VISSER, R.; PELTENBURG, H.; VAN DER ARK, A.M.; VOORTMAN, M. Sudden unexpected death due to *Taxus* poisoning. A report of five cases, with review of the literature. *Forensic Science International* 1992, 56, 81–87.

47 VON DACH, B.; STREULI, R.A. [Lidocaine treatment of poisoning with yew needles (*Taxus baccata* L.).] *Schweizerische Medizinische Wochenschrift* 1988, 118, 1113–1116.

48 FELDMAN, R.; CHROBAK, J.; LIBEREK, Z.; SZAJEWSKI, J. [Four cases of poisoning with an extract of yew (*Taxus baccata*) needles.] *Polskie Archiwum Medycyny Wewnetrznej* 1988, 79, 26–29.

49 SMITH, R.A. Comments on diagnosis of intoxication due to *Taxus*. *Veterinary and Human Toxicology* 1989, 31, 177.

50 MUSSHOFF, F.; JACOB, B.; FOWINKEL, C.; DALDRUP, T. Suicidal yew leaf ingestion – phloroglucindimethylether (3,5-dimethoxyphenol) as a marker for poisoning from *Taxus baccata*. *International Journal of Legal Medicine* 1993, 106, 45–50.

THYMELAEACEAE

1 EVANS, F.J.; SOPER, C.J. The tigliane, daphnane and ingenane diterpenes, their chemistry, distribution and biological activities. A review. *Lloydia* 1978, 41, 193–233.

2 TYLER, M.I.; HOWDEN, M.E.H. Antitumour and irritant diterpenoid esters of Thymelaeaceae species. In: *Plant Toxicology. Proceedings of the Australia–U.S.A. Poisonous Plants Symposium, Brisbane, Australia, May 14–18, 1984.* Edited by A.A. Searight, M.P. Hegarty, L.F. James and R.F. Keeler. Animal Research Institute, Yeerongpilly, Australia, 1985, 367–374.

3 NICHOLSON, J.A. *Lander's Veterinary Toxicology.* Baillière, Tindall and Cox, London, UK. 3rd Edition. 1945, 273–276.

4 GUSYNIN, I.A. [*The toxicology of poisonous plants.*] Gosudarstvennoe Izdatel'stvo Sel'skokhozyaistvennoi Literatury, Moscow, USSR. 3rd Edition. 1955, 176–177.

5 PERNTHANER, A.; LANGER, T. [*Daphne mezereum* poisoning in cattle.] *Wiener Tierärztliche Monatsschrift* 1993, 80, 138–142.

6 FORSYTH, A.A. *British Poisonous Plants.* HMSO, London, UK. Ministry of Agriculture, Fisheries and Food Bulletin 161, 1968, 66–67 (amended 1979, 66–68).

7 KINGSBURY, J.M. *Deadly Harvest.* George Allen & Unwin, London, UK. 1967, 36–37.

8 CORNEVIN, C. *Des Plantes Vénéneuses.* Librairie de Firmin-Didot, Paris, France. 1887, 160–163.

9 NATIONAL POISONS INFORMATION SERVICE, London, UK. Personal communication.

10 FROHNE, D.; PFÄNDER, H.J. *A Colour Atlas of Poisonous Plants.* Wolfe Publishing Ltd, London, UK. 1984, 226–229.

11 SKAUG, O.E. [*Daphne mezereum* poisoning.] *Tidsskrift for den Norske Lægeforening* 1984, 104, 264–265.

UMBELLIFERAE

1   MINISTRY OF AGRICULTURE, FISHERIES AND FOOD. Poisoning of Animals in Britain. Animal Disease Report 1978, 2, No.2, 9–12.

2   LONG, H.C. *Plants Poisonous to Live Stock.* Cambridge University Press, Cambridge, UK. 1917, 39–40.

3   BARR, A.G.; DAVIES, C.S. An unusual case of poisoning in a sow and litter. *Veterinary Record* 1963, 75, 457.

4   SWART, F.W.J. [Poisoning of goats with fool's parsley.] *Tijdschrift voor Diergeneeskunde* 1975, 100, 989–990.

5   VÖLKER, R. *Lehrbuch der Toxikologie für Tierärzte. (Fröhner).* Ferdinand Enke Verlag, Stuttgart, Germany. 6th Edition. 1950, 303–304.

6   TEUSCHER, E.; GREGER, H.; ADRIAN, V. [Studies on the toxicity of *Aethusa cynapium* L., fool's parsley.] *Pharmazie* 1990, 45, 537-538.

7   VON OETTINGEN, W.F. *Poisoning.* W.B. Saunders Co., Philadelphia, USA. 2nd Edition. 1958, 346.

8   CEDERSTAM, R. [Cowbane poisoning.] *Svensk Veterinärtidning* 1976, 28, 1114–1116.

9   PRIOUZEAU, M.M. [Poisoning by cowbane.] *Recueil de Médecine Vétérinaire* 1951, 127, 483–488.

10 DIJKSTRA, R.G.; FALKENA, R. [Cicutoxin poisoning in two ponies.] *Tijdschrift voor Diergeneeskunde* 1981, 106, 1037–1039.

11 NILSSON, N.S. [Cowbane poisoning, another case.] *Svensk Veterinärtidning* 1977, 29, 725.

12 TATAR, A.; OTLOWSKI, F. [Mass poisoning of cattle with cowbane (*Cicuta virosa* L.).] *Zycie Weterynaryjne* 1967, 42, 137–140.

13 TAHVANAINEN, T. [*Cicuta virosa* poisoning in cattle. A case report.] *Suomen Eläinlääkärilehti* 1993, 99, 233–234.

14 VÖLKER, H.; SCHULZ, O.; ALBRECHT, K.; SIERING, W. [Poisoning by cowbane (*Cicuta virosa*) in fattening bulls.] *Monatshefte für Veterinärmedizin* 1983, 38, 11–13.

15 LASKOWSKI, S.; MATYJEK, J.; KOPPICZ, M.; POHORSKI, A. [Cowbane (*Cicuta virosa*) poisoning.] *Polski Tygodnik Lekarski* 1975, 30, 533–534.

16 STARREVELD, E.; HOPE, C.E. Cicutoxin poisoning (water hemlock). *Neurology* 1975, 25, 730–734.

17 VAN HEIJST, A.N.; PIKAAR, S.A.; VAN KESTEREN, R.G.; DOUZE, J.M. [Poisoning caused by water hemlock (*Cicuta virosa*).] *Nederlands Tijdschrift voor Geneeskunde* 1983, 127, 2411–2413.

18 KNUTSEN, O.H.; PASZKOWSKI, P. New aspects in the treatment of water hemlock poisoning. *Journal of Toxicology. Clinical Toxicology* 1984, 22, 157–166.

19 TOKARNIA, C.H.; DÖBEREINER, J.; PEIXOTO, P.V. [Experimental poisoning with *Conium maculatum* (Umbelliferae) in cattle and sheep.] *Pesquisa Veterinária Brasileira* 1985, 5, 15–25.

20 KEELER, R.F.; BALLS, L.D.; SHUPE, J.L.; CROWE, M.W. Teratogenicity and toxicity of coniine in cows, ewes and mares. *Cornell Veterinarian* 1980, 70, 19–26.

21 KUBIK, M.; REJHOLEC, J.; ZACHOVAL, J. [Outbreak of hemlock poisoning in cattle.] *Veterinářství* 1980, 30, 157–158.

22 TUDOR, G.; ANTON, E.; DIACONESCU, G. [*Conium maculatum* (hemlock) poisoning in sheep.] *Revista de Zootehnie și Medicină Veterinară* 1969, 19, No.11, 74–80.

23 COPITHORNE, B. Suspected poisoning of goats by hemlock (*Conium maculatum*). *Veterinary Record* 1937, 49, 1018–1019.

24 MACDONALD, H. Hemlock poisoning in horses. *Veterinary Record* 1937, 49, 1211–1212.

25 ANONYMOUS. Unusual case of hemlock poisoning in swine. *California Veterinarian* 1951, 5, No.2, 26.

26 WIDMER, W.R. Poison hemlock toxicosis in swine. *Veterinary Medicine & Small Animal Clinician* 1984, 79, 405–408.

27 MARKHAM, K. Hemlock poisoning in piglets. *Veterinary Record* 1985, 116, 27.

28 HANNAM, D.A.R. Hemlock (*Conium maculatum*) poisoning in the pig. *Veterinary Record* 1985, 116, 322.

29 RICHTER, H.E. [Poisoning by hemlock, *Conium maculatum*.] *Wiener Tierärztliche Monatsschrift* 1964, 51, 404–407.

30 SHORT, S.B.; EDWARDS, W.C. Accidental *Conium maculata* poisoning in the rabbit. *Veterinary and Human Toxicology* 1989, 31, 54–57.

31 FRANK, A.A.; REED, W.M. *Conium maculatum* (poison hemlock) toxicosis in a flock of range turkeys. *Avian Diseases* 1987, 31, 386–388.

32 FRANK, A.A.; REED, W.M. Comparative toxicity of coniine, an alkaloid of *Conium maculatum* (poison hemlock) in chickens, quails and turkeys. *Avian Diseases* 1990, 34, 433–437.

33 EDMONDS, L.D.; SELBY, L.A.; CASE, A.A. Poisoning and congenital malformations associated with consumption of poison hemlock by sows. *Journal of the American Veterinary Medical Association* 1972, 160, 1319–1324.

34 DYSON, D.A.; WRATHALL, A.E. Congenital deformities in pigs possibly associated with exposure to hemlock (*Conium maculatum*). *Veterinary Record* 1977, 100, 241–242.

35 KEELER, R.F. Coniine, a teratogenic principle from *Conium maculatum* producing congenital malformations in cattle. *Clinical Toxicology* 1974, 7, 195–206.

36 KEELER, R.F.; BALLS, L.D. Teratogenic effects in cattle of *Conium maculatum* and *Conium* alkaloids and analogs. *Clinical Toxicology* 1978, 12, 49–64.

37 PANTER, K.E.; KEELER, R.F.; BUCK, W.B. Induction of cleft palate in newborn pigs by maternal ingestion of poison hemlock (*Conium maculatum*). *American Journal of Veterinary Research* 1985, 46, 1368–1371.

38 PANTER, K.E.; KEELER, R.F.; BUCK, W.B. Congenital skeletal malformations induced by maternal ingestion of *Conium maculatum* (poison hemlock) in newborn pigs. *American Journal of Veterinary Research* 1985, 46, 2064–2066.

39 PANTER, K.E.; KEELER, R.F.; BAKER, D.C. Toxicoses in livestock from the hemlocks (*Conium* and *Cicuta* spp.). *Journal of Animal Science* 1988, 66, 2407–2413.

40 PANTER, K.E.; BUNCH, T.D.; KEELER, R.F. Maternal and fetal toxicity of poison hemlock (*Conium maculatum*) in sheep. *American Journal of Veterinary Research* 1988, 49, 281–283.

41 PANTER, K.E.; BUNCH, T.D.; KEELER, R.F.; SISSON, D.V. Radio ultrasound observations of the fetotoxic effects in sheep from ingestion of *Conium maculatum* (poison-hemlock). *Journal of Toxicology. Clinical Toxicology* 1988, 26, 175–187.

42 FORSYTH, C.S.; FRANK, A.A. Evaluation of developmental toxicity of coniine to rats and rabbits. *Teratology* 1993, 48, 59–64.

43 FRANK, B.S.; MICHELSON, W.B.; PANTER, K.E.; GARDNER, D.R.; Ingestion of poison hemlock (*Conium maculatum*). *Western Journal of Medicine* 1995, 163, 573–574.

44 RIZZI, D.; BASILE, C.; DI MAGGIO, A.; SEBASTIO, A.; INTRONA, F.; RIZZI, R.; SCATIZZI, A.; DE MARCO, S.; SMIALEK, J.E. Clinical spectrum of accidental hemlock poisoning: neurotoxic manifestations, rhabdomyolysis and acute tubular necrosis. *Nephrology Dialysis Transplantation* 1991, 6, 939–943.

45 SCATIZZI, A.; DI MAGGIO, A.; RIZZI, D.; SEBASTIO, A.M.; BASILE, C. Acute renal failure due to tubular necrosis caused by wildfowl-mediated hemlock poisoning. *Renal Failure* 1993, 15, 93–96.

46 MILNE, J. Fatal poisoning in a horse by *Oenanthe crocata* – the water dropwort. *Veterinary Record* 1945, 57, 30.

47 WILSON, A.L.; JOHNSTON, W.G.; MCCUSKER, M.B.; BANNATYNE, C.C. Hemlock water dropwort (*Oenanthe crocata*) poisoning in cattle. *Veterinary Record* 1958, 70, 587–590.

48 VAN INZEN, C.; GUNN, D. Poisoned cows. *Veterinary Record* 1989, 125, 212.

49 ANGER, J.P.; ANGER, F.; CHAUVEL, Y.; GIRRE, R.L.; CURTES, N.; CURTES, J.P. [Fatal poisoning by hemlock water dropwort (*Oenanthe crocata*).] *European Journal of Toxicology* 1976, 9, 119–125.

50 MITCHELL, M.I.; ROUTLEDGE, P.A. Hemlock water dropwort poisoning – a review. *Clinical Toxicology* 1978, 12, 417–428.

51 NATIONAL POISONS INFORMATION SERVICE, London, UK. Personal communication.

52 KING, L.A.; LEWIS, M.J.; PARRY, D.; TWITCHETT, P.J.; KILNER, E.A. Identification of oenanthotoxin and related compounds in hemlock water dropwort poisoning. *Human Toxicology* 1985, 4, 355–364.

53 BALL, M.J.; FLATHER, M.L.; FORFAR, J.C. Hemlock water dropwort poisoning. *Postgraduate Medical Journal* 1987, 63, 363–365.

54 FITZGERALD, P.; MOSS, N.; O'MAHONY, S.; WHELTON, M.J. Accidental hemlock poisoning. *British Medical Journal* 1987, 295, 1657.

55 FORSYTH, A.A. Treatment for poisoning by *Oenanthe crocata*. *Veterinary Record* 1966, 79, 55.

56 MIĘDZOBRODZKI, K. [*Oenanthe aquatica* poisoning in heifers.] *Medycyna Weterynaryjna* 1960, 16, 609–610.

57 ESPEFÄLT, R. [*Oenanthe aquatica* poisoning of cattle.] *Svensk Veterinärtidning* 1995, 47, 531–532.

58 ASPIOTIS, N.; LAVRENTIADES, G.; ANDREOU, C. [Pharmacodynamic study of the poisonous plant *Oenanthe silaifolia*.] *Bulletin de l'Académie Vétérinaire de France* 1960, 33, 75–80.

59 HINTERMAN, J. [Dermatosis caused by *Heracleum mantegazzianum* Somm. et Levier in a dog.] *Schweizer Archiv für Tierheilkunde* 1967, 109, 654–656.

60 ANDREWS, A.H.; GILES, C.J.; THOMSETT, L.R. Suspected poisoning of a goat by giant hogweed. *Veterinary Record* 1985, 116, 205–207.

61 HARWOOD, D.G. Giant hogweed and ducklings. *Veterinary Record* 1985, 116, 300.

62 LAGEY, K.; DUINSLAEGER, L.; VANDERKELEN, A. Burns induced by plants. *Burns* 1995, 21, 542–543.

63 ANONYMOUS. The giant hogweed. *Lancet* 1970, II, 32.

64 DREVER, J.C.; HUNTER, J.A.A. Hazards of giant hogweed. *British Medical Journal* 1970, 3, 109.

65 LOVELL, C.R. *Plants and the Skin*. Blackwell Scientific Publications, Oxford, UK. 1993, 69–92.

66 RENNER, J.E.; GALLO, G.G.; MONTESINOS RAMOS, I.G.; BASCHAR, H.O. [Photodermatitis and keratitis in horses after contact with parsnip (*Pastinaca sativa* L.).] *Veterinaria Argentina* 1991, 8, No.77, 450, 452–454.

67 MONTGOMERY, J.F.; OLIVER, R.E.; POOLE, W.S.H. A vesiculo-bullous disease in pigs resembling foot and mouth disease. I. Field cases. *New Zealand Veterinary Journal* 1987, 35, 21–26.

68 MONTGOMERY, J.F.; OLIVER, R.E.; POOLE, W.S.H.; JULIAN, A.F. A vesiculo-bullous disease in pigs resembling foot and mouth disease. II. Experimental reproduction of the lesion. *New Zealand Veterinary Journal* 1987, 35, 27–30.

69 PERELMAN, B.; KUTTIN, E.S. Parsley-induced photosensitivity in ostriches and ducks. *Avian Diseases* 1988, 17, 183–192.

70 CAMPBELL, A.N.; COOPER, C.E.; DAHL, M.G.C. "Non-accidental injury" and wild parsnips. *British Medical Journal* 1982, 284, 708.

71 HELLIER, F.F. "Non-accidental injury" and wild parsnips. *British Medical Journal* 1982, 284, 1198.

72 BOFFA, M.J.; GILMOUR, E.; EAD, R.D. Celery soup causing severe phototoxicity during PUVA therapy. *British Journal of Dermatology* 1996, 135, 334.

URTICACEAE

1 THURSTON, E.L.; LERSTEN, N.R. The morphology and toxicology of plant stinging hairs. *Botanical Review* 1969, 35, 393–412.

2 WATT, J.M.; BREYER-BRANDWIJK, M.G. *The Medicinal and Poisonous Plants of Southern and Eastern Africa*. E. & S. Livingstone Ltd, Edinburgh and London, UK. 2nd Edition. 1962, 1042–1045.

3 OLIVER, F.; AMON, E.U.; BREATHNACH, A.; FRANCIS, D.M.; SARATHCHANDRA, P.; BLACK, A.K.; GREAVES,

M.W. Contact urticaria due to the common stinging nettle (*Urtica dioica*) – histological, ultrastructural and pharmacological studies. *Clinical and Experimental Dermatology* 1991, 16, 1–7.

4   LOVELL, C.R. *Plants and the Skin.* Blackwell Scientific Publications, Oxford, UK. 1993, 29–32.

5   ANONYMOUS. Stinging nettle (*Urtica* sp.) and dogs. *Veterinary and Human Toxicology* 1982, 24, 247.

6   SCOTT, D.W. *Large Animal Dermatology.* W.B. Saunders Co., Philadelphia, USA. 1988, 292.

7   BATHE, A.P. An unusual manifestation of nettle rash in three horses. *Veterinary Record* 1994, 134, 11–12.

8   HUGHES, R.E.; ELLERY, P.; HARRY, T.; JENKINS, V.; JONES, E. The dietary potential of the common nettle. *Journal of the Science of Food and Agriculture* 1980, 31, 1279–1286.

9   JORDAN, M. *A Guide to Wild Plants.* Millington Books Ltd, London, UK. 1976, 101–103.

10 COOPER, H.C. Personal communication.

VERBENACEAE

1   SHARMA, O.P.; MAKKAR, H.P.S.; DAWRA, R.K. A review of the noxious plant *Lantana camara. Toxicon* 1988, 26, 975–987.

2   PASS, M.A. Current ideas on the pathophysiology and treatment of lantana poisoning of ruminants. *Australian Veterinary Journal* 1986, 63, 169–171.

3   MORTON, J.F. Lantana, or red sage (*Lantana camara* L., [Verbenaceae]), notorious weed and popular garden flower; some cases of poisoning in Florida. *Economic Botany* 1994, 48, 259–270.

4   EVERIST, S.L. *Poisonous Plants of Australia.* Angus and Robertson, Sydney, Australia. 1981, 738–747.

5   LEROUX, V. [Poisoning of pets by house plants.] *Point Vétérinaire* 1986, 18, 45–55.

6   PASS, M.A.; STEWART, C. Administration of activated charcoal for the treatment of lantana poisoning of sheep and cattle. *Journal of Applied Toxicology* 1984, 4, 267–269.

7   WOLFSON, S.L.; SOLOMONS, T.W.G. Poisoning by fruit of *Lantana camara. American Journal of Diseases of Children* 1964, 107, 173–176.

8   MITCHELL, J.; ROOK, A. *Botanical Dermatology. Plants and Plant Products Injurious to the Skin.* Greengrass Ltd, Vancouver, Canada. 1979, 714–715.

VISCACEAE

1   SAMUELSSON, G. Phytochemical and pharmacological studies on *Viscum album* L. IV. Countercurrent distribution studies on viscotoxin. *Svensk Farmaceutisk Tidskrift* 1961, 65, 209–222.

2   SAMUELSSON, G.; PETTERSSON, B.M. The amino acid sequence of viscotoxin B from the European mistletoe (*Viscum album* L. Loranthaceae). *European Journal of Biochemistry* 1971, 21, 86–89.

3   JUNG, M.L.; BAUDINO, S.; RIBÉREAU-GAYON, G.; BECK, J.P. Characterization of cytotoxic proteins from mistletoe (*Viscum album*). *Cancer Letters* 1990, 51, 103–108.

4   OLSNES, S.; STIRPE, F.; SANDVIG, K.; PIHL, A. Isolation and characterization of viscumin, a toxic lectin from *Viscum album* L. (mistletoe). *Journal of Biological Chemistry* 1982, 257, 13263–13267.

5   STIRPE, F.; SANDVIG, K.; OLSNES, S.; PIHL, A. Action of viscumin, a toxic lectin from mistletoe, on cells in culture. *Journal of Biological Chemistry* 1982, 257, 13271–13277.

6   TONEVITSKY, A.G.; RAKHMANOVA, V.A.; AGAPOV, I.I.; SHAMSHIEV, A.T.; USACHEVA, E.A.; PROKOPH'EV, S.A.; DENISENKO, O.N.; ALEKSEEV, Y.O.; PFUELLER, U. The interactions of the anti-MLI monoclonal antibodies with isoforms of the lectin from *Viscum album. Immunology Letters* 1995, 44, 31–34.

7   DIETRICH, J.B.; RIBÉREAU-GAYON, G.; JUNG, M.L.; FRANZ, H.; ANTON, R. Identity of the N-terminal sequences of the three A chains of mistletoe (*Viscum album* L.) lectins: homology with ricin-like plant toxins and single-chain ribosome inhibiting proteins. *Anti-Cancer Drugs* 1992, 3, 507–511.

8   BRUNETON, J. *Pharmacognosy, Phytochemistry, Medicinal Plants.* Lavoisier Publishing, Paris, France.

1995, 190–191.

9   JORDAN, E.; WAGNER, H. [Detection and determination of lectins and viscotoxins in mistletoe preparations.] *Arzneimittel-Forschung* 1986, 36, 428–433.

10 PORA, A.; POP, E.; ROSKA, D.; RADU, A. [Effect of the host plant on the content of the hypotensive and cardioactive principles in mistletoe (*Viscum album* L.).] *Pharmazie* 1957, 12, 528–538.

11 HÜLSEN, H.; DOSER, C.; MECHELKE, F. Differences in the *in vitro* effectiveness of preparations produced from mistletoes of various host trees. *Arzneimittel-Forschung* 1986, 36, 433–436.

12 GREATOREX, J.C. Some unusual cases of plant poisoning in animals. *Veterinary Record* 1966, 78, 725–727.

13 CHAPRON, M.H. [Probable poisoning of a dog by mistletoe.] *Revue de Pathologie Comparée et d'Hygiene Génerale* 1936, 36, 400.

14 NATIONAL POISONS INFORMATION SERVICE, London, UK. Personal communication.

15 JEAN-BLAIN, C. [Mistletoe.] *Notes de Toxicologie Vétérinaire* 1977, No.1, 21–22.

16 CORNEVIN, C. *Des Plantes Vénéneuses.* Librairie de Firmin-Didot, Paris, France. 1887, 163–164.

17 STANDRING, G.; GOULDING, R. Poisonous plants. *Nursing Times* 1969, August 7, 1009–1011.

18 HARVEY, J.; COLIN-JONES, D.G. Mistletoe hepatitis. *British Medical Journal* 1981, 282, 186–187.

19 COLIN-JONES, D.G.; HARVEY, J.. Mistletoe hepatitis. *British Medical Journal* 1982, 284, 744–745.

20 SEIDEMANN, W. [Allergic rhinitis from mistletoe tea (*Viscum album*).] *Allergologie* 1984, 7, 461–463.

POISONOUS FUNGI

LARGER FUNGI

1   ZURERA, G.; RINCÓN, F.; ARCOS, F.; POZO-LORA, R. Mercury content in mushroom species in the Cordova area. *Bulletin of Environmental Contamination and Toxicology* 1986, 36, 662–667.

2   VETTER, J. Data on arsenic and cadmium contents of some common mushrooms. *Toxicon* 1994, 32, 11–15.

3   BRESINSKY, A.; BESL, H. *A Colour Atlas of Poisonous Fungi.* Wolfe Publishing Ltd, London, UK. 1990, 18–35.

4   FAULSTICH, H.; ZILKER, T.R. Amatoxins. In: *Handbook of Mushroom Poisoning. Diagnosis and Treatment.* Edited by D.G. Spoerke and B.H.Rumack. CRC Press, Boca Raton, Florida, USA. 1994, 233–248.

5   BENJAMIN, D.R. *Mushrooms: Poisons and Panaceas.* W.H. Freeman and Company, New York, USA. 1995, 198–241.

6   WIELAND, T.; FAULSTICH, H. Amatoxins, phallotoxins, phallolysin and antamanide: the biologically active components of poisonous *Amanita* mushrooms. *CRC Critical Reviews in Biochemistry* 1978, 5, 185–260.

7   FAULSTICH, H. Mushroom poisoning. *Lancet* 1980, II, 794–795.

8   ZAWADZKI, J.; JANKOWSKA, I.; MOSZCZYŃSKA, A.; JANUSZEWICZ, P. Hypouricemia due to increased tubular secretion of urate in children with *Amanita phalloides* poisoning. *Nephron* 1993, 65, 375–380.

9   ENJALBERT, F.; GALLION, C.; JEHL, F.; MONTEIL, H. Toxin content, phallotoxin and amatoxin composition of *Amanita phalloides* tissues. *Toxicon* 1993, 31, 803–807.

10 NATIONAL POISONS INFORMATION SERVICE, London, UK. Personal communication.

11 OLESEN, L.L. Amatoxin intoxication. *Scandinavian Journal of Urology and Nephrology* 1990, 24, 231–234.

12 PERTILE, N.; GALLIANI, E.; VERGERIO, A.; TIRRIN, A.; CADDIA, V. [The *Amanita phalloides* syndrome. Case of a 2-year-old girl.] *Pediatria Oggi Medica e Chirurgica* 1990, 12, 411–414.

13 BOURGEOIS, F.; BOURGEOIS, N.; GELLIN, M.; VAN DE STADT, J.; DOUTRELEPONT, J.M.; ADLER, M. [Acute hepatitis and poisoning by *Amanita phalloides*.] *Acta Gastro-Enterologica Belgica* 1992, 55, 358–363.

14 CAPPELL, M.S.; HASSAN, T. Gastrointestinal and hepatic effects of *Amanita phalloides* ingestion. *Journal of Clinical Gastroenterology* 1992, 15, 225–228.

15 GALLER, G.W.; WEISENBERG, E.; BRASITUS, T.A. Mushroom poisoning: the role of orthotopic liver transplantation. *Journal of Clinical Gastroenterology* 1992, 15, 229–232.

16 JANKOWSKA, I.; MALENTA, G.; RYZKO, J.; SOCHA, J.; WOZNIEWICZ, M. [Clinical and morphological analysis of children dying of poisoning with *Amanita phalloides*.] *Wiadomosci Lekarskie* 1992, 45, 818–823.

17 NIETER, B.; FRILLE, J. [Plasma exchange in *Amanita phalloides* mushroom poisoning – a case report.] *Nieren und Hochdruckkrankheiten* 1992, 21, 8–10.

18 MIKOS, B.; BIRO, E. [*Amanita phalloides* poisoning in a 15-year case load of a pediatric intensive care unit.] *Orvosi Hetilap* 1993, 134, 907–910.

19 RAMBOUSEK, V.; JANDA, J.; SIKUT, M. [Severe *Amanita phalloides* poisoning in a 7-year-old girl.] *Československá Pediatrie* 1993, 48, 332–333.

20 DOLFI, F.; GONNELLA, R. [Acute *Amanita phalloides* poisoning in the second trimester of pregnancy.] *Minerva Anestesiologica* 1994, 60, 153–154.

21 NAGY, I.; POGÁTSA-MURRAY, G.; ZALÁNYI, S.; KOMLÓSI, P.; LÁSZLO, F.; UNGI, I. *Amanita* poisoning during the second trimester of pregnancy. A case report and review of the literature. *Clinical Investigator* 1994, 72, 794–798.

22 MADSEN, S.; JENSSEN, K.M. [Poisoning with deadly agaric (*Amanita virosa*). Symptoms, diagnosis and treatment.] *Tidsskrift for den Norske Lægeforening* 1990, 110, 1828–1829.

23 PIERING, W.F.; BRATANOW, N. Role of the clinical laboratory in guiding treatment of *Amanita virosa* mushroom poisoning: report of two cases. *Clinical Chemistry* 1990, 36, 571–574.

24 DOEPEL, M.; ISONIEMI, H.; SALMELA, K.; PENTTILÄ, K.; HÖCKERSTEDT, K. Liver transplantation in a patient with *Amanita* poisoning. *Transplantation Proceedings* 1994, 26, 1801–1802.

25 PÉREZ-MORENO, J.; PÉREZ-MORENO, A.; FERRERA-CERRATO, R. Multiple fatal mycetism caused by *Amanita virosa* in Mexico. *Mycopathologia* 1994, 125, 3–5.

26 MARUGG, D.; REUTTER, F.W. [*Amanita phalloides* poisoning: modern therapeutic methods and clinical course.] *Schweizerische Rundschau für Medizin Praxis* 1985, 74, 972–982.

27 BEER, J.H. [The wrong mushroom. Diagnosis and therapy of mushroom poisoning, especially of *Amanita phalloides* poisoning.] *Schweizerische Medizinische Wochenschrift* 1993, 123, 892–905.

28 VESCONI, S.; LANGER, M.; COSTANTINO, D. Mushroom poisoning and forced diuresis. *Lancet* 1980, II, 854–855.

29 WAUTERS, J P; ROSSEL, C.; FARQUET, J J. *Amanita phalloides* poisoning treated by early charcoal haemoperfusion. *British Medical Journal* 1978, 2, 1465.

30 FLOERSHEIM, G.L. Treatment of human amatoxin mushroom poisoning. Myths and advances in therapy. *Medical Toxicology* 1987, 2, 1–9.

31 FLOERSHEIM, G.L. Treatment of experimental poisoning produced by extracts of *Amanita phalloides*. *Toxicology and Applied Pharmacology* 1975, 34, 499–508.

32 DUDOVÁ, V.; KUBICKA, J.; VESELSKY, J. Thioctic acid in the treatment of *Amanita phalloides* intoxication. In: *Amanita Toxins and Poisoning. (International, Amanita Symposium, Heidelberg, 1978)*. Edited by H. Faulstich, B. Kommerell, and T. Wieland. Verlag Gerhard Witzstrock, Baden-Baden, Germany. 1980, 190–191.

33 ZULIK, R.; KASSAY, S.F. The role of thioctic acid in the treatment of *Amanita phalloides* intoxication. In: *Amanita Toxins and Poisoning. (International Amanita Symposium, Heidelberg, 1978)*. Edited by H. Faulstich, B. Kommerell, and T. Wieland. Verlag Gerhard Witzstrock, Baden-Baden, Germany.

1980, 192–196.

34   BARTTER, F.C.; BERKSON, B.; GALLELLI, J.; HIRANKA, P. Thioctic acid in the treatment of poisoning with alpha amanitin. In: *Amanita Toxins and Poisoning. (International Amanita Symposium, Heidelberg, 1978).* Edited by H. Faulstich, B. Kommerell, and T. Wieland. Verlag Gerhard Witzstrock, Baden-Baden, Germany. 1980, 196–202.

35   ANONYMOUS. Death-cap poisoning. [Editorial]. *Lancet* 1972, I, 1320–1321.

36   FLOERSHEIM, G.L. [Experimental basis for the treatment of death cap (*Amanita phalloides*) poisoning.] *Schweizerische Medizinische Wochenshrift* 1978, 108, 185–197.

37   VOGEL, G. The anti-amanita effect of silymarin. In: *Amanita Toxins and Poisoning. (International Amanita Symposium, Heidelberg, 1978).* Edited by H. Faulstich, B. Kommerell and T. Wieland. Verlag Gerhard Witzstrock, Baden-Baden, Germany. 1980, 180–189.

38   KÖPPEL, C. Clinical symptomatology and management of mushroom poisoning. *Toxicon* 1993, 31, 1513–1540.

39   ZILKER, T.R.; FELGENHAUER, N.J.; MICHAEL, H.; STRENGE-HESSE, A. Grading of severity and therapy of 154 cases of *Amanita* poisoning. *Veterinary and Human Toxicology* 1993, 35, 331.

40   KLEIN, A.S.; HART, J.; BREMS, J.J.; GOLDSTEIN, L.; LEWIN, K.; BUSUTTIL, R.W. *Amanita* poisoning: treatment and the role of liver transplantation. *American Journal of Medicine* 1989, 86, 187–193.

41   WIELAND, T.; FAULSTICH, H. Fifty years of amanitin. *Experientia* 1991, 47, 1186–1193.

42   SCOTT, H.G. Poisonous plants and animals. In: *Food-borne Infections and Intoxications.* Edited by H. Riemann. Academic Press, New York and London. 1969, 543–604.

43   BASTIEN, P. A general practitioner's experience of *Amanita phalloides* poisoning. In: *Amanita Toxins and Poisoning, (International Amanita Symposium, Heidelberg, 1978).* Edited by H. Faulstich, B. Kommerell and T. Wieland. Verlag Gerhard Witzstrock, Baden-Baden, Germany. 1980, 211–215.

44   GUEST, I. Doctor survives poison. *The Guardian*, September 17, 1981, 7.

45   DUMONT, A.M.; CHENNEBAULT, J. M.; ALQUIER, P.; JARDEL, H. Management of *Amanita phalloides* poisoning by Bastien's regimen. *Lancet* 1981, I, 722.

46   FAULSTICH, H.; FAUSER, U. Amanitin poisoning in the dog. In: *Pathogenesis and Mechanisms of Liver Cell Necrosis. (A workshop on experimental liver injury, Freiburg, West Germany, 1974).* University Park Press, Baltimore, USA. 1975, 69–74.

47   CRISTEA, I. [Poisoning of goats by mushrooms of the *Amanita* genus.] *Recueil de Médecine Vétérinaire* 1970, 146, 507–512.

48   KALLET, A.; SOUSA, C.; SPANGLER, W. Mushroom (*Amanita phalloides*) toxicity in dogs. *California Veterinarian* 1988, 42, No.1, 9–11, 22, 47.

49   COLE, F.M. A puppy death and *Amanita phalloides*. *Australian Veterinary Journal* 1993, 70, 271–272.

50   SOVA, Z.; TREFNY, D.; ČIBULKA, J.; FUKÁL, L.; MADER, P.; PROSEK, J.; FUCIKOVA, A.; TLUSTA, L. [Experimental poisoning of the domestic fowl with aflatoxin B1, Agronal and *Amanita phalloides*.] *Sborník Vysoké Školy Zemědělské v Praze, Fakulta Agronomička, B* 1985, No.43, 3–16.

51   PIERCY, P.L.; HARGIS, G.; BROWN, C.A. Mushroom poisoning in cattle. *Journal of the American Veterinary Medical Association* 1944, 105, 206–208.

52   LIGGETT, A.D.; WEISS, R. Liver necrosis caused by mushroom poisoning in dogs. *Journal of Veterinary Diagnostic Investigation* 1989, 1, 267–269.

53   BRADY, L.R.; BENEDICT, R.G.; TYLER, V.E.; STUNTZ, D.E.; MALONE, M.H. Identification of *Conocybe filaris* as a toxic basidiomycete. *Lloydia* 1975, 38, 172–173.

54   TYLER, V.E.; BRADY, L.R.; BENEDICT, R.G.; KHANNA, J.M.; MALONE, M.H. Chromatographic and pharmacologic evaluation of some toxic *Galerina* species. *Lloydia* 1963, 26, 154–157.

55   KLAN, J. [A review of mushrooms containing amanitins and phalloidins.] *Časopis Lekaru Čěskych* 1993, 132, 449–451.

56   WATLING, R. *Cortinarius speciosissimus*: the cause of renal failure in two young men. *Mycopathologia*

1982, 79, 71–78.

57 RAFF, E.; HALLORAN, P.F.; KJELLSTRAND, C.M. Renal failure after eating "magic" mushrooms. *Canadian Medical Association Journal* 1992, 147, 1339–1341.

58 GRZYMALA, S. [Isolation of orellanine, the toxin of *Cortinarius orellanus* Fries and a study of its pathological effects.] *Bulletin de la Société Mycologique de France* 1962, 78, 394–404.

59 KÜRNSTEINER, H.; MOSER, M. Isolation of a lethal toxin from *Cortinarius orellanus* Fr. *Mycopathologia* 1981, 74, 65–72.

60 CADDY, B.; KIDD, C.B.M.; ROBERTSON. J.; TEBBETT, I.R.; TILSTONE, W.J.; WATLING, R. *Cortinarius speciosissimus* toxins – a preliminary report. *Experientia* 1982, 38, 1439–1440.

61 TEBBETT, I. R.; CADDY, B. Mushroom toxins of the genus *Cortinarius*. *Experientia* 1984, 40, 441–446.

62 MATTHIES, L.; LAATSCH, H. Cortinarins in *Cortinarius speciosissimus*? A critical revision. *Experientia* 1991, 47, 634–640.

63 TEBBETT, I.R. (Correspondence.) *Experientia* 1992, 48, 532–533.

64 MATTHIES, L.; LAATSCH, H. (Correspondence.) *Experientia* 1992, 48, 533–534.

65 GRZYMALA, S. [Experiences with *Dermocybe orellana* (Fr.) in Poland. B. Mass poisoning.] *Zeitschrift für Pilzkunde* 1957, 23, 138–142.

66 FAVRE, H.; LESKI, M.; CHRISTELLER, P.; VOLLENWEIDER, E.; CHATELANAT, F. [*Cortinarius orellanus*: a toxic fungus inducing severe delayed renal failure.] *Schweizerische Medizinische Wochenschrift* 1976, 106, 1097–1102.

67 SORESINA, P.; LEONI, G. [*Cortinarius orellanus* and its toxic effects.] *Micologia Italiana* 1978, 3, 9–15.

68 BOUGET, J.; BOUSSER, J.; PATS, B.; RAMEE, M.P.; CHEVET, D.; RIFLE, G.; GIUDICELLI, C.P.; THOMAS, R. Acute renal failure following collective intoxication by *Cortinarius orellanus*. *Intensive Care Medicine* 1990, 16, 506–510.

69 DELPECH, N.; RAPIOR, S.; COZETTE, A.P.; ORTIZ, J.P.; DONNADIEU, P.; ANDARY, C.; HUCHARD, G. [Outcome of acute renal failure caused by voluntary ingestion of *Cortinarius orellanus*.] *Presse Médicale* 1990, 19, 122–124.

70 DELPECH, N.; RAPIOR, S.; DONNADIEU, P.; COZETTE, A.P.; ORTIZ, J.P.; HUCHARD, G. [Voluntary poisoning by *Cortinarius orellanus*: usefulness of an original early treatment after determination of orellanine in the biological fluids and tissues.] *Nephrologie* 1991, 12, 63–66.

71 BOUSKA, I.; REHANEK, L.; MOTYCKA, K.; VESELSKY, J. [Detection of UV fluorescence in renal tissues in *Cortinarius orellanus* poisoning.]*Česka Mykologie* 1980, 34, 188–190.

72 HULMI, S.; SIPPONEN, P.; FORSSTRÖM, J.; VILSKA, J. [Mushroom poisoning caused by *Cortinarius speciosissimus*. A report on four cases.] *Duodecim* 1974, 90, 1044–1050.

73 SHORT, A.I.K.; WATLING, R.; MACDONALD, M.K.; ROBSON, J.S. Poisoning by *Cortinarius speciosissimus*. *Lancet* 1980, II, 942–944.

74 TIDMAN, M.; SJÖSTRÖM, P. [Acute renal failure caused by mushroom poisoning with *Cortinarius speciosissimus*.] *Läkartidningen* 1992, 89, 2763–2764.

75 GRZYMALA, S. [Clinical study of poisonings by *Cortinarius orellanus* Fr. mushrooms.] *Bulletin de Médecine Légale et de Toxicologie Médicale* 1965, 8, 60–70.

76 JAEGER, A. Orellanine mushrooms. In: *Handbook of Mushroom Poisoning. Diagnosis and Treatment* Edited by D.G. Spoerke and B.H. Rumack. CRC Press, Boca Raton, Florida, USA. 1994, 249–264.

77 ÖVERÅS, J.; ULVUND, M.J.; BAKKEVIG, S.; EIKEN, R. Poisoning in sheep induced by the mushroom *Cortinarius speciosissimus*. *Acta Veterinaria Scandinavica* 1979, 20, 148–150.

78 FLÅOYEN, A.; TØNNESEN, M.H.; GRØNSTØL, H.; BINDE, M. [Poisoning of cattle on pasture in Vestlandet, Sorlandet and Trondelag.] *Norsk Veterinærtidsskrift* 1992, 104, 648–650.

79 GECAN, J.S.; CICHOWICZ, S.M. Toxic mushroom contamination of wild mushrooms in commercial distribution. *Journal of Food Protection* 1993, 56, 730–734.

80 MICHELOT, D.; TOTH, B. Poisoning by *Gyromitra esculenta* – a review. *Journal of Applied Toxicology* 1991, 11, 235–243.

81 CHILTON, W.S. Chemistry and mode of action of mushroom toxins. In: *Mushroom Poisoning. Diagnosis and Treatment.* Edited by B.H. Rumack and E. Salzman. CRC Press, Boca Raton, Florida, USA, 1978, 87–124.

82 LINCOFF, G.; MITCHEL, D.H. *Toxic and Hallucinogenic Mushroom Poisoning. A Handbook for Physicians and Mushroom Hunters.* Van Nostrand Reinhold Co., New York, USA. 1977, 49–61.

83 FLAMMER. R. [The gyromitrin syndrome: poisoning by the false morel.] *Schweizerische Rundschau für Medizin Praxis* 1985, 74, 983–984.

84 TRESTRAIL, J.H. Monomethylhydrazine-containing mushrooms. In: *Handbook of Mushroom Poisoning. Diagnosis and Treatment.* Edited by D.G. Spoerke and B.H. Rumack, CRC Press, Boca Raton, Florida, USA. 1994, 279–287.

85 FRANKE, S.; FREIMUTH, U.; LIST, P.H. [Toxicity of the spring morel *Gyromitra (Helvella) esculenta* Fr.] *Archiv für Toxikologie* 1967, 22, 293–332.

86 NISKANEN, A.; PYYSALO, H.; RIMAILA-PARNANEN, E.; HARTIKKA, P. Short-term peroral toxicity of ethylidene gyromitrin in rabbits and chickens. *Food and Cosmetics Toxicology* 1976, 14, 409–415.

87 MAKINEN, S.M.; KREULA, M.; KAUPPI, M. Acute oral toxicity of ethylidine gyromitrin in rabbits, rats and chickens. *Food and Cosmetics Toxicology* 1977, 15, 575–578.

88 BRAUN, R.; GREEFF, U.; NETTER, K.J. Liver injury by the false morel poison gyromitrin. *Toxicology* 1979, 12, 155–163.

89 BRAUN, R.; KREMER, J.; RAIJ, H. Renal functional response to the mushroom poison gyromitrin. *Toxicology* 1979, 13, 187–196.

90 SLANINA, P.; CEKAN, E.; HALEN, B.; BERGMAN, K.; SAMUELSSON, R. Toxicological studies of the false morel (*Gyromitra esculenta*) embryotoxicity of monomethylhydrazine in the rat. *Food Additives and Contaminants* 1993, 10, 391–398.

91 TOTH, B. Synthetic and naturally occurring hydrazones as possible cancer causative agents. *Cancer Research* 1975, 35, 3693.

92 BERNARD, M. A. Mushroom poisoning in a dog. *Canadian Veterinary Journal* 1979, 20, 82–83.

93 TRAD, J.; PARAF, A.; OPOLON, P.; ROLLEN, A. [A para-phalloidin syndrome with severe icterus, due to *Lepiota helveola* (sensu lato).] *Semaine des Hôpitaux de Paris* 1970, 46, 2163–2169.

94 EILERS, F.I.; BARNARD, B.L. A rapid method for the diagnosis of poisoning caused by the mushroom *Lepiota morgani. American Journal of Clinical Pathology* 1973, 60, 823–825.

95 SCHULZ-WEDDIGEN, I. [Contributions to knowledge of the genus *Lepiota*. I. A case of poisoning by *Lepiota brunneo-incarnata* in north-western Germany.] *Zeitschrift für Mykologie* 1986, 52, 91–100.

96 PAYDAS, S.; KOCAK, R.; ERTURK, F.; ERKEN, E.; ZAKSU, H.S.; GURCAY, A. Poisoning due to amatoxin-containing *Lepiota* species. *British Journal of Clinical Practice* 1990, 44, 450–453.

97 PARRA, S.; GARCIA, J.; MARTINEZ, P.; DE LA PENA, C.; CARRASCOSA, C. Profile of alkaline phosphatase isoenzymes in ten patients poisoned by mushrooms of the genus *Lepiota. Digestive Diseases and Sciences* 1992, 37, 1495–1498.

98 RAMIREZ, P.; PARRILLA, P.; SANCHEZ BUENO, F.; ROBLES, R.; PONS, J.A.; BIXQUERT, V.; NICOLAS, S.; NUÑEZ, R.; ALEGRIA, M.S.; MIRAS, M.; RODRIGUEZ, J.M. Fulminant hepatic failure after *Lepiota* mushroom poisoning. *Journal of Hepatology* 1993, 19, 51–54.

99 MEUNIER, B.; MESSNER, M.; BARDAXOGLOU, E.; SPILIOPOULOS, G.; TERBLANCHE, J.; LAUNOIS, B. Liver transplantation for severe *Lepiota helveola* poisoning. *Liver* 1994, 14, 158–160.

100 HALL, A.H.; HALL, P.K. Ibotenic acid/muscimol-containing mushrooms. In: *Handbook of Mushroom Poisoning. Diagnosis and Treatment.* Edited by D.G. Spoerke and B.H. Rumack. CRC Press, Boca Raton, Florida, USA. 1994, 265–278.

101 PEGLER, D.N. *The Mitchell Beazley Pocket Guide to Mushrooms and Toadstools.* Mitchell Beazley,

London, UK. 1981, 164.

102 HATFIELD, G.M.; BRADY, L.R. Toxins of higher fungi. *Lloydia* 1975, 38, 36–55.

103 LINCOFF, G.; MITCHEL, D.H. *Toxic and Hallucinogenic Mushroom Poisoning. A Handbook for Physicians and Mushroom Hunters.* Van Nostrand Reinhold Co., New York, USA. 1977, 77–99.

104 RUMACK, B.H.; SALZMAN, E. *Mushroom Poisoning: Diagnosis and Treatment.* CRC Press Inc., Florida, USA. 1978, 177.

105 BENJAMIN, D.R. Mushroom poisoning in infants and children: the *Amanita pantherina/muscaria* group. *Journal of Toxicology. Clinical Toxicology* 1992, 30, 13–22.

106 GREATOREX, J.C. Some unusual cases of plant poisoning in animals. *Veterinary Record* 1966, 78, 725–727.

107 HUNT, R.S.; FUNK, A. Mushrooms fatal to dogs. *Mycologia* 1977, 69, 432–433.

108 RIDGWAY, R.L. Mushroom (*Amanita pantherina*) poisoning. *Journal of the American Veterinary Medical Association* 1978, 172, 681–682.

109 SMOLINSKE, S.C. Psilocybin-containing mushrooms. In: *Handbook of Mushroom Poisoning. Diagnosis and Treatment.* Edited by D.G. Spoerke and B.H. Rumack. CRC Press, Boca Raton, Florida, USA. 1994, 309–324.

110 GARTZ, J.; DREWITZ, G. [The green mushroom *Inocybe aeruginascens* – an *Inocybe* species with hallucinogenic effects.] *Zeitschrift für Ärztliche Fortbildung* 1986, 80, 551–553.

111 BRESINSKY, A.; BESL, H. *A Colour Atlas of Poisonous Fungi.* Wolfe Publishing Ltd, London, UK. 1990, 112–118.

112 COOPER, R. *A Guide to British Psilocybe Mushrooms.* Hassle Free Press, UK. 1994.

113 YOUNG, R.E.; MILROY, R.; HUTCHISON, S.; KESSON, C.M. The rising price of mushrooms. *Lancet* 1982, I, 213–215.

114 BENEDICT, R.G.; TYLER, V.E.; WATLING, R. Blueing in *Conocybe, Psilocybe* and a *Stropharia* species and the detection of psilocybin. *Lloydia* 1967, 30, 150–157.

115 SOWERBY, J. Coloured Figures of English Fungi or Mushrooms. 1803. Quoted in: *Naturaliste Canadienne* 1971, 98, 415–424. [On the hallucinogenic properties of *Psilocybe semilanceata*.] by R. Heim.

116 SCHWARTZ, R.H.; SMITH, D.E. Hallucinogenic mushrooms. *Clinical Pediatrics* 1988, 27, 70–73.

117 LASSEN, J.F.; LASSEN, N.F.; SKOV, J. [Consumption of psilobycin-containing hallucinogenic mushrooms by young people.] *Ugeskrift for Læger* 1992, 154, 2678–2681.

118 LASSEN, J.F.; RAVN, H.B.; LASSEN, S.F. [Hallucinogenic psilocybin-containing mushrooms. Poisoning by Danish wild mushrooms.] *Ugeskrift for Læger* 1990, 152, 314–317.

119 MURRAY, V.S.G.; FRANCIS, J. Review of enquiries made to the NPIS concerning *Psilocybe* mushroom ingestion, 1978–81. *Abstract, 10th International Congress of the European Association of Poison Control Centres 3-6 August, 1982.* p.78.

120 MILLS, P.R.; LESINSKAS, D.; WATKINSON, G. The danger of hallucinogenic mushrooms. *Scottish Medical Journal* 1979, 24, 316–317.

121 HATFIELD, G.M.; VALDES, L.J. The occurrence of psilocybin in *Gymnopilus* species. *Lloydia* 1978, 41, 140–144.

122 PEDEN, N.R.; BISSETT, A.F.; MACAULEY, K.E.C.; CROOKS, J.; PELOSI, A.J. Clinical toxicology of magic mushroom ingestion. *Postgraduate Medical Journal* 1981, 57, 543–545.

123 COOLES, P. Abuse of the mushroom *Panaeolus foenisecii. British Medical Journal* 1980, 280, 446–447.

124 WATLING, R. A *Panaeolus* poisoning in Scotland. *Mycopathologia* 1977, 61, 187–190.

125 HYDE, P.N. High horse. *Veterinary Record* 1990, 127, 554.

126 JONES, J. 'Magic mushroom' poisoning in a colt. *Veterinary Record* 1990, 127, 603.

127 KIRWAN, A.P. 'Magic mushroom' poisoning in a dog. *Veterinary Record* 1990, 126, 149.

128 YOUNG, A. Muscarine-containing mushrooms. In: *Handbook of Mushroom Poisoning. Diagnosis and*

Treatment. Edited by D.G. Spoerke and B.H. Rumack. CRC Press, Boca Raton, Florida, USA. 1994, 289–301.

129 HATFIELD, G.M.; BRADY, L.R. Toxins of higher fungi. *Lloydia* 1975, 38, 36–55.

130 MARETIĆ, Z.; RUSSELL, F.E.; GOLOBIĆ, V. Twenty-five cases of poisoning by the mushroom *Pleurotus olearius*. *Toxicon* 1975, 13, 379–381.

131 FRENCH, A.L.; GARRETTSON, L.K. Poisoning with the North American Jack O'Lantern mushroom, *Omphalotus illudens*. *Journal of Toxicology. Clinical Toxicology* 1988, 26, 81–88.

132 BRESINSKY, A.; BESL, H. *A Colour Atlas of Poisonous Fungi.* Wolfe Publishing Ltd, London, UK. 1990, 152–154.

133 STEIDL, V.T. [Mushroom poisoning in a dog.] *Kleintierpraxis* 1987, 32, 153–156.

134 REID, D.A. Canine poisoning by *Clitocybe* species. *Bulletin of the British Mycological Society* 1985, 19, 117–118.

135 YAM, P.; HELFER, S.; WATLING, R. Mushroom poisoning in a dog. *Veterinary Record* 1993, 133, 24.

136 KUNKEL, D.B.; CONNOR, D.A. Coprine-containing mushrooms. In: *Handbook of Mushroom Poisoning. Diagnosis and Treatment.* Edited by D.G. Spoerke and B.H. Rumack. CRC Press, Boca Raton, Florida, USA. 1994, 303–307.

137 BRESINSKY, A.; BESL, H. *A Colour Atlas of Poisonous Fungi.* Wolfe Publishing Ltd, London, UK. 1990, 124–125.

138 LINCOFF, G.; MITCHEL, D.H. *Toxic and Hallucinogenic Mushrooms. A Handbook for Physicians and Mushroom Hunters.* Van Nostrand Reinhold Co., New York, USA. 1977, 67.

139 COCHRAN, K.W.; COCHRAN, M.W. *Clitocybe clavipes*: Antabuse-like reaction to alcohol. *Mycologia* 1978, 70, 1124–1126.

140 HATFIELD, G.M.; SCHAUMBERG, J.P. Isolation and structural studies of coprine, the disulfiram-like constituent of *Coprinus atramentarius*. *Lloydia* 1975, 38, 489–496.

141 BRESINSKY, A.; BESL, H. *A Colour Atlas of Poisonous Fungi.* Wolfe Publishing Ltd, London, UK. 1990, 119–123.

142 MICHELOT, D. Poisoning by *Coprinus atramentarius*. *Natural Toxins* 1992, 1, 73–80.

143 CHILD, G.P. The inability of coprini to sensitise man to ethyl alcohol. *Mycologia* 1952, 44, 200–202.

144 JOSSERAND, M. The ability of coprini to sensitise man to ethyl alcohol. *Mycologia* 1952, 44, 829–831.

145 KÜNG, W. [The ink cap, *Coprinus atramentarius* (Bull. ex Fr.).] *Schweizerische Zeitschrift für Pilzkunde* 1972, 50, 82–85.

146 CHILTON, W.S. The chemistry and mode of action of mushroom toxins. In: *Handbook of Mushroom Poisoning. Diagnosis and Treatment.* Edited by D.G. Spoerke and B.H. Rumack. CRC Press, Boca Raton, Florida, USA. 1994, 193–194.

147 HARLEY, R.M. Royal Botanic Gardens, Kew, Surrey, UK. Personal communication.

148 LINCOFF, G.; MITCHEL, D.H. *Toxic and Hallucinogenic Mushroom Poisoning. A Handbook for Physicians and Mushroom Hunters.* Van Nostrand Reinhold Co., New York, USA. 1977, 138.

149 KRETZ, O.; CREPPY, E.E.; DIRHEIMER, G. Characterization of bolesatine, a toxic protein from the mushroom *Boletus satanas* Lenz and its effects on kidney cells. *Toxicology* 1991, 66, 213–224.

150 THIERS, H.D. Boletes and their toxins. In: *Handbook of Mushroom Poisoning. Diagnosis and Treatment.* Edited by D.G. Spoerke and B.H. Rumack. CRC Press, Boca Raton, Florida, USA. 1994, 339–345.

151 COOPER, P. *Poisoning by Drugs and Chemicals, Plants and Animals.* Alchemist Publications, London, UK. 3rd Edition.1974, 94–95.

152 BRESINSKY, A.; BESL, H. *A Colour Atlas of Poisonous Fungi.* Wolfe Publishing Ltd, London, UK. 1990, 146–148.

153 BRESINSKY, A.; BESL, H. *A Colour Atlas of Poisonous Fungi.* Wolfe Publishing Ltd, London, UK. 1990, 158–160.

154 HERMS, H. [Morel (*Helvella esculenta*) poisoning in dogs.] *Berliner und Münchener Tierärztliche Wochenschrift* 1950, 63, 161.

155 KOMMERS, G.D.; SANTOS, M.N. Experimental poisoning of cattle by the mushroom *Ramaria flavo-brunnescens* (Clavariaceae): a study of the morphology and pathogenesis of lesions in hooves, tail, horns and tongue. *Veterinary and Human Toxicology* 1995, 37, 297–302.

156 PASCHOAL, J.P.; PORTUGAL, M.A.S.C.; NAZÁRIO, W. ["Eucalyptus" disease of cattle in São Paulo State, Brazil. Ramaria poisoning.] *Biológico* 1983, 49, 15–18.

157 STEVENSON, J.A.; BENJAMIN, C.R. *Scleroderma* poisoning. *Mycologia* 1961, 53, 438–439.

158 GALEY, F.D.; RUTHERFORD, J.J.; WELLS, K. A case of *Scleroderma citrinum* poisoning in a Miniature Chinese Pot-Bellied pig. *Veterinary and Human Toxicology* 1990, 32, 329–330.

159 BRESINSKY, A.; BESL, H. *A Colour Atlas of Poisonous Fungi.* Wolfe Publishing Ltd, London, UK. 1990, 175–176.

160 BRESINSKY, A.; BESL, H. *A Colour Atlas of Poisonous Fungi.* Wolfe Publishing Ltd, London, UK. 1990, 155–156.

161 VESELSKÝ, J.; DVOŘÁK, J. [The course of a case of poisoning by *Tricholoma sulphureum* (Bull. ex Fr.) Kumm.] *Česka Mykologie* 1981, 35, 114–115.

162 HAMILTON, A.G. Clouded agarics. *British Medical Journal* 1981, 282, 825.

163 Personal communication.

164 BRESINSKY, A.; BESL, H. *A Colour Atlas of Poisonous Fungi.* Wolfe Publishing Ltd, London, UK. 1990, 126–129.

165 OLESEN, L.L. [Poisoning with the brown roll-rim mushroom, *Paxillus involutus.*] *Ugeskrift for Læger* 1991, 153, 445.

166 FLAMMER, R. [The *Paxillus* syndrome: immunohaemolysis after repeated ingestion of the mushrooms.] *Schweizerische Rundschau für Medizin Praxis* 1985, 74, 997–999.

167 BENJAMIN, D.R. *Mushrooms: Poisons and Panaceas.* W.H. Freeman and Company, New York, USA. 1995, 370.

168 WINKELMANN, M.; STANGEL, W.; SCHEDEL, I.; GRABENSEE, B. Severe hemolysis caused by antibodies against the mushroom *Paxillus involutus* and its therapy by plasma exchange. *Klinische Wochenschrift* 1986, 64, 935–938.

169 COX, A.; FOLGERING, H.T.M.; VAN GRIENSVEN, L.J.L.D. Extrinsic allergic alveolitis caused by spores of the oyster mushroom *Pleurotus ostreatus. European Respiratory Journal* 1988, 1, 466–468.

170 SPOERKE, D.G. Hypersensitivity A associated with nonoral mushroom exposure. In: *Handbook of Mushroom Poisoning. Diagnosis and Treatment.* Edited by D.G. Spoerke and B.H. Rumack. CRC Press, Boca Raton, Florida, USA. 1994, 373–389.

ERGOT

1 ANONYMOUS. St. Anthony's Fire. *Lancet* 1951, II, 436.

2 MATOSSIAN, M.K. Mold poisoning: an unrecognised English health problem, 1550–1800. *Medical History* 1981, 25, 73–84.

3 LORENZ, K. Ergot on cereal grains. *Critical Reviews in Food Science and Nutrition* 1979, 11, 311–354.

4 WATSON, R.D. The handling of risks of mycotoxicoses from an ergot epidemic in northern Scotland (a cautionary tale). *Proceedings of the Fourth Meeting on Mycotoxins in Animal Disease.* 1981, 5 pp.

5 LONG, E. Ergot – the growing menace to cereal profits. *Farmers Weekly* 1981, October 23, 87.

6 ANONYMOUS. (Ergot) Disease is building up in the East. *Farmers Weekly* 1981, October 23, 87, 89.

7   UKASTA (United Kingdom Agricultural Supply Trade Association Limited) Press Information 1981, 25.

8   BURFENING, P.J. Ergotism. *Journal of the American Veterinary Medical Association* 1973, 163, 1288–1290.

9   GRÖGER, D. Ergot. In: *Microbial Toxins.Vol. 8. Fungal toxins.* Edited by S. Kadis, A. Ciegler and S.J. Ajl. Academic Press, New York and London. 1972, 321–373.

10 DINNUSSON, W.E.; HAUGSE, C.N.; KNUTSON, R.D. Ergot in rations for fattening cattle. *North Dakota Farm Research Bulletin* 1971, 29, No.2, 20–22.

11 WHITTEMORE, C.T.; MACER, R.C.F.; MILLER, J.K.; MANTLE, P.G. Some consequences of the ingestion by young and growing pigs of feed contaminated with ergot. *Research in Veterinary Science* 1976, 20, 61–69.

12 BOURKE, C.A. The evidence against the existence of so-called convulsive ergotism in ruminants. In: *Plant-associated Toxins. Agricultural, Phytochemical and Ecological Aspects.* CAB International, Wallingford, UK. 1994, 387–392.

13 FORSYTH, A.A. *British Poisonous Plants.* HMSO, London, UK. Ministry of Agriculture, Fisheries and Food Bulletin 161, 1968, 20–21 (amended 1979, 17–19).

14 BRYSON, E. Ergot poisoning – an outbreak in dairy cattle. In: *Proceedings of the British Cattle Veterinary Association for 1989–1990.* British Cattle Veterinary Association, c/o Department of Veterinary Clinical Science, University, Liverpool, UK. 1990, 266–272.

15 HOGG, R.A. Poisoning of cattle fed ergotised silage. *Veterinary Record* 1991, 129, 313–314.

16 BRYDEN, W.L. The many guises of ergotism. In: *Plant-associated Toxins. Agricultural, Phytochemical and Ecological Aspects.* CAB International, Wallingford, UK. 1994, 381–386.

17 APPLEYARD, W.T. Outbreak of bovine abortion attributed to ergot poisoning. *Veterinary Record* 1986, 118, 48–49.

18 MANTLE, P.G. Ergotism in sheep. In: *Mycotoxic Fungi, Mycotoxins, Mycotoxicoses. An Encyclopedic Handbook. Volume 2.* Edited by T.D. Wyllie and L.G. Morehouse. Marcel Dekker Inc., New York, USA. 1978, 207–213.

19 KALLELA, K. [Unusually high alkaloid content in ergot from pasture grass.] *Proceedings of the 12th Nordic Veterinary Congress, Reykjavik.* A/S Karl Fr. Mortenson, Copenhagen, Denmark. 1974, 284.

20 GREATOREX, J.C.; MANTLE, P.G. Experimental ergotism in sheep. *Research in Veterinary Science* 1973, 15, 337–346.

21 LØKEN, T. Ergot from meadow grass in Norway – chemical composition and toxicological effects in sheep. *Nordisk Veterinærmedicin* 1984, 36, 259–265.

22 FRIEND, D.W.; MacINTYRE, T.M. Effect of rye ergot on growth and N-retention in growing pigs. *Canadian Journal of Comparative Medicine* 1970, 34, 198–202.

23 WHITTEMORE, C.T.; MILLER, J.K.; MANTLE, P.G. Further studies concerning the toxicity of ingested ergot sclerotia (*Claviceps purpurea*) to young and growing pigs. *Research in Veterinary Science* 1977, 22, 146–150.

24 WRATHALL, A.E. *Reproductive Disorders in Pigs.* Commonwealth Agricultural Bureaux, Farnham Royal, UK. 1975, 89–92.

25 BARNIKOL, H.; GRUBER, S.; THALMANN, A.; SCHMIDT, H.L. [Ergot poisoning in pigs.] *Tierärztliche Umschau* 1982, 37, 324–332.

26 ANDERSON, J.F.; WERDIN, R.E. Ergotism manifested as agalactia and gangrene in sows. *Journal of the American Veterinary Medical Association* 1977, 170, 1089–1091.

27 KAMPHUES, J.; DROCHNER, W. [Ergot contamination of feed – a contribution to the clarification of possible ergot-induced signs of disease.] *Tierärztliche Praxis* 1991, 19, 1–7.

28 DIGNEAN, M.A.; SCHIEFFER, H.B.; BLAIR, R. Effects of feeding ergot-contaminated grain to pregnant and nursing sows. *Journal of Veterinary Medicine. Series A* 1986, 33, 757–766.

29 SPESIVTSEVA, N.A. *Mikozy i mikotoksikozy.* Izdatel'stvo "Kolos", Moscow, USSR. 2nd Edition. 1964, 329.

30 RIET-CORREA, F.; MENDEZ, M.C.; SCHILD, A.L.; BERGAMO, P.M.; FLORES, W.N. Agalactia, reproductive problems and neonatal mortality in horses associated with the ingestion of *Claviceps purpurea. Australian Veterinary Journal* 1988, 65, 192–193.

31 PEARSON, A.B. Presumptive diagnosis of ergotism in red deer. *Surveillance* 1987, 14, No.1, 14.

32 BROSIG, U. Presumed ergotism in a cat. *Veterinary Record* 1993, 133, 432.

33 FRYE, F.L. Apparent spontaneous ergot-induced necrotizing dermatitis in a guinea pig. *Journal of Small Exotic Animal Medicine* 1994, 2, 165–166.

34 O'NEIL, J.B.; RAE, W.J. Ergot tolerance in chicks and hens. *Poultry Science* 1965, 44, 1404.

35 YOUNG, J.C.; MARQUARDT, R.R. Effects of ergotamine tartrate on growing chickens. *Canadian Journal of Animal Science* 1982, 62, 1181–1191.

36 BARGER, G. *Ergot and Ergotism.* Gurney and Jackson, London, UK. 1931, 279 pp.

37 CAMERON, M.L. The visions of Saints Anthony and Guthlac. In: *Health, Disease and Healing in Medieval Culture.* Edited by S. Campbell, B. Hall and D. Klausner. Macmillan, Basingstoke, UK. 1992, 152–158.

38 ANONYMOUS. The doom of St. Anthony's Fire. *Farmers Weekly* 1981, October 23, 89.

MYCOTOXINS

1 PATTERSON, D.S.P. Mycotoxins. *Environmental Chemistry* 1982, 2, 205–233.

2 WYLLIE, T.D.; MOREHOUSE, L.G. (Editors) *Mycotoxic Fungi, Mycotoxins and Mycotoxicoses. An Encyclopedic Handbook.* Volume 2. Marcel Dekker Inc., New York, USA. 1978, 570 pp.

3 CIEGLER, A. Mycotoxins: occurrence, chemistry, biological activity. *Lloydia* 1975, 38, 21–35.

4 SMITH, J.E.; HENDERSON, R.S. (Editors) *Mycotoxins and Animal Foods.* CRC Press, Boca Raton, Florida, USA. 1991, 875 pp.

5 MOSS, M.O. Secondary metabolism and food intoxication – moulds. *Journal of Applied Bacteriology* 1992, 73, Symposium Supplement No.21, 80S–88S.

6 SCUDAMORE, K.A. (Editor). *Proceedings of a UK Workshop held at Brunel, The University of West London, 21–23 April, 1993.* Central Science Laboratory, Slough, UK. 1994, 319 pp.

7 TOWERS, N. Pasture as a source of mycotoxins: the New Zealand experience and European implications. In: *Occurrence and Significance of Mycotoxins.* Edited by K.A. Scudamore. Central Science Laboratory, Slough, UK. 1994, 16–26.

8 AINSWORTH, G.C. *Introduction to the History of Medical and Veterinary Mycology.* Cambridge University Press, Cambridge, UK. 1986, 127–134.

9 BUCKLE, A.E.; SCUDAMORE, K.A. Occurrence of mycotoxins in stored grain. In: *The Occurrence and Detection of Moulds, Mycotoxins and Actinomycetes in UK Grain.* By B.G. Osborne, D.A.L. Seiler, A.E. Buckle and K.A. Scudamore. *HGCA Research Review* 1988, No.13, 59–68.

10 OSBORNE, B.G. Occurrence of mycotoxins in grain at harvest. In: *The Occurrence and Detection of Moulds, Mycotoxins and Actinomycetes in UK Grain.* By B.G. Osborne, D.A.L. Seiler, A.E. Buckle and K.A. Scudamore. *HGCA Research Review* 1988, No.13, 57–58.

11 SCUDAMORE, K.A. The occurrence of mycotoxins in food and animal foodstuffs in the United Kingdom. In: *Occurrence and Significance of Mycotoxins.* Edited by K.A. Scudamore. Central Science Laboratory, Slough, UK. 1994, 172–185.

12 MINISTRY OF AGRICULTURE, FISHERIES AND FOOD. Mycotoxins: Third Report. Food Surveillance Paper No.36. HMSO, London, UK. 1993, 66 pp.

13 KUIPER-GOODMAN, T. Risk assessment to humans of mycotoxins in animal-derived food products. *Veterinary and Human Toxicology* 1990, 32, Supplement, 6–14.

14 BEASLEY, V.R.; LAMBERT, R.J. The apparently minimal hazard posed to human consumers of products from animals fed trichothecene-contaminated grains. *Veterinary and Human Toxicology* 1990, 32, Supplement, 27–39.

15 McLEAN, M.; DUTTON, M.F. Cellular interactions and metabolism of aflatoxin: an update. *Pharmacology and Therapeutics* 1995, 65, 163–192.

16 GARNER, C. Human bio-monitoring for aflatoxin exposure. In: *Occurrence and Significance of Mycotoxins*. Edited by K.A. Scudamore. Central Science Laboratory, Slough, UK. 1994, 91–95.

17 EATON, D.L.; GROOPMAN, J.D. (Editors). *The Toxicology of Aflatoxins. Human Health, Veterinary, and Agricultural Significance*. Academic Press, San Diego, California, USA. 1994, 544 pp.

18 SMITH, J.E.; ROSS, K. The toxigenic aspergilli. In: *Mycotoxins and Animal Foods*. Edited by J.E. Smith and R.S. Henderson. CRC Press, Boca Raton, Florida, USA. 1991, 101–118.

19 WYATT, R.D. Poultry. In: *Mycotoxins and Animal Foods*. Edited by J.E. Smith and R.S. Henderson. CRC Press, Boca Raton, Florida, USA. 1991, 553–605.

20 The Fertilisers and Feeding Stuffs (Amendment) Regulations. HMSO, London, UK. Statutory Instruments 1976, No.840.

21 The Fertilisers and Feeding Stuffs (Amendment) Regulations. HMSO, London, UK. Statutory Instruments 1982, No.386.

22 BUCKLE, A.E.; SCUDAMORE, K.A. Legislation concerning mycotoxins in food and animal feeding stuffs. In: *The Occurrence and Detection of Moulds, Mycotoxins and Actinomycetes in UK Grain*. By B.G. Osborne, D.A.L. Seiler, A.E. Buckle and K.A. Scudamore. *HGCA Research Review* No.13. 1988, 10–12.

23 PHILLIPS, T.D.; CLEMENT, B.A.; KUBENA, L.F.; HARVEY, R.B. Detection and detoxification of aflatoxins: prevention of aflatoxicosis and aflatoxin residues with hydrated sodium calcium aluminosilicate. *Veterinary and Human Toxicology* 1990, 32, Supplement, 15–19.

24 MANTLE, P. A reappraisal of ochratoxin A as a factor in human renal disease. In: *Occurrence and Significance of Mycotoxins*. Edited by K.A. Scudamore. Central Science Laboratory, Slough, UK. 1994, 101–108.

25 GAREIS, M. Mycotoxins in animal feeds and effects on livestock. In: *Occurrence and Significance of Mycotoxins*. Edited by K.A. Scudamore. Central Science Laboratory, Slough, UK. 1994, 7–15.

26 SYDENHAM, E.; SHEPHARD, G.S.; GELDERBLOM, W.C.A.; THIEL, P.G.; MARASAS, W.F.O. Fumonisins: their implications for human and animal health. In: *Occurrence and Significance of Mycotoxins*. Edited by K.A. Scudamore. Central Science Laboratory, Slough, UK. 1994, 42–48.

27 SCUDAMORE, K.; CHAN, H.K. Occurrence of fumonisin mycotoxins in maize and millet imported into the United Kingdom. In: *Occurrence and Significance of Mycotoxins*. Edited by K.A. Scudamore. Central Science Laboratory, Slough, UK. 1994, 186–189.

28 GILMOUR, J.S.; INGLIS, D.M.; ROBB, J.; MACLEAN, M. A fodder mycotoxicosis of ruminants caused by contamination of a distillery by-product with *Aspergillus clavatus*. *Veterinary Record* 1989, 124, 133–135.

29 ROBB, J.; KIRKPATRICK, K.S.; NORVAL, M. Association of toxin-producing fungi with disease in broilers. *Veterinary Record* 1982, 111, 389–390.

30 KROGH, P. Porcine nephropathy associated with ochratoxin A. In: *Mycotoxins and Animal Foods*. Edited by J.E. Smith and R.S. Henderson. CRC Press, Boca Raton, Florida, USA. 1991, 627–645.

31 DIEKMAN, M.A.; GREEN, M.L. Mycotoxins and reproduction in domestic livestock. *Journal of Animal Science* 1992, 70, 1615–1627.

32 BRYDEN, W.L. Neuromycotoxicoses in Australia. In: *Plant-associated Toxins. Agricultural, Phytochemical and Ecological Aspects*. Edited by S.M. Colegate and P.R. Dorling. CAB International, Wallingford, UK. 1994, 363–368.

33 CASTEEL, S.W.; TURK, J.R.; ROTTINGHAUS, G.E.; COWART, R.P. Chronic toxicity of fumonisin in pigs.

In: *Plant-associated Toxins. Agricultural, Phytochemical and Ecological Aspects.* Edited by S.M. Colegate and P.R. Dorling. CAB International, Wallingford, UK. 1994, 319–324.

34 KIM, J.C.; LEE, Y.W. Sambutoxin, a new mycotoxin produced by toxic *Fusarium* isolates obtained from rotted potato tubers. *Applied and Environmental Microbiology* 1994, 60, 4380–4386.

POISONOUS ALGAE

1 FORSYTH, A.A. *British Poisonous Plants.* HMSO, London, UK. Ministry of Agriculture, Fisheries and Food Bulletin 161, 1968, iv (amended 1979, iv).

2 PEARSON, M.J. (Chairman) *Toxic Blue-green Algae. A Report by the National Rivers Authority.* Water Quality Series No.2. National Rivers Authority, London, UK. 1990, 125 pp.

3 PEARCE, F. Deadly blooms reach Britain's rivers. *New Scientist* 1996, 150, No.2030, 5.

4 CARMICHAEL, W.W.; FALCONER, I.R. Diseases related to freshwater blue-green algal toxins, and control measures. In: *Algal Toxins in Seafood and Drinking Water.* Edited by I.R. Falconer. Academic Press, London, UK. 1993, 187–209.

5 FALCONER, I.R. (Editor). *Algal Toxins in Seafood and Drinking Water.* Academic Press, London, UK. 1993, 224 pp.

6 KENEFICK, S.L.; HRUDEY, S.E.; PETERSON, H.G.; PREPAS, E.E. Toxin release from *Microcystis aeruginosa* after chemical treatment. *Water Science and Technology* 1993, 27, 433–440.

7 CODD, G.A. Cyanobacterial poisoning hazard in British freshwaters. *Veterinary Record* 1983, 113, 223–224.

8 CORKILL, N.; SMITH, R.; SECKINGTON, M.; PONTEFRACT, R. Poisoning at Rutland Water. *Veterinary Record* 1989, 125, 356.

9 EDNEY, A.T.B. Algal poisoning. *Veterinary Record* 1990, 126, 297–298.

10 DONE, S.H.; BAIN, M. Hepatic necrosis in sheep associated with ingestion of blue-green algae. *Veterinary Record* 1993, 133, 600.

11 LAWTON, L.A.; EDWARDS, C.; BEATTIE, K.A.; PLEASANCE, S.; DEAR, G.J.; CODD, G.A. Isolation and characterization of microcystins from laboratory cultures and environmental samples of *Microcystis aeruginosa* and from an associated animal toxicosis. *Natural Toxins* 1995, 3, 50–57.

12 CARBIS, C.R.; SIMONS, J.A.; MITCHELL, G.F.; ANDERSON, J.W.; McCAULEY, I. A biochemical profile for predicting the chronic exposure of sheep to *Microcystis aeruginosa*, an hepatotoxic species of blue-green alga. *Research in Veterinary Science* 1994, 57, 310–316.

13 CARBIS, C.R.; WALDRON, D.L.; MITCHELL, G.F.; ANDERSON, J.W.; McCAULEY, I. Recovery of hepatic function and latent mortalities in sheep exposed to the blue-green alga *Microcystis aeruginosa*. *Veterinary Record* 1995, 137, 12–15.

14 ODRIOZOLA, E.; BALLABENE, N.; SALAMANCO, A. [Poisoning of cattle by blue-green algae.] *Revista Argentina de Microbiologia* 1984, 16, 219–224.

15 BEASLEY, V.R.; COOK, W.O.; DAHLEM, A.M.; HOOSER, S.B.; LOVELL, R.A.; VALENTINE, W.M. Algae intoxication in livestock and waterfowl. *Veterinary Clinics of North America: Food Animal Practice* 1989, 5, 345–361.

16 TENCALLA, F.G.; DIETRICH, D.R.; SCHLATTER, C. Toxicity of *Microcystis aeruginosa* peptide toxin to yearling rainbow trout (*Oncorhynchus mykiss*). *Aquatic Toxicology* 1994, 30, 215–224.

17 FALCONER, I.R.; BURCH, M.D.; STEFFENSEN, D.A.; CHOICE, M.; COVERDALE, O.R. Toxicity of the blue-green alga (cyanobacterium) *Microcystis aeruginosa* in drinking water to growing pigs, as an animal model for human injury and risk assessment. *Environmental Toxicology and Water Quality* 1994, 9, 131–139.

18 NAEGELI, H.; SABIN, A.; BRAUN, U.; HAUSER, B.; MEZ, K.; HANSELMANN, K.; PREISIG, H.R.; BIVETTI, A.;

EITEL, J. [Sudden death of cattle on alpine pastures in south-eastern Switzerland.] *Schweizer Archiv für Tierheilkunde* 1997, 139, 201–209.

19 TURNER, P.C.; GAMMIE, A.J.; HOLLINRAKE, K.; CODD, G.A. Pneumonia associated with contact with cyanobacteria. *British Medical Journal* 1990, 300, 1440–1441.

20 GUNN, G.J.; RAFFERTY, A.G.; RAFFERTY, G.C.; COCKBURN, N.; EDWARDS, C.; BEATTIE, K.A.; CODD, G.A. Fatal canine neurotoxicosis attributed to blue-green algae (cyanobacteria). *Veterinary Record* 1992, 130, 301–302.

21 MILLS, A.R.; PASSMORE, R. Pelagic paralysis. *Lancet* 1988, I, 161–164.

22 SMART, D. Clinical toxicology of shellfish poisoning. In: *Handbook of Clinical Toxicology of Animal Venoms and Poisons.* Edited by J. Meier and J. White. CRC Press, Boca Raton, Florida, USA. 1995, 33–57.

APPENDIX A: PLANTS AFFECTING MILK

1 MCBARRON, E.J. *Medicinal and Veterinary Aspects of Plant Poisons in New South Wales.* Department of Agriculture, New South Wales, Australia. 1976, 150–154.

2 RICHTER, H.E. [The influence of indigenous plants (Austria) on milk quality. II. Changes in taste and smell]. *Wiener Tierärztliche Monatsschrift* 1964, 51, 266–280.

3 RICHTER, H.E. [The influence of indigenous plants (Austria) on milk quality. II. Changes in taste, smell and colour]. *Wiener Tierärztliche Monatsschrift* 1965, 52, 635–644. (Continuation of previous paper by this author, above).

4 RICHTER, H.E. [The influence of indigenous plants (Austria) on milk quality. I. Excretion of toxins of plant origin in milk]. *Wiener Tierärztliche Monatsschrift* 1963, 50, 692–699.

5 PANTER, K.E.; JAMES L.F. Natural plant toxicants in milk: a review. *Journal of Animal Science* 1990, 68, 892–904.

6 JAMES, L.F.; PANTER, K.E.; MOLYNEUX, R.J.; STEGELMEIER, B.L.; WAGSTAFF, D.J. Plant toxicants in milk. In: *Plant-associated Toxins. Agricultural, Phytochemical and Ecological Aspects.* Edited by S.M. Colegate and P.R. Dorling. CAB International, Wallingford, UK. 1994, 83–88.

7 FORSYTH, A.A. *British Poisonous Plants.* HMSO, London, UK. Ministry of Agriculture, Fisheries and Food Bulletin 161, 1968, 118–120 (amended 1979, 119–121).

8 FENTON, E.W. *Poisonous and Milk-tainting Plants.* Edinburgh and East of Scotland College of Agriculture, 1931, New Series – No.4, 56 pp. (combined with Clinical Signs and First Aid to Stock, by E.D.S. Robertson).

Index

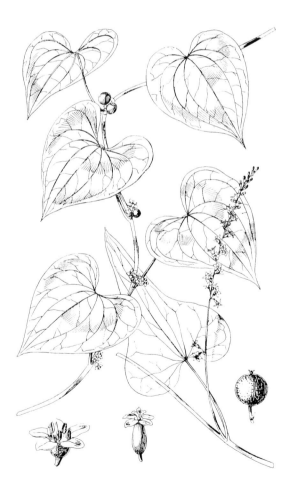

Tamus communis
Black bryony

Entries in bold refer to plate numbers in the colour section. Bold numbers precede any other numbers for each entry/sub-entry. Farm animals are referred to very frequently throughout the text and are not included in the index.